Mitchell's
Advanced Building Construction

Mitchell's Advanced Building Construction

THE STRUCTURE

by J. STROUD FOSTER, F.R.I.B.A.

B. T. BATSFORD LTD. LONDON

First published 1893

Seventeenth Edition 1963

Reprinted 1966

It should be noted that since publication of the seventeenth edition the LCC Bylaws, the Model Building Byelaws (now the Building Regulations) and Code of Practise 111 and other Codes and Standards have been revised. All reference to these documents should therefore be compared with the revised editions.

PRINTED IN GREAT BRITAIN BY
SPOTTISWOODE, BALLANTYNE AND CO. LTD, LONDON AND
COLCHESTER AND BOUND BY KEMP HALL BINDERY, OXFORD,
FOR THE PUBLISHERS
B. T. BATSFORD LTD
4 FITZHARDINGE STREET, PORTMAN SQUARE, LONDON W.1

Preface

Charles F. Mitchell, then Head of The Polytechnic School of Architecture, wrote the first edition of his book on *Advanced Building Construction* in 1893. Since then rapid advances in constructional techniques and great strides in the development of new methods and new materials have been made. It is possible, for a certain time, to take account of such advances by means of revisions of the original work but the time must come when a revision, even if conscientiously undertaken, will fail to do justice to the situation. A fresh assessment of the requirements of such a textbook must then be made in the light of current circumstances and a new approach made to the material to be covered. This has been the case with *Advanced Building Construction* and the decision has been made to commence afresh and produce a new work covering the advanced aspects of contemporary building construction as did Charles Mitchell so adequately in his day. "Mitchell" has been a standard textbook for many generations of students and the name has been retained in the title. It is hoped that the new work will meet the requirements of the present generation of students as well as the original work did for that of its own time.

The scope of the subject is so wide that it has been considered best to divide the work into two volumes, this volume to deal broadly with the structure and carcassing of buildings, the other with components, services and finishes.

The subject has been treated basically under the elements of construction. Most of these are interrelated in a building and, as far as possible, this has been borne in mind in the text. Ample cross-references are given to facilitate a grasp of this interrelationship of parts. Contract planning and site organization, and the use of mechanical plant, are both subjects relevant to constructional techniques and methods used on the site and to the initial design process for a building. These have been considered in the first two chapters. The subject of fire protection by its nature is extremely broad but it is so closely linked with the design and construction of buildings that it has been covered on broad lines in order to give an understanding of those factors which influence the nature and form of fire protection as well as to give detailed requirements in terms of construction.

At the present time there is a continual production of new and improved materials in various forms and a continuous development of new constructional techniques using both new and traditional materials. The designer can, therefore, no longer be dependent on a tradition based on the use of a limited range of structural materials, but must exercise his judgment and choice in a wide, and ever-widening, realm of alternatives. This necessitates a knowledge not only of the materials themselves but of the nature and structural behaviour of all the parts of a building of which those materials form a part. Efficiency of structure and economy of material and labour are basic

v

elements of good design. They are of vital importance today and should have a dominating influence on the design and construction of all buildings.

In the light of this, and in a period of transition and rapid development, an exemplar of constructional details would possess little value. What is required is something to give an understanding of the behaviour of structures under load and of the functional requirements of the different parts; to give some indication of their comparative economics and efficient design, their limitations and the logical and economic application of each. In writing this volume it has been the aim to deal with these aspects. The book is, therefore, not an exemplar of constructional details. Those details which are described and illustrated are meant to indicate the basic methods which can be adopted and how different materials can be used to fulfil various structural requirements. The illustrations are generally not fully dimensioned; such dimensions as are given are meant to give a sense of "scale" to the parts rather than to lay down definite sizes in particular circumstances. The function of the book is not primarily to give information on *how* things are done in detail, as this must be everchanging. Rather, the emphasis is on *why* things are done, having regard particularly to efficiency and economy in design. An understanding of the function and behaviour of the parts and of the logical and economic application of material, should enable a designer to prepare satisfactory constructional details in the solution of his structural problems.

This volume is intended primarily as a textbook for architectural, building and surveying students, but it is hoped that students of civil and structural engineering will find it useful as a means of setting within the context of the building as a whole their own studies in the realm of building structures.

In a book of this nature there is little scope for original work. The task consists of gathering together existing information and selecting that which appears to be important and relevant to the purpose of the book. The author acknowledges the debt he owes to others on whose work he has freely drawn, much of which is scattered in the journals of many countries. An endeavour has been made to indicate the sources, either in the text or in footnotes. Where this has not been done it is due to the fact that over a period of fifteen years or more of lecturing on the subject much material has been gathered, both textual and illustrative, the sources of which have not been traced. For any such omissions the author's apologies are offered. Much help and guidance has been received from many busy people who have given of their time and experience, particularly from my colleague, Raymond K. Harington, who has assisted in the writing of some of the material.

The Polytechnic, London, W.1., 1963   J. STROUD FOSTER

Acknowledgment

I am indebted to many people and organizations who have helped and guided me in the preparation of this book and from whom I have received much information. In expressing my gratitude for their kindness I find it impossible to mention all by name. I must, however, make particular mention of the following to whom my thanks are especially due:

My colleague, Raymond K. Harington, A.R.I.B.A., for his continued interest, criticism and suggestions on many points, and his assistance in writing for me the whole of the chapters on Flues and Chimney Shafts and Fire Protection, together with the section on External Facings and Claddings in Chapter 4 and that on Constructional Methods in Chapter 9.

J. E. Crofts, M.C., M.I.C.E., M.Cons.E., for the careful reading of my manuscript of Chapter 3 and for his many suggestions which have been incorporated in the final text. Much in this chapter I also owe to my reading of Capper and Cassie's very useful book, *The Mechanics of Engineering Soils*.

Kenneth A. Lock, A.R.I.C.S., A.M.F.P.A., for giving much time to the reading of the manuscript of Chapter 10 and for giving me the benefit of his expert knowledge and experience of the the subject of the chapter, much of which has been incorporated.

A. G. Stone, A.M.I.Mech.E., M.I.Plant E., F.R.G.S., to whom I am indebted for much material on Mechanical Plant in Chapter 2 and for reading my manuscript of this chapter and giving me considerable time in criticizing it and making suggestions.

Ivan Tomlin, F.I.B.E., A.I.O.B., of Messrs Howard Farrow Ltd, for his interest and for giving me so much of his time in discussing the subject of Chapter 1, reading my manuscript and making available to me details of his firm's methods of contract planning, on which I have very largely based the material in this chapter.

My friend, Z. S. Makowski, Ph.D., D.I.C., A.M.I.C.E., for help and guidance on grid structures in Chapter 9. I have, with his permission, drawn freely on his works on this subject and have used his illustrations as a basis for some of the drawings illustrating the text.

Leonard R. Creasy, B.Sc., M.I.C.E., for giving me information on various matters in Chapter 5. Much of the material on the economic aspects of this chapter and of Chapter 9 has been gathered from his excellent paper on the subject which is referred to in the text.

Kenneth W. Dale, A.M.I.H.V.E., A.M.Inst.F., who read through the manuscript of Chapter 7 and made helpful criticisms.

Peter Dunican, A.M.I.C.E., and my colleague, H. H. Hendrie, A.M.I.C.E., for their readiness to clarify and explain many points of principle and practice, and my colleague, J. W. Tiller, A.I.O.B., for reading the manuscript of Chapter 11 and of "Underpinning" in Chapter 3, and giving me the benefit of his criticism.

With the permission of the Controller of H.M. Stationery Office I have drawn freely on *Principles of Modern Building*, Vol. I., by R. Fitzmaurice, and from

Post-War Building Studies and *Building Research Station Digests* and other official publications, and from *British Standard Specifications* and *Codes of Practice*, with the permission of The British Standards Institution, 2 Park Street, W.1., from whom official copies may be obtained.

Extracts from the London Building (Constructional) By-laws, 1952, have been made with the permission of the Clerk to the London County Council and from the Model Byelaws, Series IV, Buildings, with the permission of the Controller of H.M. Stationery Office.

I am grateful for the information so freely given by many firms and organizations and for permission to base illustrations on material which they readily provided. The description of the lift-slab floor construction is based on detailed information provided by Messrs British Lift Slab Ltd.

In addition, I am grateful to the following for permission to quote from books or papers, to reproduce tables or to use drawings as a basis for illustrations in this volume: *Mechanics of Engineering Soils*, P. L. Capper and W. F. Cassie, E. and F. N. Spon Ltd; *Practical Problems in Soil Mechanics*, H. R. Reynolds and P. Proto-papadakis, Frederick Ungar Publishing Co.; *Walls and Wall Facings*, D. N. Nield, E. and F. N. Spon Ltd; *The Fabric of Modern Buildings*, E. G. Warland, Pitman & Sons Ltd; *Reinforced Concrete Chimneys*, C. Percy Taylor and Leslie Turner, Concrete Publications; *Design Problems of Heating and Ventilating*, A. T. Henley, Crosby Lockwood & Son Ltd; *Oil Fuel Applications*, A. T. Henley, Crosby Lockwood & Son Ltd; *Heating and Air Conditioning Equipment for Buildings*, F. Burlace Turpin, Pitman & Sons Ltd; *Building Elements*, R. Llewelyn Davies and A. Petty, Architectural Press; *Architectural Design*, Standard Catalogue Co. Ltd; *Architects Journal*, Architectural Press; *The Structural Engineer*, Institution of Structural Engineers; *Proceedings of the Institution of Civil Engineers*, Leonard R. Creasy; Australian Department of Labour and National Service—Industrial Services Division; Francis Kerr for drawings of his based on those in the last edition of *Advanced Building Construction* and used as a basis for a number of illustrations in Chapter 11, and for drawings used as a basis for the illustrations of excavators and compressors and pumps and of a mast crane, plate girder, retaining wall, and timbering to shafts and tunnels, and for some material on timbering for excavations and shoring. H. Werner Rosenthal for a graph and diagram relating to stanchions; and Mark Hartland Thomas for details of Universal stairs.

I must express my appreciation to D. A. Russell for his work in preparing all but a few of the illustrations in this book, and for the care and co-operation he has shown throughout in maintaining a consistently high standard of work from which the book greatly benefits.

Finally, I am grateful to John S. Walkden, F.R.I.B.A., M.T.P.I., Head of the School of Architecture, Surveying and Town Planning of the Polytechnic, W.1., for the help and encouragement which I have received from him in many indirect ways, and to W. Greville Griffiths and Miss T. M. Nye, of the publishers, for their help and endless patience in seeing the work through to press.

                                                 J. S. F.

Contents

1
Contract Planning and Site Organization

At some point before commencing work on the site, thought must be given to the way in which the building operation will be organized. Most builders plan their work in some form or another but, in the past, only a few have done so in much detail and have committed their plan to paper. Buildings, and consequently their construction, have become increasingly complex and the proper management of a contract and the control of cost, on the part of the architect at design stage and the contractor during erection, are more than ever essential if building is to be carried out efficiently both in terms of time and money. Only by proper planning can aids to productivity, such as mechanical plant, incentives, and efficient use of labour, become fully effective. With the greater mechanization of building operations and the increased use of expensive plant, the contractor must obtain maximum use of the plant and speed the construction of the job in order to keep his costs to a minimum.

The building and civil engineering industry is peculiar in that the contractor who will be responsible for carrying out the work usually plays no part in the design of a project, and has no opportunity at this point to contribute from his experience on matters of construction, planning and the nomination of sub-contractors and thus to assist in the work being carried out efficiently, quickly and economically. Although the negotiated contract is often suggested as a means of overcoming this lack of collaboration at the design stage, it is not always suitable or acceptable since the element of competitive tendering is absent. In these circumstances it is, therefore, essential that the architect should have sufficient knowledge of contract planning and of its implications to ensure a well-organized job. Reference is made later to ways in which the architect can contribute to this end at the design stage.

Whether or not such a contribution is made by the architect, the responsibility for actually carrying out the job in all its aspects is that of the contractor. In order to enable him to do this efficiently management methods common to other industries are becoming more widely used in building. The subjects of this chapter, contract planning and site organization, together with general control, are the construction aspects of production management which itself is a part only of overall management in building.[1] *Planning* makes efficient and economical use of labour, machines and materials, *organizing* is the means of delegating tasks and *control* enables planning and organization to be effective.

There appears to be little literature at the moment on building management as such, apart from a number of papers and articles which have appeared in recent years. The subject of contract planning alone would, if dealt with adequately, require a book to itself. It is possible here to deal with it in outline only, pointing out its function, advantages and implications.

CONTRACT PLANNING

This involves working out a plan of campaign or a programme for the contract as a whole and assembling the necessary data. The primary function of such a programme is to promote the satisfactory organization and flow of the various building operations during the course of erection, by planning in advance the times and sequences of all operations and the requirements in labour, materials and equipment. In order to fulfil this function and also to provide important information required during the contract, a well planned programme will have certain clear objectives and *Building Research Station Digest* No. 91 states that it should:

(*a*) show the quickest and cheapest method of carrying out the work consistent with the available resources of the builder;

(*b*) by the proper phasing of operations with balanced labour gangs in all trades, ensure continuous productive work for all the operatives employed and reduce unproductive time to a minimum;

(*c*) provide an assessment of the level of productivity in all trades to permit the establishment of equitable bonus targets;

(*d*) determine attendance dates and periods for all sub-contractors' work;

(*e*) provide information on material quantities and essential delivery dates, the quantity and capacity of the plant required and the periods it will be on site;

(*f*) provide, at any time during the contract, a simple and rapid method of measuring progress, for the builder's information, the architect's periodical certificate or the valuation of work for accounting purposes.

---

[1] For other aspects of production management, see page 37, "Management Training in the Building Industry". British Institute of Management.

If a builder's tender for any sizeable job is to be realistic, planning must start at the estimating stage and the following considerations must be taken into account: The most economic methods to be used for each operation and the sequence and timing of the operations, having regard to the resources at the contractor's disposal; whether hand or mechanical methods will be most economical and the most suitable type of plant to be used in relation to the nature and size of the job; the space available and the best positions for the various machines to be used; the best methods of handling materials and the most suitable places on the site for the storage of materials and for the placing of huts; suitable points of access to the site for lorries and machines.   In deciding what methods to use for erection and the most suitable plant for different operations, the estimator would, when necessary, consult the contract planning and plant departments of the firm.

THE OVERALL PROGRAMME

On acceptance of the tender, contract planning commences and a working, or overall, programme is prepared by the contractor's planning staff together with the plant engineers and the site agent or foreman for the job. As already indicated this will be used as a guide for site activities, for detailed planning, for buying and the delivery of materials, for the co-ordination of sub-contractors' and main contractor's work and for assessing job progress. Assumptions made at the estimating stage are borne in mind.   It is essential at this point for the contractor to have full information from the architect in the form of a site survey, a full set of working drawings including, preferably, all details and full size drawings together with those of all specialists, a specification, a copy of the bills of quantities and a complete list of all nominated sub-contractors.   Ample time should be allowed for planning before commencement of work on the site.   For most jobs, unless particularly small, at least four weeks should be allowed.   The smaller jobs must be planned in detail at the outset, since there is no time for making adjustments during the course of a short contract.   The larger jobs may be planned on broader lines, since time will be available to carry out detailed planning as the job proceeds.

The preparation of the overall programme consists broadly of

(i) breaking the job down into a series of basic operations involving only one trade;

(ii) establishing the quantities of work in each operation and the time content of each in terms of men and machines;

(iii) arranging the operations in a sequence and balancing the size of gangs to give a maximum continuity of work for each trade and the minimum delay as one trade follows another;

(iv) breaking down a large job into phases so that several operations may proceed simultaneously.

The programme is ultimately expressed in chart form which covers all the main operations throughout the contract, the phasing of the work on different parts where this is necessary and the duration of each operation, including the work of all sub-contractors and specialists.   Together with this chart a written report or schedule is prepared, which includes a description of the methods to be used, schedules of plant, giving the dates when each machine will be required, the labour requirements for each stage of the work, and information regarding site offices, storage huts, equipment and small tools.   If, for any reason, the proposals in the contract plan differ from those assumed at the estimating stage, a written cost comparison is drawn up which shows the differences and the cost implications.

The overall programme shows the major operations and phasing of the job, but detailed short-term planning at regular intervals on the site is necessary to ensure the satisfactory allocation of labour and materials to each individual operation as the work proceeds.   This is usually carried out in two stages: (i) a reasonably detailed programme is prepared at monthly intervals, to cover the four weeks ahead, and (ii) a detailed programme is prepared each week, to ensure that labour, materials and plant will be available when required.   To enable the site foreman to give his full attention during the first few weeks to starting off the job, a detailed programme is prepared for him.   This indicates in detail the materials and labour requirements of the first four weeks, together with the operational methods to be used.

The broad picture of the contract planning process given above will now be considered in greater detail.

1. Break down of Job.   For the purpose of the overall programme the job must be broken down into groups of basic operations, each of which involve only one trade.   For example, in housing, the cutting and fixing of the carcassing timber in first floor and roof or the building of the brickwork or plastering throughout.   For convenience in doing this the whole of the job is divided into stages which are commonly

(1) foundations and walling up to D.P.C.
(2) carcase to completion of roofing in
(3) finishings and all services
(4) drains and site works.[1]

[1] See *Building Research Station Digest* No. 91, "The Programming of House-building" for complete schedule of operations on this basis.

In larger jobs and multi-storey work the break-down stages can be

(1) sub-structure, or foundation work
(2) frame, or basic structure
(3) claddings, infillings, weather-proofing, etc.
(4) finishings and services
(5) drains and site works.

Each stage is planned separately at first, to allow some flexibility in relating them on the site; delays due to bad weather or other causes can be provided for by varying the intervals between or overlapping the stages during the course of the job. Compensation for any variations from the programme arising within the stages can be made by increasing the gang sizes to speed up certain operations or, at times when productivity is greater than that assumed at the planning stage, labour can be put on to ancillary works and isolated jobs which, if omitted from the overall programme, can be carried out at any time without interfering with the sequence of other operations.

2. Quantities of Work and Time Content. In order to relate the various operations throughout the job, it is necessary to define the work content of each by means of a schedule of basic quantities, from which the number of man hours and machine hours required to complete each operation can be ascertained by the application of output rates per man or machine hour, or, as they are called, labour and plant standards. These standards in each case are established on the basis of information fed back from previous contracts or from work studies,[1] having regard to the type of labour which will be available and the likely demand on plant at the time of erection. The work content for each operation is then inserted on a schedule of basic operations which can be in the form of a series of *Data Sheets*. These are lists of all operations in sequence under trade sections, each operation being

---

[1] Work study is a tool of production management and is the name given to the study of work processes to find out if they are being done efficiently and, if not, to suggest means or alternative methods by which they may be carried out more efficiently. The process involves the examination of the way operations are performed, which is called *method* or *motion study*, and the time within which they are performed, which is called *time study*. Both of these studies are extensive but interdependent and are usually carried out concurrently by an executive trained in the technique of work study and called a "Studyman" or "Work Study Engineer".

Although in normal building work a very large proportion of individual assembly operations are non-repetitive, in some of the trades there is considerable repetition in the work. In some cases 50 to 65% of the work in the bricklayer and carpenter trades may be repetitive and some 40% of work in concreting is repetitive. Work study, by establishing standard times and developing correct methods, gives considerable advantages in these spheres. In addition, methods for new work may be developed by this means and standards derived which are fair and which provide the same incentive to operatives to earn a bonus as the repetitive work.

For fuller details see *Work Study* by R. M. Currie (Pitman, London).

numbered, against each of which is placed the quantity of work involved, the amount of labour, plant and materials in each, together with the estimated cost of each operation. Operations which can be carried out concurrently are noted. These sheets together form a detailed analysis of the complete work and give information for all planning activities during the course of the contract. They provide a link between the overall programme and detailed work on the site and enable the site agent or general foreman to prepare the short term plans accurately. In addition, they provide the basis on which materials can be ordered and the correct amount of labour can be put on each operation. The sheets also provide definite operations against which operatives' time can be recorded for purposes of site bonus and costing procedures.

3. Sequence and Timing of Operations. In any section of work which contains two or more operations, one of the operations will govern the time required to complete the whole of the work. Similarly, in each stage into which a job may be divided, there will be one operation or a group of related operations governing the production time of the complete stage. This "key operation" is the one which takes the longest time when the time cycles of all the operations are based on the use of the optimum size of gang for each. The longest of the key operations in each of the stages is termed the "master operation" and fixes the rate of production for the whole job. The speed of the master operation is governed either by the time in which the work has to be completed, the size of the gang being fixed accordingly, or by the amount of labour available, in which case the size of the gang which can be put on it will fix the time required to complete the operation. In either case, it is essential to bring all other operations into phase with the master operation. This is necessary in order to ensure continuity of productive work for each trade or gang and to minimize unproductive time in preparation and clearing up at the beginning and end of each operation. The time cycles of the operations in each stage are brought into phase by adjusting the size of the gangs so that the working time of each gang is the same as that of the key operation. This avoids one trade being idle while another related trade completes its work. Although some operations might be finished in a shorter period than the time cycle for the whole stage this would result in no difference in the overall building time, so that wherever possible gangs should be balanced (p. 7). This, however, is not always possible because in some circumstances there may be physical limits to the size of gang which can be used on a particular operation, or in one trade there may be insufficient work to occupy even one man continuously throughout the complete time cycle. These operations, which must be carried out intermittently, are usually in the services installation and finishing trades which are quite often subcontracted so that arrangements can be made for the work to be done at intervals within the main cycle of operations. The diagrams on this page show the effect of the balancing of working times upon continuity of work and unproductive time in the erection of a pair of semi-detached houses. It can be seen that unproductive time is reduced and the time cycle is shortened.

4. Phasing of Work. Where the job is extensive or consists of a number of blocks, it is usual to phase the job as a whole by dividing it into a number

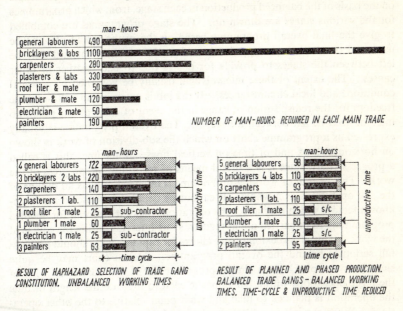

man-hours

general labourers	490
bricklayers & labs	1100
carpenters	280
plasterers & labs	330
roof tiler & mate	50
plumber & mate	120
electrician & mate	50
painters	190

NUMBER OF MAN-HOURS REQUIRED IN EACH MAIN TRADE

man-hours

4 general labourers	722	
3 bricklayers 2 labs	220	
2 carpenters	140	
2 plasterers 1 lab.	110	
1 roof tiler 1 mate	25	sub-contractor
1 plumber 1 mate	60	
1 electrician 1 mate	25	sub-contractor
3 painters	63	

unproductive time

← time cycle →

RESULT OF HAPHAZARD SELECTION OF TRADE GANG CONSTITUTION. UNBALANCED WORKING TIMES

man-hours

5 general labourers	98	
6 bricklayers 4 labs	110	
3 carpenters	93	
2 plasterers 1 lab.	110	
1 roof tiler 1 mate	25	s/c
1 plumber 1 mate	60	
1 electrician 1 mate	25	s/c
2 painters	95	

unproductive time

|time cycle|

RESULT OF PLANNED AND PHASED PRODUCTION. BALANCED TRADE GANGS - BALANCED WORKING TIMES. TIME-CYCLE & UNPRODUCTIVE TIME REDUCED

BALANCING OF TRADE GANGS

of sections, each of which is planned on the lines indicated above and so related to the other sections that trade gangs can proceed from one to another in a continuous progression.

Each operation should commence as soon as possible without necessarily waiting until the whole of the preceding one is complete, and each should have the largest practicable gang on it. In each stage and in all phases every operation should continue without a break to completion and each gang should be able to work continuously until it can leave the site altogether. Maximum production results when each member of a balanced gang is continuously engaged on the same work. It has been shown[1] that in such circumstances a definite increase in production takes place as the contract proceeds, up to a certain point, after which it tends to fall off slightly. In order to assist gangs special instruction is sometimes given on working methods by means of large scale or full-size mock-ups of parts of the structure, particularly when new systems are involved.

5. The Programme Chart. The final step is to prepare a working schedule on the basis of the balanced production in each stage, from which programmes for the various stages are drawn up. The stage programmes are combined to give the final overall programme based on the methods and plant to be used and on the balanced production of work. A short interval may be left between the stages to provide for delays due to bad weather or other causes. The extent of these intervals will usually be governed by seasonal conditions and local circumstances. If the job is extensive and allows some freedom for the redisposition of gangs in the event of delay at one point, no interval need be left between the stages. The overall programme is usually expressed as a programme chart on which the sub-division of work is shown on horizontal lines and of time on vertical lines. Sometimes this is called a progress chart, since it is a useful means of recording the progress of the work. This overall or working programme is intended only as an outline of the site operations as a whole. It cannot be detailed because so many unknown factors which may affect the operations make it essential for detailed programming to be carried out at regular, short intervals during the course of the work. This gives flexibility and allows for rapid revision should progress fall seriously behind the overall programme. Such a chart may be quite simple, or complex. As a simple progress chart it will consist of a list of the basic operations with a bar opposite each to indicate the length of time the operation is planned to take and what point relative to the other operations. When the job as a whole is phased, the bars are hatched in sections or lettered to indicate the work in each phase. Usually, the chart also indicates the dates on which orders for materials must be placed, the dates for the delivery of the various pieces of plant and the total number of men required each week, with or without a breakdown into trades.[2] A typical chart is shown on page 9.

In addition to the data sheets and the overall programme, the *schedule of contract information* is prepared giving the recommended labour force for

[1] See page 36 *National Building Studies Special Report* No. 29, "Organization of Building Sites". H.M.S.O.
[2] See *Building Research Station Digest* No. 91, "The Programming of House-building", for further details of the technique of programming. See also *National Building Studies Special Report* No. 29, "Organization of Building Sites", H.M.S.O.

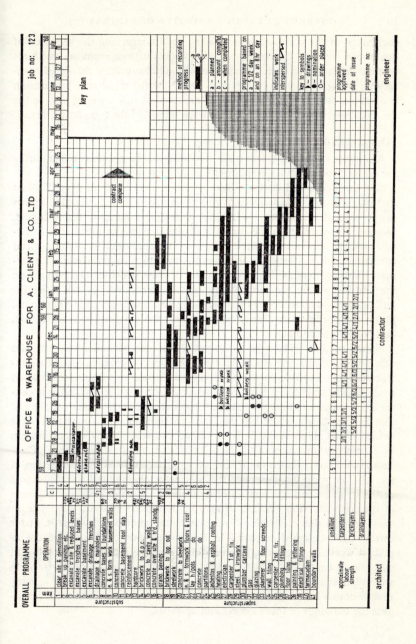

OVERALL PROGRAMME — OFFICE & WAREHOUSE FOR A. CLIENT & CO. LTD — job no: 123

key plan

contract complete

method of recording progress

a – planned
b – amount completed
c – when completed

programme based on a 5 1/2 day week and on an 8 hr day

indicates work interspersed

key to symbols
● – drawings
▲ – nomination
O – order placed

item	OPERATION
1	clear site & demolition
2	break up paving etc.
3	excavate o/site & reduced levels
4	excavate trenches & bases
5	excavate basement
6	excavate drainage trenches
7	drainage & manholes
8	concrete bases & foundations
9	e. & s. form work basement walls
10	concrete basement roof slab
11	reinforcement
12	hardcore
13	brickwork to d.p.c.
14	concrete to cavity walls
15	concrete over site & h.d. standg
16	grano pavings
17	brickwork to top out
18	steelwork
19	concrete to steelwork
20	e. & s. formwork floors & roof
21	lay h/pots
22	concrete do
23	concrete do
24	partitions
25	asbestos & asphalt roofing
26	sheeting
27	electrician 1st fix
28	carpenter 1st fix
29	steel & ironwork
30	plumber carcase
31	gas
32	glazing
33	plasterer & floor screeds
34	wall tiling
35	carpenter 2nd fix
36	plumbing fittings
37	floor tiling
38	painting & lettering
39	electrical fittings
40	tarmacadam
41	boundary walls

substructure

superstructure

approximate labour strength	
unskilled	
Carpenters	
bricklayers	
drainlayers	

architect — contractor — engineer

programme approved
date of issue
programme no:

each stage of the contract under trades, details regarding the sequence of operations given on the data sheets, and details of equipment and methods of construction to be used. This schedule will also include full details concerning all sub-contractors. A site layout plan and a site preparation programme (see page 16) will also be prepared at this stage, as well as the detailed programme for the first four week period of the contract (p. 11).

PLANNING CONSIDERATIONS

A number of factors which have a bearing on the decisions made during the contract planning stage are briefly considered here.

Site Conditions and Access. Site conditions will limit the type of plant that may be used. On wet sites it will be necessary to use tracked machines in the case of excavators and mobile cranes, and dumpers for transport. Sloping sites may make the use of rail mounted cranes unsuitable or uneconomical. On confined sites there may be insufficient room for a mixer or mixing plant and it may be necessary to use truck mixed concrete. Limitations of access may fix the maximum size of plant which can be brought on the site for use on the job. A site closely surrounded by tall adjoining buildings may dictate the use of a derricking jib crane rather than a horizontal jib crane in order to be able to rise and clear the buildings as it turns from one position to another.

Nature of Job. The type of structure and the general form, size and detailing of the building will all have an effect upon the way in which the contract is planned. Reference is made on page 15 to the significance of decisions made by the architect at the design stage. As far as the contractor is concerned, he must consider the nature of the structure in relation to the site so that he can decide where best to place his equipment and materials. It is desirable that all plant should be so placed on the site that the structure can be erected without moving the plant until most of it is completed. Plant should also be so placed that it can be removed easily at the completion of the job. In some circumstances the contractor may request the adjustment of the structure in some way, in order to permit the most efficient planning of the contract. For example, it may be desirable slightly to enlarge a lift shaft in order that a climbing crane may be accommodated within it, or for certain parts designed originally as *in situ* cast work to be carried out as precast work, or vice versa, in order fully to utilize a crane on the job. In addition to conditions round the site, the height and width of the building will influence the choice of the type of crane. As shown in Chapter 2, many mobile cranes have limitations of height and reach which make them unsuitable for buildings of three storeys and upwards.

contract: A. CLIENT & Co. Ltd
job no: 123
period 7.9.'59 to 5.10.'59

MONTHLY PERIOD PROGRAMME

method of recording progress:
- a: planned
- b: amt. completed
- c: when compl'd

OPERATION	QNT.	LAB.
clear site		4
demolition		4
break up pavings	1132 ys	2
excavate oversite	197 yc	2
excavate reduced levels	201 yc	2
excavate surface trenches & bases	250 yc	2
do.	61 yc	5
excavate basement	200 yc	2
excavate basement foundations	30 yc	5
blinding to trenches & bases	14 yc	6
concrete do.	70 yc	6
make basement wall formwork		3/1
erect do.		3/1
make formwork to stairs, slab etc		
blinding to basement foundations	9 yc	6
concrete basement floor slab	61 yc	6
brickwork to sump		1/1
reinforcement to basement walls		2
hardcore to hardstanding	421yc	6
brickwork to d.p.c.		5/2

Week headings: 7th sept. | 14th sept. | 21st sept. | 28th sept. | 5th oct.
Days: M Tu W T F S Su

Plant/equipment notes within bars: traxcavator, traxcavatpr, 10 RB backacter, 14/10 mixer and dumper, 10 R B backacter, 3 ton roller

LABOUR

	7th sept							14th sept							21st sept							28th sept							5th oct.						
unskilled	4	4	4	4	4	4		5	5	5	5	5	5		6	6	6	6	6	6		6	6	6	6	6	6		6	6	6	6	6	6	
carpenters															3/1	3/1	3/1	3/1	3/1	3/1		3/1	3/1	3/1	3/1	3/1	3/1		3/1	3/1	3/1	3/1	3/1	3/1	
bricklayers																								1/1					5/2	5/2	5/2	5/2	5/2	5/2	
drivers								1	1	1	1	1	1		1	1	1	1	1	1		1	1	1	1	1	1								
steelfixers																								2					2						

Plant. The choice of the most suitable plant for any particular operation necessitates a consideration of the capabilities, limitations and outputs of different types of plant, some indication of which is given in Chapter 2. The following paragraphs deal with a few aspects of the choice of plant at the planning stage.

Excavation can be carried out either mechanically by a number of different types of plant or by hand, the spoil can be transported in various types of vehicle and the length of haul to tip will vary with the job, so that many combinations of excavator and transporting machines are possible and the contract planner, from his experience and knowledge of plant, must in each case arrive at the most economic combination. The method adopted for excavating operations will be dependent upon

- (*a*) the type of excavation to be carried out
- (*b*) the nature of the soil to be excavated
- (*c*) the volume of soil to be excavated
- (*d*) the length of haul to tip and the terrain over which the machinery has to dig and travel.

For small quantities, hand excavation is cheaper than mechanical excavation and the type of transport will depend on the distance to be hauled, the nature of the ground to be traversed and the cost of temporary roads, where necessary.

The total work to be carried out must be reviewed in order to establish whether or not it is possible to use one machine for a number of operations rather than a number of different machines. For example, an excavator rigged as a backacter will dig trenches and, also, when rigged with a skimmer, could carry out the reduction of levels on the site if these were not too great in area, and thus avoid the use of another machine in addition to the excavator.

Work must be also phased in such a way that mechanical plant can be used. For example, if a run of drain trench sufficiently long to justify mechanical digging is situated near the building, work must be planned so that the trenches are dug before the building of the structure is commenced in order to provide room for the digger to work.

Handling of structural units and materials in fabrication and erection can be carried out satisfactorily by crane, but if the use of a crane is to prove economical the work must be planned round the crane, the influence of which will, to a large extent, determine the production cycle. Careful consideration must be given to the quantity and nature of materials to be handled and whether or not there is sufficient to keep a crane fully occupied throughout the working day. The delivery of incoming structural and fabricated elements should be phased with the building operations so that they can be off-loaded and placed immediately in their final positions by the crane wherever possible, thus avoiding double handling. In addition to the establishment of balanced gangs the most important factor in planning for high productivity is the reduction of double-handling. This involves the careful timing of materials deliveries and the delivery of all materials as near as possible to the point at which they will be used, together with the correct siting of hoisting plant, materials dumps and mixing plant in relation to the building, and to each other. Materials should be grouped near cranes and hoists so that they can be moved in order of requirement, and in such positions that the crane can hoist and place in one operation with the minimum change of position.

Bricks may be packaged by straps into multiples of fifty, or handled, together with blocks, on pallets so that the crane has a reasonable load to hoist. The sizes of precast elements or shuttering units should be related as far as possible to the lifting capacity of the crane in order to avoid excessive numbers of lifts and to speed up erection. In this respect the architect is able to consider the size of precast units, such as claddings for example, on broad lines only, bearing in mind the likelihood or not of a crane being used on a particular job. This is because the choice of crane depends on other considerations in addition to that of the size of any precast concrete units, and these, under normal contracting methods, become known to the contractor only after the design stage.

The most suitable type of crane will depend not only on the work it is required to perform but, as mentioned earlier, also on the nature of the building on which it is to be used. On large sites it is often necessary to introduce more than one crane and even on a single block if it is long, a single crane may give insufficient coverage. During the planning stage, it may be necessary to investigate the advantages and disadvantages of different combinations of cranes by means of diagrams such as shown on page 14. It will be seen that when two cranes are used, in order to obtain complete coverage of the building, the arcs of the jibs must intercept and adequate precautions on the job must be taken to avoid collision of the jibs and hoist ropes as the cranes slew. There is less likelihood of such a collision when derricking jib cranes are used, and when horizontal jib cranes are employed the booms should be set at different levels. It will also be seen from this diagram that as well as the amount of coverage given to the building, the stacking area for materials covered by the arc of the jibs is a significant factor.

Mixing. Type and size of concrete mixer are dictated to a large extent by the quality and quantity of concrete required. The suitability of the various types of mixers in these respects are described in Chapter 2.   To obtain highest efficiency, the concreting equipment must be carefully combined according to the kind of work to be done.   When small to medium quantities, say up to 30 cubic yards per day are required, a mixer, together with hand loading of the aggregate skip, some form of weigh batching and hand barrow delivery can be economical, although scraper loading, being so cheap, is generally used except for very small quantities.   If mechanical delivery is used, then the labour requirement is reduced.   When steady outputs of not less than 40 cubic yards per day are required, complete mechanization is best and this would involve a mechanical scoop or gravity loading of the mixer skip, gravity fed bulk cement and, for delivery, a crane carrying a full batch skip or, alternatively, a pneumatic concrete placer.

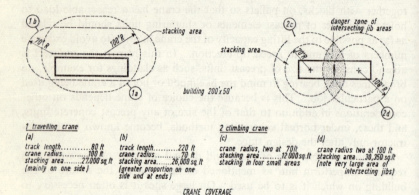

1 travelling crane

(a)
track length..........80 ft
crane radius..........100 ft
stacking area........27,000 sq ft
(mainly on one side)

(b)
track length..........220 ft
crane radius..........70 ft
stacking area.........26,000 sq ft
(greater proportion on one
side and at ends)

2 climbing crane

(c)
crane radius, two at 70ft
stacking area........12,000 sq ft
stacking in four small areas

(d)
crane radius two at 100 ft
stacking area....30,250 sq.ft
(note very large area of
intersecting jibs)

CRANE COVERAGE

When a job incorporates some *in situ* concrete work and some precast work, it is sometimes possible to arrange site precasting to occupy the idle time of a mixer and its associated handling equipment.

The decision on whether or not to set up a central mixing plant will depend on the amount of concrete to be produced, the relative costs of setting up a central plant and a number of individual mixers, and the relative costs of mixing by the two methods.   In addition, the cost of transport from the central mixer to the various points of placing will also affect the decision.

Type of Plant.   In considering alternatives for the same operation, it must be borne in mind that the cost of mechanical operations is influenced by the nature of the particular job, the sequence of work dictated by the design of the structure and the methods used for erection, and by the amount of work to be done. The efficiency of any mechanized system cannot, therefore, be judged solely on the cost of equipment, but on the influence the system has upon all the related operations and thus upon the overall cost. It is often the case that a combination of plant which is dearer than an alternative combination, permits the work to be carried out with greater continuity and in a shorter time, so that the overall cost is cheaper.[1]

Design Factors. The importance of a contribution from the architect at the design stage toward improvement in job organization is stressed on page 1, and some indication is given here of the manner in which this might be made.

If, in designing, account is taken of the operations which the craftsmen must perform in carrying out the work, and unnecessary labours are avoided, greater speed in construction will result. Simplicity of construction and detailing leads to economies by enabling work to proceed quickly, thus reducing the contract period. Site operations can be simplified in many ways such as by reducing variations in the widths of foundations so that changes in trench-digger shovels are kept to a minimum; by maintaining floor slabs at a uniform level and allowing for variations in finishes by different thicknesses of screed rather than by variations in the floor slab; by designing openings and lengths of wall to brick dimensions in order to avoid the cutting of bricks. By avoiding breaks and returns in walls as far as possible, in order to simplify brick and block work, or shuttering in the case of concrete work, and to keep foundation runs straight to simplify digging.

Interference and delay arise on the job when more than one trade has to work on one item at the same time, or one trade has to wait on another before completing work it has partly finished. This can be avoided by the separation of trades at the design stage. For example, by designing the brick walls to a single-storey building as panels running from floor slab to roof, with no openings in them, and the doors and windows as units running from floor to roof with no brickwork over, the bricklayer and carpenter can carry out their operations independently. If the roof is of timber construction, since no concrete lintels are required over openings, the concretor does not have to wait after having formed the floor slab in order to follow the carpenter and place the lintels. Finishing work is also simplified as the plasterer has only to work on plain surfaces.

Detailing which results in the division of work and the mixing of materials can prevent the use of the most efficient arrangement of mechanical plant.

---

[1] See *The Structural Engineer*, February 1958: "The Problem of Mechanical Handling in Building Operations" by J. F. Eden and D. Bishop, where this is discussed and illustrated by comparative priced programmes.

This can occur, for example, on small contracts of domestic work in which cross-walls in some blocks are of concrete and in others are of brick, so that the main contractor is not provided with sufficient concrete work to justify him setting up an efficient mechanized concrete mixing plant. Similar circumstances can arise when there is a division of similar work between the main contractor and a nominated sub-contractor.

The absence of continuity of work is an important factor which reduces the value of the mechanization of most building operations because so much time is spent on preparatory work between operations rather than on productive work. Continuity is more likely if the operations are simple and repetitive. This should be dealt with at the design stage by detailing which results in (i) as few operations as possible for each aspect of the work, and (ii) the separation of the work of fabrication from that of erection, since the problems of each are so different that any mechanization must be independent. The detailing of elements which must be moved into position should be such that the loads to be handled closely approach the capacity of the plant likely to be used. (See also page 24.)

SITE ORGANIZATION

SITE PLANNING

As described earlier, a programme covering operations during the first four weeks will have been drawn up at planning stage, in the preparation of which, where possible, the general foreman or agent responsible for the contract will have assisted, so that he is in agreement with the proposals laid down. This programme will be generally in two parts:

(a) Site preparation programme, which will cover the demolishing of any existing buildings, the setting out of the site and marking out of storage areas, the erection of huts and the construction of temporary access roads where necessary.

(b) Period I programme, on the lines of that shown on page 11, which will cover work during the first four weeks or so of the contract.

Together with these will be provided site layout plans to show (a) traffic routes, on which will be indicated any areas requiring particular attention, such as levelling-off or covering with temporary Summerfield track, and any direction signs required; (b) the location of offices, huts and stores; (c) the position of bulk storage areas both during and after excavation together with the location of any equipment.

The general foreman or agent will in addition also be provided with copies of the overall programme, schedule of contract information and data sheets as well as all other necessary documents such as bills of quantities, specification, set of contract drawings, details of all material orders placed and to be placed at various dates during the contract, and finally details of the type and quantity of equipment to be used and the approximate periods when they will be required on the site.

Period Planning. Work on the site will commence on the basis of the first monthly programme and during the third week of this period, and all subsequent stages, the next monthly programme will be prepared on the basis of the overall plan and data sheets. In the preparation of the monthly plan consideration must be given to the labour force desirable and that practicable in the circumstances at the time, to plant requirements and availability, to the phasing and overlapping of operations to ensure completion of the work in the minimum time and to the planning of labour to maintain group identities. Steps must be taken to give adequate warning to all subcontractors when they will be required on the site.

Weekly Planning. Towards the end of each week progress will be reviewed and the next week's planned progress confirmed or modified if necessary. The following week's planned labour requirements will be reviewed and an estimate made of materials required for the next week but one and of any action required to be taken regarding equipment. This weekly review will be prepared by the general foreman in consultation with his trade foremen and any sub-contractors' foremen, and a written report will be submitted to the contractor's planning department. In certain cases where close integration of fully mechanized operations is required over a short period, particularly in the case of reinforced concrete structures, a weekly programme would be drawn up in chart form by the planning department. Such a chart is illustrated on page 18. In addition to weekly planning, the general foreman will hold a brief meeting each day with his trade foremen and sub-contractor foremen to review the next day's work and to make the necessary preparations in regard to the placing of materials and equipment in readiness for the next day's operations.

The general foreman will, at the beginning of the job whenever possible, indicate to the local employment office his anticipated "build up" of labour force during the course of the contract.

Progress Control. Good site planning is a prior necessity to smooth and effective progress in construction work, but a regular review of the progress of all operations and its comparison with the programme or plan is essential.

Progress is maintained by the foreman, or on larger jobs by a progress engineer, by the proper organization of the delivery and placing of materials,

WEEKLY PROGRAMME — **QUANTITIES FOR TYPICAL UPPER FLOOR** — job name and number

concrete		steel		formwork	
floor slabs	= 60 yc	floor	= 2.35 tons	floors	= 2700 f.s.
walls	= 27 yc	walls & columns	= 1.00 tons	walls	= 3120 f.s.
columns	= 4 yc	P.C. beams	= 1.15 tons	columns	= 490 f.s.
P.C. beams total	= 91 yc	total	= 4.50 tons	total	= 6310 f.s.
total	= 6 yc				

labour force
carpenters = 10
steel fixers = 4
trade labourers = 10
crane drivers = 1
total = 25

HOURS: 8 16 24 32 40 44

OPERATION	
A	fix wall and column steel
B	bend and fix slab steel
A	erect wall and column formwork lift and place p.c. lintels
A	concrete walls
A	fix p.c. beams
B	bend steel and make up p.c. beams
A	strike walls, complete erection columns
A	erect slab formwork, lift and place p.c. balconies
A	concrete column-
B	concrete slab
A	complete slab formwork
B	fix wall and column steel place p.c. beams
A	fix slab steel
B	erect wall and column form-work, lift and place p.c. lintels
B	concrete walls
B	fix p.c. beams
A	bend steel and make up p.c. beams
B	strike walls, comolete erection columns
	lift and place p.c. stairs and landings etc.
A	erect slab formwork lift and place p.c. balconies
A	concrete slab
B	concrete columns
B	complete slab formwork
A B	hoist and stack bricks

Legend: steel fixer — carpenter — concretor — brick stacking by ensuring that all equipment and plant is in its correct position at the right time, and by adjusting the size of labour gangs when progress is likely to fall behind the programme because of unforeseen circumstances. Progress is checked during weekly planning by estimating or measuring the work completed, the percentage of each operation or group of operations completed being established and compared with the programme. Progress is marked on the programme charts as indicated on page 9. When progress varies appreciably from the overall programme and where for this and any other reason it is considered desirable to alter the planned sequence of operations, the general foreman would consult the planning department before making such changes. Close co-operation between the site staff and the planning department is often maintained by means of regular and formal site production meetings between the general foreman and the planning engineer responsible for the job. When considering any changes, the effect on the supply of materials must be borne in mind, and when progress is faster than planned, the supply of materials in time for the work becomes the predominating factor. All sub-contractors must be notified immediately of any changes in the planned programme of work.

The general foreman should maintain a record of current and planned labour strength in the form of a schedule or chart on which the following week's planned labour requirements will be entered during weekly planning. In addition, all incoming material will be recorded on a form, one for each main item, which should show amongst other information dates of order and receipt, quantity delivered and the balance of material outstanding.

As an aid to progress control on a job of any size, in addition to the site production meetings mentioned above, other regular site meetings should be held at which should be present the contract manager, site agent or general foreman, architect, clerk of works, quantity surveyor and any sub-contractors when necessary. At these meetings all aspects of the job requiring attention are discussed and decisions for future action made. To ensure that maximum benefit is obtained from such a site meeting, an agenda should be prepared and circulated some days prior to the meeting and minutes should be prepared and circulated as soon as possible after the meeting.

SITE LAYOUT

The layout of every site may be divided into an administrative area and a construction area. In the former will be located stores, offices, sub-contractors' huts and canteen and similar accommodation if this is provided, and in the latter, which will be the actual site of the buildings being constructed, will be located consumable stores adjacent to the various buildings and all equipment required for construction purposes.   The layout of both these areas forms an essential part of early planning in every contract, the neglect of which will lead to delay in the initial progress of the job, the tying up of more capital than necessary in materials and financial loss on the part of the contractor.

Proper access and departure routes for lorries should be provided and these should be clearly signposted.   In determining the traffic routes, attention must be paid to the position of all main services, such as water, gas and electricity, and to drains and excavations.   Temporary roads must be positioned with sufficient distance between them and future buildings to allow for the movement or positioning of all mechanical plant.

The *administrative area* should be located to give quick access to that area of the site which will require maximum labour control and the main storage area, sub-contractors' huts and canteen, should be so located that accessibility for unloading materials is good and so that they are a minimum distance from the construction areas.   The site office should be sited on the route into the administrative area and with as good a view as possible of the construction areas.   The size of the site office will vary with the accommodation to be provided, which will depend in turn upon the size of the contract.   It should provide accommodation for all or any of the following: Agent, general foreman, quantity surveyor, timekeepers, bonus surveyor, checker, clerk of works, resident engineer, small lock-up store and conference room.

All contracts of any size in the present day require adequate telephone facilities for communication, electricity for power, compressed air for equipment, and lighting and heating facilities for office huts.   At a very early point in the planning stage the necessary arrangements for these services will be put in hand, particularly requests for telephone facilities and electricity.

The stores area should be situated near the site office and will consist of covered huts for valuable or non-weatherproof stores, such as paint and ironmongery, and a locked pen for larger valuable stores which are weatherproof, such as metal window frames and pipes.   Storage for sub-contractors will be located near the sub-contractors' huts and sometimes they will be situated within the stores area.

Where possible the moving of the administrative area to another part of the site during the course of a contract should be avoided by careful initial site planning, but where this is essential because of the nature of the site or the job, a further site layout plan would be prepared for each move involved.

The *construction area* should contain the minimum practical quantities of materials and of necessary equipment and these should be so positioned that handling and movement is kept to a minimum. As the position of equipment, particularly mixers, hoists and cranes, will influence the position of materials such as sand, aggregates and bricks, the position of all plant should be planned before that of the materials. Materials arrive on the site in the order decided at planning stage, or in accordance with instructions issued from the site, and sufficient area must be provided to accommodate the size of batch ordered. In addition, overflow areas should be allocated. In planning the layout of the site, consideration must be given to the excavation stages as these may seriously restrict proposed storage areas.

Standardized materials, such as bricks, tiles and drainpipes, should be stacked in unit dumps, the numbers in which remain constant although the length, breadth and height may be varied to suit site conditions. Aggregates, sited round the mixer, should be accommodated in light bays which will keep the material separate, prevent waste and facilitate the checking of quantities in stock. If dumps are clearly identified by signboards, preferably put in position a day or two prior to the arrival of the materials, this saves time in giving instructions to lorry drivers on entering the site and avoids the possibility of dumping materials in the wrong position.

2
Contractors' Mechanical Plant

In its widest sense "contractors' plant" implies the machinery, tools (other than craftsmen's personal tools) and other equipment used in the contractor's yard and workshop, and on the site. In this chapter contractors' mechanical plant and power tools only will be discussed, in particular those used on the building site. Machinery used solely in the workshop, such as woodworking and stonecutting machinery, some of which is discussed in *Mitchell's Elementary Building Construction*, will not be considered nor will contractors' general equipment such as ladders, lifting tackle and wheelbarrows. Scaffolding, the erection of which often presents minor structural problems, is discussed in Chapter 11.

The machines and power tools which are the subject of this chapter are divided into three classes according to their degree of mobility: (i) fixed, (ii) portable, (iii) mobile. The first group includes machines which operate from a fixed position on the site, the second group, machines and tools which can be moved about by pulling, pushing or carrying by hand, and the third group, those which can move from one place to another under their own power. They may further be divided into classes according to their function and are later discussed on this basis.

THE MECHANIZATION OF BUILDING OPERATIONS

The use of suitable mechanical aids on the site can reduce building costs considerably and speed up building operations. The off-site production of most building materials and components is generally highly mechanized; the mechanization of site operations has been far less general. But during the last ten to fifteen years there has been in Great Britain a marked trend towards a greater degree of mechanization. To a large extent this is due to the rising cost of labour. The introduction of mechanical aids reduces labour costs and, by increasing the speed of construction, results in earlier completion and enables the building owner to occupy the building and recover his capital outlay at an earlier date.

It has been pointed out[1] that there are a number of obstacles in the way

[1] "Recent Research into the Use of Mechanical Aids for Building" by N. S. Farrow and J. F. Eden—paper presented to the Building Research Congress 1951.

of complete mechanization of building. Compared with other industries, building work is less repetitive and involves the movement of plant from one place to another as one job is completed and the next commenced. Most jobs present different constructional problems and site conditions vary. Perhaps the greatest hindrance lies in the fact that the greater majority of building designs, building techniques and sequences of operations on the site are still based on manual methods. Unless a building is so designed and the contract work so organized that machines can be operated for continuous periods at full capacity their use will not be economic.

The Department of Scientific and Industrial Research, through the Building Research Station, has carried out valuable work in the development of plant, especially that designed for use on housing and other small scale work. The most marked development is probably to be seen in the use of the crane, originally employed in this country primarily for erection and fixing and now widely used for the handling and movement of materials. This has been possible because of the introduction of tall, long jib cranes from the continent, where they had long been used for this purpose. This has been followed by the development and production of similar cranes in Britain.

The high cost of the more expensive plant can be justified only if the plant is kept in more or less continuous use. Many firms, especially the smaller contractors, experience difficulty in maintaining the necessary sequence of operations over a period long enough to justify the high initial cost of the plant. There are now, however, a considerable number of specialist firms with the necessary equipment who can be hired to carry out a particular operation, as well as firms who only stock plant for hire, so that with adequate and careful planning it is possible for even the smaller contractor to mechanize those operations which can thereby be performed more cheaply.

The efficient employment of mechanical plant depends on a number of factors which must be given careful consideration at the outset of each job. Haphazard mechanization will not necessarily either reduce costs nor reduce the total construction time. Careful planning of the work throughout is essential.

PLANNING FOR THE USE OF MECHANICAL PLANT

Nature of Job and Site

While it is true that on large contracts, provided the work is satisfactorily planned, mechanization will usually be advantageous, on smaller contracts other means of rationalization alone may be more effective, such as careful programming of the work, flexible methods of working, efficiently planned site organization and the use of production aids to normal manual methods.

These include ready dry-mixed mortars, building jigs and frame scaffolding. Site conditions must also be suitable and some of the limitations arising from these are mentioned on page 10.

Relationship Between Operations of Plant and of Men

It is essential, particularly in mechanical handling, that the number of men working on any operation should be correctly related to the output of the mechanical plant serving them.   This is necessary in order to avoid the plant being idle from time to time while the men use the material already delivered to them.   Concreting gangs, for example, must be related in size and number to the size of concrete mixer used so that each load of concrete can be received and placed by the time the next load is delivered.   The number of men who can work efficiently on any one site is, of course, limited by the size of the job, the nature of the structure and other considerations, so that this will set a limit to the size of mechanical plant capable of being used to advantage (see also page 6).

Careful Planning and Programming of the Contract as a Whole

This is essential in order that the plant, which is expensive to hire or to purchase and maintain, is occupied to the maximum extent while on the site. Ideally, the sequence of all operations throughout the job, whether mechanized or manual, should be so arranged that no plant on the site is ever idle. This requires careful consideration in the choice of the most appropriate plant for each particular operation to ensure that it will always be working to its full capacity, yet neither too quickly nor too slowly for the manual work to which it is related (see pages 6, 12).

Suitability of the Design of the Building

The design of a building determines the work to be done in its erection and, to a large extent, the sequence in which that work is carried out.   If, therefore, full benefit is to be derived from the use of mechanical plant all aspects of mechanization and building methods must be considered at the design stage, so that when the contractor takes over the work can be arranged in a manner suited to mechanical rather than to wholly manual operations. It is essential that the architect should be aware of the advantages of mechanized methods, of the nature and capabilities of various types of mechanical plant and of the factors which are likely to make their use of greatest value.   These include continuity of operations and the use of plant at maximum capacity every time it is operated.   For example, precast concrete cladding panels can be designed as large or small units.   A crane will be more economically employed in hoisting them if the panels are designed as large units approaching in weight the maximum lifting capacity of the crane likely to be used on the job, rather than if they are smaller in size and weight. The cost of hoisting one large or one small panel will be much the same so that the relative cost of hoisting a number of the small panels equivalent in area to one of the larger panels will be high.

Simplification of design, particularly in constructional detailing, is necessary to assist the mechanization of building, and must become a normal process in architectural practice if greater advantage is to be taken of plant commonly used and if the development of new plant is to be encouraged (see page 15).

MECHANICAL PLANT

In addition to the classification according to mobility already given, page 22, most mechanical plant may be classified according to function and will be described under the following headings:

Excavating—Hoisting—Transporting—Mixing.

EXCAVATING

The process of excavating covers both surface and deep excavation of soil and often involves the movement of the excavated soil by the excavating equipment itself.

Excavating plant, apart from a few special machines such as trenchers, may be broadly divided into equipment based (i) on an excavator, which is a tracked or wheeled self-propelled machine consisting of a chassis carrying a revolving platform and a power-operated jib or boom controlled by wire ropes, together with a driver's cabin, and which is designed to be used for a number of different excavating operations by changing the booms and buckets, and (ii) that based on a tractor, either tracked or wheeled.

The nature of the excavation to be performed, the type of soil to be excavated, the distances which the excavated soil must be carried to transport and the condition and gradients of the site are among the factors which must be borne in mind in selecting the equipment for any particular job. Excavating plant cannot have much influence on architectural design, but the machines are expensive if kept idle or are only partly worked, so that careful planning of the work relative to the job and the plant to be used is essential.

Excavators

An excavator may be rigged as a face shovel, backacter, skimmer, dragline or crane and grab as shown on page 26, all of which can be used to load the

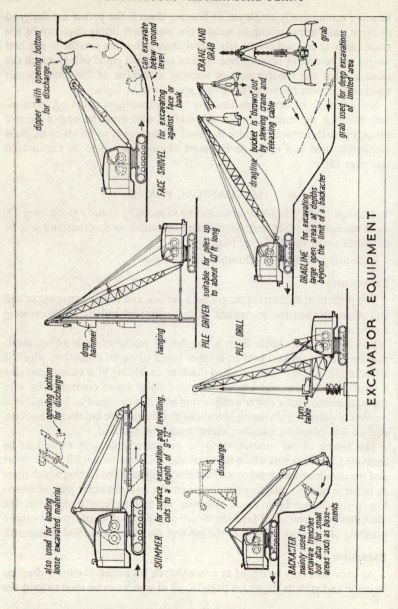

EXCAVATOR EQUIPMENT

FACE SHOVEL for excavating against face or bank

dipper with opening bottom for discharge

can excavate below ground level

CRANE AND GRAB

grab

dragline for excavating large open areas at depths beyond the limit of a backacter

bucket is 'thrown' out by slewing crane and releasing cable

grab used for deep excavations of limited area

DRAGLINE for excavating large open areas at depths beyond the limit of a backacter

PILE DRIVER suitable for piles up to about 40 ft long

drop hammer

hanging

PILE DRILL

turn table

SKIMMER for surface excavation and levelling, cuts to a depth of 9"-12"

opening bottom for discharge

also used for loading loose excavated material

discharge

BACKACTER mainly used to excavate trenches but also for small areas such as basements

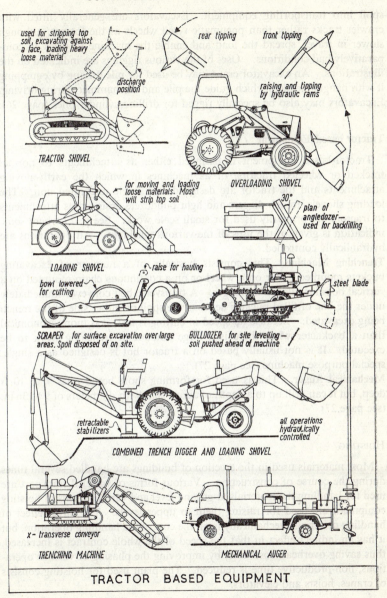

used for stripping top soil, excavating against a face, loading heavy loose material

discharge position

TRACTOR SHOVEL

rear tipping

front tipping

raising and tipping by hydraulic rams

OVERLOADING SHOVEL

for moving and loading loose materials. Most will strip top soil

30°

plan of angledozer— used for backfilling

LOADING SHOVEL

raise for hauling

bowl lowered for cutting

steel blade

SCRAPER for surface excavation over large areas. Spoil disposed of on site.

BULLDOZER for site levelling — soil pushed ahead of machine

retractable stabilizers

all operations hydraulically controlled

COMBINED TRENCH DIGGER AND LOADING SHOVEL

x- transverse conveyor

TRENCHING MACHINE

MECHANICAL AUGER

TRACTOR BASED EQUIPMENT

spoil into transporting equipment. Excavators are generally fitted with crawler tracks rather than pneumatic tyred wheels as the former, although slower in travel, spread the load and enable the machine to work in comparatively bad conditions. Uses of the various riggings are indicated on the illustrations. An excavator crane may be used for pile driving by equipping it with hanging leaders which guide the pile and the hammer during driving. Excavators may also be specially rigged for drilling cylinder piles (page 26).

Tractor based Equipment

Tractor-based equipment is designed either as attachments to normal tracked or wheeled tractors, or as machines in which the earth-moving attachments and the tractor are designed as a single integrated unit. The loading shovels, trench diggers and light bulldozers designed as attachments to tractors are primarily used for small scale work. See p. 27 where some indication is given of the uses of the various machines. All operations are hydraulically controlled.

Trenching Machine. This consists basically of a number of excavating buckets mounted either on a wheel or on a continuous chain mounted on a vertical boom similar to a dredger. A transverse belt conveyor immediately under the line of filled buckets deposits the spoil on either side of the trench being excavated. Because its speed in cutting is fast, it is more economical than a backacter when there is a large amount of trenching work to be executed. It is not usually based on a tractor but is designed as a single, special purpose machine (see page 27).

Mechanical Auger. This is used for forming short bored piles 7 to 10 ft deep, but it can drill up to a depth of about 20 ft with diameters of 9 to 36 in. (see page 27).

HOISTING

Most materials used in the erection of buildings are handled several times during the course of construction. Various forms of wheeled transport are used for handling the materials at ground level and various forms of hoisting equipment are used for raising them to upper levels. The direct effect of handling materials mechanically is on the cost of the handling operation, but it has an indirect effect in that the speed of the whole contract is increased, thus saving overhead costs and, by improving the phasing of various operations, non-productive time is reduced. The plant used for hoisting consists of cranes, hoists and elevators.

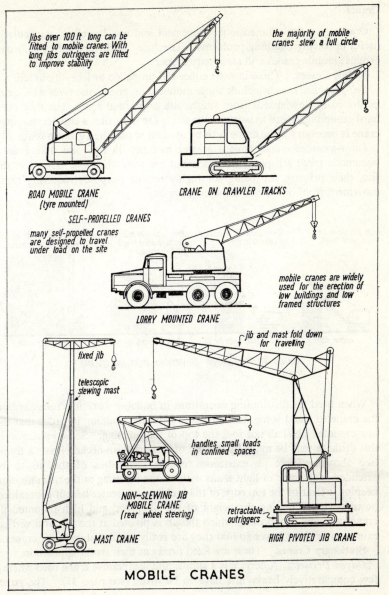

Jibs over 100 ft long can be fitted to mobile cranes. With long jibs outriggers are fitted to improve stability

the majority of mobile cranes slew a full circle

ROAD MOBILE CRANE
(tyre mounted)

CRANE ON CRAWLER TRACKS

SELF-PROPELLED CRANES

many self-propelled cranes are designed to travel under load on the site

mobile cranes are widely used for the erection of low buildings and low framed structures

LORRY MOUNTED CRANE

jib and mast fold down for travelling

fixed jib

telescopic slewing mast

handles small loads in confined spaces

NON-SLEWING JIB
MOBILE CRANE
(rear wheel steering)

retractable outriggers

MAST CRANE

HIGH PIVOTED JIB CRANE

MOBILE CRANES

Cranes

Cranes give three-dimensional movement and are, therefore, particularly useful in solving handling problems. They may be divided into two broad groups: mobile cranes and stationary cranes.

Mobile Cranes. These may be either self-propelled or lorry-mounted.

Self-propelled cranes include those mounted on pneumatic tyres which can be driven at slow speeds from site to site on normal roads, but they need hard ground on which to work on the site. On most sites a crawler mounted crane is necessary if the crane is to be used on unprepared ground (page 29).

Lorry-mounted cranes have a greater mobility on the road than even a pneumatic tyred self-propelled crane but are somewhat less mobile on the site, their primary use being for highly mobile purposes requiring rapid movement from one site to another (page 29).

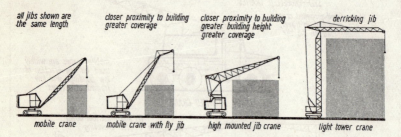

all jibs shown are the same length

closer proximity to building greater coverage

closer proximity to building greater building height greater coverage

derricking jib

mobile crane   mobile crane with fly jib   high mounted jib crane   light tower crane

CRANES - RELATIVE AMOUNT OF WORKING AREAS AND COVERAGE

When used for distributing operations in building work it is necessary for the crane to stand some distance away from the building in order that the low-mounted jib shall not foul the top of the building. Some reduction in this distance may be made by the use of a short swan-necked jib or a fly jib (see above). These jib extensions enable the radius of the jib to be extended in the case of light loads without the lowering of the main jib, thus keeping it clear of the top edge of the building. Greater benefit is obtained, however, by increasing the height of the jib pivot, and high mounted jib cranes are now produced in which the jib is pivoted at the top of a vertical extension or short tower so that they are really small mobile tower cranes.

Stationary Cranes. These are fixed firmly at their working position.

Guyed Derrick. A derrick is a simple and inexpensive crane used where a few comparatively heavy lifts have to be made (see page 31). The guyed

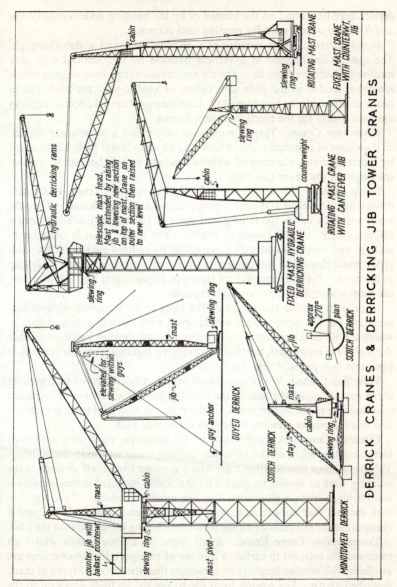

DERRICK CRANES & DERRICKING JIB TOWER CRANES

ROTATING MAST CRANE

FIXED MAST CRANE WITH COUNTERWT.

slewing ring

ROTATING MAST CRANE WITH CANTILEVER JIB

counterweight

cabin

slewing ring

cabin

hydraulic derricking rams

telescopic mast head. Mast extended by raising jib & lowering new section on top of mast. Crane on outer section then raised to new level

FIXED MAST HYDRAULIC DERRICKING CRANE

slewing ring

approx 270°

plan

SCOTCH DERRICK

jib

mast

slewing ring

mast

elevated for slewing within guys

GUYED DERRICK

guy anchor

jib

SCOTCH DERRICK

stay

mast

cabin

slewing ring

mast

MONOTOWER DERRICK

slewing ring

mast pivot

counter jib with ballast counterwt.

derrick may be erected on the ground or on the building under construction and it is very widely used for erecting steel frames.

Scotch Derrick. This consists of a slewing mast and a derricking jib. The mast is maintained in a vertical position by two latticed steel stay members which run from its top to the extremities of two base sleepers which are either loaded at the ends with ballast or kentledge or are anchored to heavy concrete blocks (see page 31). Like the guyed derrick, Scotch derricks are used widely for the erection of steel frames.

Monotower Crane. This is more accurately called a monotower derrick as it consists of a braced tower, which may be up to 200 ft high, surmounted by a derrick crane, the mast of which extends to a pivot bearing well down the height of the tower (see page 31).

Tower Crane. This is actually a form of monotower crane, electrically driven, light in weight and easily transported and quickly erected. They are made with jibs up to 100 ft long and some of the largest machines have a lifting capacity at this radius of 5 tons. The lattice mast is built up in sections and may be fitted with a derricking jib or fixed horizontal jib. All types rotate through a full circle and the driver's cabin is mounted high up in the mast. Typical examples are shown on pages 31 and 33. It is probably the most widely used crane on building sites.

In order to permit the height of the mast to be increased without dismantling the jib, some cranes are designed with extending mast heads in which the jib is carried on a short length of mast moving inside or outside the top of the main mast, the two being secured together when the crane is in operation (see pages 31 and 33).

Travelling Crane. Where conditions permit, a rail mounted or travelling crane moving along the side of the building has the advantage of increased coverage due to the movement along the rails. A firm level track is essential and this sometimes presents difficulties on sloping sites.

Climbing Crane. An alternative to the telescopic mast as a means of increasing the height of the jib is the climbing crane set inside the building. This has a short non-rotating mast which is raised from floor to floor as the building rises as shown on page 33. An inside mounted crane requires a shorter jib to cover a given area than one mounted outside. This, together with the fact that a short mast only is needed, makes the climbing crane a cheap crane for tall buildings if the structure is strong enough to take the load.

Transportable Tower Crane. Apart from the mobile cranes with high mounted jibs referred to earlier, a number of transportable tower cranes are available with smaller heights and capacities than the standard types of crane described above. For towing from site to site the jib folds down on to the

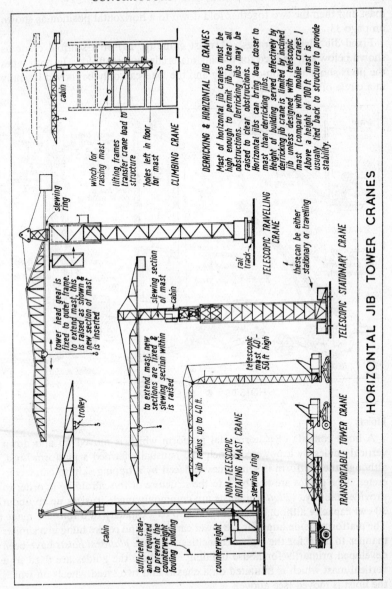

CLIMBING CRANE

cabin

winch for raising mast

lifting frames transfer crane load to structure

holes left in floor for mast

DERRICKING & HORIZONTAL JIB CRANES

Mast of horizontal jib cranes must be high enough to permit jib to clear all obstructions. Derricking jibs may be raised to clear obstructions.

Horizontal jibs can bring load closer to mast than derricking jibs.

Height of building served effectively by derricking jib crane is limited by inclined jib unless designed with telescopic mast (compare with mobile cranes.)

Above a height of 100 ft mast is usually tied back to structure to provide stability.

slewing ring

tower head gear is fixed to outer frame. to extend mast, this is raised as shown & new section of mast is inserted

slewing section of mast

cabin

rail track

TELESCOPIC TRAVELLING CRANE

these can be either stationary or travelling

TELESCOPIC STATIONARY CRANE

trolley

to extend mast, new sections are fixed & slewing section within is raised

jib radius up to 40 ft.

telescopic mast 40 - 50 ft high

NON-TELESCOPIC ROTATING MAST CRANE

slewing ring

TRANSPORTABLE TOWER CRANE

cabin

sufficient clearance required to prevent the counterweight fouling building

counterweight

HORIZONTAL JIB TOWER CRANES

mast and then the two together fold down to a horizontal position as shown on page 33.

Fixed Jib Slewing Cranes. A mast crane (p. 29) or a scaffold crane as shown below can be used for placing materials on a scaffold.   In both types the jib is short and non-derricking and the load can only be moved laterally in a circle of fixed radius.

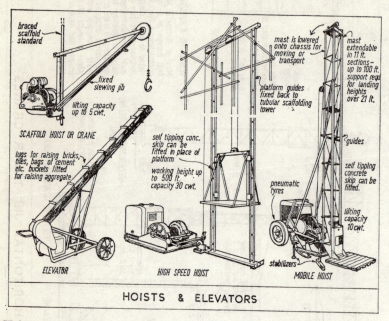

braced scaffold standard

fixed slewing jib

lifting capacity up to 5 cwt.

SCAFFOLD HOIST OR CRANE

lugs for raising bricks, tiles, bags of cement etc. buckets fitted for raising aggregate

ELEVATOR

self tipping conc. skip can be fitted in place of platform

working height up to 500 ft. capacity 30 cwt.

HIGH SPEED HOIST

mast is lowered onto chassis for moving or transport

platform guides fixed back to tubular scaffolding tower

pneumatic tyres

stabilizers

MOBILE HOIST

mast extendable in 11 ft. sections – up to 100 ft. support req'd for landing heights over 21 ft.

guides

self tipping concrete skip can be fitted.

lifting capacity 10 cwt.

HOISTS & ELEVATORS

Hoists

A hoist consists of a horizontal platform which is moved up and down vertical guides by a powered winch and is usually termed a platform hoist, although the platform is sometimes replaced by a tipping skip to carry concrete.   The guides are tied back to the structure or to scaffolding in order to provide stability.   *Platform hoists* are commonly made in sizes up to about 30 cwt capacity although larger models up to a capacity of 3 tons are made. The platform is side hung for the lower capacities and centre hung in a similar manner to a lift for the higher capacities.   *Mobile platform hoists* have been developed primarily for house building.   In these the guides are fixed to a vertical mast which is mounted on a chassis and two tyred wheels on which the hoist is moved (see above).

Elevators

These consist of a rotating belt or chain to which are fixed buckets or lugs depending on the nature of the materials to be raised (page 34).

TRANSPORTING

The term transporting implies horizontal movement primarily but it can involve some vertical movement, as in the case of conveyors and concrete pumps, and the plant used for this purpose varies widely in its nature.

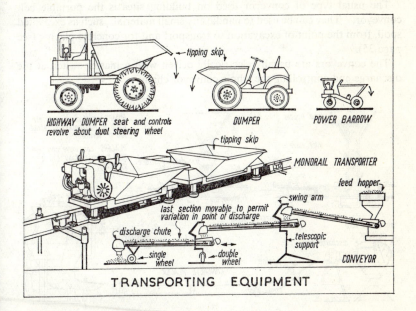

HIGHWAY DUMPER seat and controls revolve about dual steering wheel

DUMPER

POWER BARROW

tipping skip

MONORAIL TRANSPORTER

last section movable to permit variation in point of discharge

discharge chute

single wheel

double wheel

swing arm

feed hopper

telescopic support

CONVEYOR

TRANSPORTING EQUIPMENT

Dumpers

These are designed for the transport of materials such as excavated spoil, hardcore and concrete. They are powered by a diesel engine or, on the smaller types, by petrol engine.

The smaller types (5–14 cu. ft), generally called power barrows, are three-wheeled, driven and steered on the backwheel by a pedestrian driver. The larger types (up to 7 cu. yds) have four tyred wheels with front-wheel drive and rear-wheel steering, with a driving seat or saddle placed so that the hopper or skip is in front to give a view for placing the load (see above).

Monorail Transporter

This is a powered wagon or skip running on a single, easily laid rail as shown on page 35, and is intended primarily to carry concrete from the mixer to the point of placing. No driver is required as the wagon is despatched by engaging the clutch and at the end of the journey the clutch is disengaged either manually or by a trip device fitted to the rail.

Conveyors

The usual type of conveyor used on building sites is the portable belt conveyor. They can be used to handle any small materials, such as excavated spoil, from the point of excavation to transport and for concrete placing (see page 35).

The conveyors are usually electrically driven with a master switch at the discharge end controlling the whole conveyor chain.

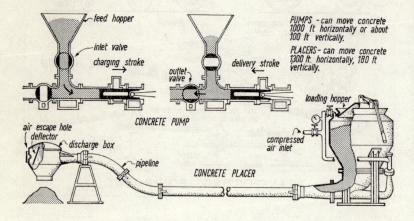

Concrete Pumps and Placers

Pumps are mechanically operated by ram and placers are pneumatically operated by compressed air (see above).

In the *mechanically operated pump* the concrete is pumped along a pipeline from the hopper by means of a ram pump and the pipe is always full of concrete, which comes out as a continuous discharge at the end. With a *pneumatically operated placer*, the concrete is blown from the hopper in batches along the pipeline and the pipe is clear most of the time.

MIXING

In modern building construction a large amount of material must still be mixed with water, mainly concrete, mortar and plaster. Of these concrete is probably made in most quantities and the mixing of it has been most highly mechanized. Except on jobs requiring only an extremely small amount of concrete, a concrete mixer of some form is now used on every building site. The advantages of mechanical mixing over hand mixing, except for very small quantities, are greater economy, certainty of thorough mixing without loss of cement and accurate gauging of the water content.

Concrete Mixers

Concrete mixers are made in various types and sizes, the most commonly used being drum mixers of which there are two forms, non-tilting and tilting drum. These are designated in B.S. 1305 according to size and type as 5NT or $3\frac{1}{2}$T, for example.[1] The figure denotes the quantity in cubic feet of mixed concrete delivered per batch. Mixers larger than 14 cu. ft are usually designated by their actual output in cubic yards per batch.

Concrete mixers may be classified as follows: 1. Non-tilting drum mixers (closed drum, reversed discharge). 2. Tilting drum mixers. 3. Split drum mixers. 4. Pan mixers. 5. Truck mixers.

Drum mixers smaller than 5 cu. ft are tilting type only and those larger than 7 cu. ft usually non-tilting only. 5 and 7 cu. ft mixers are made in both types.

The smaller sizes of tilting drum mixer are portable and in some cases are designed for towing. Most of the larger sizes are semi-portable. Power is generally supplied to concrete mixers by petrol or diesel driven engines.

Whereas the quantity of concrete required dictates the size of mixer to be used, the quality of concrete required dictates the type of mixer, since the different characteristics of the various types have an effect on the quality of concrete produced. Non-tilting and tilting drum mixers are suitable for ordinary structural quality concrete but not for dry-rich or dry-lean mixes. Split drum mixers produce good dry-lean concretes and pan and turbo-mixers produce all qualities.

Non-tilting Drum Mixer. In this type the drum is cylindrical with partially closed ends and rotates in a vertical plane, the mixed concrete being discharged either by means of a chute or by reversing the direction of rotation of the drum. Charging of the drum is carried out by a power loading side hopper

---

[1] The designations previously used, such as 5/$3\frac{1}{2}$ or 7/5, indicated by the first figure the quantity in cubic feet of dry material the mixer would hold.

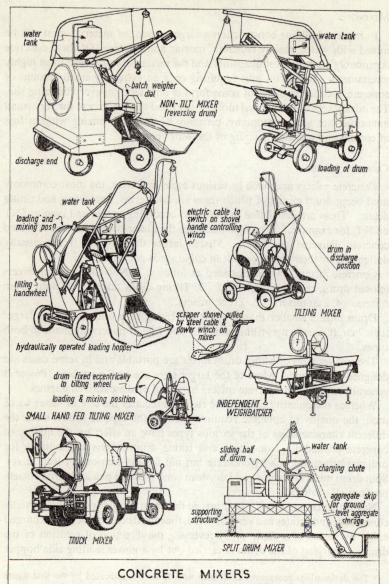

water tank

batch weigher dial

NON-TILT MIXER
(reversing drum)

discharge end

water tank

loading of drum

water tank

loading and mixing posn

electric cable to switch on shovel handle controlling winch

drum in discharge position

tilting handwheel

scraper shovel pulled by steel cable & power winch on mixer

TILTING MIXER

hydraulically operated loading hopper

drum fixed eccentrically to tilting wheel

loading & mixing position

INDEPENDENT WEIGHBATCHER

SMALL HAND FED TILTING MIXER

sliding half of drum

water tank

charging chute

TRUCK MIXER

supporting structure

aggregate skip for ground level aggregate storage

SPLIT DRUM MIXER

CONCRETE MIXERS

or skip (see page 38). Some models are automatic in action, producing one batch after another only needing to be supplied with materials and with skips or other transport to take each batch as it is discharged.

Tilting Drum Mixer. This consists of a pear-shaped drum open at the narrow top end and revolving on a tilting axis which permits the drum to be tilted in one direction for loading into the open end, and in the opposite direction for discharging the batch of mixed concrete (page 38).

Split Drum Mixer. This consists of a circular drum in two halves rotating on a horizontal spindle. One half is arranged to slide along the spindle to discharge the mix (page 38). Loading is through a feed-hole at one side.

Pan Mixer. This consists of a shallow drum or pan, 3 to 8 ft in diameter, revolving on a horizontal plane. A set of rotating paddles on a vertical spindle projects down into the drum in close contact with its side. Water is fed through a pierced tube round the perimeter edge of the pan and discharge is through the bottom at the centre. Pan mixers are expensive and are not readily portable, but they work faster than other mixers.

Turbo-mixer. A form of pan mixer in which the pan is stationary is called a turbo-mixer. The paddles project from the side of a rotating cylinder set within the pan, so that they move in the annular space. Discharge is through a "half-moon" door situated at one point at the bottom of the annular mixing space (see page 40).

Truck Mixer. These are used mainly by manufacturers of ready-mixed concrete to deliver freshly mixed concrete to sites where it is uneconomic or impossible to instal a mixing plant. An example is shown on page 38.

Weighbatchers

These are used for batching materials for concrete by weight.

Small Independent Weighbatcher. This is primarily for use with small portable mixers and consists of a pair of hoppers each connected by weighing mechanism to its own calibrated dial (see page 38).

Weighbatcher Incorporated with Mixer. Some mixers incorporate a hydraulic weighbatcher on which the loading hopper rests.

Mobile and Semi-Mobile Weighbatcher. A mobile weighbatcher is mounted on wheels and jacked up for use and is usually large enough to supply one or two mixers.

Central Mixing Plant

This is the concentration of batching and mixing operations in a single static plant instead of by a number of mobile mixers and is often used on large, extensive sites and when large amounts of concrete per hour are

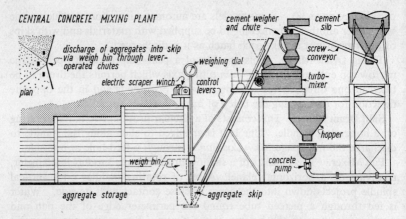

CENTRAL CONCRETE MIXING PLANT

cement weigher and chute

cement silo

discharge of aggregates into skip via weigh bin through lever-operated chutes

weighing dial

screw conveyor

plan

electric scraper winch

control levers

turbo-mixer

hopper

weigh bin

concrete pump

aggregate storage

aggregate skip

required. A central mixing plant may be arranged in many ways. The above shows an example using ground level weighbatching controlled from an elevated position by the mixer driver.

COMPRESSORS AND PUMPS

These pieces of contractors' plant do not fall within the preceding categories.

Compressors

These are used to provide compressed air for a wide variety of tools and are made in many sizes (page 41). Very large compressors may be used to supply compressed air through a suitable main to various points on a large site.

Pumps

Apart from concrete pumps mentioned earlier, most pumps used on building sites serve to keep the surface of the site and the excavations free from water; they are also used sometimes to lower the water table in water-logged ground. Pumps are operated by petrol or diesel engine or by electric motor. Typical examples are shown on page 41.

Well points are used in lowering the water table. The driving and draining action is shown on page 41. They are placed 6 to 10 ft from the excavation at 3 to 12 ft intervals and are connected together at the top and to pumps by means of header pipes. Well points are effective only up to a depth of about 12 to 15 ft. For greater depths they must be set in stages.

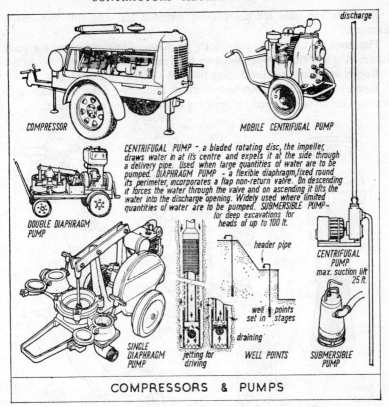

discharge

COMPRESSOR

MOBILE CENTRIFUGAL PUMP

CENTRIFUGAL PUMP - a bladed rotating disc, the impeller, draws water in at its centre and expels it at the side through a delivery pipe. Used when large quantities of water are to be pumped. DIAPHRAGM PUMP - a flexible diaphragm, fixed round its perimeter, incorporates a flap non-return valve. On descending it forces the water through the valve and on ascending it lifts the water into the discharge opening. Widely used where limited quantities of water are to be pumped. SUBMERSIBLE PUMP - for deep excavations for heads of up to 100 ft.

DOUBLE DIAPHRAGM PUMP

header pipe

CENTRIFUGAL PUMP
max. suction lift 25 ft.

well points
set in stages

draining

SINGLE DIAPHRAGM PUMP

jetting for driving

WELL POINTS

SUBMERSIBLE PUMP

COMPRESSORS & PUMPS

POWER TOOLS

This term covers a very large number of tools, held or controlled by hand, but operated by electricity, compressed air or petrol. They are used for many purposes and the range of variety in each type of tool is so great that it is only possible here to list and illustrate the principal types (pages 42,43).

The majority of power tools have the engine or motor incorporated as an integral part of the tool. Some, however, are driven by a flexible shaft, the prime mover of which may be operated by any of the three forms of power and may be situated up to about 15 ft away from the working position of the tool. Flexible shaft drive is mainly used for grinders, sanders and vibrators.

Picks, Breakers and Rock Drills. These are used for breaking up and cutting into materials such as brick, concrete, stone, asphalt.

Rammers are used for compacting returned soil and for compacting hardcore.

Hammers are used for cutting holes or chases in brickwork and for bush hammering and similar operations on hard material.

Rotary drills are used for drilling holes in all types of materials.

Grinders are used for such operations as smoothing down the faces of *in situ* cast concrete walls and for grinding down all types of materials.

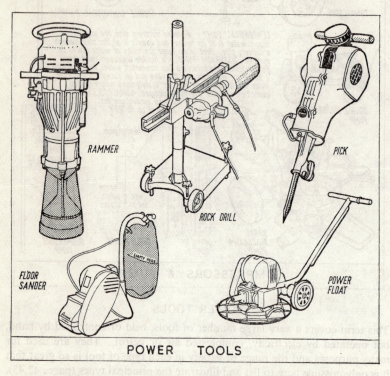

RAMMER

ROCK DRILL

PICK

FLOOR SANDER

POWER FLOAT

POWER   TOOLS

Saws. These may take the form of a circular or rotary saw, a reciprocating saw, or a chain saw.

Planers and rebaters are fitted with two bladed, high-speed rotary cutters. *Routers* are used with bits of varying profiles for grooving and moulding.

Cartridge Hammers. These are also known as rivet or bolt guns and are used for making fixings to timber, brick, concrete and metal by means of steel pins.

CARTRIDGE HAMMER

HAMMER

HAND GRINDER

DISC SANDER

BELT SANDER

CHAIN SAW

RECIPROCATING SAW

CIRCULAR SAW

PLANER

ROTARY DRILL

POWER TOOLS

Sanders are used for smoothing down wood surfaces. There are four types: (i) the *rotary* or *disc sander*, (ii) the *belt sander*, (iii) the *orbital sander*, which makes an oscillating-orbital motion at high speed, (iv) the *drum sander* which is used for sanding floors. The disc and belt sanders can be used with the appropriate types of abrasive discs or belts for metal and masonry surfaces and for removing paints and varnishes.

Power floats are used for trowelling screeds, monolithic finishes and the surfaces of large areas of concrete. They produce a very dense, smooth surface. These machines work satisfactorily on lean, dry mixes which produce much better results in paving work than do rich, wet mixes.

3
Foundations

The function of a foundation is to transmit all the dead, super-imposed and wind loads from a building to the soil on which the building rests in such a way that settlement, particularly uneven or relative settlement of the structure, is limited and failure of the underlying soil is avoided. Wind loads may result in uplift forces on foundations particularly in the case of extensive lightly loaded single-storey buildings and of slender, tall structures. In such circumstances the foundations may be required to assist in holding the structure down against the wind uplift.

Superstructure, foundations and soil act together. The design of the foundations cannot therefore be satisfactorily considered apart from that of the superstructure they carry. Nor should the superstructure be designed without reference to the nature of the soil on which the foundations rest. In the case of probably 75% of new buildings, similar in size and character and founded on the same type of soil as the surrounding existing buildings, no problems arise in this respect. The structure and foundations of a new building can be similar to those already erected. But when a new building is much higher than those already existing or varies radically in some other way, or is built on a virgin site, its design should be developed having regard to the type of foundation likely to suit the ground. Only in this way can a satisfactory and economic solution to the design as a whole be obtained. An overall picture of the condition below the surface of the site is an essential factor in the selection of the type of superstructure, since it may affect fundamentally the whole planning of the building. In addition, it may affect the placing of a building or a group of buildings on a site. It is therefore necessary for the designer to have not only some knowledge of the nature and strength of the materials to be used for the foundations and superstructure, but also some knowledge of the nature, strength and likely behaviour under load of the soils on which the building will rest.

The science of soil mechanics, by means of site explorations and tests, provides this essential information, which geology alone does not provide, and therefore permits a more rational approach to foundation design than is possible by empirical methods. The aim of a site exploration,[1] or subsoil

[1] The term site exploration is used here rather than site investigation as the latter implies a broader study of a site than just the investigation of the subsoil. For the scope of site investigations, and for full details of site explorations, see B.S. Code of Practice 2001 (1957) "Site Investigations".

survey, is to provide a picture of the nature and disposition of the soil strata and to obtain samples of the soils in the different strata for subsequent laboratory tests and examination. These involve classification of the soils, mechanical tests for establishing the physical properties of the soils and chemical tests.[1] Such an exploration should be carried out at a very early stage of a building project, beginning at the same time as the preliminary design of the structure. Because of the close connection between the soil conditions and the design of the superstructure it is inadvisable to complete the exploration before the design has been considered. This avoids unnecessary expenditure in obtaining unwanted information or the possibility of obtaining insufficient information for design purposes.

The extent of an exploration will depend on the size and type of structure, the nature of the site and the availability of local geological information. Full information from an extended exploration enables the foundations to be designed in the knowledge of the ground conditions which actually exist with consequent economies in the foundations. These can be considerable in large, heavily loaded buildings. The exploration should be taken deep enough to include all strata likely to be significantly affected by the building and this depth will depend on the type of structure, on its weight and, particularly, on the size and shape of the loaded area. Usually investigations must be made to a depth of at least one and a half times the total width of the foundation. The cost of an exploration will, of course, vary with the type of structure and the nature of the soil. It is low when compared with the total building cost: usually in the region of 1% of the cost of the structure.

FOUNDATION DESIGN

Two main considerations enter into the design of foundations: (i) The soil must be safe against failure by shear which may cause plastic flow under the foundation, (ii) the structure must be safe against excessive settlement due to the consolidation of soil under the foundation, and particularly against differential or unequal settlement under various parts of the building. In order to investigate the stability of any foundation it is necessary, therefore, to know firstly, something of the distribution and intensity of pressure between the foundation and the soil and of the intensity of pressure and shearing stresses at various points within the soil. Secondly, to know something of the mechanism of failure of the soil when over-loaded.

PRESSURE DISTRIBUTION

Distribution of Contact Pressure. The assumption usually made that a uniformly loaded foundation will transmit its load so that the soil is uniformly

[1] For information on these, see standard textbooks on practical soil mechanics.

stressed, is generally incorrect. The manner in which the load is distributed to the soil depends on the nature of the soil and on the rigidity or stiffness of the foundation. This is shown in Table 1 and in the diagram below. It will be seen that there is a considerable variation of pressure under rigid foundations, although in practice the pressure distribution tends to become more uniform. It will also vary with the relative density of the soil. Foundations, of course, vary between the perfectly rigid and the perfectly flexible type, in addition to which the soil may combine both cohesive and frictional properties in varying degree.[1]

Table 1. Distribution of Contact Pressure

| Foundation | Soil Type | |
	Cohesive	Cohesionless
Approaching fully flexible	Tendency to uniform distribution of pressure	Tendency to uniform distribution of pressure
Approaching fully rigid	Tendency to high stresses at edges — becoming more uniform as ultimate load is approached	Tendency to high stresses in centre—at all loads

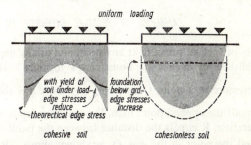

CONTACT PRESSURE DISTRIBUTION UNDER RIGID FOUNDATIONS

[1] Soils may be divided into two broad groups: (i) coarse-grained including gravels and sand, (ii) fine-grained silts and clays. Coarse-grained or granular soils derive their shear strength almost entirely from the resistance due to friction between the particles. As vertical pressure squeezes the particles closer together the shear resistance increases. These are called cohesionless or non-cohesive soils. Fine grained soils depend on cohesion only. That is the resistance due to the tendency of the particles to hold together. However much these soils are loaded the particles develop no friction so that the shear resistance remains constant and equal to the cohesion of the soil. These are called cohesive soils. Intermediate soils naturally exhibit both forms of resistance.

This knowledge permits preliminary decisions to be made before the detailed design of a foundation is undertaken and also acts as a guide to the choice of the type of foundation by which the load will be transferred to the soil. The distribution of contact pressure has little effect on the stresses in the soil at depths greater than the width of the foundation. Its greatest significance lies in establishing the stresses which are set up in the foundation itself. In practical foundation design, based on a uniform pressure distribution, the factor of safety normally used generally covers the under-estimate of bending moments on cohesive soils. On cohesionless soils the estimate will usually be greater than the actual bending moments in the foundation.

Distribution of Vertical Pressure.   A knowledge of the distribution of the normal vertical stress in the soil is required for the solution of settlement problems.

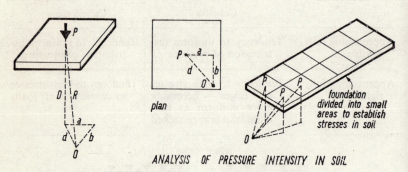

ANALYSIS OF PRESSURE INTENSITY IN SOIL

The intensity of vertical pressure at any point and at any depth in the soil may be established by means of Boussinesq's formula. This gives the intensity of pressure at a point O as $q = \dfrac{3PD^3}{2\pi R^5}$ where q = the intensity of pressure, P equals the applied point load, D equals the depth of the point O under consideration, R equals the distance between the point of application of the load and the point in the soil, O, as shown above. $R = \sqrt{d^2 + D^2}$ for which d may be obtained as $\sqrt{a^2 + b^2}$. The stress intensities at any point in the soil due to a number of concentrated loads may be added. Thus a foundation transmitting a uniformly distributed load may be divided into a number of smaller areas and the load on each regarded as a concentrated load. From this the general pattern of pressure distribution under the whole of the foundation may be established. Division into 2 ft squares gives sufficient accuracy for depths below 10 ft.

In practice this process involves an excessive amount of labour which may be reduced by the use of charts or tables.[1] For most practical purposes, however, the distribution of pressure at any level may be ascertained reasonably accurately by adopting a load spread of 60 degrees from the edges of the foundation. At any depth the load is then assumed to be spread over the area enclosed by the "spread" lines. Thus the unit pressure may be determined by dividing the applied load by the area of spread. The increased pressure at any level due to the overlapping pressures from a group of closely spaced independent foundations may be determined in the same way. The 60 degrees spread is taken from the edges of the outermost foundations in the group and the applied load is the sum of the combined foundation loads.

A diagram may be drawn by joining points of equal pressure in the soil to produce what is known as a bulb of pressure diagram as shown on page 50. It will be seen that the larger the loaded area, the deeper is its effect upon the soil. If a number of loaded foundations are placed near each other the effect of each is additive and if they are closely spaced one large pressure bulb is produced similar to that produced were the whole area uniformly loaded. This is shown on page 50. If the increase in pressure at a given depth due to building is not greater than 10% of the original over-burden pressure (see page 52) at that depth, the effect on the soil at that particular depth will usually be negligible. It has been shown in many cases that beyond the bulb of pressure bounded by the line joining points stressed to one-fifth of the applied pressure, consolidation of the soil is negligible and has little effect upon the settlement of a foundation. For practical purposes this is considered to be the significant or effective bulb of pressure. For a uniformly loaded square or circular foundation this bulb extends to a depth of approximately one and a half times the width of the foundation. For a strip foundation it extends to as much as three times the foundation width. As already noted, the pressure bulb, together with the geology of the site, indicates the depth to which investigations of the soil should be made. This is particularly important in the case of wide foundations where deep, underlying weak strata, which would not be affected by the pressures from narrow or isolated foundations, would be stressed by the wider foundations.

Distribution of Shear Stress. The distribution of shear stress and the position of maximum shear stress is important when there is a possibility of shear taking place in the soil. The maximum shear stress in the soil may be established analytically or graphically by Mohr's circle. The maximum shear stress set up by a single strip foundation carrying a uniform load of

[1] Neumark charts or Terzaghi tables.

p lb per sq. ft is p/π lb per sq. ft. This occurs at points lying on a semicircle having a diameter equal to the width of the foundation. Thus at the centre of the foundation the maximum shear occurs at a depth equal to half its width. The bulb of shear stresses is shown on this page.

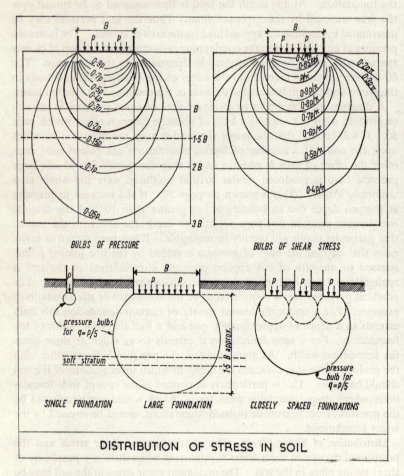

BULBS OF PRESSURE

BULBS OF SHEAR STRESS

SINGLE FOUNDATION

LARGE FOUNDATION

CLOSELY SPACED FOUNDATIONS

DISTRIBUTION OF STRESS IN SOIL

ULTIMATE BEARING CAPACITY OF SOIL

Should the load on a foundation be excessively high, plastic failure of the soil would occur and the foundations would sink into the ground. When a cohesive soil is surface-loaded this type of failure occurs by a wedge of soil directly under the foundations being forced downwards. This pushes the soil on each side outwards causing it to shear along a curved slip plane, so that heaving of the surface on each side takes place, as shown below (A). The depth of a foundation therefore must be such that the weight of soil above the base on each side together with the shear resistance of the soil is sufficient to prevent this. In practice, it is unusual for both sides of a foundation to be equally strong and failure is likely to occur on one side only, as shown at (B). The larger section of the slip plane is assumed to be a circular arc.

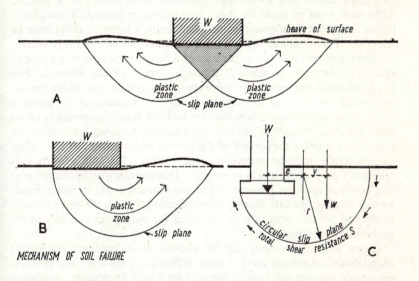

MECHANISM OF SOIL FAILURE

The intensity of loading at which failure occurs is known as the ultimate bearing capacity of the soil and is related to the shear strength of the soil. The bearing capacity may be found by an analysis of plastic failure or by a graphical method. The circular arc method, illustrated above at (C), is useful when the strength of the soil varies with depth. The critical slip circle is found by trial and error, the centre being located approximately by the use of tables or graphs based on accumulated data. Moments of the load W, the weight w of the soil within the arc and the total shear resistance, S, along the slip surface are taken about the centre of the arc (S = length of slip plane × shear strength of soil per unit area). For stability the sum of the moments of soil weight and shear resistance must be at least equal to We, the moment of the foundation load. The factor of safety against failure is the sum of the resisting moments divided by the moment of the foundation load:

$$\text{Factor of Safety} = \frac{(S \times r) + (w \times y)}{W \times e}$$

It is generally assumed that when a clay is loaded uniformly on the surface by a strip load, the ultimate bearing capacity is about $5\frac{1}{2}$ to 6 times the shear strength of the clay. In practice, foundations are not always in the form of long strips, nor do they always apply their load to the surface of the ground. Allowances must be made for this. In addition, in order to avoid plastic failure and to keep settlement within small limits, a factor of safety must be adopted. For structures such as brick buildings, which can safely accommodate themselves to a certain amount of differential movement, a factor of safety of two might be allowed, although three is usually adopted. For structures which are sensitive to movement, such as rigid, monolithic frames, or flexible frames with light stone facings, it is necessary to allow a factor of at least three. Thus the safe uniform bearing pressure is about twice the shear strength of the soil when surface is loaded. Normally the foundation is below the surface of the ground and a volume of soil, called the *overburden*, must be removed to form the pit. The soil below is thus relieved of the pressure due to its weight. This pressure may be allowed over and above that of the pressure due to the building load, so that for subsurface loading, the safe bearing pressure becomes twice the shear strength of the soil per unit area to which is added the weight per unit area of the excavated overburden.

Higher bearing pressures may be allowed on independent rectangular foundations. Although there is some difference of opinion, it is generally considered that the safe bearing pressure for a strip foundation on cohesive soils may be increased by about 30% for a square foundation.

There is less risk of plastic failure with cohesionless soils than with clay, and with these the limiting conditions depend on settlement rather than on shear failure. In most cases serious settlement takes place before the ultimate bearing capacity of the soil is reached. The ultimate bearing capacity for granular soils may be calculated from Ritter's formula, involving the depth of the foundation below the surface, the breadth of the foundation and the unit weight and angle of internal friction of the soil. In practice considerable regard is paid to the results of Standard Penetration Tests which give an indication of relative density of the soil.

SETTLEMENT OF FOUNDATIONS

The vertical downward movement of the base of a structure is called settlement and its effect upon the structure depends on its magnitude, its uniformity, the length of time over which it takes place, and on the nature of the structure itself. Provided that the settlement is uniform over the whole area of the building and is not excessive, the movement does little damage. If, however, the amount of settlement varies at different points under the building, giving rise to what is known as relative or differential settlement, stresses will be set up in the structure. These may be relieved in the case of a brick structure, for example, by the setting up of a large number of fine cracks at the joints, but in more rigid structures overstressing of some structural members might occur. The maximum amount of settlement which should be permitted, that is, the allowable settlement, in any particular circumstances is discussed on page 61.

Settlement may be caused by:

(i) the imposed weight of the structure on the soil,

(ii) changes in moisture content of the soil,

(iii) subsidence due to mining or similar operations,

(iv) general earth movement.

Settlement under the load of the structure may be due first to elastic compression, which is the lateral bulging of the soil and which takes place without a change in volume. It is usually small and occurs as construction proceeds. Secondly, it may be due to plastic flow, which has already been discussed, and which must be prevented by adopting sufficient depth and bearing area for the foundations. Thirdly, settlement may be due to consolidation.

Cohesive Soils. Settlement due to the consolidation of cohesive soils may continue for years after the completion of the building. The compressibility of clay is appreciable, but as the reduction in volume takes place by the expulsion of some pore water, and as the permeability of clay is low, consolidation takes place very slowly. The amount of settlement in a layer of clay of thickness $H = \dfrac{e' - e''}{1 + e'} \times H$ where e' is the voids ratio[1] from the initial consolidation due to the overburden, p', and e'' is the voids ratio due to the total pressure, p'', set up by the foundation load plus the overburden. The values for both e' and e'' are taken from the p-e curve (such as that

---

[1] This is the ratio of the volume of voids to that of solids in a soil.

3

shown on this page), constructed from a consolidation test carried out on a sample of the soil. It is possible to establish the time required for a given degree of consolidation to take place as the time is directly proportional to the square of the thickness of the soil layer, inversely proportional to the coefficient of permeability and directly proportional to the slope of the p-e curve. So that if the thickness of a clay stratum is known, together with the nature of the drainage conditions at its boundaries, it is possible to prepare a curve such as that shown on page 55, showing the probable progress of settlement over a period of time.

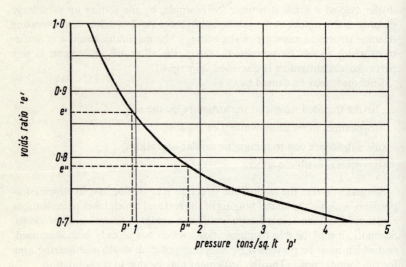

LABORATORY COMPRESSION CURVE (p — e curve)

Cohesionless Soils. In sands and gravels the amount of compression under load is small and the rate of settlement keeps pace with the construction of the building. On completion of the building no further settlement takes place unless caused by unforeseen circumstances such as the erosion of sand by water outside the limits of the building, the removal of surcharge by adjacent excavations or consolidation of the soil by vibration. This is because these types of soil are to a large extent incompressible, the particles resting on one another, so that under load they do not move very far and settlement is not large. What settlement does occur takes place quickly because the permeability is high.

Bearing Pressures on Soils

In the design of foundations a distinction must be made between the bearing pressure which a soil is safely capable of withstanding and the pressure which it is advisable not to exceed in practice.

The maximum safe bearing capacity is the maximum pressure that a soil will bear without risk of shear failure, irrespective of any settlement which may result. It is obtained, as described above, by dividing the ultimate bearing capacity by an appropriate factor of safety.[1]

The allowable bearing pressure is the maximum pressure which should be applied to the soil taking into account shear failure, settlement and the ability of the particular building to withstand settlement. The allowable bearing pres-

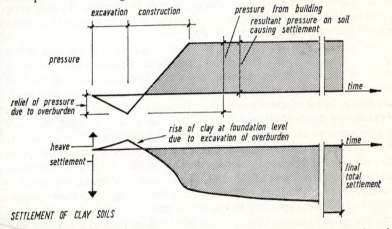

SETTLEMENT OF CLAY SOILS

sure thus depends both on the ground and the type of building concerned, and is generally less than, and never exceeds, the maximum safe bearing capacity.

As explained earlier, if the soil is overloaded shear failure of the soil will result. To avoid this type of failure the ground pressure immediately beneath the foundations must not at any point exceed the maximum safe bearing capacity of the soil. If the foundations rest on ground such as rock or deep beds of compact gravel (so that settlement need not be considered) it is sufficient to ensure that the maximum safe bearing capacity is nowhere exceeded. If the ground is such that possible settlement must be considered, the ground pressure immediately beneath the foundations must not exceed the allowable bearing pressure and should, as far as possible, be equal at all points.

[1] Values for maximum safe bearing capacities of various types of soil are given in Table 1 of C.E. Code of Practice No. 4, "Foundations", which also gives factors which will permit an increase in these values—paras 1.631 and 1.641.

Where possible uneven loading of the soil should be avoided, under both individual and combined foundations. This is achieved by arranging the centre of gravity of applied loads to coincide with the centre of area of the foundation. Where some eccentricity is unavoidable the design must ensure that the allowable bearing pressure is not exceeded at any point.

Equality of applied ground pressure cannot be achieved beneath a number of independent bases if the loads on some are almost entirely dead loads but the loads on others have a high proportion of live load, since the dead loads are applied all the time but the live loads, which must be provided for, may never occur. The use of a suitably low allowable bearing pressure may, in such cases, reduce the differential settlement to an acceptable amount. It is, however, a better arrangement, particularly on grounds of low bearing capacity, to plan the building so that the dead to live load ratio is approximately uniform in the various columns.

Variation in moisture content is particularly important in the case of fine grained cohesive soils which change rapidly in volume with changes in moisture content. The shrinkable clays found in the south-east of England are most susceptible to these changes, which may be caused either by climatic changes or by the effects of tree roots. The effect of normal seasonal changes extends to a depth of about 3 ft, except in times of long drought, so that if the foundations are placed at or below this depth, the structure is unlikely to be affected by settlement due to this cause. Since the depth of foundations to small and lightly loaded structures need not be great for structural reasons, this moisture movement of clay soils often dictates the foundation depth in smaller types of buildings. Tree roots can extend radially greater than the height of the tree, depending on the type of tree, and they extract water from the soil to considerable depths. The proximity of trees to a building site, particularly fast growing and water-seeking trees such as poplars, elms and willows, should therefore be noted in any site investigation. Within a few years of planting the roots of these trees will extend 50 ft or more and dry out clay soil below any nearby building. Movements of 1 to 2 in. are common and settlements as much as 4 in. have been known to occur in buildings as far as 80 ft from black poplars.

Settlement due to mining subsidence is confined to certain localities and this, together with general earth movement is discussed on pages 62–65.

CHOICE OF FOUNDATION TYPE

The foundations and sub-structure together with the superstructure of a building are interrelated and interdependent. In order to obtain maximum strength and economy in the total structure they must be considered and designed as a whole. The larger and taller the building the more important this becomes.

The type of foundation adopted very often depends largely upon the form of construction used for the structure above. But with soils such as clay or silts, and in subsidence areas, the building itself must often be designed to react to differential settlement with no ill effect.

It is a comparatively easy matter to provide adequate foundations to small buildings, but as the size, particularly the height, of the building increases, so does the need for economy in cost of foundations increase. An increase in height increases the load on the foundations in two ways. Firstly, because the total weight of the building is greater, and secondly, because the greater horizontal forces due to wind pressure shift the resultant load on the foundations to one side, causing a local increase in ground pressure (as in the case of walls, Chapter 4). Generally, unless conditions are exceptional, the dead weight of the building will keep the resultant within the middle third of the base. Although new methods such as power boring for cylinder piles make it economically possible to build much higher on soils the nature of which previously limited the height of building, problems of settlement are intensified. Overall settlement may be greater with the liability of greater differential settlement and the possibility of tilting of the whole structure.

In terms of overall building costs the problem of dealing with settlement must be considered from the point of view of the structure as well as of the foundation on which it rests. In extreme cases it may be essential to use a high factor of safety against ultimate failure but for economic reasons, as far as the foundations are concerned, a factor of not more than three is often desired and this may lead to considerable settlement. Although forms of structure can be designed which are flexible enough to resist safely such settlement those forms of construction which are economic in material often involve rigidity of structure, resulting in sensitivity to differential movement. The cost of structure must therefore be balanced against the cost of foundations and in some circumstances it may prove cheaper to limit settlement by using a high factor of safety so that a rigid and economic superstructure may be used.

Many factors are involved in the choice of a foundation type. The actual arrangement required in any particular case will depend upon the nature and strength of the subsoil, the type of foundation indicated by considerations of economy in the structure as a whole, the nature of the structure, the distribution of the loads from the superstructure and the total weight of the building and its parts.

Foundations Relative to Nature of Soil. A knowledge of the general manner of pressure distribution in different soils according to the type of foundation acts as a guide in making a preliminary choice of foundation. By a careful distribution of the loads from the superstructure it is possible to reduce and sometimes eliminate uneven pressure.

When it appears that settlement would be large, the bearing pressure may be reduced by adopting a greater spread of foundations, or by using a raft. It should be remembered, however, that although this procedure may be beneficial when the foundation rests directly on the compressible soil, it is not effective in preventing settlement when consolidation takes place in a deep-seated compressible stratum. This is because the wider the foundation the greater will be the depth at which the soil will be stressed. This can be seen in the comparative pressure bulb diagrams shown on page 50. When the building rests on a comparatively shallow compressible stratum, it may be cheaper to carry the foundations down to firmer soil at a lower level by means of piers or piles.

When the compressible layers are deep-seated it is possible to limit consolidation by excavating basements so that the pressure imposed by the weight of the building is wholly or partly offset by the reduction in overburden pressure. The provision of deep basements may also be used as a means of reducing differential settlement under buildings in which some parts are heavier than others, such as a tall tower block with lower surrounding parts of the building forming a "podium". A deep basement under the tower block will have the effect of reducing the pressure in the soil at that point due to the relief of overburden pressure thus equalizing the pressures under the whole building (page 60, A). The application of this method is, however, limited by the expense of the excavation which, if to be effective, may need to be very deep, and by the effect of soil movement during excavation (see page 82).

For greatest economy both in superstructure and foundations, all loads should, as far as possible, be carried directly from the point of application to the point of support. This is particularly important when the loads are great. A raft foundation may be an economic way of transferring to a weak soil the load from a large number of lightly loaded columns but when heavy load concentrations are to be transferred to the soil, deep piles passing through the weak soil to bed rock may be the cheapest solution.

Foundations Relative to Nature of Structure. The consideration of the behaviour of soils under load shows that rigidity or flexibility of structure can influence the design of slab and raft foundations. Similarly, the behaviour of the structure under load depends not only upon the dead and imposed loads, but also upon the nature of the foundations and the manner in which the structure is supported upon them, since some of the forces acting upon the structure are those developed at its junction with the foundations (see Ch. 9). Accordingly, as indicated earlier, consideration must be given on the one hand to the choice of a foundation appropriate to the type of structure likely to be most economic, and on the other hand to the possibility of using a structure suited to the soil conditions and to foundations which appear most appropriate. For example, in some circumstances on sites with weak soils the most economic building might result from the use of a few expensive types of foundation, rather than from the use of a larger number of more lightly loaded and cheaper foundations. In such circumstances the structural frame would be designed with this in mind, the columns being widely spaced in order to reduce the number of foundations required.

Design of Structure to Resist Settlement. Since a certain amount of settlement is usually inevitable, it must be reckoned with and provision made for it in the design of the structure. The effects of differential settlement depend to a large degree upon the rigidity of the structure. For example, in structures in which beams rest simply on brick walls, unequal settlement unless excessive will not affect the internal stresses in the structural elements, although finishes may be affected. But in rigid continuous structures even a small amount of differential settlement of the supports will cause secondary shearing forces and bending moments in the beams and columns due to the distortion of the frame arising from the rigid joints (see page 60, B). Buildings with rigid frames may be supported upon a stiff raft foundation (page 60, C), or the foundations of individual columns can be connected by a series of continuous beams so that the structure settles as a whole, the frame being designed to act as a very deep girder to resist any secondary stresses set up by settlement. Although secondary stresses may be set up in rigid structures by settlement of the foundations, such structures do permit forms of construction which require less resistance from the soil than non-rigid forms. This applies especially to single-storey structures where rigid frames with hinged bases may be used to prevent the transfer to the foundations of bending stresses set up by the wind pressure on the superstructure above. This is discussed more fully in Chapter 9.

Although the structure of a building supported on a non-rigid foundation may be of comparatively flexible construction, so that its stability is not impaired by movement, differential settlement is usually limited in order to avoid damage to claddings and finishes and excessive unevenness in the floors. The limit of this movement will depend not only upon the type of structure and the nature of the finishes, but also upon the extent to which damage and

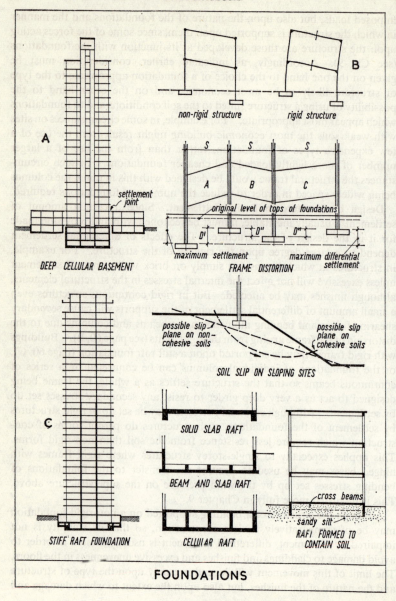

A DEEP CELLULAR BASEMENT

settlement joint

B non-rigid structure   rigid structure

FRAME DISTORTION

S   S   S   S

A   B   C

original level of tops of foundations

D'   D''   D'''

maximum settlement   maximum differential settlement

SOIL SLIP ON SLOPING SITES

possible slip plane on non-cohesive soils

possible slip plane on cohesive soils

C STIFF RAFT FOUNDATION

SOLID SLAB RAFT

BEAM AND SLAB RAFT

CELLULAR RAFT

cross beams

sandy silt

RAFT FORMED TO CONTAIN SOIL

FOUNDATIONS

subsequent repair to finishes is acceptable. The acceptable limit may vary with different buildings. Where large movements such as occur on subsidence sites must be accommodated, special forms of construction to deal with this problem must be devised and this is discussed on page 83.

It has been suggested that the differential settlement of uniformly loaded continuous foundations and of equally loaded spread foundations of approximately the same size, is unlikely to exceed half of the maximum settlement, and that normal structures such as office buildings and flats can satisfactorily withstand differential settlements of $\frac{3}{4}$ in. between adjacent columns spaced about 20–25 ft apart. It is suggested that an allowable pressure should be selected such that the maximum settlement of any individual foundation is 1 in.[1] These figures relate only to foundations on cohesionless soils, clay being too variable to generalize.

Since most damage arising from differential movement is due to distortion of the rectangular panels between beams and columns, and since the angle of "racking" depends on the distance between the columns as well as on the actual amount of settlement, it is possible to formulate rules on the same principle as the deflection limitations used in beam and slab design, in which the maximum differential settlement between adjacent columns is limited to a certain fraction of the span between them. Thus the difference in the settlements of two adjacent columns, that is, the differential settlement between them, divided by their distance apart, is a measure of the severity of the settlement. There is considerable risk of damage in a normal framed building when this fraction exceeds about 1/300, so that at design stage it is advisable to so limit the estimated differential settlement that this fraction does not exceed 1/500. This is illustrated on page 60. It will be seen that the distortion in frame panel A is greater than that in the centre panel B. This is obvious from inspection and also from the fact that D/S in panel A is greater than D/S in panel B. The differential settlement in panels B and C is the same, but as the distance between the columns of panel C is greater than that between those in panel B, the severity of "racking" in panel C is less and therefore the likelihood of damage is less than in panel B. This again is clear from a comparison of the fraction D/S in each case. Having established in this way the safe estimated differential settlement, the building frame should be designed so that the strains due to the settlement are not excessive. Although this method of relating estimated settlement to the structure is useful, the relative uncertainty and approximate nature of settle-

[1] See *Soil Mechanics in Engineering Practice*, by K. Terzaghi and R. B. Peck, Wiley, 1948. See also "The Allowable Settlements of Buildings", by A. W. Skempton and D. H. McDonald. *Proceedings of the Institution of Civil Engineers*, Part III, 1956, 5.

ment calculations compared with structural calculations must be borne in mind. This limits their application—more refined calculations will not make the soil more uniform. Further, the flexibility of structure, generally speaking, is not continuous throughout a building due to the stiffening effect of structural walls and lift shafts. This tends to localize distortion in different parts and the resultant damage may be greater than that anticipated on the basis of a ratio of 1/500.

Foundations Relative to Ground Movement. Reference to ground movement has already been made on page 56, where the effect of seasonal moisture variations and of tree roots in causing settlement on clay soil is discussed. Frost heave, the lifting of foundations due to the expansion of some soils when frozen, occurs in certain conditions. In the British Isles a depth of foundation 18 in. below ground level is sufficient to give protection in most places. These volume changes cause local movements of the soil, but mass movement of ground takes place in unstable areas: these occur as a result of subsidence in mining areas and in areas of brine pumping, landslips on unstable slopes and creep on clay slopes.

Subsidence. When subsidence takes place, in addition to the total vertical movement there is a horizontal movement which exerts forces on any structure resting on or built into the subsiding ground. This can best be understood by considering the subsidence caused by the extraction of a coal seam. As the working face moves forward and support is removed from the ground behind, settlement will take place after a certain time depending on the nature of the overburden and the method of extracting the coal. This will cause a depression of the ground at the surface which will move in advance of the working face causing a tilt and curvature in the ground which is termed the "subsidence wave". This is illustrated on page 63.

As the wave passes beneath a building it will subject it to changing forces according to the position of the building on the wave:

(a) At the crest of the wave a cantilever effect will be produced in the foundations and tensile forces will be set up in the ground. This tension will be transmitted to the foundations (2).

(b) On the flank of the wave the building will be subjected to eccentric loads because it is tilted out of the vertical (3).

(c) In the trough of the wave support will be removed from the centre of the foundation and a beam effect will be produced setting up tension in the foundation. Compressive forces will be set up in the ground (4).

(d) When the subsidence wave has finally passed, the building will resume its vertical position but at a lower level (5).

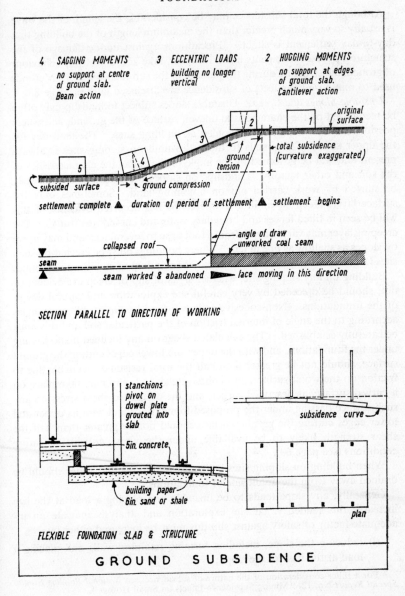

4 SAGGING MOMENTS no support at centre of ground slab. Beam action

3 ECCENTRIC LOADS building no longer vertical

2 HOGGING MOMENTS no support at edges of ground slab. Cantilever action

original surface

total subsidence (curvature exaggerated)

ground tension

subsided surface — ground compression

settlement complete ▲ duration of period of settlement ▲ settlement begins

angle of draw
unworked coal seam

collapsed roof

seam

seam worked & abandoned ◀ face moving in this direction

SECTION PARALLEL TO DIRECTION OF WORKING

stanchions pivot on dowel plate grouted into slab

5in. concrete

building paper
6in. sand or shale

subsidence curve

plan

FLEXIBLE FOUNDATION SLAB & STRUCTURE

GROUND SUBSIDENCE

Although the total subsidence may be considerable the length of the wave is usually so very much greater than the maximum length of the building that day-to-day settlement is slight.[1] Precautions against undue damage of the structure by these movements must, however, take account of this behaviour of ground and structure during the passage of the subsidence wave. Methods used to minimize the effects of subsidence are discussed later on page 83.

Unstable Slopes and Creep. Unstable slopes subject to landslip may often be recognized by the characteristic uneven surface of the ground, and where possible such areas should be avoided as building sites. The tendency for the upper strata of clay soils to move downhill on sloping sites is always present and will be governed by the angle of the slope, the characteristics of the soil and other factors. Landslips on slopes previously just stable may be started by work carried out on adjoining land. Sometimes only the surface layers creep downhill and where this has occurred evidence of this will be seen in tilted fences and boundary walls and curved tree trunks. The creeping layer may vary in depth from a foot or so to several feet, and may move on slopes as shallow as one in ten. Where buildings must be erected on such sites large scale and expensive works may be required to stabilize the ground.

Building on any sloping site, whether signs of slip or creep are evident or not, should be preceded by very careful site exploration and careful design of the foundations. Non-cohesive soils will tend to slip at different angles according to the angle of internal friction of the particular soil and this must be carefully established. The calculated shear on any inclined plane passing under the foundations, and with the upper and lower edges cutting the ground surface, should not be greater than half the total resistance available due to friction on the worst surface. In cohesive clay soils slip may take place on a curved surface, as described earlier, and the calculated shear stress on any such surface passing under the proposed foundations and with its upper and lower edges cutting the ground surface should not be greater than half the shear strength likely to be available under the worst anticipated future conditions (see page 60).

When building on sloping sites it is most important that water should be drained away from the uphill side of foundations.

Generally, any slope tends to be unstable and placing a load at the top increases this tendency. If site exploration and analysis indicate an inadequate factor of safety against slip this must be increased either by

(i) reducing the slope, including forming retaining walls and placing a load at the base of the slope;

[1] For a fuller consideration of the nature of subsidence, see *National Building Studies Special Report* No. 12, "Mining Subsidence-Effects on Small Houses".

(ii) reducing the load;

(iii) placing the load below the line of failure of the slope;

(iv) maintaining or increasing the ground strength by drainage or water diversion, having regard to ground water movements which will obtain when the building is erected;

(v) maintaining ground strength by placing filter layers to prevent erosion.

Differential settlement which would cause little damage on level sites tends to be more serious on sloping sites, as the parts which settle tend to move downhill, causing large cracks. Longitudinal tensile reinforcement in simple footings is very useful in such cases.

FOUNDATION TYPES

In the earlier part of this chapter consideration has been given to the resistance of the soil to the loads imposed by the building, to its behaviour under load, and to the factors which affect the choice of foundation. It now remains to examine in detail the actual types of foundations used in various circumstances to transfer the building loads to the soil.

Foundations are now invariably made of concrete, either mass or reinforced, and range from a simple strip to a deep, piled foundation.

The many forms of foundations used in building work may be divided broadly into *shallow* foundations or *deep* foundations. Shallow foundations are those which transfer the load to the soil at a level close to the lowest floor of the building and include the spread foundations: strips, slabs and rafts. These, of course, may be formed at great depth below ground where there is a basement. Deep foundations include piles and various types of piers. Unless conditions make the use of deep foundations essential, shallow foundations are always used as these are nearly always the cheapest. An exception is possibly the use of short bored piles instead of strip foundations in shrinkable clays.

Various types of strip and slab foundations (page 66) are commonly used on sites where a sufficiently deep strata of reasonably strong subsoil exists near the surface of the ground or, in the case of a building with a basement, at or near the level of the proposed basement floor.

Raft foundations, by which the whole of the available site is covered, may be used for a number of reasons already mentioned in the previous section on the choice of foundation type. They may be used where no firm strata of soil exists at a reasonable depth below the surface and a maximum area of

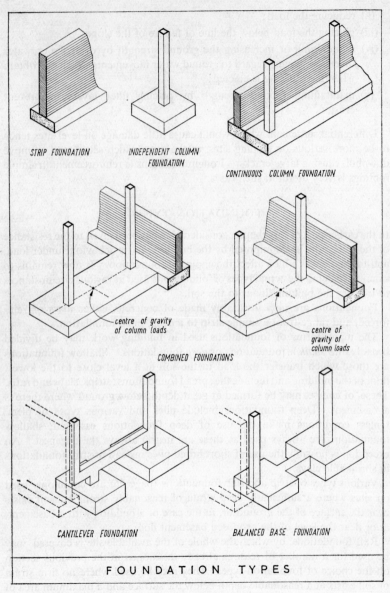

STRIP FOUNDATION

INDEPENDENT COLUMN FOUNDATION

CONTINUOUS COLUMN FOUNDATION

centre of gravity of column loads

COMBINED FOUNDATIONS

centre of gravity of column loads

CANTILEVER FOUNDATION

BALANCED BASE FOUNDATION

FOUNDATION TYPES

foundation is required to bring the imposed pressures within the safe bearing capacity of the soil, or, more frequently, to restrict settlement. They are also used to provide a stiff foundation under a building, the structure of which is sensitive to differential movement. Where the soil lacks uniform resistance, a stiff raft may also serve to bridge weak areas. A raft may also be used as part of a stiff basement to reduce the imposed pressure by means of a relief of overburden pressure. Finally, rafts, either stiff or extremely flexible, are used on sites on which subsidence is likely to occur due to mining activities below or in the neighbourhood of the site.

Piles are used to transmit the loads to lower strata where the pressure can be safely resisted. Pile foundations may be used on sites where no firm strata exists at a reasonable depth and the applied loading is uneven, making the use of a raft inadvisable. They are also used as an alternative to piers in cases where a firm bearing strata exists at a reasonable depth but yet too deep to permit the economical use of strip or slab foundations.

These foundation types may be broken down further into the following sub-divisions each of which will be considered in detail.

Strip and Slab Foundations:	Strip Foundation
	Independent Column Foundation
	Continuous Column Foundation
	Combined Column Foundation
	Cantilever Foundation
	Balanced Base Foundation
Raft Foundations:	Solid Slab Raft
	Beam and Slab Raft
	Cellular Raft
Piled Foundations:	Friction Piles
	End Bearing Piles
Piers:	Masonry
	Mass Concrete
	Cylinders and Monoliths

Which type of foundation will be most appropriate in any particular case depends upon a number of factors, to some of which reference has already been made in the previous section. These are amplified and extended later.

SPREAD FOUNDATIONS GENERALLY

In the design of spread foundations, that is strips, slabs and rafts, two prerequisites form the basis. First, that the soil must not be overloaded and secondly, that settlement beneath the foundations must at no point be excessive and, as far as possible, must be equal at all points. Means of ensuring this are discussed on page 55 where the safe bearing capacity of the soil and the allowable bearing pressure are defined. Design is based on these to avoid shear failure and excessive settlement respectively. Uneven loading of the soil and the resulting differential settlement is avoided or limited by arranging the centre of gravity of the applied loads to coincide with the centre of area of the foundation.

In *Elementary Building Construction* simple strip footings to continuous walls are considered, and it is shown that in cases of light loading on reasonably strong soils, a foundation strip no wider than the wall it carries can, in some cases, provide sufficient width as not to overstress the soil or cause excessive settlement. In practice, however, some spread is usually provided, about twice the thickness of the wall. This provides some stability to the wall before it is tied in by floors and roof. For hand excavation a minimum width of 2 ft to 2 ft 6 in., depending on the depth, is needed to give sufficient working space.

The Model Building Byelaws include a table relating load per foot run of wall of domestic buildings to various subsoil types and giving the minimum widths of foundations required. The L.C.C. By-laws lay down a minimum width of foundation equal to three times the width of the base of the wall it carries, but this may be reduced or increased at the discretion of the District Surveyor.[1]

Area and Thickness. The area of a foundation slab should be related to the imposed load and to the bearing strength and settlement characteristics of the soil. In all cases the size of the foundation must be such that the soil is not overstressed, and for strip foundations this is considered in terms of width to give sufficient area per foot run. For isolated piers or columns both width and length are involved.

In most cases the edges of a foundation will project beyond the faces of the wall or column it supports so that as a result of the resistance of the soil, bending due to cantilever action will occur and bending and shear stresses will be set up in the foundation. The tensile strength of unreinforced concrete is low, and in order to keep these stresses within the capacity of the concrete the strip or slab must be of adequate depth. Concrete fails under a compressive load usually by shearing along planes lying at an angle of 45° to 60° to the horizontal and it is on this basis that the requirements regarding thickness of concrete foundations are formulated in the Model and L.C.C. By-laws. This results in the thickness being not less than the projection of

---

[1] M.B. Byelaw 19; L.C.C. By-law 4.05.

the base beyond the face of the wall it carries (page 70). In practice, if there is no blinding layer, it is prudent to increase the thickness by 3 to 4 in. as the bottom of the base may be weakened by loose or wet soil. If pressures are high and the quality of the concrete is low an angle of dispersion of 60° should be used although generally 45° is sufficient.

When loads are heavy or the soil is weak considerable projection of the foundation results. The thickness of mass concrete required under the Byelaws may then make the foundation excessively deep, and it is normal to provide reinforcement to take up the bending stresses and to reduce the thickness of the concrete to that required to give sufficient resistance to shear. In extreme cases only is shear reinforcement also provided. If the depth of the foundation can be enough to obviate the need for shear reinforcement, the risk of cracks and the consequent corrosion of the steel by ground moisture is avoided. The detailed design of such foundations is covered in textbooks on reinforced concrete. They will be considered here in terms of their types and applications. In spite of the greater depth of foundation considerable benefit may be derived from the use of mass concrete bases in waterlogged ground. These may often prove cheaper than the continuous pumping needed to permit the fixing of the reinforcement and the placing of concrete around it in the dry.

Strip Foundation. This foundation may be used to carry load-bearing walls, including brick or concrete walls to multi-storey buildings. The bending stresses set up by the double-cantilever action of the foundation across the base of the wall are likely to be high and to resist these reinforcement is placed at the bottom of the slab, which will be the tensile zone, usually in the form of rods at right-angles to the length of the wall.

Independent Column Foundations. This is the most commonly used type of foundation in framed buildings (see page 70).

(i) Reinforced Concrete. This is a square or rectangular slab of concrete carrying a single column and with an area sufficient to keep the soil stresses within the allowable bearing capacity of the soil. Reinforcement is placed at the bottom in both directions to resist the bending stresses set up by the double-cantilever action of the slab about the column base. Shear reinforcement is normally not provided. The critical plane for bending in the case of a reinforced concrete column, is at the face of the column, but in the case of a steel stanchion it is at the centre of the base-plate. When bending moments due to wind pressure on the structure above will be transferred to the foundation slab through a rigid connection, allowance must be made for this in the design of the slab. The critical plane for shear is assumed to be at a distance from the face of the column equal to the effective depth of the slab. If the required area gives a size of base relative to the thickness required for shear resistance such that the load can be spread entirely

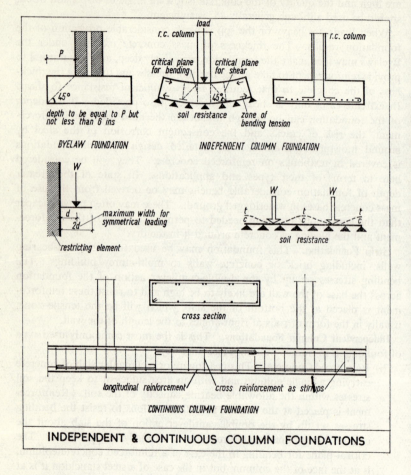

INDEPENDENT & CONTINUOUS COLUMN FOUNDATIONS

by dispersion at an angle of 45° over the whole area of the slab, any reinforcement provided need only be nominal in amount. The thickness of the slab may be reduced towards the edges to economize in concrete either by stepping or tapering the top face. Slopes greater than 25° require top shuttering to prevent the concrete building up at the edges when poured. Stepped bases should not be provided unless site supervision is sufficient to ensure that the concrete in each base will be placed in one operation.

A cover of at least 2 in. is normally provided to the steel (3 in. in the L.C.C. area), and in order to protect steel and concrete from the soil during construction a blinding layer of concrete, 2 to 4 in. thick, is usually laid over the bottom of the excavation.

(ii) Steel Grillage. This form of foundation makes use of steel joists to take up the shear and bending stresses in the foundation. For single columns with a square foundation the joists are in two tiers or layers each the width of the slab, the dimension of the slab being such as to give the required area according to the strength of the soil. The stanchion base-plate is bolted to the top of two, three, or more, deep R.S.J.'s forming the top tier and these transfer the load to a bottom tier of smaller joists spaced along the length of, and at right angles to, the upper tier. The joists in both tiers must be spaced apart to permit concrete to pass between the flange edges and fill the internal spaces completely. To prevent movement during concreting the joists are connected through the webs by bolts and barrel spacers or, as an alternative on the bottom tier, a spacing angle may be fixed across the ends of the joists on the top flanges. Web stiffeners to resist buckling may be required, particularly in the top tier under the stanchion.

The L.C.C. By-laws require a minimum concrete cover of 4 in. and, as far as structural design is concerned, permit a $33\frac{1}{3}\%$ increase of the normal permissible stresses in the steel if the joist flanges are spaced not less than 3 in. apart and the concrete mix is not less than 1:2:4, with the concrete tamped solidly round each joist.

The grillage foundation was used originally in cases where the stanchion load was so great that a conventional gussetted base sufficient to reduce the pressure on the concrete to within safe limits became too large. It is expensive in steel and is now rarely used.

Continuous Column Foundation. This type of foundation supports a line of columns and is one form of combined foundation (page 66). Although it is, in fact, a strip foundation the term "continuous column foundation" is used here to distinguish it from the normal strip foundation carrying a wall which is subject only to transverse bending, whereas the continuous column foundation is subject to both transverse bending and longitudinal bending due to the beam action between the columns (see page 70). Circumstances in which it might be used are: (i) where the spacing in one direction and loading of the columns are such that the edges of adjacent independent column foundations would be very close to each other or would overlap, and (ii) where there exists some restriction on the spread of the foundations at right-angles to a line of columns, such as a site boundary or an existing building adjacent to a line of outer columns, which would exclude the possibility of an independent foundation of adequate size to each. This is common in urban areas where a new building is to be erected between the existing party walls of adjoining buildings, and it is inadvisable or unnecessary to cut under the party walls to form foundations.

Assuming that sufficient width of foundation, relative to the spacing of the columns, is available to provide the necessary area of foundation, the strip is designed as a continuous beam on top of which the columns exert downward point loads and on the underside of which the soil exerts a distributed upward pressure. The stresses set up are the reverse of those in a normal continuous floor beam. The main tensile reinforcement is therefore required near the upper face between columns and near the bottom under the columns to resist the negative bending stresses (page 70). Transverse reinforcement must always be provided to locate the main bars during concreting, whether or not it is required to resist transverse bending.

Combined Column Foundation. It has been suggested that a continuous column foundation may be used when there exists some restriction on the spread of independent foundations at right-angles to a line of columns. This assumes that the columns can be placed far enough away from the restriction to provide sufficient area of foundation since, in order to obtain a symmetrical disposition of column relative to foundation (to ensure even stressing of the soil), the maximum width available is twice the distance from the centre line of the columns to the restriction (see page 70). When this distance is too small to provide adequate width of foundation the columns close to the restriction may be linked to an inner line of columns on what is called a combined foundation, by means of which sufficient area and an even distribution of pressure may be obtained (see page 66).

One or more pairs of columns may be combined in this manner. but the problem of design is the same in each case. This is the provision of a slab with an area sufficient to prevent overstressing of the soil and excessive settlement under the combined column loads, and of such a shape and proportion that its centre of area lies as nearly as possible on the same vertical line as the centre of gravity of the column loads.

In the case of a pair of columns which are equally loaded or of which that next to the restriction is more lightly loaded, a simple rectangular shaped

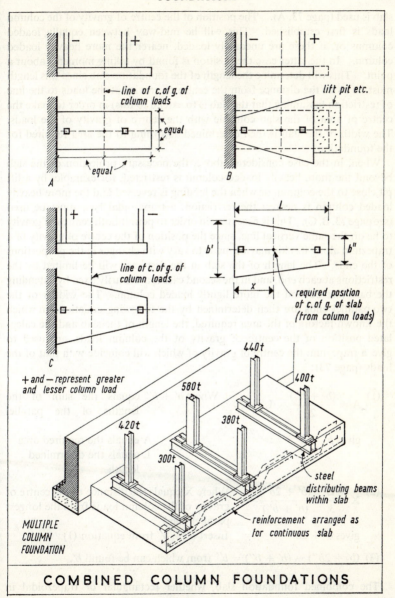

line of c.of g. of
column loads

equal

equal

A

lift pit etc.

B

line of c. of g. of
column loads

C

+ and − represent greater
and lesser column load

L

b'

b"

x

required position
of c. of g. of slab
(from column loads)

440 t

580 t

400 t

420 t

380 t

300 t

steel
distributing beams
within slab

MULTIPLE
COLUMN
FOUNDATION

reinforcement arranged as
for continuous slab

COMBINED COLUMN FOUNDATIONS

slab is used (page 73, A). The position of the centre of gravity of the column loads is first established. This will lie mid-way between equally loaded columns or, if these are unequally loaded, nearer the more heavily loaded column. In the latter case the position is found by taking moments about a point. This will determine the length of the foundation slab since this length must be twice the distance from the centre of gravity of the loads to the line of restriction (assuming that the slab is to extend to this) in order to make the centre of area of the slab coincide with the centre of gravity of the loads. The width of the slab is then determined according to the area required for the foundation.

When, in the case considered above, the necessary projection of the slab beyond the more heavily loaded column is restricted, for example, by a lift pit close to the column, or when the loading is reversed and the more heavily loaded column is nearest the restriction, a trapezoidal base must be used (see page 73, B, C). This is necessary in order to permit both centres of gravity to lie on the same vertical line, since the position of the centre of gravity of a trapezium along its axis may be made to vary with changes in the proportions of the ends. The length of the slab in the first case will be limited by the restrictions at each end, and in the second case is arbitrarily fixed by extending the base just beyond the more lightly loaded column. The widths of the two parallel ends are then determined by the following equations in which the known factors of the area required, the length of the slab and the calculated position of the centre of gravity of the column loads, are used to give a trapezium the centre of gravity of which will coincide with that of the loads (page 73):

(1) $$A = \frac{(b' + b'')}{2} \times L$$

gives $b' + b''$

Where $b' + b''$ equals the sum of the lengths of the parallel sides

A equals the required area

L equals the determined length

(2) $$X = \frac{L}{3} \times \frac{(b' + 2b'')}{(b' + b'')}$$

gives $b' + 2b''$

Where X equals the distance of the centre of gravity of the column loads from the longest parallel side b'

Insert $b' + b''$ from equation (1)

(3) $(b' + 2b'') - (b' + b'') = b''$ from which can be found b'.

The combined foundation slab, whether rectangular or trapezoidal in shape, will be reinforced along its length on the line of the columns, in a similar manner to the continuous column foundation, to resist the tensile stresses set up by the beam action between the columns and any cantilever action in the ends. Transverse reinforcement will also be provided.

As indicated earlier, this type of foundation may be in the form of a multiple slab, carrying two or three pairs of columns, in which, as before, it is desirable that the centres of gravity of column loads and slab coincide (page 73). This, however, is not always practicable and a certain amount of eccentricity may have to be accepted within the safe limits of soil strength and settlement. Combined foundations may be constructed as a single or double tier steel grillage in conjunction with steel stanchions. The loading and spacing of a pair of stanchions may be such that sufficient width of slab will be obtained when the necessary number of R.S.J.'s in a single tier linking the stanchions have been encased with concrete to give the required 4 in. cover. If this is not the case the alternative to a bottom tier of joists at right-angles to the line of stanchions is to reinforce the concrete with transverse rods. The use of combined foundations is not limited to the circumstances visualized above and a common or combined foundation may be provided for a number of adjacent columns where the size of independent foundations would be such that they would overlap.

Balanced Foundations. These consist of the cantilever foundation and the balanced base foundation which may be used in the following circumstances instead of a combined column foundation:

(i) As an alternative to a trapezoidal combined foundation slab.

(ii) When some obstruction at a column position prevents an adequate foundation being placed directly under the column. For example, when the column is placed close to the wall of an adjoining building, the foundations of which project under the column, or when a sewer passes directly under a column. In these circumstances a cantilever foundation would be used.

Cantilever Foundation. The foundation consists of a ground beam one end of which, cantilevering beyond a base set a short distance in from the obstructed column and acting as a fulcrum to the beam, picks up the foot of the column while the other end is tailed down by an internal column (see page 66).

The loads on the beam and the two base slabs are quite simply ascertained from the loads on the two columns, and from these the beam size and slab area may be calculated (see page 76):

$$W_1 \times X = W_3 \times Y$$

Therefore $\quad W_3 \quad = \quad \dfrac{W_1 \times X}{Y}$ (this "uplift" at the end of the cantilever beam must be resisted by an equal force supplied by W_2)

$$W_4 = W_1 + W_3 \text{ (i.e. load on fulcrum slab)}$$

$$W_5 = W_2 - W_3 \text{ (i.e. load on internal slab)}$$

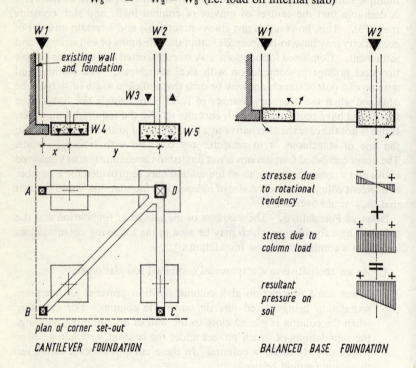

CANTILEVER FOUNDATION

BALANCED BASE FOUNDATION

The counterbalancing force supplied by the internal column must be provided wholly by the dead load on this column. This must be at least 50% greater than the combined dead and live loads on the outer column to provide an adequate margin of safety. Care must be taken to maintain this margin during construction. When the dead load on the internal column is insufficient for counterbalancing purposes, added weight must be provided by increasing the size of the internal base as necessary or alternatively anchorage must be provided in the form of tension piles under the slab. Tension piles, or a mass concrete counterweight, must be used when no suitably placed column is available for counterbalancing the cantilever beam. When a corner column is involved, a diagonal cantilever beam may be used as shown on page 76.

It should be noted that the short fulcrum column, shown in the illustrations is not essential. The cantilever beam may rest directly on the top of the fulcrum slab.

As indicated earlier, maximum economy is achieved if loads are transferred axially. Cantilever foundations should not, therefore, be resorted to unless it is impossible to re-align the column to permit axial support of its load.

As in a combined foundation, the cantilever foundation may be constructed in reinforced concrete or in steel. In the latter case the steel cantilever beam in conjunction with steel stanchions may bear on steel grillages or on normal reinforced concrete slabs.

Balanced Base Foundation. In this form of balanced foundation the beam is dropped to the level of the base slabs. It can be used when a base can be placed under, although eccentric to, the outer column and may be viewed as a beam balancing, or resisting the tendency to rotate on the part of the eccentrically loaded foundation slab (see pages 66 and 76).

In design, the foundation slab to the outer column is made large enough to take the load W_1 from the column. The tendency of this slab to rotate due to the eccentric loading is resisted by a balancing beam linking it with the inner foundation slab which, in turn, will tend to rotate under the action of the balancing beam. The spread of this slab must, therefore, be sufficient not only to distribute safely to the soil the load from its own column, but also to prevent overstressing of the soil at its far edge due to the rotational tendency (page 76). If, for this reason, the spread became excessive, it would be necessary to use a cantilever foundation. The balancing beam must be stiff enough to fulfil its function satisfactorily. In both the cantilever and balancing beams the tensile zones would be at the top where the main reinforcement would be placed.

Raft Foundations

A raft foundation is fundamentally a large combined slab foundation designed to cover the whole or a large part of the available site. The broad circumstances in which raft foundations are used have been mentioned on page 65 and they may now be considered in greater detail.

A raft may be used when the soil is weak and the columns are so closely spaced in both directions, or carry such high loads, that independent column foundations would overlap or would almost completely cover the site. In these circumstances it may be cheaper to use a raft when it appears likely that more than three-quarters of the site will be covered by independent column foundations. When a raft is indicated the following considerations should be borne in mind before a final decision is made:

(1) When the depth of the weak strata down to firm soil is not much greater than about fifteen feet, it may be cheaper to use foundation piers, as these can be economically constructed to this depth.

(2) When the weak soil extends to a depth greater than this, bearing piles might, in some circumstances, form a cheaper foundation than a raft.

(3) When the weak soil extends to such a great depth that bearing piles would be uneconomic, a raft can be used provided that the building is reasonably compact in plan and fairly evenly loaded. When the loading is very uneven, friction piles could be used as an alternative and possibly simpler solution to the problem.

(4) Treatment of the ground to improve its bearing capacity, such as vibro-compaction of sand, may be economical.

The choice of method depends on the extent of the individual loads, the size of project and the ground conditions. Each method must be compared with the others on an economic basis.

When a raft is used this reduces the ground pressure immediately beneath the foundation, but the pressures at greater depths are little less than they would have been under closely spaced independent column foundations (see page 49). Care must be taken to ensure that the pressures at such depths are acceptable.

A raft used to distribute the building loads over a large area of weak soil may be flexible or rigid in form, as required by the characteristics of the soil, the distribution of loading and the form of structure used for the building it supports. As already explained, the rigidity of a raft has an important effect upon the distribution of pressure and upon settlement. It is possible to use a stiff raft to minimize differential settlement. For example, in the case of a building bearing on a cohesionless soil and having high load concentrations round the edges, the use of a rigid raft would result in a greater uniformity of pressure under the raft than if a flexible form were used. However, a high degree of rigidity results in a most expensive structure and a certain amount of differential settlement usually has to be accepted, the safe limits depending upon the construction of the building which is supported.

A raft may also be used as a means of bridging over weak areas on a site which otherwise is generally fairly firm. A raft should not, however, be carried directly over a local hard area in an otherwise fairly weak site. In such circumstances the hard area should be excavated to a suitable depth and backfilled with a material compacted so as to bring its bearing capacity to an amount not exceeding that of the remainder of the site.

The use of basements in foundation problems was mentioned earlier. A basement may be used as a means of reducing the nett intensity of pressure on the soil by a relief of overburden pressure, in order to reduce the overall settlement under the whole area of a building. One may also be used under the heavier parts of a building in which large variations of loading occur, as in a building with a tall tower block surrounded closely by lower blocks, to produce a uniform distribution of pressure. In such circumstances the basement must be provided with a rigid raft foundation or, if the basement is deep, the whole of the basement must be constructed as a stiff rigid structure (page 60).

Stiff rafts may be used in some circumstances to overcome the difficulties of subsidence sites or, alternatively, these difficulties may be overcome by the use of an extremely flexible raft carrying a building of sufficient flexibility to deal with the movements arising during actual subsidence. This is discussed more fully on page 83. The flexibility of a raft foundation varies, as in the case of normal beams, with the depth and the degree of stiffness between the parts and, where great stiffness is required, a deep beam or cellular structure is essential.

Design of Rafts Generally. In order to distribute evenly the pressure on the soil, the centre of gravity of the building loads as a whole should lie on the same vertical line as that of the raft. This is particularly important since the raft form is used on weak yielding soils where a slight unevenness of pressure will cause considerable differential settlement. Although, as seen in combined slab foundations, equal loading of the columns is not essential in order to make the centre of gravity of the loads coincide with the centroid of the raft, this is facilitated if the plan of the building is symmetrical and without projecting elements. The ideal is a simple, regular shaped raft carrying symmetrically arranged, equally loaded columns and on which any heavier parts of the structure are grouped symmetrically about the axis. If practical limitations on the extent of the raft at the sides make it impossible to bring about the coincidence of the two centres of gravity, it may be necessary to make the raft irregular in shape in order to reduce the eccentricity to a minimum. In circumstances where some part of the raft must be unevenly loaded to an excessive degree, or where a considerable projection or arm in the plan form is unavoidable, the unevenly loaded or the projecting section should be on a separate raft with the building structure above also separated. This will avoid adverse effects on the structure arising from differential settlement due to the uneven loading on the subsoil.

Problems due to subsoil water arise during the construction of basements on account of the upward pressure of the water. The total dead weight of the basement and building above must, when completed, exceed the maximum upward pressure of the water. When the basement is under construction, however, it is without the superstructure load and must be prevented from floating. If the dead weight of the basement alone is insufficient for this, one of a number of methods can be used to do so.

(a) The subsoil water level may be lowered by pumping or other means. This is usually essential in the initial stages of construction at least.

(b) The basement may be temporarily filled with water to a height such that its weight, together with the dead load of the basement, resists the upward pressure of the subsoil water.

(c) Holes may be formed in the floor through which the subsoil water may enter the basement and prevent the build up of external pressure. When construction has advanced enough to provide sufficient dead load, the holes are sealed.

Pumping to keep the water level down is most commonly used, but when construction is sufficiently far advanced the use of the other methods, particularly (b) which is the simpler of the two, enables pumping to be stopped. If a basement was to be used only to reduce pressure on a weak soil, it might prove cheaper to use piles in order to avoid the construction of a basement in such conditions.

The weight of a building structure is not uniformly distributed over the raft, but is concentrated at the wall or column points and, since a completely rigid raft is not practicable in most cases, there is the tendency for greater pressure to occur under these points, giving a non-uniform distribution of pressure under the raft. Nevertheless, to simplify design procedure, other than in the case of an extremely flexible raft, the assumption is frequently made that the pressure distribution is uniform or varies uniformly under the raft, and that the upward reaction of the soil on the raft is uniform. To find the reaction of the soil per sq. ft, the total load from the structure is divided by the area of the raft and from this may be calculated the thickness of the slab and the reinforcement required for the raft, the design process being similar to that for an inverted floor.

Rafts may be divided into three types according to their design and construction.

(a) Solid slab.

(b) Beam and slab.

(c) Cellular.

All are basically the same, in consisting of a large, generally unbroken area of slab covering the whole or a large part of the site. The thickness of slab and size of any beams will be governed by the spacing and loading of the columns and the degree of rigidity required in the raft.

Solid Slab Raft. This type of raft consists of a solid slab of concrete reinforced in both directions. Light solid slab rafts are used for the small load-bearing wall type of building, such as houses, or for light framed structures where the bearing pressures are relatively low.[1] For larger and more heavily loaded buildings, this type of raft is often economic only up to a thickness of about 12 in. Unless the column and wall loads are very heavy, the slab is reinforced top and bottom with two-way reinforcement. When loads are heavy, more reinforcement is required on the lines of the columns to form column bands similar to a plate floor. The reinforcement to the panels between would then be two-way reinforcement mainly at the top. If the slab is situated at ground level, it is generally desirable to thicken the edge of the slab or to form a downstand beam of sufficient depth to prevent weathering away of the soil under the perimeter of the raft (page 60). In some cases deep edge beams are required to contain the soil under the slab to transfer the load to a lower level. This is illustrated in the three-storey building shown on page 60. The ground floor slab, 12 in. above ground level, is stiffened by cross and edge beams to act as a raft, the pressure from which is transferred to the ground below through soil filled within and contained by the deep edge beams before the floor slab is cast.

A thin solid slab raft divided into small sections, held together by steel mesh at mid-thickness, may be used for light framed buildings on sites liable to subsidence. For design reasons, discussed later, the raft rests on the surface of the ground, acting as the ground floor slab and no downstand edge beams are provided, soil erosion being avoided by a few feet of paving round the building.

Beam and Slab Raft. When loading or requirements of rigidity necessitate a slab thickness greater than 12 in. it may be cheaper to use beam and slab construction, which may be visualized as an inverted floor, the slab bearing directly on the ground and the beams projecting above it (page 60). The reinforcement is arranged accordingly. On sites where the weak strata is overlaid by a thin layer of comparatively stiff soil at building level, economy in construction could be effected by placing the beams below rather than above the slab. The beams could then be cast in excavated trenches of the appropriate size without the use of shuttering, and the necessity of a sub-floor would be avoided. The slab at the bottom, however, has the advantage

[1] See *Elementary Building Construction.*

of providing stiffness to the bottoms of the beams, which will be in compression in the zones of negative bending moment between columns. Where possible, the raft should be cantilevered beyond the outside lines of columns so that the bending moments in the inner slabs are reduced.

When there is some unevenness of loading on the columns of a frame, but where loading and strength of soil are such that a full raft is not required, beams may be used to link independent column foundations to give some degree of rigidity in order to limit differential settlement.

Cellular Raft. When stresses in the raft are high, and particularly when great rigidity is required, the beams must be deep and when the overall depth is likely to exceed 3 ft, a cellular form of construction is adopted. This consists of top and bottom slabs with edge and intermediate beams in both directions forming a hollow cellular raft (page 60). When such a raft is extensive in area and great rigidity is required to reduce differential settlement, the depth may need to be as much as a full basement storey or more. The cellular basement is also necessary when very deep basements are used to reduce overall settlement by a relief of overburden pressure. As already explained cellular basement construction is one means of dealing with these problems in the case of very tall buildings, as both the need to limit overall settlement and to reduce differential settlement often arise. (Typical examples are shown on page 60.)

A normal cellular raft is completely cellular, but in the case of a basement, reinforced concrete walls, monolithic with the floors and dividing the basement area into small compartments, makes it unsuitable for many purposes. An alternative method may be used in which heavy reinforced concrete columns and floor beams are framed together to form Vierendeel girders in both directions. To obtain sufficient rigidity, the junctions of top and bottom of the columns with the beams will normally need large haunches. This restricts the floor area of the basement and in some circumstances it may be preferable to use pile foundations instead of a basement as an alternative, although possibly more expensive, method.

In deep excavations, there is an upward movement of the excavated surface called "heave" which is caused by the pressure of the overburden at the sides of the excavation forcing up the base of the excavation. If a very deep basement is needed in soft clay the heave and, subsequently, the ultimate settlement of this, may be the determining factor in deciding the depth to which the foundation should be taken. If sufficient relief of overburden pressure cannot be obtained the excess pressure may be taken by piles and if the piles are driven prior to the excavation, the amount of heave can be reduced.

Foundations on Subsidence Sites

The behaviour of soil and buildings under the action of subsidence has been described on page 62. A number of methods are used to minimize the effects of mining subsidence upon a building; of these the following are commonly used.

(i) The foundation of the building may be designed as a strong reinforced concrete raft, generally in cellular form to give adequate stiffness, or as a system of beams and slabs with three-point support on the soil. The foundation structure, together with the building supported by it, will tilt as the ground moves, but the building will not distort and will, therefore, be free from damage. These methods are expensive, particularly the construction of stiff cellular rafts, and are generally used only for larger and more important structures, since the cost of the foundations is likely to be much in excess of the value of any damage caused.

(ii) The building itself may be designed as a rigid frame structure or be strengthened by reinforcement to act as a single structural element, capable of resisting without cracking all the stresses set up as it tilts, and as the support from the ground reduces in area and varies in position with the movement of the ground. With both these methods it is desirable to break up long buildings into short blocks, connected only by some form of flexible joint.

(iii) In contrast to the above methods, the building and its foundation can both be designed as flexible elements, the construction of the structure and its cladding being detailed to accommodate the differential movements of the soil without damage either to structure or finishes.

(iv) Hydraulic jacks may be used to raise or lower the building at different points to keep pace with the subsidence movement and thus avoid tilting. With this method the building structure would rest on reinforced concrete or prestressed concrete foundation beams bearing on concrete bases, provision being made for the jacks to be inserted at the points of support where adjustment is required.[1]

When the method adopted requires a long building to be broken down into short independent units, these should not exceed about 60 ft in either direction in order to keep differential settlement within reasonable limits. If the independent units must be connected this is accomplished by movement or slip joints in walls, roof and floor slab. These gaps must be sealed in such a manner that freedom of movement is permitted—thin corrugated metal could be used at the walls and some form of sliding element at roof and floor.

[1] See "Underpinning and Jacking Buildings Affected by Mining Subsidence", by J. F. S. Pryke, M.A. (Cantab.). A.M.I.Struct.E., *The Chartered Surveyor*, April 1960.

As an alternative to corrugated metal, rendering on expanded metal has been used. When notice is given by the National Coal Board that movement will take place the rendering is cut down to permit "concertinaing" to take place, and when the movement is complete and the gaps have again opened up they are made good permanently.

Protection within the limits of these small units should provide resistance against the stresses set up in the ground and against those set up by the cantilever and beam actions of the foundation. This is done by providing steel reinforcement disposed according to the stresses set up in the foundation slab by the different external forces. The amount of the ground forces transmitted to the slab may be limited by reducing as much as possible the friction between the slab and the ground. This is accomplished by laying the ground or foundation slab on building paper on a bed of sand, shale or other granular material 6 to 12 in. thick.

Resistance to the stresses due to the flexure of the foundation at the crest or trough of the wave can be provided only at considerable expense by means of a stiff and rigid foundation, often in heavy and deep cellular form. In small and light structures the cost of such foundations, sometimes as much as 10% of the cost of the building, is likely to be greater than the cost of repairing any damage caused by unrestricted flexural movements, and foundations of this type would be economical only in large, multi-storey structures in which the high cost of the foundations would be distributed over a total floor area much greater than that of the foundation itself.

Damage to the structure arising from the flexural movements of the foundation when this is not rigid are minimized by using, as far as possible, flexible forms of construction such as timber framing and brickwork bedded in weak mortar to prevent serious cracking. Light reinforcement introduced in brickwork at top and bottom and around openings also assists in this respect, especially when the differential movements are likely to be severe. In addition to these precautions flexural movement can be reduced by siting the building with the shorter axis in the direction of the likely maximum curvature when this can be ascertained.

These methods accept as inevitable a considerable amount of damage to the structure, requiring repair after subsidence is complete, or they make use of heavy, rigid and costly foundations designed to resist the flexural stresses. Even so in many cases experience has shown these to be inadequate to prevent extensive damage to the structure. This is probably due to the fact that the deeper the structure is in the ground the more likely it is to be affected adversely by the horizontal ground movements.

An alternative method suitable for buildings of light construction, in which the foundation and superstructure are integrated into a wholly flexible structure, uses a foundation designed as a thin, flexible slab which accommodates itself to the curves and tilt of the subsidence wave. The building structure is formed as a light, completely pin-jointed frame capable of adjusting itself to the differential vertical movements transferred to it through the foundation slab (see page 63). Claddings designed to permit free movement, such as tile hanging, weatherboarding or hung concrete slabs, are used and windows are designed in timber with sufficient clearances to accommodate the maximum anticipated distortion.

The foundation slab, laid on sand or shale, consists of a 5 in. thickness of concrete reinforced at the centre of the thickness and divided into panels not greater in area than 200 sq. ft. The panel edges are painted with bitumen so that the slab will bend fairly freely with the ground. The primary function of the reinforcement is to hold these slabs together. The sand or shale bed, together with the lightness of structure, reduces friction and minimizes the amount of ground forces transmitted to the slab.

Where the loading on columns is such as to require spreading over a relatively large area local top and bottom reinforcement is placed in the slab but no thickening of the slab occurs.

Since no flexural stresses are set up in the slab as a whole the need to limit its length in order to keep differential settlement within small limits does not arise. The length of the building is not, therefore, dictated by this consideration but rather by that of the maximum length which can economically be held together by tensional reinforcement. This appears to be about 180 ft for a single-storey building reducing to 140 ft for one of three or four storeys, up to which height it is considered that this form of foundation is applicable.

Rigidity is provided in the pin-jointed frame structure by specially designed diagonal steel braces incorporating coiled springs at the ends. These do not move under normal wind and dead loads but react to the greater stresses due to subsidence. One of the springs always acts in compression, the other remaining inoperative. When the subsidence wave has passed the springs bring the frame back to its normal position and continue to control it under normal loads.[1]

This type of flexible foundation and building structure is, of course, suitable for soft, or made up ground, on which differential settlements are likely to develop after the building is completed as well as for normal sites. There

[1] For full details of this system and of problems connected with it, such as the passing of services through the floor slab, see *RIBA Journal*, December 1957. *Architects' Journal*, October 10 and 24, 1957.

is no reason why its use for lightly loaded buildings, for which it was designed, should be limited to subsidence sites.

A form of roller bearing has been used for heavy single storey structures, in which two sets of rollers at right angles to each other in a tray, are situated at the foot of portal frames to permit free horizontal movement of the soil and foundations in any direction without transfer to the structure.

PILE FOUNDATIONS

These may be defined as a form of foundation in which the loads are taken to a low level by means of columns in the soil on which the building rests.

It is a method of support adopted (a) instead of a raft foundation where no firm bearing strata exists at any reasonable depth and the loading is uneven, (b) when a firm bearing strata does exist but at a depth such as to make strip, slab or pier foundations uneconomical, that is at depths over 10 to 15 ft, but not so deep as to make use of a raft essential. Piles to depths of 60 ft are common and in exceptional circumstances they are used to depths of 100 ft or more, but piles over 100 ft are considered long, (c) when pumping of subsoil water would be too costly or timbering to excavations too difficult to permit the construction of normal foundations.

Irrespective of the type piles may be divided into two categories according to the manner in which they lower the level of the applied pressure (i) friction piles, (ii) end bearing piles (page 87). Most piles do, in fact, carry the load by a combination of friction and end bearing.

Friction piles, transferring their load to the surrounding soil by means of the friction between their surfaces and the soil, and to a slight extent by end bearing, are used in deep beds of clay and silt as an alternative to a raft. They may also be used in conjunction with a raft, as already described, when the latter cannot be taken deep enough to obtain sufficient relief of over-burden pressure to keep settlement within acceptable limits. Such foundations should be designed with great care as they may result in unacceptable differential settlement. The friction pile has the effect of carrying the bulb of pressure to a low level so that the high stresses are set up in the soil at a level where it is strong enough to resist them rather than near the surface where it is weaker. It may be assumed that friction piles form a raft imposing the load upon the soil about two-thirds down their depth. In order to obtain an effective lowering of the bulb of pressure it is essential that the ratio of pile length to building width should be high. The wider a foundation is the deeper will its bulb of pressure penetrate and unless the piles in a wide building are long relative to its width they will make little difference to the actual depth of the bulb of pressure (see page 87).

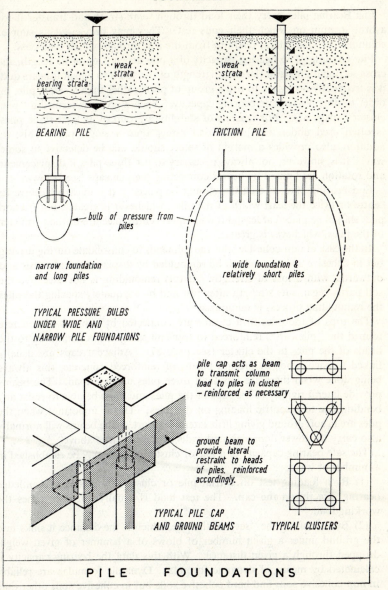

BEARING PILE

FRICTION PILE

bulb of pressure from piles

narrow foundation and long piles

wide foundation & relatively short piles

TYPICAL PRESSURE BULBS UNDER WIDE AND NARROW PILE FOUNDATIONS

pile cap acts as beam to transmit column load to piles in cluster – reinforced as necessary

ground beam to provide lateral restraint to heads of piles. reinforced accordingly.

TYPICAL PILE CAP AND GROUND BEAMS

TYPICAL CLUSTERS

PILE   FOUNDATIONS

End Bearing piles carry their load through weak strata and transfer it to a firm stratum on which their ends rest. They may be viewed as simple columns receiving lateral restraint from the soil through which they pass.

Pile Groups. The bearing capacity of a pile depends upon its length, its cross-sectional area and the shear strength of the soil into which it bears and it is frequently necessary to use a group of piles, rather than a single pile, in order to obtain adequate bearing capacity. Such a group is termed a "pile cluster" (page 87). For reasons of stability a group of at least three piles is often used under any heavy load rather than a single pile. This, in addition, also provides a margin of safety should one be defective in some way. It is, however, not always necessary to use three piles if displacement and rotation are limited by beams connecting the pile caps (see below).

End bearing piles in a cluster should be placed 2 ft 6 in. apart centre to centre or twice the least width of the piles, whichever is greater, but friction piles should be placed at least 3 ft 6 in. apart centre to centre or the perimeter of the piles, whichever is greater.

In the case of non-cohesive soils the soil tends to consolidate during driving but in cohesive soils it tends to be remoulded by displacement upwards and outwards, with a loss of strength. If this remoulding is not excessive the soil partly regains its strength after rest and by adequately spacing the piles the remoulding process is minimized.

The tops of the piles in a cluster are connected by a block of concrete termed the "pile cap", reinforced to transmit safely the column load to the heads of the piles in the cluster (see page 87). Adjacent caps are usually linked to each other by ground beams of reinforced concrete, this always being done when there are less than three piles under a load. The beams provide lateral rigidity to the tops of the piles and must be able to resist any bending due to eccentric loading on the piles. This is important when the piles are in soft ground giving little lateral support. The beams will normally also carry the lower floor slab and walls of the structure above.

The safe bearing capacity of a pile or cluster of piles may be established in a number of ways:

(1) By a loading test on a trial pile or cluster, by means of kentledge bearing directly on the cap. The test load is usually up to $1\frac{1}{2}$ times the working load.

(2) By measuring the "set" of the pile, which is the distance it sinks into the ground under a given number of blows of a hammer of given weight dropped through a given distance. With this data the bearing capacity is calculated by means of dynamic formula. Dynamic formulae are reliable in non-cohesive soils and hard cohesive soils but in cohesive soils other than

"hard" a check by calculation based on measured shear strength of soil should be made.

(3) In cohesive soils, by calculation based on the measured shear strength of the ground at various levels.

(4) By means of a small diameter penetration test, making use of apparatus developed to measure the soil resistance at its foot and the frictional resistance along its outside surface. These measurements can be taken at varying depths over a building site and the lengths and bearing capacities of the piles predetermined before work begins.

(5) By previous experience with similar piles nearby.

As will be seen from the earlier part of this chapter, tests will not give a complete picture of the final settlement of the completed structure as a whole, since it will produce a deeper bulb of pressure than the single pile or cluster of piles (page 50), and this must be considered separately having regard to the factors on which this depends.

Compacting and Short Bored Piles. Piles may be used in non-cohesive soils such as loose sand as a means of compacting it by the vibration of driving in order to increase its bearing capacity.

A particular form of pile foundation makes use of unreinforced short-bored piles. These are used for small-scale buildings on shrinkable clays where it is essential for the foundations to be at least 3 ft below the surface in order to be beyond the zone of seasonal moisture movement. This method is described in *Elementary Building Construction.*

Types of Piles

Piles are considered as *driven* or formed *in situ* according to whether they are preformed and driven into the ground by blows of a hammer or are formed on site by placing concrete and reinforcement in a borehole.

Some types of piles are, in fact, basically formed *in situ* but a shell or former into which the concrete is poured is driven into the soil and from the point of view of soil mechanics are considered as driven piles. To distinguish them from driven precast concrete, timber or steel piles they may be termed "driven tube" piles.

Driven Piles. These may be of timber, steel or precast concrete. The latter, either normally reinforced or prestressed, is most commonly used in building work. Timber piles are not much used in building work, except for minor purposes, such as supports to manholes in running sand for example. The use of timber piles is restricted by the limitations in cross sections and lengths available. Splices are unsatisfactory. In addition the supply of large numbers of timber piles is difficult at short notice. Timber tends to rot if not always submerged and difficulties are encountered in the use of timber piles if there is hard driving in the early stages. Steel piles in the form of open ended box or H-sections, or pipes, are used when the length is very great, especially when driven to rock to carry heavy loads. These conditions would require large section heavy concrete piles, difficult to handle and liable to damage, and in such circumstances they would be used instead of steel only in situations where the latter would be subject to heavy corrosion.

Precast concrete piles may be square, hexagonal or round in section and may be solid or hollow. 60 ft long precast piles are normal and lengths up to from 50 to 60 ft can be obtained from stock. Large section piles over 100 ft long have been used; they are usually cast on or near the site. The toe of a precast pile is usually fitted with a cast iron or steel protective shoe and the top is protected during driving by a steel cap or "helmet" in order to prevent spalling. Shoes are not essential in soft ground but special shoes are provided for entering rock.

The reinforcement in precast concrete piles is designed to resist the stresses set up in transport and slinging and in driving, as well as those set up by the working load. Prestressing may be used, in which case the whole pile may be prestressed as cast, or long piles can be formed of factory made precast sections transported to the site where they are made up into full pile lengths and post-tensioned prior to driving.

The pile is supported between guides or "leaders" in a vertical steel piling frame (see page 91) sufficiently high to take the pile and to allow room above the cap for a hammer, or for the drop of a weight, by means of which the pile is driven into the ground. Pile driving frames are normally mobile and arranged to rake over to drive piles at an angle when required. For piles less than 40 ft in length an excavator may be equipped with hanging "leaders" to act as a pile driver (see page 26). Driving by a weight or drop hammer is performed by allowing a weight, or "monkey", attached by cable to a steam or diesel operated winch, to fall on to the head of the pile in successive blows. The winch raises the monkey each time to the top of the drop and is then released to allow the monkey to fall. The distance of drop is usually about 5 ft although drops up to 10 ft are sometimes used.

Pile driving hammers rest directly on the pile and travel down with it. Driving is more rapid than by a drop hammer because of the large number of blows delivered per minute. They are operated by steam or compressed air as single- or double-acting hammers. Petrol operated hammers are also available, acting on the principle of earth rammers. With a single-acting hammer the motive power simply lifts the hammer after which it falls by its own weight. With a double-acting hammer the steam or air assists in forcing it down on to the pile after having raised it. The weight of the striking parts of a double-acting hammer is much less than that in a single-acting hammer but the former gives a more rapid succession of blows.

Driven piles are most suitable for open sites where the length required will be constant and where there is ample headroom for the driving frames.

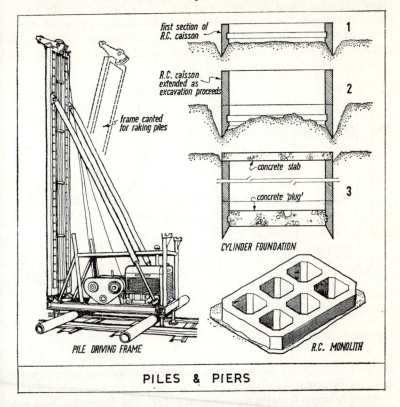

first section of R.C. caisson — 1

R.C. caisson extended as excavation proceeds 2

frame canted for raking piles

concrete slab

concrete 'plug' 3

CYLINDER FOUNDATION

PILE DRIVING FRAME

R.C. MONOLITH

PILES & PIERS

Considerable vibration and noise is set up during driving and on some sites this would preclude the use of this type of pile.

In certain types of soil, such as fine, clean sands and fine gravels, driving is facilitated by the use of a jet of water discharged under pressure at the toe of the pile to displace the soil underneath. Various arrangements of jets are used and the water is taken to the toe through a pipe or pipes running through the pile from the top. Towards the end of driving the water is cut off so that the pile is driven to rest for the last 4 or 5 ft through undisturbed soil.

Driven Tube Piles.   These are more suitable than driven precast concrete piles on sites where there is likely to be a considerable variation in the lengths of piles.   They may be formed in various ways using steel or concrete tubes.   In some forms driving is from the top, in others from the toe by means of a mandrel or by a drop hammer falling through the length of the tube.   In some forms the tube or shell is left permanently in position, in others it is withdrawn as concreting proceeds.   In common with driven piles

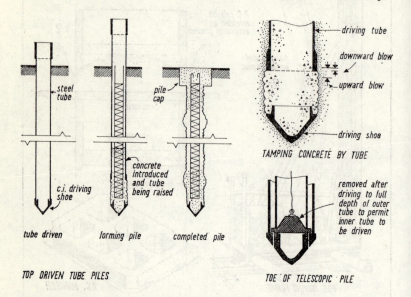

vibration occurs under the blows of the hammer, the degree of which depends upon the particular system used.

Where driving is from the top a steel tube of required diameter is fitted with a cast-iron conical shoe, placed in a driving frame and driven down by a drop or a steam hammer in the same way as a precast concrete pile (see above). Reinforcement, in the form of a cage made up of longitudinal rods linked by helical or horizontal binding with spacers at intervals to ensure adequate concrete cover, is lowered into the tube.   Concrete is then poured in through a hopper or skip as the tube is gradually withdrawn leaving the driving shoe behind.

Tamping of the concrete may be done by a drop hammer falling on to each charge of concrete as the tube is slowly withdrawn, consolidating it and forcing it into close contact with the surrounding soil. In other systems, using a tube with a thickened bottom rim, the concrete is tamped by the tube itself which, as it is withdrawn, is subjected to rapid up and down blows from a steam hammer, causing it to vibrate and consolidate the concrete by its thickened edge (page 92).

The normal tube length is from 40 to 50 ft, but this may be extended when necessary by screwing on a further length when the first has been driven or, alternatively, the tube may be used as a leader for a precast concrete extension pile driven through the tube and taking the conical shoe with it. This has the advantage of reducing frictional resistance since the driving force has to overcome only the resistance of the extension pile as it is being driven, the upper tube remaining fixed in position. The same result may be obtained by the use of telescopic tubes in which the upper length after it has been driven to its full extent acts as a leader to an inner tube which is driven to the full required depth (p. 92). Both these methods can be used where piles must pass through the water of a river or lake, the upper tube being left in position as a casing to the concrete filling.

Driving from the toe substantially reduces the amount of vibration set up during the driving operations. One type of pile driven in this way uses a steel tube of the appropriate diameter held in a driving frame with the open bottom end resting on the ground (see page 94). The first 2 or 3 ft of the tube are filled with dry gravel which is compacted by blows from a drop hammer falling within the tube. When the friction between the gravel and the inside of the tube is sufficiently great subsequent blows pull the tube down into the soil. By means of marks on the hammer cable a check is kept on the depth of the plug and more gravel is introduced when necessary so that the tube is continually sealed to prevent the entry of soil or subsoil water. Reinforcement and a semi-dry concrete mix is placed as described earlier and tamping is carried out by the drop hammer as the tube is gradually withdrawn. In this type and in all types in which the tube is withdrawn, particularly where the tamping is carried out by a drop hammer, it is possible to form an enlarged bulb base of concrete which increases the bearing area of the pile (page 94). Light tube piles driven in this way may be used when vibration must be limited but the nature of the sub-soil, such as waterlogged soil or running sand, might make boring impossible. The tubes are left permanently in position and are filled with reinforcement and concrete.

Another type of pile driven from the toe uses a tube or shell of concrete round a steel mandrel, the tube being left in the soil to act as a permanent

4*

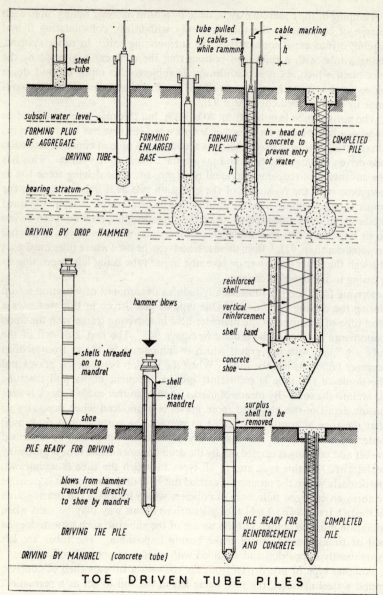

steel
tube

tube pulled
by cables
while ramming

cable marking

h

subsoil water level

FORMING PLUG
OF AGGREGATE

DRIVING TUBE

FORMING
ENLARGED
BASE

FORMING
PILE

h = head of
concrete to
prevent entry
of water

h

COMPLETED
PILE

bearing stratum

DRIVING BY DROP HAMMER

hammer blows

reinforced
shell

vertical
reinforcement

shell band

concrete
shoe

shells threaded
on to mandrel

shell

steel mandrel

shoe

surplus
shell to be
removed

PILE READY FOR DRIVING

blows from hammer
transferred directly
to shoe by mandrel

DRIVING THE PILE

PILE READY FOR
REINFORCEMENT
AND CONCRETE

COMPLETED
PILE

DRIVING BY MANDREL (concrete tube)

TOE DRIVEN TUBE PILES

casing to a core of reinforced concrete cast inside (see page 94). The concrete tube is built up from precast reinforced concrete sections threaded over the mandrel, at the bottom of which is a solid concrete shoe. The hammer blows are transmitted to the shoe through the mandrel and by means of a special device at the top of the mandrel sufficient force is also transmitted to the tube to overcome skin friction and to enable it to follow the shoe. After being driven to a set the mandrel is withdrawn, any surplus sections of tube are removed from the top and the reinforcement and concrete is placed inside.

Bored Piles. On sites where piling is to be carried out close to existing premises, or for underpinning buildings with the minimum of disturbance, driven or driven tube piles are unsuitable because of the amount of vibration set up. In such cases some form of bored pile is used in which the vibration is much less. The system requires only a light shear-leg type of rig instead of a large driving frame and is useful, therefore, on sites where levels vary and where space or headroom is restricted. The use of bored piles is usually cheaper than any form of driven pile when a few only are required or when the required bearing capacity is very small.

In forming a bored pile a steel tube is sunk by removing the soil from inside it by means of a coring tool, the tube then sinking under its own weight or being driven down by relatively light pressure, generally by means of the coring tool itself acting through a steel channel passed horizontally through the clearing holes in the sides (see page 96).

The tube is made up from screw-coupled sections varying from 3 ft 6 in. to 4 ft 6 in. in length, so that work can be carried out with the headroom restricted to as little as 6 ft, fresh sections being coupled on until the final pile length is reached. When headroom is as low as this boring must be done by hand with a low rig. Labour costs are greater than when a coring tool can be used. Hand boring may also be used to eliminate vibration due to the dropping of a coring tool.

The coring tool is raised and dropped inside the tube by a winch driven by a petrol or diesel engine to which it is attached by a steel cable running over a pulley at the top of the shear-legs. A clutch enables the operator to drop the tool as required.

The type of coring tool used varies according to the nature of the subsoil. In clay a steel cylinder with a bottom cutting edge is used. It has rectangular holes in the sides to enable stiff clay to be more easily removed by a spade or crowbar when the cutter is brought up full from the tube. In sands and ballast a cylinder similar to the clay cutter is used, but without the extracting holes in the side, with a hinged flap at the bottom opening upwards to allow

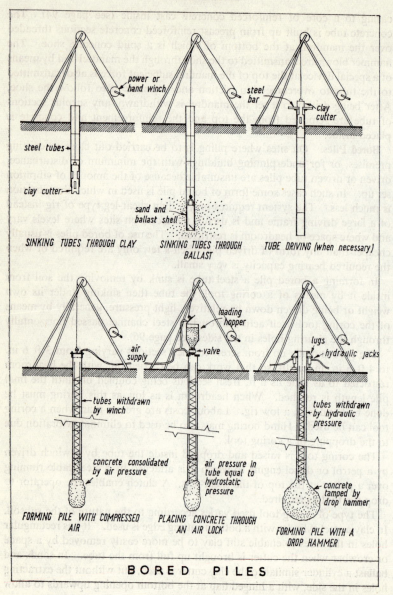

SINKING TUBES THROUGH CLAY

SINKING TUBES THROUGH BALLAST

TUBE DRIVING (when necessary)

power or hand winch

steel tubes

clay cutter

sand and ballast shell

steel bar

clay cutter

FORMING PILE WITH COMPRESSED AIR

PLACING CONCRETE THROUGH AN AIR LOCK

FORMING PILE WITH A DROP HAMMER

air supply

tubes withdrawn by winch

concrete consolidated by air pressure

loading hopper

valve

air pressure in tube equal to hydrostatic pressure

lugs

hydraulic jacks

tubes withdrawn by hydraulic pressure

concrete tamped by drop hammer

BORED PILES

the soil to enter the cylinder as it drops and then closing to retain it when the cylinder is raised. This is called a sand and ballast shell.

When the required depth is reached, a cage of reinforcement is lowered into the tube and concrete is introduced in batches through a hopper as the tube is gradually withdrawn either by block tackle operated by the winch or by hydraulic jacks operating against lugs on the top of the tube (page 96). Tamping can be carried out by a drop hammer or by compressed air.

In the latter method, which eliminates vibration during the tamping process, after each batch of concrete is introduced a pressure cap is screwed on the top of the tube and compressed air is admitted which forces the concrete down and out against the surrounding ground (page 96). With this method a bulb foot, similar to that formed by a drop hammer, may be formed in ballast by forcing cement grout into the ballast surrounding the foot of the pile.

When ground water is present it can be kept out of the tube during concreting by compressed air, in which case the concrete is placed through an air-lock attached to the top of the tube in place of the normal pressure cap as shown on page 96. This consists of a cylindrical steel hopper with a feed hole at the top and a large valve at the bottom. Admission of air first blows out the water through a pipe lowered down the tube. This pipe is then closed, and by maintaining the air at sufficient pressure to balance the head of subsoil water, the tube is kept free of water. Concrete is then placed in batches through the air-lock, each batch being forced down and out by a temporary increase in the air pressure as the tube is being raised.

In using bored piles or driven tube piles where the tube is withdrawn, the possibility of "necking" must be borne in mind. This is liable to occur when the external water pressure is more than the pressure of the concrete where it flows out of the bottom of the tube. It may also occur when the pile is in very soft clay which will try to press back into the pile when the tube is withdrawn if the concrete pressure is insufficient. Compressed air on the concrete helps to overcome this if it is maintained at the critical time.

Cylinder Piles. These are large diameter bored piles which may be from 2 to 7 ft or more in diameter and possess the advantages of the traditional cylinder foundation which has been used for many years by engineers to carry very large loads.

One system, developed essentially for use in cohesive soils, uses an auger for drilling the hole. The auger is fixed to the end of a long square vertical kelly bar which passes through a turntable by means of which it is rotated. A standard excavator may be rigged specially for this purpose as shown on page 26, or specially designed gear consisting of a high retractable vertical jib to carry the rotating kelly bar may be fixed to a heavy mobile wagon. These piles are generally unreinforced except where they pass through a soft stratum near the ground level and may be sunk to a depth of 100 ft or more in suitable conditions. A lining is not normally used except in cases where a granular stratum overlays a clay stratum, when the hole may be lined to a depth of from 25 to 30 ft. Drilling is rapid and shafts can be sunk into firm clay at a speed of up to 10 ft per hour. The base of the piles may be expanded up to two or three times the diameter of the shaft by means of an under-reaming tool consisting of a cylinder from which cutting wings are made to extend when at the base of the shaft.

Another system uses steel linings from 3 to 4 ft in diameter for the full length of the boring, which is carried out by a specially designed turn grab carried on a square kelly bar in the same way as the augers described above. The grab is capable of boring through most types of soil up to the hardness of soft rock so that the system is not limited to firm cohesive soils. The steel lining is made up of inter-locking systems each about 10 ft long, the first of which has a cutting edge. The lining is forced down, and ultimately drawn up, by means of hydraulic jacks working on a steel collar clamped tightly to the top section by a horizontal jack. The rotating grab is fitted with three hinged blades which are opened for drilling and then closed to retain the excavated material for withdrawal. The blades are also used to form an under-reamed base when this is required.

Cylinder piles have a number of advantages over normal types of piles in terms of cost and construction time, particularly when heavy column loads have to be carried. A group of normal piles can be replaced by a single large diameter cylinder pile which reduces drilling costs and construction time. In many cases a group of friction piles can be replaced by a single under-reamed cylinder pile which carries its load mainly in end bearing. For example, loads of 2,000 tons can be carried on a single cylinder in suitable soil, such as the lower levels of the London clay. In most cases, because a column can be carried by a single cylinder, pile caps can be greatly reduced or eliminated, thus shortening the construction time and reducing the cost. In addition, the soil strata in the boring can be inspected as the work proceeds and concreting can be carried out more satisfactorily than in the case of normal *in situ* piles, and can be properly inspected. These piles, because of their capacity to carry very heavy loads, are valuable as foundations to very tall buildings founded on soft soils where the alternative to cylinder piles would be a large number of long friction piles.

In practice little is known about the relation between base and shaft resistances, but tests indicate that if the base resistance is to be fully developed large settlements are to be expected. This must be carefully considered when under-reamed piles are used. The under-reamed pile can resist large tensile forces and is therefore useful where tension piles are required.

Jacked Piles. Where complete freedom from vibration and noise is essential a jacked-in pile can be used in which precast sections of reinforced concrete are successively jacked down one after the other. The jack works either directly on solid precast sections joined together by lengths of tubular steel grouted in a central hole as they sink into the ground (page 107), or on the top of a built-up steel mandrel which forces down a concrete shoe and tubular precast sections, the completed tube being filled with reinforcement and concrete.

When these piles are used for underpinning work the jack operates against the underside of the foundation, otherwise it works against a travelling kentledge. The expense of jacked-in piles limits their use.

PIER FOUNDATIONS

Brick and Concrete Piers. When a good bearing stratum exists up to 15ft below ground level, brick, masonry or mass concrete foundation piers in excavated pits may be used. At this depth, unless the nature of the ground necessitates considerable timbering or continuous pumping, piles are not always economical. The size of the piers, which are generally square, will depend upon the material used and upon the strength of the soil, but the smallest hole in which excavation can be carried out is about 3 ft square.

Cylinder and Monolith Foundations. These are a form of pier foundation used when very heavy loads must be carried through waterlogged or unstable soil down to bed rock or to a firm stratum.

A *cylinder foundation* is constructed by means of a caisson, a cylinder of steel or concrete which provides support to the sides of the excavation and by means of which soil and water can be excluded. The caisson is from 6 ft upwards in diameter and is built up as high as is practicable before excavation begins (see page 91). The soil is excavated from within by grabbing, hand clearing being used usually only at the cutting edge, and the caisson sinks to the required depth under its own weight or with the aid of kentledge. The bottom edge of a concrete caisson is formed into a cutting edge usually protected by a steel shoe. After sinking, the caisson is left permanently in position. It may either be filled with concrete or sealed at the bottom with a concrete "plug" and at the top with a concrete slab. The interior may be left empty or filled with sand or water.

Open caissons, or cylinders which are open at top and bottom, are used where ground conditions permit. When it is necessary to keep the excavation free of water and silt, a *pneumatic caisson* is used. This has a working chamber with a closed top fitted with an air-lock through which men and materials must pass in order to permit the air within the caisson to be maintained at sufficient pressure to prevent the entry of water. Open caissons can be taken to depths up to 150 ft or more; theoretically there is no limit to the depth. In stiff clay soils considerable weight is required to overcome the skin friction as the caisson sinks and in these conditions cylinder piles, already described, form a suitable alternative. Pneumatic caissons may be used for any types of soil, but the depth to which they may be sunk is limited to about 110 to 120 ft below the water surface level. This corresponds to an air pressure of about 50 lbs per sq. in. which is the greatest pressure in which men can work. In practice pneumatic caissons are generally not sunk much beyond 100 ft.

A *monolith* is a rectangular open caisson of steel or concrete with a number of wells for excavation, used when loading necessitates a very large area of foundation (see page 91). Heavy mass or reinforced concrete monoliths have the advantage of greater weight. These can be very large depending upon the nature of the job. The initial lift of a monolith might be as high as 10 ft or more constructed on a temporary concrete slab which would be smashed and removed prior to sinking. Further lifts about 6 ft high would be constructed until the required depth had been reached. As with cylinders monoliths may be sealed at the top and bottom or be filled in solid according to the requirements of a particular job.

The advantages of cylinder and monolith foundations over normal pile foundations are that the soil may be inspected at the base and during the course of excavation and the concrete can reliably be placed in position. The area of a caisson should be so related to that of the superstructure above that it is great enough to allow for some deviation from its correct position during sinking.

UNDERPINNING

The term underpinning is applied to the process of excavating under an existing foundation and building up a new supporting structure from a lower level to the underside of the existing foundation, the object being to transfer the load from the foundation to a new bearing at a lower level. This may be necessary for any of the following reasons:

(i) when excessive settlement of a foundation has occurred;

(ii) to permit the level of adjacent ground to be lowered, for example where a new basement at a lower level is to be formed;

(iii) to increase the load bearing capacity of a foundation.

Before underpinning operations commence, the structure of the building should first be examined for weaknesses such as poor brickwork or masonry and for effects of settlement which may be accentuated during the course of the work.   In very old or badly damaged buildings, the structure may require strengthening by grouting up cracks and loose rubble masonry, for example, or by tying-in walls by tie rods or prestressing cables.   Temporary support should be provided by adequate shoring and by strutting up of openings (see Ch. 11).   In some circumstances a wall or column must be relieved of all loads bearing on it by strutting floors and beams down to a solid bearing clear of the underpinning.   During the course of underpinning high structures it may be advisable to keep a check on any possible movement by taking readings of plumb bobs suspended from high points on the structure and by making checks on levels from time to time.   "Tell-tales" should be fixed to check any further movement at points where it had previously occurred.

CONTINUOUS UNDERPINNING

Where possible walls should be underpinned with the minimum of disturbance to the structure and to the occupants of the building, and in most cases the work can be carried out without the support of needles passing through the wall to the interior.   The work should be carried out in sections or "legs" in such a sequence that the unsupported lengths of existing foundation over excavated sections are equally distributed along the length of the wall being underpinned (page 102, A).   In buildings other than small lightly loaded structures, the sum of these unsupported lengths should not at any one time exceed one-quarter of the total length of the wall, or in the case of a very weak wall, or one carrying heavy loads, one-fifth to one-sixth of the total length.   Unless unavoidable, a section should not be excavated immediately adjacent to one which has just been completed.   On a low, lightly-loaded building such as a two-storey house with the walls in good condition, it is common practice to work to a sequence in which not more than one-third of the length is unsupported at any one time.   The lengths of wall which can be left temporarily without support over the excavated sections will depend upon the thickness and general state of the wall and its foundation and upon the load which it will be carrying during the course of the work.   Advantage is taken of the "arching action" of normally bonded brick and stone walls over openings and the length of sections can usually be from 3 to 5 ft.

As each section is excavated, timbering will generally be required, the depth of each stage of excavation depending upon the firmness of the soil. Poling boards or, in loose soils permitting only small depths to be excavated at a time, horizontal sheeting will be used to support the soil faces under the

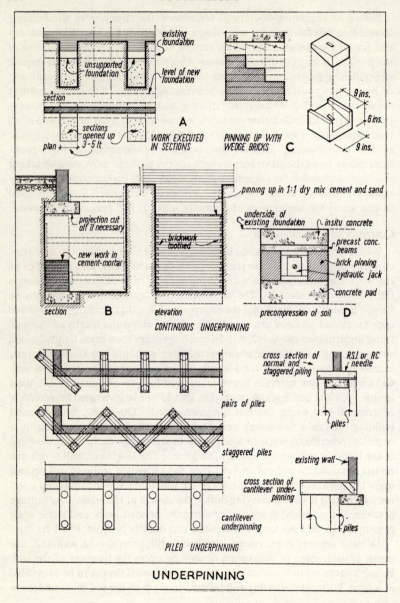

existing foundation

unsupported foundation

level of new foundation

section

sections opened up 3 - 5 ft

plan

A

WORK EXECUTED IN SECTIONS

PINNING UP WITH WEDGE BRICKS

C

9 ins.

6 ins.

9 ins.

projection cut off if necessary

new work in cement-mortar

section

B

pinning up in 1:1 dry mix cement and sand

brickwork toothed

elevation

CONTINUOUS UNDERPINNING

underside of existing foundation

insitu concrete

precast conc. beams

brick pinning

hydraulic jack

concrete pad

precompression of soil

D

cross section of normal and staggered piling

RSJ or RC needle

pairs of piles

piles

staggered piles

existing wall

cross section of cantilever underpinning

cantilever underpinning

piles

PILED UNDERPINNING

UNDERPINNING

wall. When the nature of the soil or other circumstances precludes the withdrawal of poling boards or sheeting as underpinning proceeds, these are usually of precast concrete about 3 ft × 1 ft × 2 in. thick. Holes through the thickness permit grout to be pumped through to fill solidly any voids between the soil face and the back of the boards. This is essential in order to prevent the voids closing up afterwards and causing settlement at the back of the wall. When the full depth of the excavation is reached, the new concrete foundation will be placed if brick underpinning is being used or, if concrete is being used either for a normal wall or a retaining wall, the first lift of the concrete. (For details of retaining wall construction see "Timbering for Excavations", Ch. 11.) The ends of the brickwork in each section should be left toothed ready for bonding with the next section (p. 102, B); all concrete work should have grooves formed to provide a key for the next section of concrete. Any horizontal reinforcement must project, being turned up against the sides until the adjacent section is excavated. It is then turned down to be spliced with that in the next section. All brickwork should be in cement mortar.

After cleaning off the underside of the existing foundation, brickwork is built up to within about 1 to $1\frac{1}{2}$ in. of the foundation. When time has been allowed for the mortar to set and shrink, it is pinned up with half-dry 1:1 cement and sand rammed in hard with a 1 in. board to make solid contact with the foundation above. In thick walls it is necessary to step down the brickwork from back to front in order to pin up satisfactorily, each step being pinned up in turn, commencing at the back. It is possible to pin up with specially made 2-piece wedged-shaped engineering bricks, bedded in stiff mortar at the top of each step which, as they are driven home, reduce the mortar thickness to a minimum. The two pieces are keyed together by mortar squeezed into a vertical slot in each as the wedge is tightened (see page 102, C). Concrete underpinning, which must be placed over front shutters, can generally be taken only to within about 3 in. of the existing foundation. This, after the concrete has had time to set and shrink, is filled with half-dry 1:1 cement and sand or a dry mix fine aggregate concrete, rammed home with a mechanical tamper. Many Local Authority surveyors insist on a 3 in. gap being left over brickwork so that it may be pinned up in this way, particularly in the case of thick walls. Alternatively, pressure grouting can be used to pin up. Daywork joints in concrete walls which are to be water resistant must be freed of laitance. This can be washed away from freshly-placed concrete by high-pressure water spray within $1\frac{1}{2}$–2 hours of placing, leaving a good, clean key. When the adjacent sections are opened up the exposed concrete faces may need to be hacked to form a good key and wire brushed to remove any remaining laitance and loose material. The keyed surface should be thoroughly wetted and brushed over with a thin coat of 1:2 cement and sand mortar immediately before fresh concrete is placed against it.

Underpinning in each section should commence as soon as possible after the bottom has been exposed, and be carried out as quickly as possible. No earth face should be exposed overnight. If delay is likely the bottom should be protected by a blinding layer of concrete or the last few inches of excavation should be held over.

When the walling is weak or when sections must be opened up in lengths greater than those suggested above, it may be necessary to provide temporary intermediate supports in the form of needles passing through the wall or under the foundation, or vertical struts placed directly under the foundation. Needles of timber or steel should be of ample size to avoid deflection and should be kept in close contact with the structure by means of folding wedges or jacks. Supports must be well clear of the area of underpinning work and taken on to a solid bearing. When the needles pass through the wall above foundation level, subsidiary needles hung from the main needles may be required to carry the section of wall below the level of the main needles, particularly if the walling is weak (see page 107 A). In order to minimize the number of needles penetrating within the building it is possible to use widely spaced main needles which pass through the wall and carry a beam parallel to the outside face of the wall. This acts as a fulcrum to intermediate counterweighted cantilever needles which penetrate only the thickness of the wall (page 107, B). When support by needles is impracticable, temporary steel struts bearing on concrete pads may be inserted beneath the existing foundation. The underpinning work may then be built up or cast between them before they are removed or, alternatively, they may be left in position and eventually cast in with new concrete work.

The method of underpinning and final pinning up described above, if carefully executed, will result in negligible movement due to settlement of the new work, but in large and important buildings, a system of precompressing the soil on which the new work will bear is adopted. By this means consolidation of the soil is effected before the load from the underpinning above is applied and subsequent settlement is avoided. In this method a pad of reinforced concrete is cast on the bottom of the excavation and when it has matured a hydraulic jack of the normal type or a Freyssinet flat jack is fixed to it at the centre of the underpinning section. Precast concrete beams are then placed on top of the jack and concrete is placed on them up to the underside of the existing foundation (page 102 ,D). Before this has set it is jacked up so that all voids in the underside of the foundation are completely filled with the concrete. When the concrete on the beams has matured a pre-determined load is applied by the jacks so that the soil is compressed and its bearing capacity is "pre-tested" in advance. When all the work has been carried out in this way, the spaces between the jacks in adjacent sections are pinned up with engineering bricks in cement mortar which, when set, permits the jacks to be removed and the remaining spaces to be filled up tightly.

Hydraulic jacking may also be used to ensure a positive contact between the face of the excavated soil at the back of each section and any supporting poling boards or sheeting. Each stage of excavation is supported at the back by 4 to 6 in. of *in situ* reinforced concrete acting as a permanent poling board. Temporary struts back to the opposite excavated face incorporate hydraulic jacks by means of which a predetermined pressure is applied to the concrete poling board about 24 hours after casting, while it is still green: at this stage the concrete is still flexible and this ensures with greater certainty close contact with the soil face and the elimination of any voids behind the concrete.

Prestressing can be applied to continuous *in situ* concrete underpinning carried out in the normal way to form a continuous beam under the existing foundations. This is done by sinking some sections to the full required depth to act as supporting piers to a beam formed between them by the intermediate sections which are not sunk so deep. These are formed into a continuous beam by post-tensioning with cables, passed through holes formed in the sections as they are cast and anchored at the ends. In addition to providing continuous support under the foundations, which may be essential when the superstructure is in a very poor condition, this method keeps to a minimum the amount of deep excavations which must be carried out.

PILED UNDERPINNING

Continuous underpinning as described above may in some circumstances be impracticable or uneconomic. The presence of subsoil water with certain types of soil might make the work extremely difficult, or when the load has to be transferred to a great depth, the cost of continuous underpinning might be excessive. In such circumstances piles may be used with the load from the wall transferred to them by beams. In order to avoid vibration which would be undesirable in many cases of underpinning, bored or jacked-in piles are used.

The arrangement of beams and piles depends on many things, including the state of the structure and the necessity or otherwise of avoiding disturbance to the use or contents of the building. The most straightforward method is probably to sink pairs of piles at intervals along the wall, one on either side, connected by a needle or beam passing through the wall just above or immediately below the foundation, whichever best suits the circumstances (see page 102). Reinforced concrete or R.S.J.'s can be used for the beams. The latter occupy less space and are generally simpler to fix. An alternative method which may sometimes be more suitable is to stagger the piles on each side of the wall. This has the effect of halving the number of piles required, although each will take a greater load, and of lengthening the beams. If the positions most convenient for sinking the piles do not coincide with the most suitable positions for the needles, two beams, one on each side of the wall and parallel to it may be carried by the piles and will support the needles which will pass through the wall at the most suitable points.

These methods, because of the internal piles, necessitate work within the building being underpinned. Where this is not possible, groups of two or more piles along the outside of the building may be used to support the wall by means of cantilever capping beams projecting under the wall (see page 102).

When the superstructure and its foundation is in a weak condition, continuous beam support to the wall may be essential. In small, lightly-loaded buildings such a beam, projecting beyond the wall face, can sometimes be supported adequately on a line of single piles only outside the building. In other cases the beam must be carried by needles bearing on piles on each side of the wall or on cantilever capping beams as described above. The supports may, however, be spaced at greater intervals and the beam designed to span between them. When support to the wall may be given above the level of the foundation the beam can be formed in a number of ways which simplify construction. First by the use of "stools". These are concrete blocks with holes in them through which reinforcing bars can be passed. When very deep beams are required the stools are formed of a number of vertical steel bars welded to top and bottom plates. Holes are cut in the wall at approximately 3 ft centres at the required level and the stools are inserted. These act as props to the wall above when the intervening sections of the wall between them are cut away. When this has been done for the full length of the underpinning, reinforcement may be threaded through the stools and tied in position. Shuttering is then erected and the concrete placed to form a continuous beam incorporating the stools as part of it. The gap at the top of the beam is pinned up as described earlier (see page 543).

Another similar method makes use of prestressed concrete beams and involves no *in situ* casting of concrete. Precast blocks or segments, with holes cast through them for a prestressing cable, are inserted in turn next to

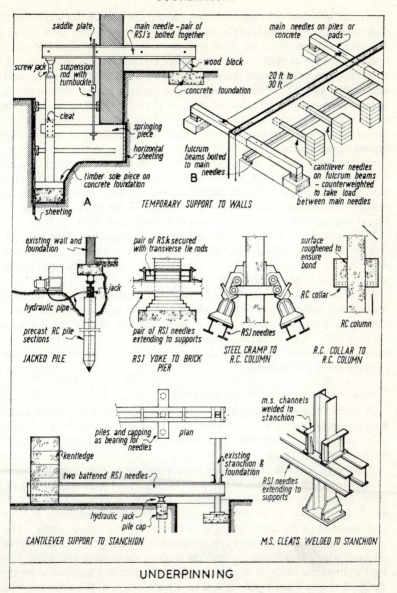

TEMPORARY SUPPORT TO WALLS

saddle plate
main needle – pair of RSJ's bolted together
main needles on piles or concrete pads
screw jack
suspension rod with turnbuckle
wood block
concrete foundation
20 ft to 30 ft
cleat
springing piece
horizontal sheeting
fulcrum beams bolted to main needles
timber sole piece on concrete foundation
cantilever needles on fulcrum beams – counterweighted to take load between main needles
A
B
sheeting

existing wall and foundation
jack
hydraulic pipe
precast RC pile sections
pair of RSJ's secured with transverse tie rods
pair of RSJ needles extending to supports
surface roughened to ensure bond
RC collar
RC column

JACKED PILE
RSJ YOKE TO BRICK PIER
STEEL CRAMP TO R.C. COLUMN
R.C. COLLAR TO R.C. COLUMN

RSJ needles

piles and capping as bearing for needles
plan
m.s. channels welded to stanchion
kentledge
two battened RSJ needles
existing stanchion & foundation
hydraulic jack
pile cap
RSJ needles extending to supports

CANTILEVER SUPPORT TO STANCHION
M.S. CLEATS WELDED TO STANCHION

UNDERPINNING

each other in holes cut in the wall, each being pinned-up on top and wedged underneath until the whole of the wall is supported by a line of these blocks. The joints between them are filled with dry mix mortar rammed tight and openings are left at each end for anchorage and stressing of the cable. A post-tensioning cable is then threaded through the full length, tensioned and anchored at each end to form a single, homogeneous beam. Alternatively, stressed steel underpinning beams are now available made up in 2 to 5 ft lengths of steel joists with steel diaphragm plates welded to each end and drilled for high tensile torque bolts. Each length is inserted in turn and pinned up in the same way as the segments of a post-tensioned concrete beam, so that the wall above is continually supported. The beam is inserted in the wall with the joints between the lengths of joist left slightly open on the tension side, and after packing solid at the top, the bolts are tightened by a torque wrench. In closing the joints, the lower flange of the beam is stressed so that the beam takes up its load without deflecting (see p. 543).

The methods just described are also useful when new openings must be formed in existing walls and permit the work to be carried out without the dead shoring and strutting which is otherwise necessary as described in the section on shoring in Chapter 11.

As an alternative to cantilevered supports, jacked-in piles can be used immediately under the existing foundations in order to avoid internal work. These piles have been described on page 99 and the method is illustrated on page 107. It is, of course, essential that the weight of the structure be sufficient to provide adequate dead weight as a reaction to the jacks as the piles are being forced down.

UNDERPINNING TO COLUMN FOUNDATIONS

In underpinning framed structures, the main problem is to provide satisfactory support to the columns while they are being underpinned. Before excavation is begun these must be relieved of load by dead shores under all beams bearing on them.

Reinforced concrete columns and brick piers can be supported by means of a horizontal yoke formed of two pairs of rolled steel joists set in 1 to 2 in. deep chases in the sides of the columns. The bottom pair are large enough and long enough to act as needles to transfer the load to temporary support and the upper pair are at right-angles to the needles and bear on them. The pairs of joists are tied together by transverse tie rods or angles. An alternative method, which avoids chasing into the sides of the column and which can deal with greater loads, is to grip the column or pier in a heavy steel cramp designed to grip more tightly as it takes up the weight of the column. The base of the cramp bears on needles on opposite sides of the column which transfer the load to supports well away from the column base.   R.C. columns may be supported by an R.C. collar.   Steel stanchions can be supported on R.S.J. needles by steel angles or channels welded to the stanchion flanges and bearing on the needles.   Lightly loaded stanchions can sometimes be carried by a large diameter steel pin, passed through a hole drilled in the web and bearing on the needles.   These methods are illustrated on p. 107.

In all cases the supports to the needles must be far enough away from the column or pier to avoid collapse by dispersion of the pressure on to the sides of the excavation, and also to allow sufficient working space.   The needles must have good solid bearings, strong enough to take the loads transferred to them from the columns and this may sometimes necessitate the use of piles at the bearings.   If underpinning is due to the excavation of a new basement under the columns, the temporary pile supports may have to penetrate below the level of the new basement to a depth sufficient to permit them to act as free standing columns when the main excavation is carried out and while the column is being underpinned.

Circumstances may make it impossible to provide support to the needles on two sides of a column or stanchion and a counterweighted cantilever support must then be used.   This would be formed of a pair of long, deep R.S.J. needles bearing on a fulcrum support some distance from the column in the form of a base slab or piled foundation (see page 107).   One end of the needles would pick up the yoke or cleats attached to the column and the other would be tailed down by kentledge or tension piles.   A hydraulic jack placed between the needles and the fulcrum support enables the latter to be "precompressed" and any settlement taken up to prevent movement of the column.

Ground Treatment

Suitable soil such as gravel and sand may be strengthened by chemical consolidation or by pressure grouting, and water in sand and silts can be frozen by refrigeration.   The task of underpinning can often be simplified by the application of these processes to the soil and in some circumstances they can be used as an alternative to underpinning.   In the latter case, where permanent effects are required, consolidation or grouting would be used, since freezing is only practicable as a temporary measure.[1]

[1] See *Civil Engineering Code of Practice* No. 4, "Foundations", Part 6, for a description of these methods.

4
Walls and Piers

FUNCTIONAL REQUIREMENTS

The primary function of the wall is to enclose or divide space. In addition it may have to provide support. In order to fulfil these functions efficiently there are certain requirements which it must satisfy. They are the provision of adequate:

> Strength and Stability
> Weather Resistance
> Durability
> Fire Resistance
> Thermal Insulation
> Sound Insulation.

The fire resistance of walls is discussed in Chapter 10, thermal and sound insulation in *Advanced Building Construction* (*Components, Services and Finishes*) and the important subject of durability in *Elementary Building Construction*, Chapter 5, so that the requirements of strength, stability and weather resistance only will be discussed here.

Types of Wall

Walls may be divided into two types, loadbearing and non-loadbearing. Each type may be further divided into external, or enclosing walls, and internal dividing walls.

The external non-loadbearing wall, which nowadays is invariably related to a framed structure, is termed a panel wall.

The term partition is applied to walls, either loadbearing or non-load-bearing, dividing the space within a building rather than to internal walls which separate different occupancies within the same building or divide the building into compartments for purposes of fire protection (for separating walls see page 147 and for division walls see Chapter 10).

In addition there are retaining walls, the primary function of which is to support and resist the thrust of soil and, perhaps, subsoil water, on one side. The most important functional requirements of the retaining wall are strength and stability and durability.

It is not possible to place the functional requirements of walls in order of importance since this will vary with the main function of the wall. For example, all, with the exception possibly of sound insulation, must be considered in the external loadbearing wall, whereas in the case of the loadbearing separating wall only strength and stability, fire resistance and sound insulation need usually be considered. In the case of panel walls the same considerations will apply as to external walls but compressive strength will be of less importance.

In studying the functional requirements of walls it is necessary to consider the form of construction and the following terms are used:

Masonry Wall, in which the wall is built of individual blocks of material, such as bricks, clay or concrete blocks or stone, usually in horizontal courses, cemented together with some form of mortar. The binding strength of the mortar is usually disregarded as far as the strength of the wall is concerned.

Monolithic Wall, in which the wall is built of a material requiring some form of support or shuttering in the initial stages. The traditional earth wall and the modern concrete wall are examples of this. The monolithic reinforced concrete wall is considered in Chapter 5 and in this chapter reference will be made only to the plain concrete wall of either normal, no-fines or lightweight concrete.

Both these forms of construction can be used as external loadbearing walls or as panel walls. A third form, adopted for framed buildings, consists of relatively light sheets or framed panels secured to the frame of the building to form the enclosing element. These are generally termed *Claddings* and are discussed later in this chapter. A typical traditional example is timber weatherboarding fixed to a timber-framed wall.

STRENGTH AND STABILITY

The strength of a wall is measured in terms of its resistance to the stresses set up in it by its own weight, by superimposed loads and by lateral pressure such as wind; its stability by its resistance to overturning by lateral forces and buckling caused by excessive slenderness.

CAUSES OF FAILURE

Crushing. This is avoided by adequate thickness at all points to keep the stresses in the wall within the safe compressive strengths of the materials of which it is built. In masonry walls both the strength of the unit and the type of mortar have a bearing upon the strength of the wall as a whole (see page 119).

Eccentric Loading. Floor and roof loads on walls are frequently applied on one side, rather than on the axis of the wall. In addition, the deflection of a floor tends to concentrate the load on the bearing edge of the wall and this tendency will be greater with flexible floors, such as normal timber construction, than with reinforced concrete floors which are stiffer. With timber floors, the eccentricity of load may be as much as one-third of the wall thickness. With concrete floors about one-sixth. Even if the bearing of a timber joist floor covers the full width of the wall it is desirable to assume an eccentricity of about one-sixth due to the deflection.

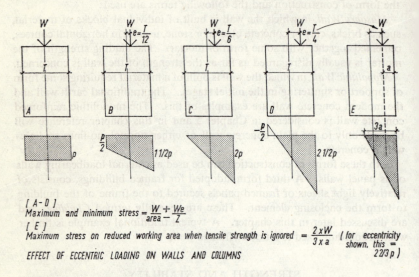

$$[A-D]$$
$$\text{Maximum and minimum stress} = \frac{W}{area} + \frac{We}{Z}$$

$$[E]$$
$$\text{Maximum stress on reduced working area when tensile strength is ignored} = \frac{2 \times W}{3 \times a} \quad \left(\begin{array}{l} \text{for eccentricity} \\ \text{shown, this} = \\ 2\,2/3\,p \end{array} \right)$$

EFFECT OF ECCENTRIC LOADING ON WALLS AND COLUMNS

Such eccentric loading tends to cause bending in the wall and has the effect of increasing the compressive stress in the wall on the loaded side and of decreasing it on the opposite side. This must be borne in mind for the result can be twofold: (i) the increased stress could become greater than the safe compressive strength of the wall, and (ii) if the eccentricity is too great, tensile stresses will be set up in the side opposite that on which the load is applied (see this page D). This has a marked effect upon the strength of the wall, particularly so in masonry walls in which the tensile strength is small and which, in practice, is usually ignored.[1] It is assumed that cracking occurs

---

[1] The tensile strength of the wall is governed not by the tensile strength of the mortar used but by the adhesional strength or bond between the units and the mortar. Failure

when tensile stresses are set up. Thus when the eccentricity is greater than one-sixth of the thickness and tension occurs, part of the wall will cease to function structurally. It is also assumed that on cracking a redistribution of the compressive stress takes place such that the resultant passes through the centroid of the stress triangle (see page 112, E). The working portion of the wall is thus reduced to three times the distance of the point of application of the load from the bearing face of the wall.

Overturning. Lateral loads, such as the pressure of wind or of stored materials on normal walls and of earth on retaining walls, tend to bend and overturn the wall. This causes the line of resultant pressure to become eccentric and sets up a stress distribution similar to that caused by eccentric loading, with a reduction in working area when cracking occurs. In free-standing walls this may be overcome by making the wall thick enough to bring the resultant well within the base or by buttressing. In buildings account is taken of horizontal and vertical lateral supports, which may be present in the form of floors and cross walls or a structural frame, to provide added resistance against overturning to that of the wall itself.

Buckling. Short walls or piers ultimately fail by crushing, but as the height increases they tend to fail under decreasing loads by buckling. The terms "short" and "high" in this context are relative to the thickness of the wall and are measured, broadly, in terms of the ratio of unsupported height to horizontal thickness. The height is generally based on the distance between floors, assuming these give adequate lateral support to the wall. The actual proportion of the floor to floor dimension to be considered for this purpose and the method of providing adequate lateral restraint by means of floors are discussed later. Buckling may be controlled either by restricting the height, increasing the wall thickness, stiffening by buttresses or intersecting walls or by reducing the permissible working stresses.

The manner in which all these possible causes of failure are accounted for in the regulations governing the minimum thickness of walls is discussed under the section on "Calculation of Wall Thickness".

invariably occurs as a result of a breakdown of this bond rather than from a failure of the mortar or units in tension. Bond is extremely variable and average ultimate values range from 40–80 lb per sq. in. depending on the mortar mix, workmanship and weather conditions at the time of building. B.S. Code of Practice 111, 1948, "Structural Recommendations for Load Bearing Walls", recommends that no reliance should be placed on the tensile strength of masonry. But most local authorities do permit some allowance, ranging from 5 to 20 lb per sq. in., usually on the basis of experience rather than on calculations based on tensile strength, particularly when the tensile strength is an important factor in the design. (Table 12.6, page 166, of *Principles of Modern Building*, Vol. 1, 3rd Ed. (H.M.S.O.), shows the effect of different mortar mixes and walling units upon the transverse strength of walls.)

LOADING

This is considered in terms of (i) the dead load, (ii) the live load.

The *dead load* is the weight of all parts of the structure bearing upon the wall together with its own self-weight. Weights of building materials used as a basis for estimating such dead loads are given in B.S.S. 648.

The *live load* is the weight of superimposed floor and roof loads including snow, and wind pressure. Tables of minimum loading on floors and roofs are given in by-laws and codes of practice; reference is made to these in Chapters 6 and 9.

In most types of building it is unlikely that all floors would be fully loaded at the same time. In the design of walls and piers, building regulations allow for this by permitting varying percentage reductions of the total superimposed floor loads according to the number of floors carried (see Table 2).[1] No reduction is permitted for warehouses, storage buildings and garages nor for

Table 2—Reductions of total imposed floor loads on walls, columns, etc.

Number of floors carried by member under consideration	Per cent reduction of imposed load on all floors above member under consideration
1	0
2	10
3	20
4	30
5 or more	40

workshops unless designed for loadings of 100 lb. per sq. ft or more and provided the loading assumed for the wall or pier is not less than it would have been if all floors had been designed for 100 lb per sq. ft with no reductions. When a wall or pier supports a beam, the reduction permitted in respect of a single span of beam supporting not less than 500 sq. ft of floor (see "Loading", Chapter 6) may be compared with that given by Table 2 and the greater of the two taken into account in the design of the wall or pier.

Apart from the necessity of investigating the effect of wind on individual wall panels and on the foundations, regulations permit wind loading on a building as a whole to be disregarded in the case of (i) a building or part of a building of which the height does not exceed twice the effective width, and (ii) a wing of a building if it does not project more than twice its own width.[2] Code of Practice 3 (Ch. V) also includes (iii) a section joining two parts of a

---

[1] B.S. Code of Practice 3 (Ch. V), L.C.C. By-laws and the Model Building Byelaws all permit the same reductions.

[2] L.C.C. By-law 2.03(3) and C.P. 3 (Ch. V).

building if the height of the section exceeds twice its width, but its length does not exceed four times its width. In both the L.C.C. By-laws and the Code these relaxations depend upon adequate stiffening being provided by walls and floors.

Wind pressure on a wall will vary with the velocity of the wind and the height of the wall above ground level, and the maximum velocity of wind will vary with the locality and exposure. Table 3, from B.S. Code of Practice 3

Table 3—Basic Wind Pressure (p)

Effective height of building* (ft)	Wind pressure (lb/sq. ft)			
	Exposure A ($V = 45$ m.p.h.)	Exposure B ($V = 54$ m.p.h.)	Exposure C ($V = 63$ m.p.h.)	Exposure D ($V = 72$ m.p.h.)
Up to 10	4	6	8	10
20	5	7	9	12
30	5	8	11	14
40	6	9	12	16
50	7	10	14	18
60	8	11	15	20
80	9	12	17	22
100	9	13	18	24
120	10	14	19	25
140	11	15	21	27
160	11	16	22	28
180	12	17	23	30
200 or more	12	17	24	31

* Half-way between eaves and ridge levels.

Exposure: A Exceptionally Sheltered. B General case, altitude up to 500 ft; not near sea. C Open country, altitude up to 800 ft; not near sea. D Sites above 800 ft or within five miles of sea.

(Ch. V), gives the basic wind pressure for various building heights under four degrees of exposure. Local Authorities adopt the degree of exposure appropriate to their area. The L.C.C. By-laws use the values given under Exposure B. A formula is given in the Code by means of which the pressure can be calculated for velocities other than those tabulated. Wind blowing on a building will create a pressure on the side against which it blows and a suction of equal intensity on the opposite or leeward side. The pressures given in Table 3, which are used in the design of the building as a whole, are considered as being made up of these two equal forces, $0 \cdot 5\,p$ pressure and $0 \cdot 5\,p$ suction.

Outward suction is also created on the flank walls parallel to the direction of
the wind (see this page).   In the design of the walls provision is made for the
effect of openings by allowing for a pressure of $0·7\,p$, inwards or outwards, or
p when openings are very large.   Special consideration should be given to
wide, low buildings and the Code lays down that when the width is more than
twice the height to the eaves and the roof pitch is less than 30° the walls should
be designed to resist a total pressure, inwards or outwards, of $0·8\,p$.   The
structure of buildings such as hangars and sheds having large openings on one
side should be designed for internal pressures of $\pm\,0·5\,p$ in addition to external
pressures.

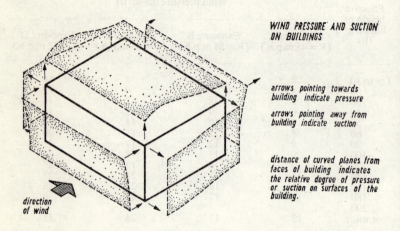

WIND PRESSURE AND SUCTION
ON BUILDINGS

arrows pointing towards
building indicate pressure

arrows pointing away from
building indicate suction

distance of curved planes from
faces of building indicates
the relative degree of pressure
or suction on surfaces of the
building.

direction
of wind

In practice few buildings of loadbearing wall construction will require
wind-loading calculations in respect of overall stability, but in the case of
wall panels, panel infillings in framed buildings, areas of light sheet wall
claddings and large areas of glazed openings this would be necessary.   The
wind pressures in Table 3 are average values only, and in the design of
individual wall panels and wall sheeting, a pressure of $0·8\,p$, inwards or
outwards, should be allowed for.   The distribution of wind pressure on walls
is not uniform.   It is greater near the eaves, and near the ends of a wall high
suctions are possible.   The Code therefore recommends that fastenings for wall
sheeting within 15% of the height or the length from the eaves or corner
respectively should be designed to resist a suction of $1·5\,p$.   Other forms of
cladding and panel walls in the same positions would, of course, have to resist
a similar suction.

For buildings other than those rectangular in shape the pressure values must be modified by a "shape factor".

SOLID MASONRY WALLS

For many years loadbearing brick-work has provided the cheapest structure for blocks of flats from three to five storeys in height, and, broadly speaking, loadbearing brick or block wall construction will still produce the cheapest structure for small-scale buildings of all types where planning requirements are not limited by its use.[1] Until masonry walls were calculated on a scientific basis, great heights required great thickness of wall but in Great Britain there are at present on the drawing board schemes using calculated brickwork for eleven-storey blocks with only 11 in. external cavity walls and 9 in. solid internal loadbearing walls, and for five-storey blocks using only 4½ in. internal loadbearing walls. Calculated brickwork is being used in Switzerland for blocks as high as eighteen-storeys with external walls 15½ in. maximum thickness and 6 in. internal walls. This necessitates careful consideration of such design aspects as (i) the choice of a suitable cellular plan form, (ii) maintaining a suitable proportion of height to width of building to keep wind stresses to a minimum (see page 114), (iii) running concrete floor slabs through to the outer face of external walls to reduce the eccentricity of floor load (see page 112).

In the case of buildings over three storeys the wall thicknesses are invariably determined by means of calculations. This is common practice also with smaller types of loadbearing wall structures other than two-storey domestic buildings, especially when a large proportion of openings is required which would reduce the effective wall area to a minimum. The load on the wall of a two-storey domestic building pierced with average size window and door openings is quite small and well within the bearing capacity of a normal half-brick wall. This results in functional requirements other than that of strength being the determining factors as far as thickness is concerned. The latter is not normally, therefore, calculated in terms of strength.

The L.C.C. By-laws and the Model Building Byelaws which lay down regulations governing the calculation of wall thicknesses do, in addition, provide means for determining thicknesses other than by a process of calculation.[2] This is still often termed "the prescribed method" because in earlier L.C.C. By-laws the conditions with which a wall had to comply, for its

---

[1] See graph on page 138 and also page 211.
[2] L.C.C. By-laws 5.05 to 5.16; M.B. Byelaws, Third Schedule, Rule 3(1).

thickness to be determined in this manner, were termed "the prescribed conditions". Although this method has limitations it is, nevertheless, simple to use and for many small traditional types of buildings up to three storeys high, gives the same solution as by calculation. Thicknesses are prescribed for two classes of buildings—the warehouse class, which in the Model Byelaws also covers public buildings, and buildings other than the warehouse or public building class. Strength and stability are ensured by limiting the width of openings to provide adequate bearing area of wall,[1] and by relating the thicknesses to the height and to the length of the wall between adequate lateral supports in the form of cross or buttressing walls or piers. Reference should be made to these regulations for the variations between the two and for other conditions laid down in both, but not referred to here.

In the County of London, the London Building Acts (Amendment Act), 1939, Part III, Section 26, confers discretionary powers on the District Surveyor in respect of the construction of all public buildings. These come directly under the jurisdiction of the District Surveyor as regards all structural matters. In examining proposals for a public building he may consent to their being in accordance with the L.C.C. Constructional By-laws in respect of wall thicknesses for loadbearing or panel walls, or he may require a higher standard than that required by the By-laws.

In using the prescribed method it is not possible to take into account stronger materials than those laid down as a minimum, thus to gain the advantage of reduced thicknesses, or the actual loads likely to bear upon the walls in various parts. The limitation on the width of openings necessitated by an assumed maximum loading and a specified minimum strength of material tends to be restricting in design. The determination of wall thickness by calculation, having regard to actual loads and varying strengths of materials, leads to more economic construction in most cases and to a greater freedom in the disposition of openings. The thickness of a wall or pier determined in this manner is based upon the calculated load to be carried, the actual strength of the materials used and the slenderness of the wall or pier.

Strength of Masonry Walls

The strength of a masonry wall depends primarily upon the strength of the units and of the mortar. In addition the quality of workmanship is important. Variations of 25 to 35% in the strength of brickwork have been found due to bad workmanship, mainly on account of badly mixed mortar and imperfect bedding of the bricks. This is an important consideration in

[1] L.C.C. By-law 5.11; M.B. Byelaws, Third Schedule.

high-strength masonry walls where all units should be properly bedded and all vertical joints flushed up solid.

The effect of the strength of the units and of the mortar is illustrated by the graphs on this page which are based on tests on brickwork. It will be seen that the strength of the wall increases with the strength of the individual bricks, but not in direct proportion to the unit strength. This is due to the significant effect of the mortar, which is shown in the adjoining graph, where

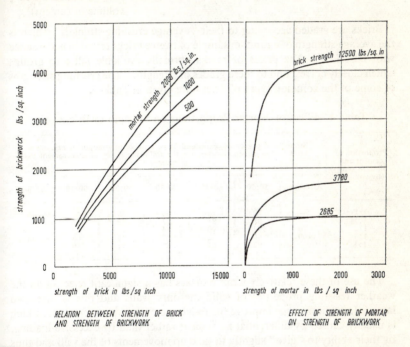

RELATION BETWEEN STRENGTH OF BRICK
AND STRENGTH OF BRICKWORK

EFFECT OF STRENGTH OF MORTAR
ON STRENGTH OF BRICKWORK

the effect of varying mortar strengths is related to the strength of the wall. It can be seen that little advantage is gained from the point of view of ultimate wall strength, in increasing the strength of the mortar beyond a certain point for any particular grade of brick. In terms of actual mortar mixes this is illustrated in Table 4 which shows that although a cement mortar will give greatest strength a cement-lime mortar with 50 or 60% of the cement replaced by lime gives only a slightly lower strength of brickwork. A straight non-hydraulic lime mortar will generally give only a brickwork strength of less than half that attained with a cement or cement-lime mortar. It should be noted that the optimum strength of wall was obtained with a 1:3 basic proportion for the mortar. The mortars suggested to give maximum strength with various grades of brick are:

Low strength bricks (1,500 lb per sq. in.)   1 cement : 2 lime : 9 sand
Medium strength bricks (3–5,000 lb per sq. in.)   1 cement : 1 lime : 6 sand
High strength bricks (7,000 lb per sq. in. or more)   1 cement : 3 sand : (Lime may be added up to $\frac{1}{4}$ volume of cement)[1]

Bricks are graded according to their "average crushing strength" which is the average strength of a random sample of twelve bricks tested in accordance with B.S. 1257. The prices of bricks normally available fall into groups which closely correspond to these grades of strength. The crushing strengths of some of the common types of bricks are given in Table 5.

Table 4—Effect of Mortar Proportions on Strength of Brickwork

Proportion of cement and lime to sand (by volume)	Strength of brickwork expressed as percentage of strength of brickwork built in 1:3 cement mortar, for the following ratios of lime:cement by volume						
	All cement	50:50	60:40	70:30	80:20	90:10	All lime
1:1	—	72	70	66	58	47	—
1:1½	—	87	84	77	68	56	—
1:2	96	94	90	84	74	60	—
1:3	100	96	92	87	79	65	48
1:4	—	92	87	81	71	59	—

The use of these relatively weak mortars has a significant effect upon the weather resisting properties of solid masonry walls and this is discussed later. In addition, they improve the resistance of the wall to cracking, which is usually caused by differential movement rather than by excessive loading, by their ability to "give" slightly to take up movements of the wall and thus often prevent cracking or, should movement be so great, distribute the cracking throughout the joints.

CALCULATION OF WALL THICKNESS

The L.C.C. By-laws [2] lay down requirements for the calculation of wall thicknesses. The Model Building Byelaws accept the recommendations of

---

[1] For a full discussion on the strength of masonry walls see *Principles of Modern Building*, Volume 1, 3rd Ed. (H.M.S.O.), from which much of the above has been extracted.
[2] L.C.C. By-laws 5.17 to 5.23.

Table 5—Compressive Strength of Bricks

Type of brick	Mean strength (lb/sq. in.)
Engineering Bricks:	
British Standard, Grade A (Blue Staffs pressed, Cattybrook, Accrington pressed red)	10,000 upwards (max. about 20,000)
British Standard, Grade B (Southwater, Blue Staffs) .	7,500–10,000
Facing Bricks:	
Hand made—	1,000–8,500
Extreme range	1,000–2,500
Kentish stocks	About 4,000
Leicester sand stocks	
Machine made—	500–15,000
Extreme range	500–2,500
London stocks (1st grade)	
Boulder clay wirecuts (reds from Northern England and Northern Ireland)	4,000–7,500
White Gault wirecuts (white commons and facings from Beds, Cambs and Kent) . . .	2,000–3,000
Keuper marl wirecuts (Leicester reds) . . .	4,000–6,500
Carboniferous shale pressed or wirecuts (bricks from parts of Scotland, N. England, N. Ireland, Lancs, Yorks, Staffs, N. Wales, etc., buffs, browns, reds, blues, brindles)	5,000–15,000
Flettons, rustic or sandfaced	2,000–4,500
Common Bricks:	
Machine made London stocks (common) . . .	500–1,500
Boulder clay wirecuts	3,000–6,000
Keuper marl wirecuts (Birmingham, Leicester, Nottingham, etc.)	3,000–4,000
Carboniferous shale (pressed)	1,500–10,000
Flettons, any make	2,000, 4,500
Sand Lime and Concrete:	
Special purpose sand lime (B.S. 187) . . .	3,000
Special purpose concrete (B.S. 1180) . . .	2,500
Class "A" sand lime (B.S. 187)	2,000
Class "A" concrete (B.S. 1180)	1,750
Class "B" sand lime and concrete (B.S. 187 and 1180) .	1,000

B.S. Code of Practice 111 as satisfying the requirements of Byelaw 22 in respect of strength and stability.

Reference has already been made to the failure of walls and piers under decreasing loads with increasing height. The ratio of height to thickness as a measure of this tendency is termed the *slenderness ratio*. It is defined in both the L.C.C. By-laws and Code of Practice 111 as the ratio of effective height to effective thickness, but the Code permits it to be based alternatively on the effective length if this is less than the effective height. This takes account of the stability which is provided by vertical as well as by horizontal lateral supports. The slenderness ratio of a pier[1] is the ratio of effective height to the horizontal dimension lying in the direction of the lateral support. When the pier dimensions are unequal or where there is support in one direction only, two ratios result and the larger is used. When there is no top support the ratio is the effective height to the least dimension of the pier.

The *effective height*, in the case of a wall, is based on the distance between adequate lateral supports[2] provided by floors and roof, termed the storey height. It is three-quarters of the storey height where there is lateral support at the top, and one-and-a-half times the storey height where there is none. For piers, the respective proportions are the actual storey height and twice the storey height. The latter is also the effective height relative to the pier thickness at right-angles to the direction of a single lateral support.

The *effective length* in the Code of Practice is the distance between the centre lines of adjacent piers, buttresses or intersecting walls.

The *effective thickness* is the actual thickness of a solid wall excluding plaster, rendering, or any other applied finish or covering. Allowance is made for any stiffening piers which may be bonded to the wall by multiplying the actual thickness by a factor which varies with the size and spacing of the piers, resulting in an effective thickness greater than the actual thickness. Table 6, from the L.C.C. By-laws, gives these factors, the values being the same as those in the Code. Buttressing or intersecting walls may be considered as piers of width equal to the thickness of the intersecting wall and of a thickness equal to three times the thickness of the stiffened wall.[3] These definitions are illustrated on page 123.

---

[1] A pier is defined as a member of which the width does not exceed four times its thickness. Code of Practice 111 limits the term "pier" to such a member bonded to a loadbearing wall. It defines a similar but isolated member as a "column".

[2] Defined as "support which will restrict movement in the direction of the thickness of the wall, or, in relation to a column or pier, movement in the direction of the thickness or width of the pier or column".

[3] Code of Practice 111 does not permit these modifications to the effective thickness when the slenderness ratio is based on the effective length of the wall.

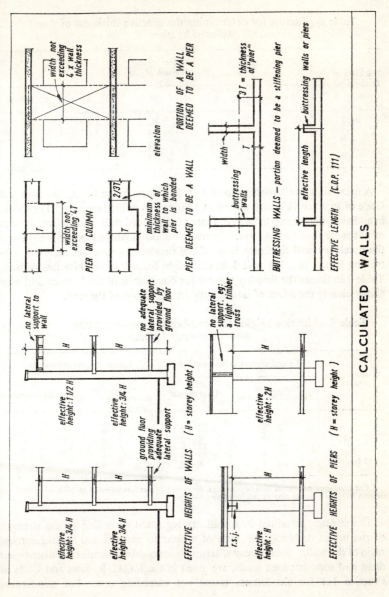

width not exceeding 4 x wall thickness

elevation

PORTION OF A WALL DEEMED TO BE A PIER

T

width not exceeding 4T

PIER OR COLUMN

2/3T

minimum thickness of wall to which pier is bonded

PIER DEEMED TO BE A WALL

3T = thickness of "pier"

width

buttressing walls

T

BUTTRESSING WALLS — portion deemed to be a stiffening pier

effective length

buttressing walls or piers

EFFECTIVE LENGTH   (C.O.P. 111)

no lateral support to wall

effective height: 1 1/2 H

H

effective height: 3/4 H

H

no adequate lateral support provided by ground floor

ground floor providing adequate lateral support

effective height: 3/4 H

H

effective height: 3/4 H

H

EFFECTIVE HEIGHTS OF WALLS   (H = storey height)

no lateral support. eg: a light timber truss

H

effective height: 2H

EFFECTIVE HEIGHTS OF PIERS   (H = storey height)

H

r.s.j.

effective height: H

CALCULATED WALLS

Table 6—Factors for determining the effective thickness of a wall stiffened by piers

Thickness of pier Thickness of wall	Pier spacing Width of pier				
	6 or less	8	10	15	20 or more
1·0	1·0	1·0	1·0	1·0	1·0
1·5	1·2	1·15	1·1	1·05	1·0
2·0	1·4	1·3	1·2	1·1	1·0
2·5	1·7	1·5	1·3	1·15	1·0
3·0	2·0	1·7	1·4	1·2	1·0

A maximum slenderness ratio of 18 is laid down in the L.C.C. By-laws and Code of Practice 111, with a limit of 12 for walls in lime mortar. The Code, in addition, permits up to 24 in the case of reinforced walls and walls to houses of not more than two storeys. In many buildings where loading is light and the necessary wall thickness is small the slenderness ratio becomes the controlling factor, limiting as it does the height for any given thickness of wall. Table 7 indicates the limiting heights for common wall thicknesses and also shows clearly the effect of lateral support at the top of the wall.

Table 7—Limiting heights for load-bearing masonry walls without stiffening piers

Wall thickness (inches)	Lateral support at base and top		Lateral support at base only	
	*Cement or cement:lime mortar	Lime mortar	*Cement or cement:lime mortar	Lime mortar
	ft. in.	ft. in.	ft. in.	ft. in.
4	8 0	5 4	4 0	2 8
4½	9 0	6 0	4 6	3 0
9	18 0	12 0	9 0	6 0
13½	27 0	18 0	13 6	9 0
11 (cavity)	12 0	8 0	6 0	4 0

* For houses of not more than two storeys, for which a slenderness ratio of 24 is permitted, the heights in these columns may be increased by one-third.

The stresses permitted in a wall are regulated according to the strength of the bricks or blocks, the type of mortar to be used and the slenderness ratio of the wall. Basic stresses, arising from combined uniformly distributed dead and superimposed loads, are given in the L.C.C. By-laws and Code of Practice 111 for slenderness ratios not exceeding one. For slenderness ratios exceeding one these basic stresses must be reduced by multiplying by a reduction factor. The Tables of basic stresses and reduction factors are given on this page. The permissible stresses in italics are in tons per square foot and are those given in the L.C.C. By-laws. The other figures are those given in Code of Practice 111. Reduction factors for slenderness ratios up to 18 are identical in the Code and L.C.C. By-laws. The By-laws include a formula for establishing the permissible basic stress when bricks or blocks having a crushing strength greater than 10,000 lb per sq. in. are to be used.

Table 8—Permissible compressive stress on masonry members with slenderness ratio not exceeding one

Mortar mix (parts by volume)			Maximum uniformly distributed stress in lbs/sq. in. (*tons/sq. ft*) corresponding to units with crushing strength in lbs/sq. in. of:								
					6th	5th	4th	3rd	2nd	1st	L.C.C. strength ← designation
Cement	Lime	Sand	400	1,000	1,500	3,000	4,000	5,000	7,500	10,000	10,000 + x
1	0–¼	3	40	100	150	210	250	360	510	660	⎰ 660+0·042x
					10	*13*	*16*	*23*	*33*	*42*	⎱ but 900 max.
1	0–¼	4			*9*	*12*	*15*	*20*	*24*	*28*	
1	1	6	40	100	140	190	230	260	350	350	350
					9	*12*	*15*	*17*	*22*	*22*	
1	2	9	40	80	120	170	210	250	350	350	350
					8	*11*	*13*	*16*	*22*	*22*	
1	3	12	30	70	100	130	170	200	200	200	200
					6	*8*	*11*	*13*	*13*	*13*	
Hydraulic: 1		2	30	70	100	130	170	200	200	200	200
Non-hyd.: 1		3	30	60	80	100	100	100	100	100	100
					5	*6*	*6*	*6*	*6*	*6*	

These stresses have been based on certain ratios of strength of wall to strength of unit (see page 119) where the proportion of the height to thickness of the unit is about that of the normal brick. It has been shown[1] that these stresses are unnecessarily low when deeper blocks are used and the Code allows for this by permitting the basic stresses to be doubled when blocks with a height of not less than twice the thickness are used.

Table 9—Reduction Factors for slenderness ratio (masonry members)

Slenderness ratio	Reduction factor	Slenderness ratio	Reduction factor
1	1·0	12	0·50
2	0·96	14	0·40
4	0·88	16	0·35
6	0·80	18	0·30
8	0·70	21	0·25
10	0·60	24	0·20

In the case of walls and piers having slenderness ratios exceeding one, the following increases in the permissible stresses may be made when local

[1] See *Principles of Modern Building*, Vol. 1, 3rd Ed., page 165 (H.M.S.O.).

5*

loading such as girder bearings, eccentric loads or lateral forces are borne in addition to uniformly distributed loads: 25% for eccentric loads or lateral forces, 50% for local loads or a combination of all three types of loading. In the latter case the contribution to the excess stress made by the eccentric loads or lateral forces must not exceed 25%. The following provisos are made: (i) The compressive stress due solely to the uniformly distributed load shall not exceed the maximum permissible stress arrived at by the use of the reduction factors. That is to say, the excess must be due solely to the other loads. (ii) The maximum permissible stress plus the percentage increase permitted shall not exceed the basic stress.

In order to keep the thickness of the walls within reasonable limits and, preferably, of the same thickness for the full height of the building, particularly in the case of cross wall construction, variations in the types of bricks and in the mortar mixes are made according to the stresses at different heights. Excessive variation is uneconomic and leads to difficulties in supervision on the site. Sufficient flexibility in strength can, however, be obtained in most buildings by the use of three to four grades of bricks with one or two mixes of mortar. Ordinary fletton bricks, which are cheap, generally come within the fifth grade (see Tables 5, 8) and when used in 9 in. thick imperforate cross walls are adequate for flat blocks up to four or five storeys in height when the floor spans are short. Concrete blocks may be used instead of bricks. When these are specified advantage may be taken of the permitted increase in the basic stresses on blocks having a height of twice or more times their thickness. The L.C.C. By-laws lay down that a calculated brick or block wall shall have a thickness at any level not less than one-sixteenth of the height measured from that level to the top of the wall, with a minimum thickness of $8\frac{1}{2}$ in. at any point in the case of an external wall.

Walls or piers built of materials of differing strengths bonded together are less important now as loadbearing structures since the general practice is to use a thin "veneer" of facing material attached to a structural backing, but provision is made for dealing with such a combination in two ways. The weakest material may be considered to be used throughout any storey height and the thickness calculated on that basis. Alternatively, the area of that portion of the wall or pier built of the strongest material only may be considered as carrying the load, in which case the maximum permissible stress for that material may be used but the slenderness ratio may be calculated on the total thickness of the wall or pier.[1]

Random rubble walling should be based on permissible stresses of 75% of the corresponding stresses for coursed walling of similar materials.

[1] L.C.C. By-law 5.20 (4). Code of Practice 111 gives the first of these alternatives only.

The design process may be summarized as follows:

1. Calculate total load (W) per ft run of wall or on pier at level under consideration ("Loading"—Ch. 4, 6, 9).

2. Assume wall thickness and establish slenderness ratio (p. 122).

3. Ascertain appropriate stress reduction factor (R.F.) where slenderness ratio exceeds unity (Table 9).

4. Establish bearing area per ft run of wall or of pier (A).

5. Establish "equivalent basic stress" $= \dfrac{W}{A \times R.F.}$. (Allow for any increase in stress for local loading—p. 125).

6. Select grade of brick and mortar with strength not less than equivalent basic stress (Table 8).

PLAIN MONOLITHIC CONCRETE WALLS

A plain monolithic concrete wall means a wall of cast *in situ* concrete containing no reinforcement other than that which may be provided to reduce shrinkage cracking, together with a certain amount round openings.

As with reinforced concrete walls they are most economic when used both to support and to enclose or divide, provided they are at reasonably close spacing. That is to say, up to about 18 ft apart. They are, therefore, used mainly for housing of all types, both as external and internal loadbearing walls, when low building costs can be attained.

Dense concrete is generally used for high buildings and no-fines concrete is used for heights up to five storeys, although in Europe blocks as high as 19-storeys have been constructed with no-fines loadbearing walls more cheaply than with a frame.

Plain monolithic concrete walls suffer certain defects which, in some respects, makes them less suitable as external walls than other types. With normal dense aggregates the thermal insulation is low[1] and the appearance of the wall surface may be unsatisfactory, requiring some form of finishing or facing. In addition the unreinforced concrete wall, and particularly the no-fines wall, is unable to accommodate itself to unequal settlement as does a reinforced wall by virtue of the reinforcement or a brick or block wall by the setting up of fine cracks in the joints. Thus, as a result, large cracks tend to form in the wall. Nevertheless, where foundations

[1] See Tables 1 and 2, B.S. Code of Practice 123.101, "Dense Concrete Walls", for thermal transmittance coefficients for solid and cavity dense concrete walls with and without internal linings.

are designed to reduce unequal settlement to a minimum such walls can successfully be used.

Aggregates used for dense plain concrete are natural aggregates conforming to the requirements of B.S. 882, air-cooled blast furnace slag and crushed clay brick. Aggregates for light-weight concretes are foamed slag, clinker, pumice and any artificial aggregate suitable for the purpose. No-fines concrete may be composed of heavy or lightweight aggregate.

Dense concrete walls are constructed from concrete made with a well-graded aggregate giving a concrete of high density. The L.C.C. By-laws require the thickness of any concrete wall to be not less than 4 in. thick and Code of Practice 123.101 "Dense Concrete Walls", recommends a minimum thickness of 6 in. for external walls.

In most buildings the thickness of any type of plain concrete wall must, by reason of other functional requirements, be thicker than the minimum dictated by loadbearing requirements. An example of this is the dense concrete separating wall, which must be 7 in. thick in order to provide an adequate degree of sound insulation between houses and flats. (See *Advanced Building Construction* (*Components, Services and Finishes*).

A normal 1:2:4 mix is commonly used for dense concrete walls but weaker mixes are permitted. Code of Practice 111.201 permits under certain conditions, the use of high grade concretes (see page 131).

Lightweight aggregate concrete walls of greater thickness than dense concrete will be sufficiently strong for reasonably lightly-loaded buildings and they will give better thermal insulation when used for external walls. Care must be taken, however, in the choice of aggregate for external use because of the danger of excessive shrinkage and moisture movement occurring with certain types. Clinker has a corrosive action on steel and should not be used if shrinkage reinforcement is to be incorporated.

All types of lightweight aggregate concrete are more permeable than dense concrete, and where the wall is exposed to the weather a greater thickness of cover to the steel is required, with possibly the further protection of rendering. Concrete with a wide range of density and compressive strength can be obtained by the selection of appropriate aggregate and mix (see Table 10).

No-fines concrete walls are constructed with a concrete composed of cement and coarse aggregate alone, the omission of the fine aggregate giving rise to a large number of evenly distributed spaces throughout the concrete. These are of particular value in terms of rain exclusion. No-fines concrete is suitable for external and internal loadbearing walls or for panel wall infilling to structural frames.

Table 10—Concretes

Aggregate	Density of aggregate lb/ft³	Density of concrete lb/ft³	Compressive strength lb/in²	Thermal conductivity B.t.u./ft² h °F in.	Particular use
Expanded vermiculite and perlite	4–15	25–70	70–500	0·75–2·0	For thermal insulation
Aerated concrete	—	25–90	200–1500	0·75–2·5	
Pumice	30–55	45–70	200–550	1·50–2·0	
Foamed slag	30–60	60–95	200–800	1·50–3·0	
Sintered p.f.a.	40–60	70–80	400–1000	—	
Expanded clay or shale	35–65	60–75	800–1200	2·30–3·20	
Clinker	45–65	65–95	300–900	2·80–4·0	For fire protection / Fire resistance Class 1
Foamed slag (structural concrete)	30–60	105–130	2000–5000	—	
Sintered p.f.a. (structural concrete)	40–60	85–110	2000–5000	—	
Expanded clay or shale (structural concrete)	35–65	85–115	2000–5000	—	For load-carrying and durability
Crushed brick	70–85	105–135	2000–4000	—	
Crushed limestone	85–100	135–150	3500–5000	—	Fire resistance Class 2
Flint gravel, and crushed stone	85–100	140–155	(i) 2000–6000 (ii) 6000–10,000 (special purpose)	—	

The weight of no-fines concrete is about two-thirds that of dense concrete made with a similar aggregate. It is, consequently, less strong. Aggregates graded from $\frac{3}{4}$ in. down to $\frac{3}{8}$ in. are used with mixes of 1 to 8 or 10 for gravel aggregate and 1 to 6 for lightweight aggregates. The aggregate should be round or cubical in shape and no more water should be used than that required to ensure that each particle of aggregate is thoroughly coated with cement grout without the voids being filled. The hydrostatic pressure on formwork is only about one-third of that of normal concrete. This is an advantage since horizontal construction joints should be minimized and formwork one or two storeys high can be employed without it being excessively heavy. Any normal type of shuttering can be used or open braced timber frames faced with small-mesh expanded metal are suitable. These permit inspection of the work during pouring. The economies which can be effected in the formwork are important in view of the high proportion of the total cost of concrete work accounted for by the formwork alone.

No-fines concrete walls should not be subjected to bending stresses nor to excessive eccentric or concentrated loads. Slender piers and wide openings are, therefore, unsuited to no-fines construction. Isolated piers should not be less than 18 in. in width or one-third the height of adjacent openings.

The bond strength of no-fines concrete is low but for openings up to about 5 ft wide the walling itself may be reinforced to act as a lintel, provided there is a depth of wall not less than 9 to 12 in. above the opening. As a precaution against corrosion the steel should be galvanized or coated with cement wash and bedded in cement mortar. For wider openings an *in situ* or precast reinforced lintel of dense concrete is generally necessary. Even when the wall above openings is not required to act as a lintel to carry floor or roof loads, horizontal reinforcement equivalent to a $\frac{1}{2}$ in. steel bar should be placed above and below all openings. In buildings with timber floors the steel above the openings in external walls is usually made continuous.

For small scale domestic buildings a wall thickness of 8 in. is usually structurally sufficient. For external walls, unless a lightweight aggregate or internal insulating lining is used, a 12 in. thickness will be necessary. Wall thicknesses of 12 in. are used for multi-storey loadbearing wall construction. Lateral support to the walls must be provided by positively anchoring the floors to the walls by some means such as vertical steel dowels set in the wall and secured to the floor reinforcement or to timber joists.

Because of its weakness in tension, walls of no-fines concrete are sensitive to differential settlement. Particular attention must, therefore, be paid to the design of the foundations. For small buildings the lower part of the walls and the strip foundation should be of dense concrete, reinforced if necessary. For high buildings adequate stiffness is usually obtained by the use of rigid reinforced dense concrete cellular foundations.[1]

Thickness of plain concrete walls. This may be established either by the prescribed method, in the same manner as for masonry walls, or by calculation. The procedure in calculating is the same as for masonry walls but using different permissible stresses based on varying grades of concrete for slenderness ratios up to one, together with a different set of reduction factors to apply to the basic stresses for slenderness ratios over one. When the reinforcement specified for shrinkage and around openings is incorporated, Code of Practice 111.201 permits slenderness ratios up to 24 but otherwise sets a

Table 11—Maximum permissible compressive stress on plain concrete walls with slenderness ratio not exceeding one.

Nominal mix	L.C.C. grade	Minimum cube strength at 28 days lb/sq. in.	Maximum permissible stresses	
			lb/sq. in.	tons/sq. ft
1:1:2	I	2,925	780	50 (L.C.C.)
1:1½:3	II	2,550	680	44 (L.C.C.)
1:2:4	III	2,250	600	39 (L.C.C.)
1:3:6	—	1,650	350	22·6
1:4:8	—	1,250	250	16·1
1:6	IV	1,600	311	20 (L.C.C.)
1:8	V	1,200	233	15 (L.C.C.)
1:10	—	800	156	10
1:12	—	400	78	5
Note: Figures in italics correspond to those in adjacent columns.	Concretes with lightweight aggregates	2,000	389	25
		1,600	311	20
		1,200	233	15
		800	156	10
		400	78	5

limit of 18 as do the L.C.C. By-laws. Table 11, showing basic stresses is based on that in the Code, and Table 12, showing reduction factors is from the L.C.C. By-laws. The factors are the same as those produced by the use of the appropriate equation given in the Code.[2] The Code of Practice alone permits higher stresses (not shown in Table 11) for what is termed "structural grade concretes" for use in plain concrete walls. These are the same as the higher strength grades given in the L.C.C. By-laws but which are not included in the latter for this purpose. The Code permits their use only under qualified supervision which will ensure a high standard of workmanship and construction.

[1] For detailed recommendations for the use of no-fines concrete see *Post-War Building Studies* No. 1, "House Construction": Appendix (H.M.S.O.).
[2] Reduction Factor = $1·03 - (0·03 \times \text{Slenderness Ratio})$.

The By-laws, permitting the use of concrete down to Grade V, allow the use of the denser types of lightweight aggregate concretes. For example, foamed slag and expanded clay concretes with 1 : 6 mix will give a test strength of up to 2,000 lb per sq. in. The lower strengths permitted in the Code enable leaner mixes and less dense concretes to be used. No-fines concrete will not give such high strengths as dense concretes, but with a gravel aggregate can be made to give a test strength of 1,000 lb per sq. in. or more at 28 days. Code of Practice 111.201 does not specifically refer to no-fines concrete, but the recommendations apply to the design of walls in which it is used.

Shrinkage reinforcement is required by the L.C.C. By-laws not less in volume than 0·4% of the volume of the concrete in the wall, and arranged so that half is disposed vertically and half horizontally. Code of Practice 111 indicates that the provision of the same amount is desirable.

Table 12—Reduction Factors for slenderness ratio (concrete)

Slenderness ratio	Reduction Factor	Slenderness ratio	Reduction factor
1	1·0	10	0·73
2	0·97	12	0·67
4	0·91	14	0·61
6	0·85	16	0·55
8	0·79	18	0·49

This is to restrain setting shrinkage and to control any subsequent moisture movement in the wall and is most effective when small, closely spaced bars are used in two layers near the wall faces. A minimum cover of ½ in. is recommended in the Code, but in most cases this will be too small to give protection against corrosion, unless the concrete face is protected by cladding. Extra reinforcement should be provided round door and window openings where the shrinkage effects are greatest, together with adequate reinforcement over the openings.[1] As the drying shrinkage of no-fines concrete is low, reinforcement for this purpose is not usually necessary except, perhaps, with some lightweight aggregates, because the stresses set up by the slight shrinkage are relieved by the formation of fine cracks round the individual particles of aggregate. Shrinkage reinforcement may also be omitted from dense concrete walls where the mix is lean and of low shrinkage and where end restraints on the walls are small and work can be carried out continuously.[2]

---

[1] See Code of Practice 111, Sub-code 201, "Concrete Cast *In Situ*", Clause 303.
[2] See page 268.

LATERAL SUPPORT

Adequate lateral support or restraint to a wall as defined in the footnote on page 122 is provided by a concrete floor or roof slab bearing on the wall. Restraint is less certain with a timber floor, the joists of which bear on the wall. It is non-existent when the joists run parallel to the wall. Adequate restraint may be obtained, however, with timber floors and roofs by means of positive metal anchors. These should be at least $1\frac{1}{4}$ in. by $\frac{1}{4}$ in. cross section and 16 in. long with split and upset ends for building into solid walls. 2 in. anchors, split and bent up or down at least 6 in., should be used for cavity walls. They should be securely fastened to the joist ends at 4 ft intervals in buildings over two storeys high or up to 6 ft for buildings of one or two storeys. Where the joists run parallel to the wall similar anchors engaging three joists are used at not more than 6 ft intervals, or at not more than 8 ft intervals in buildings of one or two storeys. Experience has shown that the stiffening effect of partitions in small houses usually makes unnecessary the special anchoring of floors to the walls.

It is not usually necessary to provide such anchorage at loadbearing partitions but the joists should be securely spiked together where they bear on the wall in order to ensure an effective tie. In the case of cross wall construction where the joists must not pass through the wall, metal ties fixed to the ends of opposite joists may be used at similar intervals. Lateral support to gable walls should be provided by similar anchors fixed to the ceiling joists. Since ceiling joists are normally lighter than floor joists, and are not stiffened by floor boards, it may be desirable to provide sufficient lateral stiffness by fixing binders across joists running parallel to the wall. These details are illustrated on page 134.

Stiffening of floor joists is also necessary should a sound insulating floating floor be used. In this case the floor boards will not stiffen the floor structure and the necessary stiffness should be provided by solid strutting right across the floor on the line of the anchors. 6 in. by 1 in. boards should also be notched and spiked into the ends of the joists where they bear on loadbearing walls. Since a floor or roof providing lateral support must act as a horizontal beam resisting lateral forces, this must be borne in mind in its construction.

Timber wall plates should not be built into the walls and when a spreader is required a 2 in. by $\frac{1}{4}$ in. W.I. bearing bar should be used. The reduction in wall thickness caused by the built-in ends of joists will result in higher stresses at the floor levels. Care must be taken, therefore, to ensure that there is sufficient strength and brick- or blockwork should be of a high standard at these points. When joists bear on both sides of the wall, as in cross-wall

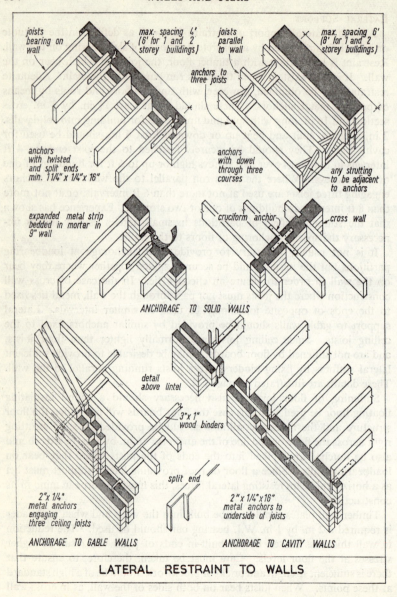

joists bearing on wall

max. spacing 4' (6' for 1 and 2 storey buildings)

joists parallel to wall

max. spacing 6' (8' for 1 and 2 storey buildings)

anchors to three joists

anchors with twisted and split ends min. 1¼" x ¼" x 16"

anchors with dowel through three courses

any strutting to be adjacent to anchors

expanded metal strip bedded in mortar in 9" wall

cruciform anchor

cross wall

ANCHORAGE TO SOLID WALLS

detail above lintel

3" x 1" wood binders

split end

2" x ¼" metal anchors engaging three ceiling joists

2" x ¼" x 16" metal anchors to underside of joists

ANCHORAGE TO GABLE WALLS

ANCHORAGE TO CAVITY WALLS

LATERAL RESTRAINT TO WALLS

construction, and good bonding may be difficult, the infilling between the joists may be of *in situ* concrete.

Piers and walls providing lateral support to a loadbearing wall must be of sufficient height and thickness to provide efficient support and must be effectively bonded at the intersection. Block bonding should not normally be used but always a fully bonded junction. Where large blocks are used or where block bonding is necessary, satisfactory bond at the intersections may be obtained by the use of $1\frac{1}{2}$ in. by $\frac{1}{4}$ in. metal ties, about 2 ft long with the ends bent up 2 in. These should be spaced not more than 4 ft apart.

CROSS WALL CONSTRUCTION

This is a particular form of loadbearing wall construction in which all loads are carried by internal walls running at right angles to the length of the building (see page 136).

The majority of buildings require dividing up by internal partitions or separating walls. In certain types in which these occur at sufficiently close and regular intervals and where a high degree of fire resistance and sound insulation is required, necessitating relatively thick and heavy walls, an economic structure results when the walls are made to carry the loads from floors and roof. Typical examples are terraces of houses, maisonette, flat and hostel blocks and schools.

The advantages of this form of construction are:

(i) Simplicity of construction—the walls consist of simple unbroken runs of brick- or blockwork, or *in situ* concrete.
(ii) Projecting beams and columns are eliminated.
(iii) It lends itself to repetition and standardization of both structural and non-structural elements and thus to the prefabrication of the latter.
(iv) The external walls, being free from load, may be designed with greater freedom in the choice of materials and finish.
(v) As a result of these factors, construction costs are low.

Concrete cross wall construction in multi-storey buildings over four to five storeys in height is normally reinforced and is called box-frame construction. It is discussed later in Chapter 5. At this point smaller buildings only will be considered, built of bricks, blocks or plain concrete.

Although not a disadvantage in the type of building to which cross wall construction is most suited, planning is restricted by the fact that the walls must run up in the same plane on all floors, from foundations to roof. It is desirable for economic reasons that the walls should also run in an unbroken line on plan from front to back of the building although this is not structurally

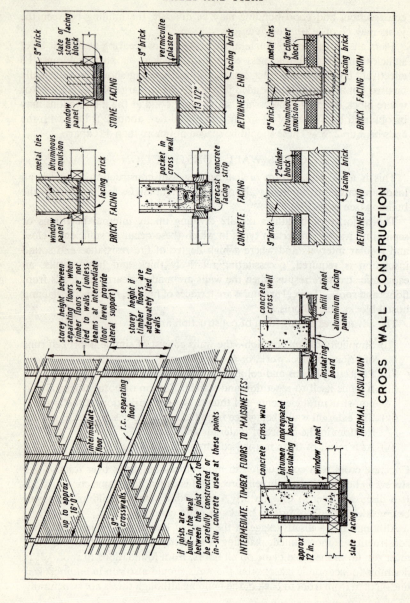

CROSS WALL CONSTRUCTION

essential. For maximum economy the walls should also be free of openings as far as possible. A further restriction on planning is the limitation which must be placed on the spacing of the walls in order to obtain an economic combination of walls and other elements of the structure. Of these, the floors and external walling are the most important.

Spacing of Walls. Cross walls should be spaced at regular or regularly repeating intervals along the building in order that a limited number of floor spans can be standardized in terms of thickness, reinforcement and formwork. Thus also, external wall elements, other than those of brick or blocks, may be standardized in a limited number of units.

The optimum spacing is about 13 to 14 ft but spacing may range from 11 to 18 ft without varying the cost of the structure itself by more than a few per cent. Within this range any increase or decrease in the cost of the floor structure is balanced by the respective decrease or increase in the cost of the walls. This can be seen from the graph on page 138. Although within the limits of 11 to 18 ft the cost of the structure remains reasonably constant, the cost of external cladding increases directly with the increase of wall spacing. Analysis shows that while there is usually little to be gained from the point of view of cost and structure in using intermediate cross walls within plan units of up to 18 ft in width, they should be introduced for greater widths.

Design Generally. The design of the walls is carried out on the basis of Code of Practice 111 or the L.C.C. By-laws for calculated walls, the loading and the stresses in the walls being determined in the manner described in the previous pages.

A cross wall structure will normally be stable against the pressure of wind parallel to the walls but will, in most cases, require some longitudinal bracing against wind pressure at right angles to the walls. This is because there is little rigidity at wall and floor junctions and the materials of which the walls are constructed have little tensile strength. The floor loads and the self-weight of the walls set up "precompression" in the walls which enables the latter and the floor-to-wall joints to resist tensile stresses up to the limit of this "precompression".[1] In many cases this may be insufficient to prevent the development of tensile stresses and the following methods may be adopted, either singly or in conjunction with each other, to provide longitudinal bracing and to ensure overall stability:

(i) The use of a staircase or lift tower of which the walls at right angles to the cross walls act as buttresses and are assumed to take all lateral forces.

[1] See "Overturning" on page 113.

(ii) The provision of longitudinal walls in the plan to take the lateral forces.

(iii) The return of the ends of the cross walls as an "L" or "T" for the same purpose.

(iv) The introduction of certain piers and walls in reinforced concrete, or the forming of the joints between walls and floors in reinforced concrete.

(v) The introduction of longitudinal reinforced concrete beams.

External cavity panel walls of brick and clinker block alone can provide sufficient rigidity to the structure of buildings up to five storeys high and of reasonable length, provided the area of window is not excessive and the workmanship is sound, especially at the bonding of panels to cross walls.

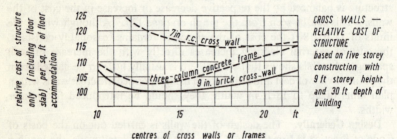

CROSS WALLS —
RELATIVE COST OF
STRUCTURE
based on five storey
construction with
9 ft storey height
and 30 ft depth of
building

centres of cross walls or frames

Bricks, blocks or plain *in situ* concrete are all suitable materials for cross wall construction. The advantage of blocks in terms of stress allowances has already been mentioned. They have the added advantage of being quickly laid, especially in areas such as Scotland, for example, where they are widely used. Plain concrete walls have in some cases proved as cheap as comparable block walls, particularly where the opportunity has been taken to use a crane for rationalizing the building operations.

The graph on this page shows the relative costs of brick and concrete cross walls together with those of a reinforced concrete frame for five-storey buildings. At this height the unreinforced wall, typified by brick, and the frame become competitive. But the reinforced concrete wall,[1] even at its most economic spacing of about 18 ft is not economic for such low buildings.

In cross wall construction the *in situ* solid reinforced concrete floor gives greatest rigidity. Hollow tile floors and precast floors may be used if the junction with the wall can be cast *in situ*, their effectiveness depending upon

' See page 268 for reference to the omission of reinforcement from concrete cross walls.

the degree of rigidity which can be obtained at this point.   This rigidity can be increased, whatever the type of floor, by introducing vertical reinforcement in the wall at the floor level.   This, however, is more practicable for concrete walls than for those of bricks or blocks where the rods would complicate the laying of the units.   When timber floors are used, for example in three-storey houses or as the intermediate floors in maisonettes (see page 136), lateral support to the walls must be obtained by anchoring the joists to the walls in the manner described on page 133.   Where the joists run parallel to the walls and bear on precast concrete cross beams the latter, if spaced not too far apart, may provide adequate restraint.   No longitudinal rigidity to the structure as a whole is provided when timber floors are used.

REINFORCED MASONRY WALLS

Reinforced masonry, usually in the form of reinforced brickwork, has been used to a considerable extent in the United States of America and in earthquake countries such an India and Japan.   It has been used to a limited extent in Great Britain since the nineteenth century.   The reinforcement enables the brickwork to withstand tensile and shear stresses in addition to the compressive stresses which it is capable of bearing alone.

The subject is discussed briefly in *Mitchell's Elementary Building Construction*, where methods of building horizontal reinforcement in walls to provide increased resistance to stresses set up by unequal settlement are described and illustrated.   Reinforced brick piers are also illustrated.   It should be emphasized again here that care should be taken not to use brickwork for work which clearly calls for reinforced concrete.

Prestressing in the form of post-tensioned high-strength brickwork can be used for tall piers to overcome the tensile stresses caused by eccentric loading and lateral wind pressure.   This permits the overall size to be kept to a minimum.   It can be done by building a hollow pier, the central space accommodating post-tensioning cables or bars (see Chapter 5, page 288) which are anchored to the foundation and to a steel plate at the top of the pier.   This is simpler than building up a combination of solid brickwork and normal reinforcing bars.

Masonry work, particularly brickwork, can act as a beam or lintel over an opening.   Methods involving soldier courses are shown in *Mitchell's Elementary Building Construction*.   With normal coursing the reinforcement, either rods or expanded metal, is placed in the first and, perhaps, second bed joint with $\frac{1}{8}$ to $\frac{1}{4}$ in. diameter wire stirrups in every vertical joint of the bottom course.   The ends of these are hooked over the tops of the bricks in the bottom course as shown on page 140 of this volume.   To give sufficient effective depth there should be at least four courses of bricks in the lintel with a greater depth for wide spans. Reinforcement must extend 6 to 9 in. into the brickwork at each bearing, with adequate end anchorage.

The design of reinforced masonry follows the general principles for reinforced concrete and should be based on recommendations given in Code of Practice 111.102.[1]

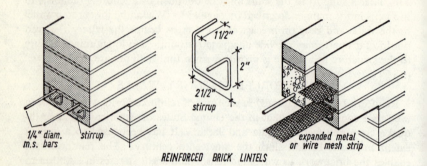

REINFORCED BRICK LINTELS

CAVITY LOADBEARING WALLS

The cavity wall possesses two important advantages over the solid wall. It provides better resistance to rain penetration and it gives a greater degree of heat insulation than a corresponding thickness of solid wall of the same material. General details are given in *Elementary Building Construction*. It will be seen that in order to avoid rain penetration no solid bridging of the cavity such as might make the two leaves act together is permissible unless carefully designed to avoid the passage of water from outer to inner leaf.

The function of the wall ties is to link the two leaves so that the lateral deflections are shared by both, particularly when one only is loaded, the other leaf then acting as a stiffener. To function satisfactorily in this way the ties must be sufficiently stiff and be adequately bonded to the leaves. Any of the ties conforming to B.S. 1243 (1954) spaced not more than 3 ft apart horizontally and 18 in. vertically in staggered arrangement will be satisfactory. Code of Practice 111 recommends in addition that ties at 12 in. vertical intervals should be placed near the sides of all openings. To ensure a satisfactory bond with the leaves a cement-lime mortar at least should be used.

[1] For a fuller discussion of reinforced masonry see *New Ways of Building*, Ed. Eric de Maré (Architectural Press, London).

Floor loads are usually carried entirely by the inner leaf, and in the case of a timber floor the joists should bear directly on the leaf. If a spreader is used a W.I. bearing bar is preferable to a built-in timber wall plate. The use of metal hangers to support the joist ends should be avoided because of the excessive eccentricity of load which is caused. At eaves level the cavity may safely be bridged and advantage should be taken of this to allow some of the roof load to be carried by the outer leaf.

Differential movement between the two leaves is likely to occur in large areas of external cavity walling, which over a period of time may weaken the bond of the ties in the joints. This, together with slight deformations of light wire ties, will reduce their effectiveness as a stiff link between the leaves. These movements can be sufficiently limited by dividing the wall into separate panels not exceeding 40–50 ft in length nor three storeys in height. In such circumstances strip metal ties are preferable to the lighter wire ties. The detailing of the vertical break will depend on the type of structure (see page 224). The horizontal sub-division may conveniently be formed by running floor slabs through to the outer face at appropriate levels, since in most buildings over three storeys in height some of the floors, even in maisonette blocks, will be of reinforced concrete.

Code of Practice 111 provides for calculation on the same basis as for solid walls, provided that the effective thickness of the wall is taken as two-thirds of the sum of the thicknesses of the two leaves. This takes into account the fact that a cavity wall has less lateral stiffness than a solid wall equal in thickness to the sum of the thicknesses of the two leaves.

Where one leaf only supports the load the permissible stress for that leaf may be based on the slenderness ratio calculated from either (i) the effective thickness given above, or (ii) the effective thickness taken as the actual thickness of the loadbearing leaf. Except where the supporting leaf is more than twice the thickness of the other leaf, a lower slenderness ratio and a higher permissible working stress result by using (i). When the load is carried by both leaves, one of which is of weaker material, as is the case when a lightweight inner leaf is used with a brick outer leaf, the permissible stress to be used for both leaves should be based on the weaker of the two materials, and determined by using an effective thickness equal to two-thirds of the sum of the two leaves. This is in accordance with the provision made for solid walls built of two materials in Clause 301 (b) of Sub-Code 111:101.

The Model Building Byelaws relate cavity loadbearing walls in terms of thickness to the prescribed method given in the Third Schedule, making no limitation on the class of building. They also allow for calculation by virtue of the fact that Code of Practice 111 is accepted as a basis for satisfying the requirements of the byelaws in respect of masonry and plain monolithic walls.

The present L.C.C. By-laws permit loadbearing external or party walls to be constructed as cavity walls in buildings other than public buildings or buildings of the warehouse class, provided they do not exceed 25 ft in height or 30 ft in length. They lay down definite conditions regarding their construction[1] but make no provision for the calculation of the thickness.

The Council does, however, on application being made, now grant relaxations of the by-laws (a) to permit the topmost two storeys of a building exceeding two storeys in height to be in cavity walling, so long as this portion does not exceed 25 ft in height or 30 ft in length, (b) to permit cavity walls to be calculated in accordance with the provisions for solid walls, subject to the thickness being deemed to be two-thirds of the sum of the thicknesses of the two leaves. These relaxations will form the subjects of amendments when the by-laws are next revised.

Generally, both the L.C.C. By-laws and the Model Building Byelaws in the Third Schedule require each leaf to be at least 4 in. thick. An exception is made in the Model Byelaws in the case of walls not exceeding 25 ft in length and 20 ft in height (25 ft if a gable wall) which, if complying with certain requirements regarding height of blocks, mortar mix and numbers of ties, may be built with leaves not less than 3 in. thick. Code of Practice 111 lays down a general minimum thickness for both leaves of 3 in. The Model Building Byelaws and the Code permit the use of hollow blocks in both leaves but the L.C.C. By-laws only in the inner leaf of an external wall.

In normal domestic construction an inner loadbearing leaf of lightweight concrete (400 lb per sq. in. minimum strength) will not usually need to be more than 4 in. thick on the ground floor of a two-storey house, but probably 6 in. in the case of a three-storey building. In the upper storey, provided the roof load is shared by both leaves, 3 in. will generally be sufficient using double the normal number of ties. It is essential that all chases for pipe runs and electric conduits in thin loadbearing leaves should be settled and allowed for in the design. A careful check should be made on concentrated loads at the bearings of lintels over wide openings. At these points it may be necessary to use a spreader or thicker blocks, or to form a pier.

Block construction, which is commonly used in America and on the Continent, can be carried out more rapidly than brickwork. The hollow clay blocks, known as "V-bricks", shown on page 143, have been developed by the Building Research Station as a facing brick which permits cavity walls to be constructed with one unit. They are made in two sizes $8\frac{5}{8} \times 8\frac{5}{8} \times 2\frac{5}{8}$ in.

[1] L.C.C. By-law 5.16.

and $8\frac{5}{8} \times 8\frac{5}{8} \times 4\frac{1}{8}$ in. With $\frac{3}{8}$ in. bed and vertical joints the final building sizes relate to those of standard bricks and permit bonding with normal brickwork. They are vertically perforated in such a way as to form two "perforated bricks" linked by thin bridging pieces across a cavity. One side has a normal brick facing finish so that rendering is not required. Although twice the volume, each block is the same weight as a normal brick so that a wall may be built with less effort and more quickly than a standard two-leaf wall, but of comparable strength and weather resistance. The danger of mortar squeezing into the cavity is minimized by the use of a mortar-laying guide which enables a strip of bedding mortar of the appropriate width to be laid quickly over each of the leaves.

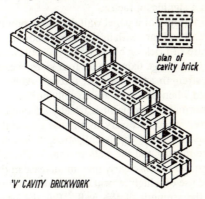

plan of
cavity brick

'V' CAVITY BRICKWORK

PANEL WALLS

Masonry and monolithic walls are often used as filling to the panels formed by the structural columns and beams of a framed building and the L.C.C. By-laws refer to such a wall as a "panel wall". The term is used here in this sense although it is sometimes used in a wider sense to include other forms of enclosing wall elements.

In a framed structure most of the wall elements are assumed to sustain no loads from floors and roof. Compressive strength is therefore of less importance than transverse strength to withstand pressure from wind or stacked materials. Although heavy construction can provide good fire resistance, durability and sound insulation, the compressive strength of materials such as brickwork and concrete is not, therefore, generally fully utilized when they are used for panel walls, and considerable weight is added to the structural frame. To overcome this disadvantage, in addition to the use of lightweight concrete for masonry and monolithic panel walls, other means of providing the infilling or enclosing element have been devised to reduce the deadweight while still fulfilling the functional requirements of a non-load-bearing external wall. These are dealt with later under "External Facings and Claddings". Although the compressive strength of a masonry panel wall is at present not normally utilized, investigations by the Building Research Station show that panel walls and the supporting frame act together giving considerable rigidity and strength to the frame. In some tests the supporting beam was wholly in tension, the wall acting with it as the compression element. If this composite action is taken into account in order to economize on the actual beam elements or to provide lateral rigidity to the frame against wind pressure on the building as a whole, then the compressive strength of a panel wall becomes a significant factor.

The strength and stability of a panel wall depends upon its stiffness, which in an unreinforced wall will vary with its thickness, upon the nature of the edge fixing and, in the case of brick or block walls, on satisfactory bond between mortar and unit. Good edge fixing on all four sides is essential in order to develop maximum strength against lateral forces. Although greatest pressure can be sustained when the edges are actually built into the frame to give a rigid fixing, the normal mortar joint is usually adequate for this purpose. This can be improved when necessary by the use of metal ties built in wall and frame. In masonry walls the lateral strength is related to the bond existing between the mortar and the walling units. The table referred to in the footnote on page 113 shows clearly that an increase in the tensile strength of the mortar by the use of a high cement content does not result in a proportional increase in the strength of the wall. But the use of walling units which provide a better bond with the mortar, such as hollow clay blocks, especially those with undercut grooves on the bed faces, does result in a significant increase in the lateral strength of the wall.

The Model Building Byelaws make no specific reference to panel walls. These would be designed in accordance with the appropriate sections of Code of Practice 111 having regard to the dead weight of the wall, the lateral pressure to be resisted and the high pressures and suctions caused by wind near the eaves and corners of a building (see page 116). For normal conditions and panel size, a 9 in. solid or 11 in. cavity wall is usually sufficient.

The L.C.C. By-laws impose[1] a minimum thickness of $8\frac{1}{2}$ in. for a solid masonry panel wall and a maximum height of 25 ft. The actual thickness must be at least one-eighteenth of either the height or the length, whichever is the less. Cavity panel walls are permitted and these must comply with the requirements for cavity loadbearing walls except that the inner leaf may

[1] L.C.C. By-law 5.24.

be 3 in. instead of 4 in. thick and may be of hollow blocks. The height must not exceed 25 ft and the area must be kept within 200 sq. ft. The height or length (whichever is the less) must not exceed 13 ft (see page 146).

These provisions, in the case of a 9 in. solid wall, permit a panel 13 ft 6 in. high and of unlimited length, or of the maximum height of 25 ft and 13 ft 6 in. long. In the case of a cavity wall, working to the maximum figures given for either the height or length, the limits of the panel are 13 ft by approximately 15 ft 4½ in. and 25 ft by 8 ft.

The L.C.C. By-laws limit the extent to which a panel wall may project beyond its supporting beam (see page 146). A solid panel must not overhang by more than one-third of its thickness and a cavity panel by not more than one-third of the thickness of the overhanging leaf, unless the base of the wall is built solid for a height equal to the full thickness of the wall, in which case it may overhang by one-third of the full thickness.

This leads to some practical difficulties when it is desired to carry a brick panel over the structural frame to give a continuous brick facing to the building. With a 13½ in. thick panel no problem arises since one-third of the thickness will allow a half-brick cover to the structural members. But such a thick wall is excessively heavy and, in any case, would rarely be required for most normal frame spacings. The usual 9 in. wall, or cavity wall, with a 4½ in. outer leaf have permissible overhangs of only 3 in. and 1½ in. respectively, both less than a half-brick. Cut bricks have been avoided by the use of special briquettes, 3 in. or 1½ in. on bed, to face the supporting beam, but some difference in colour is to be expected at times, particularly in the case of the thinner briquettes which are actually only a little over 1 in. thick. These will dry out after rain more quickly than the thicker brickwork above and below and will show up as bands of lighter tone.

An alternative is to use metal supporting angles fixed to the structural beam and accommodated in the thickness of a brick bed-joint. This permits a 4½ in. brick cover to the beam and at the same time keeps the projection over the support down to one-third of the leaf thickness. The angle support must be of non-ferrous metal to comply with the provisions of L.C.C. By-law 3.21 (revised). These methods are illustrated on page 146.

Monolithic concrete panel walls may be used and if constructed of lightweight concrete they may provide a high degree of thermal insulation in external walls. Satisfactory edge fixing is given by the normal bond with structural members either of concrete or encased steel, and by tying in the shrinkage reinforcement to the structural members. The L.C.C. By-law requirements in respect of minimum thickness and shrinkage reinforcement are as for loadbearing walls.

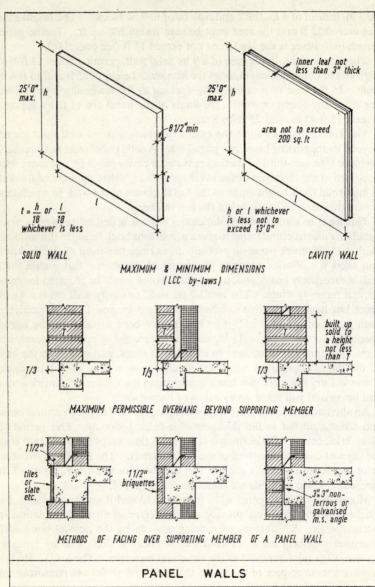

inner leaf not
less than 3" thick

25'0"
max. h

8 1/2" min

25'0"
max. h

area not to exceed
200 sq. ft

t

l

$t = \dfrac{h}{18}$ or $\dfrac{l}{18}$
whichever is less

h or l whichever
is less not to
exceed 13'0"

SOLID WALL

CAVITY WALL

MAXIMUM & MINIMUM DIMENSIONS
(LCC by-laws)

T

T

T

built up
solid to
a height
not less
than T

T/3

T/3

T/3

MAXIMUM PERMISSIBLE OVERHANG BEYOND SUPPORTING MEMBER

11/2"

tiles
or
slate
etc.

11/2"
briquettes

3"x 3" non-
ferrous or
galvanised
m.s. angle

METHODS OF FACING OVER SUPPORTING MEMBER OF A PANEL WALL

PANEL WALLS

Although reinforced concrete may be used for panel walls it is more logical to use a material such as this, with its high loadbearing capacity, in load-bearing members. In this context it is discussed in Chapter 5.

PARTY WALLS AND SEPARATING WALLS

A party wall in the L.C.C. By-laws means a wall separating adjoining buildings belonging to different owners or occupied by different persons. In the Model Building Byelaws these are referred to as separating walls.[1]

In the L.C.C. area the term "separating wall" means a wall separating different occupancies within the same building, such as the walls between flats and maisonettes, and such walls are not required to comply with the provisions for party walls given below. Concrete walls 6 or 7 in. thick may, therefore, be used and 9 in. calculated brickwork can be used for heights greater than those permitted by the prescribed method.

A party wall may, or may not, be loadbearing. Its primary function is to prevent the spread of fire between adjoining buildings and to provide an adequate degree of sound insulation. In the L.C.C. area a party wall may not be constructed with hollow bricks or blocks, of reinforced concrete, nor as a steel or concrete structural frame with panel infilling. Its thickness must be established in accordance with the prescribed method which results in a minimum thickness of $8\frac{1}{2}$ in.[2] The only limitations in the Model Byelaws are that such a wall shall be incombustible throughout and of a stated degree of fire-resistance according to the type of building. In addition, any structural frame supporting it shall have the same fire resistance as required for the wall it carries.[3] As mentioned under "Cavity Walls", within certain limits of height and length, and for certain classes of building, a party wall may be constructed as a cavity wall. But the cavity party wall, once considered desirable for reasons of sound insulation, is for all practical purposes now known to be no better in this respect than a 9 in. solid wall (see *Advanced Building Construction* (*Components, Services and Finishes*)).

The L.C.C. By-laws prohibit the building-in of timber or other combustible material to the required thickness of a party wall. The Model Building Byelaws permit the building-in of the ends of timber beams, joists and purlins provided they are satisfactorily protected by not less than 4 in. of brickwork or other non-combustible material. Although separating walls in the L.C.C. area are not governed by the regulations covering party walls, it is unlikely that building-in of timber joists would be permitted.

[1] M.B. Byelaw 42, although the words "party wall" are used in the Third Schedule.
[2] L.C.C. By-laws 5.02; 5.04; 5.30.
[3] For the general requirements regarding fire resistance, see Chapter 10.

MOVEMENT CONTROL

The nature of movements in buildings generally is referred to in the next chapter on page 220, where references are given to more detailed discussions of the subject elsewhere. Only the practical steps necessary to prevent damage to walls through movement will be discussed at this point.

Settlement Movement. The methods used to minimize differential settlement have been described in the previous chapter. In masonry walls, provided the mortar is not too strong, slight movements can be taken up in the joints without damage to the wall and in normal circumstances no special provision is made. Monolithic concrete walls are more sensitive to movement, and when these are not reinforced, particularly with no-fines concrete, reinforced foundations may be required. Tall buildings may require a cellular raft to provide a foundation of sufficient stiffness.

Moisture Movement. Most walling materials absorb water and in doing so they expand; on drying out they contract. This is termed moisture movement, and it is usually reversible except in concrete, mortars and plasters. These have an initial drying shrinkage on first drying out after setting which exceeds any future reversible movement. The magnitude of moisture movement varies with the material and in some it is so great as to necessitate special measures in construction. Table 13, taken from *Principles of Modern Building*, Volume 1, gives a broad grouping of materials relative to their moisture movement.

Special structural precautions[1] should be taken with walls built of sand-lime or concrete bricks or blocks and these are primarily the use of weak mortars and the provision of vertical movement joints which may be detailed in a similar manner to expansion joints. Shrinkage in structural concrete is normally restrained by reinforcement (see page 132). When shrinkage or contraction joints are considered desirable in a concrete wall to control random cracking and the joint must be water resistant, as in the case of retaining walls, a P.V.C. water bar or stop is incorporated in a similar manner to that shown in expansion joint (B) page 224. At a contraction joint, however, the reinforcement would carry across the joint line and no gap would be formed in construction although precautions would be taken to prevent bonding of the concrete on each side of the joint. Those materials with large moisture movements are generally most suited to internal use and some slab and sheet materials in this category are commonly used in the construction

---

[1] These are described in detail in *Building Research Station Digest* No. 6, "The Avoidance of Cracking in Masonry Construction of Concrete or Sand-lime Bricks", and in *Principles of Modern Building*, Volume 1, 3rd Ed. (H.M.S.O.).

of partitions. Methods of providing for movement are suggested in Table 16, pages 202–203.

Thermal Movement. The cause and magnitude of thermal movement is described in the next chapter (page 221). Masonry walls up to about 100 ft in length which are free to expand can usually safely accommodate thermal movements in the normal range of temperatures. When a wall exceeds this

Table 13

Degrees of moisture movement

Materials having very small moisture movement.	Well-fired bricks and clay goods.* Igneous rocks. Most limestones. Calcium sulphate plasters.
Materials with small moisture movement.	Some concrete and sand-lime bricks. Some sandstones.
Materials with considerable moisture movement calling for precautions in design and use.	Well-proportioned ballast concretes. Cement and lime mortars and renderings. Some concrete and sand-lime bricks. Light-weight concrete products. Some sandstones.
Slab and sheet materials with large moisture movement calling for special technique of treatment at joints and surrounds.	Wood-cement materials. Fibrous slabs and wallboards. Asbestos-cement sheeting. Plywoods and timber generally.

Note: Fired clay products may show an initial expansion on wetting that is irreversible and is not revealed by the drying shrinkage test laid down in B.S. 1257:1945. It has been shown in Australia, that walls built with "kiln-fresh" bricks may expand twice as much as similar walls built with bricks that had been exposed to the weather for a fortnight. A slow moisture expansion, greater than that shown by the standard tests, may also take place over a period of years. Some striking failures due to this effect have been reported from the United States of America.

length, or where movement is restrained in some way such as shown on page 221 (F), the effect of stresses set up by thermal movement should be examined. Vertical expansion joints should be provided to break the wall into sections of limited length and to provide space for the unrestrained movement of each section. Such joints in the external walls of buildings must be made weather-proof by the use of non-extruding resilient filling or crimped copper strips. A form of crimped strip suitable for masonry work is shown at F, page 224. The wall on one side of the joint is built up first and one wing of the strip fixed to it by screws inserted and driven through the slots formed by the cut-out lugs in the opposite wing. The latter is then secured by the lugs which are bedded in as the wall is built up. Joints in boundary walls need not necessarily be filled in. Expansion joints not greater than 50 ft apart should normally be provided in dense concrete walls. These may be formed as shown on page 224 A, B. Reference is made on page 141 to the use of vertical expansion joints to limit differential thermal movement between the inner and outer leaves of large areas of cavity walling.

Unless the roof slab is arranged to slide on the head of a wall a joint should be provided in the wall where one is provided in the roof slab.

Thermal movement in partitions is usually quite small. Only in the case of long partitions near boiler rooms or cold stores need consideration be given to this type of movement. An expansion joint must be formed in a partition when the latter crosses a joint carried through the floors of a building. Methods of detailing this are shown on page 224, F and G.

Methods of dealing with thermal movement in curtain walling are described on page 173.

EXTERNAL FACINGS AND CLADDINGS

The traditional masonry technique of bonding stone with a brick backing produces a structure which combines strength and satisfactory appearance and in which the facing material acts structurally with the backing material. The advent of the framed structure with solid infilling panels led to the use of thin applied slabs of stone or precast concrete as an external facing rather than ashlar work, and the increasing use of framed structures naturally resulted in attempts to reduce the dead load of the non-structural enclosing construction. This factor, together with the development of lifting devices for use on building sites, has led to the technique of constructing walls with large, light elements or "claddings" attached to the structural frame. This separation of the finishing process from that of the basic structure helps to reduce the number of operatives on the site at any given time and reduces the risk of finishes being damaged by following trades.

Fixing techniques will vary according to the nature of the "background" structure, the type of facing or facing system used and whether the facing is applied as the work proceeds or after the completion of the structure. In discussing the various methods by which building structures may be finished externally it is convenient to subdivide them under the following headings:

Facings.   Methods of finishing which require a continuous "background" structure to give the necessary support and fixing facilities for the materials forming the external face of the building.   In no case, except in ashlar work, will the facing materials take loads other than their own weight.

Claddings.   The term "cladding" is here taken to mean a method of enclosing a building structure by the attachment of elements capable of spanning between given points of support on the face of a building, thus eliminating the necessity for a continuous "background" structure.   A cladding element will generally be large enough to take a large part of the wind force acting on the building and must be strong enough to transfer this load to the basic structure.   Claddings may be heavy elements such as precast concrete slabs, or lightweight elements such as metal or asbestos cement profiled sheetings, or glass curtain walling.

Infilling Panels.   A method of providing enclosure by large, fairly light elements which are generally based on some light framing of timber or metal. These elements differ essentially from claddings in that they are fixed between the members of the structural frame of the building, rather than being applied to the face of the frame to form a skin.   In addition to supporting their own weight, infilling panels must be strong enough to support wind loads and transfer them to the main structure through properly designed fixings.

These categories of external finishes are shown diagrammatically, page 152.

FACINGS

Brickwork.   Although brickwork is naturally associated with load-bearing structures its weathering properties and excellent appearance and range of colour make it a very suitable facing to other materials such as structural concrete.   When used as a non-structural facing, bricks need not be laid to a bonded pattern and various straight jointed patterns may be employed. The brickwork should be tied to the background structure with twisted wire ties or metal cramps at 3 ft centres horizontally and vertically arranged in a diagonal pattern.   The weight of the brick facing should be taken at each storey level by projections from the structure or by metal angles.   See pages 146 and 152.   The facing over openings should be supported on nibs or metal angle supports unless the brickwork is reinforced to act as a lintel as shown on page 140.[1]   Where brick facing is applied to a concrete background, the latter

---

[1] In the L.C.C. area the application of both external and internal claddings is covered by the requirements of By-law 3.21 (revised).   The District Surveyor must approve the nature and thickness of material and method of support.   Metal fixings to all external facings or claddings must normally be of stainless steel or non-ferrous metal other than aluminium or zinc, unless their position in the work ensures adequate protection from corrosion.

should be painted with bituminous paint to prevent staining of the exterior by salts in the concrete.

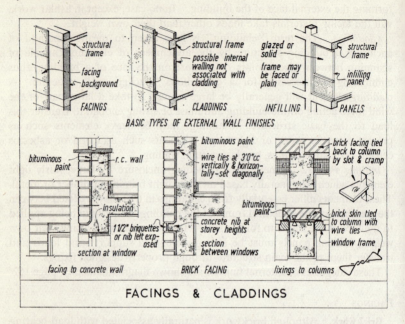

BASIC TYPES OF EXTERNAL WALL FINISHES

FACINGS & CLADDINGS

Natural Stone. The choice of stone for facing will be influenced by such factors as the design of the building, its situation and the aesthetic and technical considerations relevant to each particular case. Natural stone may be broadly classified as follows in order of hardness and durability and approximate weight:

Igneous rocks, such as granite   162/169 lbs/cu. ft
Metamorphic rocks, which include marbles, slates,
    quartzite   165/180 ,,   ,,
Sedimentary rocks, such as limestone and sandstones   109/147 ,,   ,, [1]

Igneous rocks and metamorphic rocks are extremely hard, durable and water resistant and are capable of taking a high polish. They are of high density and strength which permits them to be used as facing slabs in thicknesses of between $\frac{1}{2}$ in. and 2 in. (See Table 14.) Due to the strength of these stones comparatively thin slabs may be fixed with light cramps and wires

[1] See also *Elementary Building Construction*, Chapter 8.

Table 14. Thickness of Natural Stone External Facing Slabs

Stone	Slab Size (in.)	Minimum Thickness (in.)	Mortar for bedding and jointing
Limestones			
Ancaster Freestone	24×18	1	Lime and stone dust
	48×24	1½	
	60×30	2	
„ Weatherbed	36×18	1	Lime and stone dust
	60×24	1½	
	72×36	2	
Doulting Freestone	30×24	2	2:5:7 cement, lime, stone dust
Hornton	42×18	1½	Spot bedding: with 1:3 cement/sand; jointing: lime with 10% cement
Painswick	30×18	3	2:5:7 cement, lime, stone dust
Portland	30×30	2	2:5:7 cement, lime, stone dust
	60×36	3	
	72×48	4	
St. Adhelm (Box Ground)	30×18	2	ditto
Sandstones			
Auchinlea Freestone	24×18	4	1:1:6 cement, lime and sand
Berristall	48×24	2	
Bolton Wood	36×24	2	
Crosland Hill (York Stone)	72×12	2	1:3 cement and sand
	96×27	3	
Darley Dale	60×36	3	1:1:4 cement, lime, stone dust
Dunhouse	30×24	3	
Pennant	36×24	2	1:5 cement and stone dust
Woodkirk (York Stone)	96×36	3	Hydraulic lime and stone dust
	120×60	4	
White Mansfield	24×18	1	1:3 cement/sand or stone dust
	24×24	1½	
	36×30	2	
Granites			
Corrennie	60×30	1½	Lime or cement and sand
Kemnay	96×48	1½	ditto
Rubislaw	36×24	1	
Shap	48×24	2	
Slates			
Sawn	60×30	1½	Up to 72×30 in. available in some slates but 48×24 in. recommended as average size slab
	48×24	1	
	48×24	¾	Only in string or apron courses up to 21–24 in. high
	36×18	½	Only for small areas of small slabs bedded solid to wall (see *Elementary Building Construction*)
Natural Riven	24×24	1	
	18×12	½	ditto
Marbles	Irrespective of slab size	¾	For facing only up to First Floor level
	ditto	1	For facing rising above First Floor level
	ditto	1½	Many Local Authority surveyors require this as a minimum

NOTE: The maximum size against each stone indicates that recommended by the quarry for facing slabs, or the maximum size available from the quarry.

The mortar, where indicated, is that recommended by the quarry.

without risk of the edges splitting. Sedimentary rocks, formed by the redisposition of older rocks by the action of air or water, are generally softer, less durable and more absorbent and exhibit a highly laminar structure. Such stones should be laid with their natural bed at right-angles to the face of the wall. This principle applies whether the stone is bonded into a brick or block background or used as a non-bonded slab facing. Consistent with this, certain minimum thicknesses are desirable for facing slabs according to the nature of the stone and Table 14 indicates the thicknesses recommended by the quarries for a number of typical building stones suitable for external facings. This list, of course, is not comprehensive, and does not imply that other good building stones are not suitable for this purpose. It will be seen that some sedimentary rocks may be used as thin as $1\frac{1}{2}$ to 2 in. for slab facings, but this thickness does not afford much material at the edges to give a secure anchorage for cramps. A thickness of 3 in. or even 4 in. is usually recommended. Very thin slabs are not always the most economic, depending upon the fixing problems on the job. Slabs should be about 3 to 4 sq. ft. face area and limited to 120 to 150 lb in weight if they are to be man-handled. Care should be taken that limestone and sandstone are not used in juxtaposition in such a way that the soluble salts formed by the decomposition of the limestone are washed on to the sandstone, since this may produce rapid decay of the sandstone. Similar decay may occur where cast stone and sand-stone are placed in juxtaposition and brick can be damaged in the same way. Stone facing on a background of brick or concrete should always be coated on the back with bitumen, or the back-ground itself should be similarly coated. This is necessary in order to provide a barrier against the movement of salts in the bricks, mortar or concrete. These, taken up in solution by rain passing through the joints or the slabs, are deposited in the stone when the rainwater evaporates through the facing and cause staining and decay of the stone.

Metal Anchorages. Natural stone facings are fixed to the "background" structure by means of metal fixings which are designed primarily to hold the slabs back to the wall and keep the faces in correct alignment.[1] The fixings can assist in relieving stones below of the weight of those above, but the weight of the facing should usually be brought back to the structure at 8 to 10 ft intervals by suitable projections or by angles bolted to the structure. All metal anchorages should be of non-ferrous metal such as copper or bronze, since galvanizing and bitumen painting of iron or steel give temporary protection only and may result in subsequent staining and spalling of the

---

[1] Non-bonded slab facings only are covered here. See *Elementary Building Construction*, Ch. 8, for ashlar facing.

stone (see footnote page 151).   All metal ties should be non-ferrous and not inferior to the specification given in B.S. 1243.

On page 156 are shown various types of metal anchorages and supports. Those for sedimentary stones are usually in strip form and reasonably substantial when supporting the weight of a thick slab.   The ends are accommodated in mortices or grooves cut in the edges of the slabs.   The thinner igneous and metamorphic slabs are invariably secured with wire cramps and dowels which necessitate less labour on the hard dense stone, drilling and surface sinking only being required.   Dowels are sometimes used with cramps in the vertical joints of large sedimentary slabs to hold back and align the adjacent slabs.   The ends of all forms of anchors and corbels must be fixed firmly to the background and this is usually done by bedding in mortar in mortices cut or, in the case of concrete, cast in the background material. Forming of individual mortices in concrete can be avoided by casting in dovetail section pressed metal channels to form horizontal or vertical slots which accommodate the dovetail-shaped ends of various types of cramps (see page 156).

Setting, Jointing and Pointing.   Sedimentary stones are usually bedded and backed up solidly in mortar, and suitable mortars must be used.[1]   The widths of the joints should not be less than $\frac{3}{16}$ in., metal strips being used as screeds.   The finish to the face of the mortar joints may be carried out as the work proceeds in the same mortar used for bedding.   Alternatively, joints may be raked back $\frac{3}{4}$ in. and pointed with specially prepared mortar of selected colour and equal strength to the bedding mortar.   Marble, granite and slate facings are fixed with a $\frac{1}{2}$ in. air space behind the slab formed by setting the stone against mortar dabs, page 156.   This technique allows for differential movement of the facing and structural background and also prevents staining and "blooming" of the faces of the slabs.   In addition the backs of marble slabs are painted with shellac or bitumen paint.

In recent years there have been cases of the loosening of facing slabs at the fastenings, particularly on the gable walls of very high reinforced concrete buildings.   This is thought to be due to the accumulative effect of "creep" in the great height of concrete wall and to overcome this, mastic joints at every floor, or not more than 20 ft apart, are now generally required.

Fixing.   An example of sedimentary stone slab facing is shown on page 156. In this instance the stones are secured by metal fixings which give each stone some support and keep the faces in alignment.   Support over openings is given by an angle rag-bolted to the structure.   As already mentioned, the

---

[1] Code of Practice 121.201, " Masonry.   Walls ashlared with natural or cast stone", gives suitable mortars for various stones.   See also Table 14.

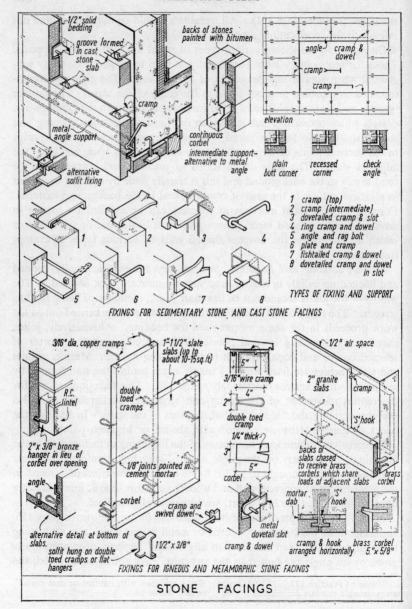

1/2" solid bedding

groove formed in cast stone slab

backs of stones painted with bitumen

metal angle support

cramp

alternative soffit fixing

continuous corbel

intermediate support—alternative to metal angle

angle   cramp & dowel

cramp

cramp

elevation

plain butt corner

recessed corner

check angle

1   cramp (top)
2   cramp (intermediate)
3   dovetailed cramp & slot
4   ring cramp and dowel
5   angle and rag bolt
6   plate and cramp
7   fishtailed cramp & dowel
8   dovetailed cramp and dowel in slot

TYPES OF FIXING AND SUPPORT

FIXINGS FOR SEDIMENTARY STONE AND CAST STONE FACINGS

3/16" dia. copper cramps

1"-11/2" slate slabs (up to about 10-15 sq. ft)

R.C. lintel

double toed cramps

3/16" wire cramp

double toed cramp

1/4" thick

1/2" air space

2" granite slabs

cramp

'S' hook

2"x 3/8" bronze hanger in lieu of corbel over opening

angle

1/8" joints pointed in cement mortar

corbel

cramp and swivel dowel

alternative detail at bottom of slabs.

soffit hung on double toed cramps or flat hangers

11/2" x 3/8"

corbel

metal dovetail slot

cramp & dowel

backs of slabs chased to receive brass corbels which share loads of adjacent slabs

brass corbel

mortar dab

'S' hook

cramp & hook arranged horizontally

brass corbel 5." x 5/8"

FIXINGS FOR IGNEOUS AND METAMORPHIC STONE FACINGS

STONE FACINGS

weight of the facing should be brought down to a positive bearing on the structure at 8 to 10 ft intervals by similar angles or concrete corbels or by using "bonding" courses as shown in *Elementary Building Construction*.

Fixing methods for igneous and metamorphic stones are also shown on page 156. "S"-hooks are used to align the edges of adjacent slabs when fixing is by wire cramps into one edge only of two adjacent edges. The mortar dabs position the "unfixed" edge relative to the background and the "S"-hook prevents it falling outwards. Small slabs of slate and quartzite are bedded solid and supported by flat cramps every third or fourth course. (See *Elementary Building Construction*.) Thin stone slabs, such as marble and slate, may also be fixed by screwing and pelleting.

Natural stone may be used as permanent shuttering to a concrete wall. The backs of the slabs are grooved to provide adequate key or the slabs are cramped back as the work proceeds, page 158. The backs of the slabs should be painted with bituminous paint. Adequate temporary support to the facing is essential since it would be impossible to re-align the slabs if they were displaced when the concrete was being poured or by the subsequent use of a mechanical vibrator. The use of asbestos fibre or plastic cord set in grooves in the edges of the slabs is advisable in order to avoid "weepage" through the joints and staining of the stone face.

Cast Stone. Cast stone is described in *Elementary Building Construction*. The manufacture of this material is essentially the job of specialist firms, and it is most important that the stone be fully matured before building it in since the material shrinks on setting and hardening.

Cast stone may be used as a facing in a similar manner to natural stone but as the material is cast it is possible to lightly reinforce the slabs and cast fixings into the backs (see page 158). Reinforced slabs can be thinner than their natural stone equivalent, although it has been shown that by careful manufacture slabs of $1\frac{1}{2}$ to $2\frac{1}{2}$ in. thickness may be unreinforced. This avoids the possibility of surface staining which results from insufficient cover to steel reinforcement.

Concrete. Facing slabs may be cast in concrete in a similar way to cast stone slabs. They are about 2 in. thick lightly reinforced and may have fixings cast into the back. Alternatively they may be fixed with conventional non-ferrous fixings. Large slabs are normally trough shaped to reduce their weight whilst maintaining strength. If the slabs are to be man-handled by two men the weight should be kept down to about 120 to 150 lbs. This will limit the area of 2 in. slabs to about 5 sq. ft. The slabs should be carried at about 10 ft vertical intervals by corbels or by bonding-in blocks

6*

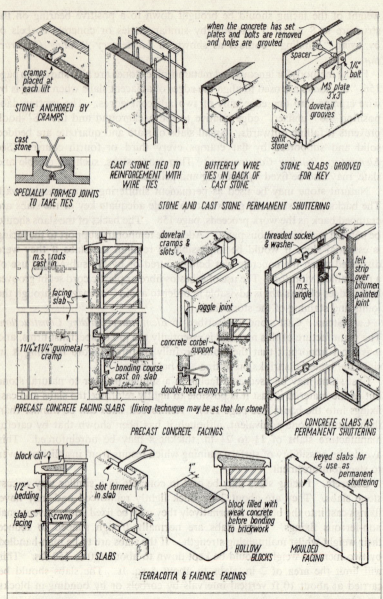

when the concrete has set plates and bolts are removed and holes are grouted

cramps placed at each lift

STONE ANCHORED BY CRAMPS

cast stone

SPECIALLY FORMED JOINTS TO TAKE TIES

CAST STONE TIED TO REINFORCEMENT WITH WIRE TIES

BUTTERFLY WIRE TIES IN BACK OF CAST STONE

spacer

1/4" bolt

MS plate 3"x3"

dovetail grooves

soffit stone

STONE SLABS GROOVED FOR KEY

STONE AND CAST STONE PERMANENT SHUTTERING

m.s. rods cast in

facing slab

11/4"x11/4" gunmetal cramp

dovetail cramps & slots

joggle joint

concrete corbel support

double toed cramp

bonding course cast on slab

threaded socket & washer

felt strip over bitumen painted joint

m.s. angle

PRECAST CONCRETE FACING SLABS (fixing technique may be as that for stone)

PRECAST CONCRETE FACINGS

CONCRETE SLABS AS PERMANENT SHUTTERING

block cill

1/2" bedding

slab facing

cramp

slot formed in slab

1"

block filled with weak concrete before bonding to brickwork

keyed slabs for use as permanent shuttering

HOLLOW BLOCKS

MOULDED FACING

SLABS

TERRACOTTA & FAIENCE FACINGS

STONE, CONCRETE & TERRACOTTA FACINGS

cast on the backs of the slabs (see page 158). Since the dimensions of concrete slabs will vary, sufficient tolerance must be provided in the joints. Mortar joints should be not less than $\frac{1}{4}$ in. wide and mastic or dry jointing not less than $\frac{1}{8}$ in. wide. The panels may be finished in a variety of colours and textures by careful choice of aggregate which may be exposed by washing or spraying the surface before hardening or by scrubbing or wire brushing. Polishing or acid spraying may be carried out after manufacture. Patterned timber, plastic or rubber moulds may be used to provide surface texture. Reinforcements should have at least $1\frac{1}{4}$ in. outer cover. Concrete slabs used as permanent shuttering are shown on page 158. In this example the slabs are held by adjustable bolts and square washers on steel angle framing to ensure alignment whilst the concrete is poured. The joints are rebated and allow plenty of tolerance.

Terrazzo Slabs. These are composed of concrete with a $\frac{5}{16}$ in. facing of terrazzo. The slabs, which should be painted on the backs and rear edges with a sealing compound, are fixed in similar ways to stone and concrete slabs.

Terracotta and Faience. These materials are described briefly in *Advanced Building Construction* (*Components, Services and Finishes*). For external work they are produced in the form of slabs 12 in. × 8 in., 18 in. × 12 in. and 24 in. × 18 in. by 1–1$\frac{1}{4}$ in. thick. They are scored or dovetailed on the back to give a good key and may be fixed with non-ferrous metal cramps in a manner similar to thin stone slabs, or used as permanent shuttering to concrete, page 158. Hollow blocks are also produced which are filled with fine concrete and bonded into brickwork. The blocks are limited to 3 cu. ft volume and are usually used for such elements as sills and copings, page 158. The protective glaze on faience only covers the face and a small strip of the return surfaces. Arrises are rounded. Joints should be $\frac{1}{4}$ in. wide.

Glazed Tiles. Tiles for external use are made from a plastic clay which produces an "open" body capable of resisting the action of frost. Tiles should be specified as "exterior frost resisting glazed tiles", and are bedded on a rendered backing in mastic or mortar. Concrete surfaces, particularly soffits, should be well hacked for key. When covering a large surface tiles are best contained in panels, or broken up into separate panels to reduce the risk of cracking due to movement of the background. The edges of the panels should have open weathered or mastic filled joints to allow for movement.

Tile and Slate Hanging. Roofing tiles and slates may be used as facings to vertical surfaces both as decoration and protection. They should not be hung in positions where they are vulnerable to damage. Tiles are hung on

battens, preferably fixed over counter battens at about 16 in. c/c. A lap of
1½ in. is adequate, the tiles being double nailed and laid to break joint, as in
roofing practice.   Some examples are shown on page 161.   Slate hanging is
similar to roofing practice, the same gauges relative to each size of slate
being used.   Although not recommended as a general practice, slates may
be nailed directly into brick jointing and a suitable size can be chosen to
work in with the courses.   Nibless tiles may be fixed in the same manner.

Asbestos Cement.   This material may be used in the following ways:

(*a*) *Asbestos slate and tile hanging, siding:* Asbestos slates are rectangular
and are centre nailed.   Asbestos tiles are square, laid diamond pattern, and
are double nailed at the centre.   In addition a loose rivet is used to hold the
slates or tiles together in threes.   Asbestos siding is basically flat sheeting
used in long strip sizes.   Fixing is to battens with a 1 in. or 1½ in. lap at the
head and vertical joints are protected by felt backing strips. (See page 161.)

(*b*) *Asbestos cement sheeting:* This may be fixed to grounds either with
lapped horizontal joints with a felt strip behind the vertical joints, or with
horizontal butt joints, z-flashings and vertical cover strips.   Fluted sheeting
is usually fixed with countersunk screws (page 161).

(*c*) *Permanent shuttering:* For limited areas of facing such as to spandrels,
it is possible to use flat or profiled sheeting as a shutter lining to be retained
as a permanent facing, bonded to the concrete.   This avoids evidence of
fixings and provides a solid backing to the sheeting, which is brittle and otherwise easily cracked in vulnerable positions.

Timber.   Where local byelaws permit, timber may be used to face walls in
the following ways:

(*a*) *Weatherboarding*, nailed to grounds plugged to concrete or brickwork
at about 4 ft centres for 1 in. boards fixed horizontally (16–18 in. for ⅝ in.
boards) and 2 ft centres for 1 in. boards fixed vertically.   Diagonal boarding
1 in. thick should be fixed to vertical grounds at about 2 ft 6 in. centres.
Nails used to fix the boarding should be composition nails, since hammering
may break the coating of sherardized or galvanized nails.   Copper nails will
usually produce characteristic staining.   Secret nailing, where appropriate,
helps to prevent corrosion staining of unpainted boarding.   Hessian based
bituminous felt or similar waterproof and windproof backing should be
placed immediately behind the boarding.   Boarding should be free to move
on at least one side and the lower edge should be kept at least 6 in. above any
horizontal surface to prevent splash staining.   Vertical boarding should be
fixed so that the lower edges are free to allow water to drain off easily, but
where this is not possible, for example when the boards are in grooves or
rebates, they should be treated with preservative or be sealed (see page 162).

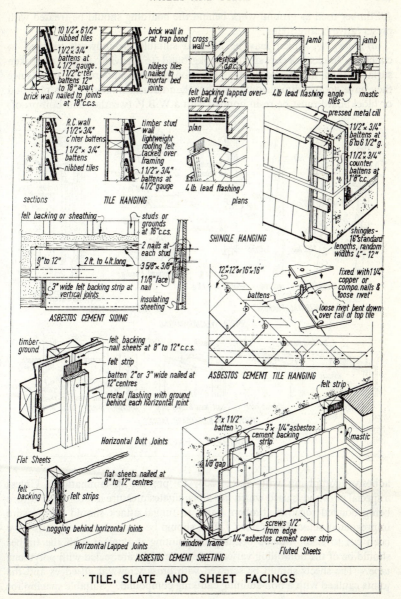

sections   TILE HANGING

SHINGLE HANGING

ASBESTOS CEMENT SIDING

ASBESTOS CEMENT TILE HANGING

Flat Sheets

Horizontal Butt Joints

Horizontal Lapped Joints

ASBESTOS CEMENT SHEETING

Fluted Sheets

TILE, SLATE AND SHEET FACINGS

All timber used as ground work behind the boarding should be treated with preservative before fixing.

(b) *Panelling*, which may be fixed to suitable groundwork plugged to concrete, brickwork or similar background to provide larger unbroken surfaces than weatherboarding. Plywood and blockboard are used since they have greater dimensional stability than natural timbers. The plywood or blockboard must be resin bonded with a W.B.P. (weather and boil-proof)

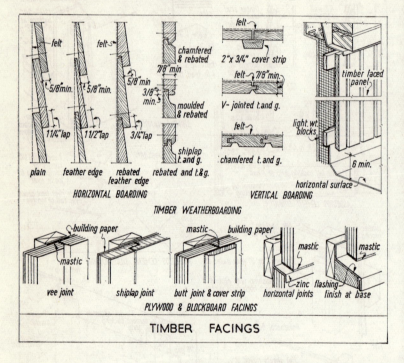

adhesive complying with B.S. 1204, to prevent de-lamination. Unless a special plywood is used which has all laminates pressure impregnated before being bonded together, timbers liable to fungal attack should be pressure impregnated before being fixed. This should be done after the boards have been cut to size. Mastic bedding or pointing in contact with the timber should be of the non-oiling variety unless the edges are sealed with polythene tape. The sheets should be screwed with brass screws at all edges and the joints caulked with a non-staining caulking compound. Suitable spacing for grounds is: $\frac{3}{8}$in. sheet —24 in., $\frac{1}{2}$ in. sheet—32 in. $\frac{5}{8}$ in. and $\frac{3}{4}$ in. sheet—42 in. (See page 162).

(c) *Shingle hanging*: Edge grain sawn cedar shingles hung vertically are twice nailed at the centre to battens at 6 in. or 6$\frac{1}{2}$ in. gauge. Each shingle is held by two other nails from the course above it and the resulting covering is extremely weather tight. Composition, copper or best hot spelter galvanized nails should be used, page 161.

Metal. Metals such as steel, stainless steel, copper, bronze, aluminium and lead may be used for facings to masonry and concrete structural backings in the following ways:

(a) *Fully supported sheeting*. This is similar to roofing technique, the sheets being joined together with welts and standing seams and secured by cleats nailed to horizontal timber insets in concrete or battens in screed as shown on page 164. Lead sheet is too heavy to rely on cleat fixing and the sheets are held by a number of brass screws driven into lead plugs in the backing and finished-off with lead burned dots.

(b) *Profiled metal sheeting and panelling*. This application of metal sheeting consists of sheets pressed or extruded into various profiles to give rigidity, thus enabling fewer fixings to be used. Alternatively, thin panels may be stiffened by welding ribs or angle stiffeners to the backs of the sheets or the panels may be cast. Metals used in this way include:

Aluminium alloys. These are available in different types and various finishes (see Chapter 2, *Advanced Building Construction*: *Components, Services and Finishes*). Typical profiled sections and applications of aluminium panel facings to masonry and concrete walls are shown on pages 164, 165. Aluminium should be protected from damp mortars and plasters since it is liable to alkaline attack. A protective paint should be used to dissociate it from steel or other metals. Plastic or fibre washers may be used to keep sheeting clear of steel fixing bolts and similar fixings.

Steel. Carbon steel panels require protection against rusting. This can be achieved in various ways (see Chapter 2, *Advanced Building Construction*: *Components, Services and Finishes*). Some of these methods give colour and variation in texture. The most effective protective finish is vitreous enamelling, which can be applied in any colour and finished in full gloss, matt, semi-matt and eggshell surface textures. Other finishes include the application of stone dust by a refractory process and asbestos, applied as a felt or by spraying on a zinc coating or primer. Chemical colouring of plated surfaces is possible but needs to be given a lacquered finish; weathering will depend on the efficacy of the lacquer. An example of steel panels fixed with clips and lugs screwed to timber ground-work is shown on page 165. The panels are butt-jointed and caulked with a mastic compound.

Stainless steel. This is a general name for a number of steel alloys. The material is pressed into panels using 20 to 22 gauge metal and is more economic when used in narrow strips, say 10 in. to 1 ft wide, than in large sheets. The apparent waviness of flat sheets can be reduced by embossing or by profiling, keeping the flat surfaces down to 4 or 5 in. in width. Fully corrosion resistant welds are possible which are invisible when polished. All fixings should be of stainless steel or be heavily protected carbon steel. On this page is shown an example of pressed stainless steel applied as a facing on metal fixings bolted to the structural background.

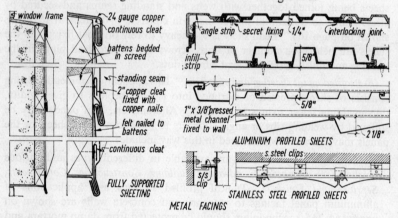

MELAL FACINGS

Bronze. This copper alloy has greater mechanical strength than sheet copper. It is expensive, can be obtained in plain and profiled sheets and weathers to a dark brown/black with a slight green patina. Bronze facing to a concrete wall, screwed to a supporting framework of mild steel flats, angles and channels, is shown on page 165.

(*c*) *Metal tile hanging*: Copper and aluminium roof tiling may equally well be used on vertical surfaces as facings.

Plastics. Of the vast number of plastics at present in existence, only certain types are suitable for external use as facings, and only limited experience is available as to the weathering capacities. The phenolformaldehyde laminates are generally recommended for exterior use. These plastics are laminated with paper, cloth, wood veneer or glass fibre, which increase their mechanical strength and insulation properties (e.g. "Holoplast" and "Corro-

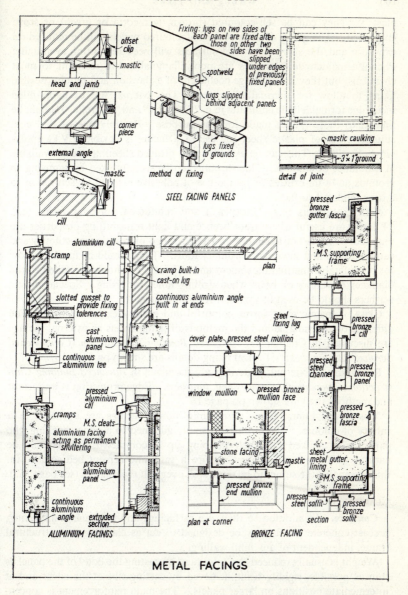

head and jamb
offset clip
mastic

external angle
corner piece

cill
mastic

Fixing: lugs on two sides of each panel are fixed after those on other two sides have been slipped under edges of previously fixed panels

spotweld
lugs slipped behind adjacent panels
lugs fixed to grounds

method of fixing

mastic caulking
3 × 1" ground

detail of joint

STEEL FACING PANELS

aluminium cill
cramp
slotted gusset to provide fixing tolerances
cast aluminium panel
continuous aluminium tee

plan

cramp built-in
cast-on lug
continuous aluminium angle built in at ends

pressed bronze gutter fascia
M.S. supporting frame

steel fixing lug
pressed bronze cill

cover plate pressed steel mullion
window mullion
pressed bronze mullion face

pressed steel channel
pressed bronze panel
pressed bronze fascia

pressed aluminium cill
M.S. cleats
cramps
aluminium facing acting as permanent shuttering
pressed aluminium panel
continuous aluminium angle
extruded section

ALUMINIUM FACINGS

stone facing
mastic
pressed bronze end mullion

plan at corner

sheet metal gutter lining
M.S. supporting frame
pressed steel soffit
pressed bronze soffit

section

BRONZE FACING

METAL FACINGS

plast "). They can be self-coloured (brown, terracotta or green) or stove enamelled. The glossy surface of the selfcoloured panels will be reduced on exposure and the stove enamelled surfaces will need repainting eventually. Phenolformaldehyde laminates are non-inflammable and resistant to most chemicals, but they have a large coefficient of expansion and require flexible fixing to allow for thermal movement. The external use of paper-filled melamine formaldehyde laminates (e.g. "Formica" and "Wareite") should be limited to those grades made for this purpose. Possibly one of the most suitable types of plastic sheet for use as a facing is flexible P.V.C. (polyvinyl chloride). This can be extruded into profiled sheeting and is available in a number of colours. This sheeting can be secretly fixed by screwing to grounds at 18 in. centres or by the use of adhesive assisted by screws on to a true, rendered surface.

Acrilyc polymers (e.g. "Perspex") and reinforced polyester resins (e.g. "Filon") are useful where translucence and light transmitting properties are required. Sheets are available in a large range of translucent colours and can be drilled and sawn with ordinary tools. They should be fixed to allow for considerable thermal movement and at least $\frac{1}{8}$ in. should be added to the diameter of screws or bolts when drilling holes for fixing. Special plastic washers should be used to weatherproof the fixing.

Glass. Opaque glass forms colourful and easily cleaned surfaces. The different types available and the methods of fixing sheets as external facings are discussed in Chapter 11, *Advanced Building Construction* (*Components, Services and Finishes*). Typical fixing details are shown on page 167.

Renderings. External renderings are discussed in *Advanced Building Construction* (*Components, Services and Finishes*). Edge protection is important and methods used are shown on page 167.

Mosaic and Flint. Glass or ceramic mosaic facings are available in a variety of colours. The mosaic is usually gummed to a paper backing, the paper being soaked off when slabbing up is completed. Flints may be natural or "knapped". They require a sand and cement bed some 5 in. thick to enable the stones to be set in well over half their length (see page 167).

CLADDINGS

Concrete. In addition to their use as facings and permanent shuttering, precast concrete panels may be designed to act as cladding to a structural frame, independent of any infill walling.

Weight is usually reduced to a minimum by casting the body of the panel as thin as possible, rigidity being achieved by casting ribs at the edges and at intermediate positions on larger panels. The main reinforcement is concentrated in the ribs, the thinner body of the panels being lightly reinforced with galvanized wire or left unreinforced in many cases. Thin slabs (say, 2 in. thick) of constant thickness without ribs should be reinforced with welded galvanized mesh to reduce the risk of rust staining on the faces. In all cases reinforcement should be kept back 1 in. to $1\frac{1}{4}$ in. from the weather face of any concrete panel or slab.

Panels may be cast in factories or on site, and in either case joints must provide adequate tolerance since panels can rarely be produced to finer dimensional tolerances than plus or minus $\frac{3}{16}$ in. In most cases greater allowances should be made. To assist in obtaining the correct width bed joint between panels, pieces of hemp or asbestos rope are often laid across the

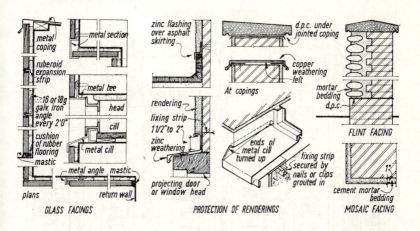

tops of the lower panels. These act as distance pieces and relieve the joint from load to prevent extrusion of mortar bedding. Edges of panels may be designed to give a simple, self-drained, anti-capillary joint or the joint may be sealed with mastic. In the latter case the joint width should not exceed about $\frac{3}{8}$ in. Pointing in mastic is either applied in strip form or gunned into position. The backs of panels should be drained and precautions taken against entry of moisture into the interior of the building in a similar manner to that employed in cavity wall construction, since some water penetration is almost inevitable, particularly where large panels are used. Various joint details are illustrated on page 168.

Cladding panels may be designed to span vertically between floors from which they obtain support or to span horizontally between columns.

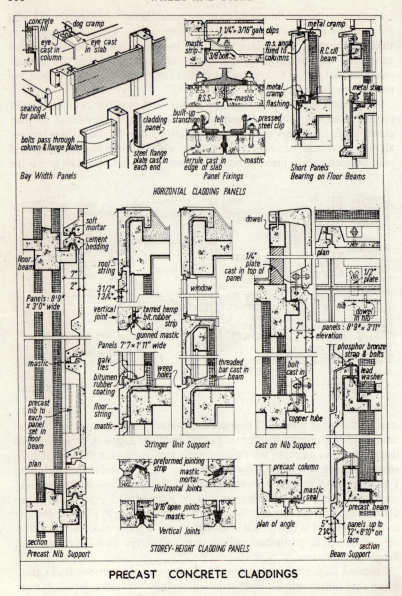

Bay Width Panels

concrete nib — dog cramp — eye cast in slab — eye cast in column — seating for panel — bolts pass through column & flange plates — cladding panel — steel flange plate cast in each end

Panel Fixings

1 1/4" x 3/16" galv. clips — mastic strip — 3/8 bolt — m.s. angle fixed to columns — R.S.S. — mastic — built-up stanchion — felt — ferrule cast in edge of slab — mastic — pressed steel clip

Short Panels Bearing on Floor Beams

metal cramp — R.C. cill beam — metal strap — metal cramp — flashing

HORIZONTAL CLADDING PANELS

Precast Nib Support

soft mortar — cement bedding — floor beam — 7" — 2" — Panels: 8'9" x 3'0" wide — mastic — precast nib to each panel set in floor beam — plan — section

Stringer Unit Support

roof string — 3 1/2" — 1 3/4" — vertical joint — tarred hemp bit. rubber strip — gunned mastic — Panels 7'7" x 1'11" wide — galv. ties — bitumen rubber coating — floor string — mastic — weep holes — threaded bar cast in beam — window

Cast on Nib Support

dowel — plan — 1/4" plate cast in top of panel — 7" — 2" — elevation — 1/2" plate — nib — dowel in nib — panels: 8'9" x 3'11" — bolt cast in — copper tube — phosphor bronze strap & bolts — lead washer

Horizontal Joints

preformed jointing strip — mastic mortar

Vertical Joints

3/16" open joints — mastic

STOREY-HEIGHT CLADDING PANELS

Beam Support

precast column — mastic seal — plan of angle — 5" — 2 1/4" — precast beam — panels up to 12' x 8'10" on face — section

PRECAST CONCRETE CLADDINGS

Vertical panels in principle are "hooked" on to the structure to which they are often secured in various ways by non-ferrous or galvanized steel dowels, plates or angles. Horizontal panels may pass over the columns and butt against each other on the face, or they may extend only to the return faces. Fixing is by metal plates or clips and bolts or by projecting stirrups and *in situ* concrete filling. Examples of vertical and horizontal cladding are shown on page 168. Horizontal cladding is generally used as the panel filling between windows on adjacent floors, and an alternative to column fixing is to design the slabs to bear on the structural floor and to be stabilized at the top by attachment to an intermediate support spanning between the columns at cill level, as shown on page 168. In this case the slab need not extend the full bay width in one piece but a number of smaller slabs can be used to fill the space between the columns. Rebates on the columns avoid straight through joints.

Surface finishes may be obtained as for facings (page 159) or grooved natural stone slabs can be cast on the face as for in situ work (page 158).

Asbestos Cement. Profiled asbestos cement has been used for many years as cladding to lightweight industrial and temporary buildings. Where greater thermal insulation is required, the sheeting may form the outer skin to a cavity wall lined with insulating blocks or slabs as shown on page 170, A. In recent years manufacturers have produced underlining sheets which may be used to produce a double skin cladding or sandwich sheet, the cavity being filled if desired with a suitable flexible insulation material such as slag wool or glass fibre quilt (page 170). A comprehensive range of accessories such as flashings, filler pieces and internal and external angles, is available, and in many instances the cladding may accommodate integral window frames. All such cladding panels are lap jointed at the sides, and concealed fixings are available with some types (page see 170, B). Upper and lower edges may be either lapped or butt jointed. Where panels are lapped, it is necessary to shoulder the diagonally opposite panels in a similar manner to interlocking tiling to avoid excessive thickness at the junction of four sheets. Horizontal butt joints are rendered waterproof by the use of a Z flashing and additional fixings. A variety of metal fixings is available to attach the cladding to steel angle framing, steel tubing, concrete rails, or timber rails or inserts. These are illustrated on page 170, C. The general details shown on this page are of the application of one type of sheet which is typical of others.

Metal. The metals used for facings may be employed in the form of sheet claddings. Generally, aluminium and steel are used for this purpose. Metal cladding sheets are profiled to give the necessary strength to span between fixing rails and may be fixed directly to these members or be lined with

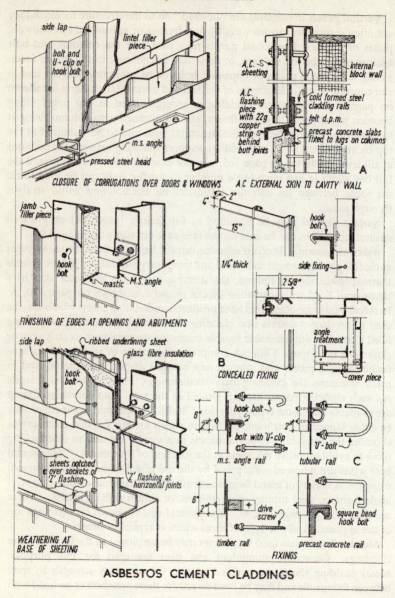

CLOSURE OF CORRUGATIONS OVER DOORS & WINDOWS

A.C. EXTERNAL SKIN TO CAVITY WALL

FINISHING OF EDGES AT OPENINGS AND ABUTMENTS

CONCEALED FIXING

WEATHERING AT BASE OF SHEETING

FIXINGS

m.s. angle rail   tubular rail

timber rail   precast concrete rail

ASBESTOS CEMENT CLADDINGS

an insulating material as shown on page 172, A, B. Alternatively, panels may be fabricated with internal and external metal surfaces and an insulating material sandwiched between them (page 172, C.) Methods of attachment vary from simple fixings such as hook bolts and screws for single thicknesses of sheeting to secret fixings based on concealed clips or specially designed cover strips which accommodate square bolt heads in concealed slots (page 172, A, B). Large pressed aluminium cladding panels can be in storey height units, suitably profiled to obtain rigidity and prevent vibration, with integral window units (page 172, D). These panels have interlocking vertical joints, which allow for thermal movement, and drained horizontal joints. Water penetrating the vertical jointing is drained downwards in cavities formed within the joint, trapped in catch pans at the base and conducted to the face of the cladding through the horizontal jointing.

Curtain Walling. This term is here taken to mean a system of cladding comprising a frame or grid of members fixed to the face of a structure, usually at each floor level, and an infilling of panels, glazed or solid, as may be required to perform both the functions of window and wall.

The curtain wall must fulfil the same functional requirements as any other system of external walling and it will be considered here under these headings. The main problem in the design of curtain walls lies in the framework which holds the panels and this may be of metal or timber. Three methods are adopted in the construction of metal curtain walling based on (i) the patent glazing principle, (ii) metal window fabrication technique, (iii) box mullions and transoms, page 173. Patent glazing, with its carefully arranged drainage channels and weep holes, and the metal window technique of "factory cladding" were both used long before the term "curtain wall" was introduced. In the majority of proprietary systems of curtain walling, the framing is principally composed of vertical members fixed to and spanning between the floor slabs. Horizontal members—heads, sills and transoms, are fitted between these verticals. A method of fixing to the structure in which the principal members are horizontal, thus permitting the employment of "normal" weathered jointing technique, uses "stub" columns to support the framing. These form a projection on the inside of the building unless absorbed in the cavity between the outer panel and a back-up wall, should this be required by fire regulations (see page 173).

Strength and Stability. Curtain walling, like other claddings, carries only its own weight between supports, but it must be capable of resisting wind forces and of transmitting them to the structure. Wind loads increase in severity as the height above ground and the degree of exposure increase and the members of the framing and their fixings must be designed accordingly.

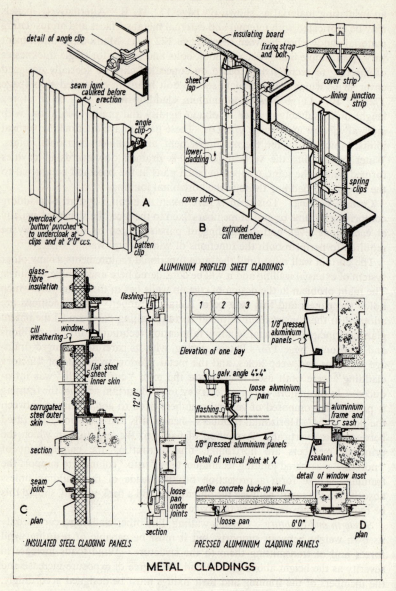

detail of angle clip

seam joint
caulked before
erection

angle
clip

overcloak
'button' punched
to undercloak at
clips and at 2'0"c.c.s.

batten
clip

A

insulating board

fixing strap
and bolt

cover strip

sheet
lap

lining junction
strip

lower
cladding

spring
clips

cover strip

extruded
cill member

B

ALUMINIUM PROFILED SHEET CLADDINGS

glass-
fibre
insulation

flashing

cill
weathering

window

flat steel
sheet
inner skin

corrugated
steel outer
skin

section

seam
joint

C   plan

INSULATED STEEL CLADDING PANELS

12'0"

loose
pan
under
joints

section

Elevation of one bay

1 2 3

galv. angle 4"×4"

loose aluminium
pan

flashing

1/8" pressed aluminium panels

Detail of vertical joint at X

perlite concrete back-up wall

X

loose pan   6'0"

D
plan

1/8" pressed
aluminium
panels

aluminium
frame and
sash

sealant

detail of window inset

PRESSED ALUMINIUM CLADDING PANELS

METAL CLADDINGS

This is shown in Table 3. The variations in the basic average wind pressures recommended for claddings, panels and fixings are described on page 116. Fixings should be of stainless steel or non-ferrous metal (see footnote on page 151 regarding the L.C.C. requirements) and so designed that two-thirds of the fixings employed are capable of resisting the wind forces on the walling. This provides a margin of safety in the event of the failure of one fixing and prevents progressive failure of a number of fixings.

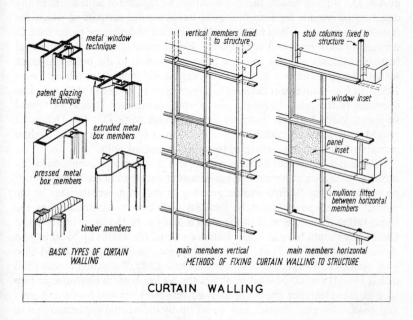

CURTAIN WALLING

Thermal movement of all parts will occur. In order to maintain dimensional stability this movement must be limited or be allowed to take place freely. Differential movement is likely to occur between (i) the framing and the structure, (ii) the vertical and horizontal members of the framing, (iii) the framing and the infilling panels, (iv) the inner and outer surfaces of composite panels.

Differential movement between framing and structure is due to the fact that the curtain walling is more exposed to varying external influences than the structure which it protects. The latter, in addition, may achieve a fairly constant temperature due to its higher thermal capacity and to internal heating and air conditioning. Movement between the framing and the structure and between the members of the framing system is provided for in the detailed design of joints and fixing devices. To prevent the accumulation of thermal movement[1] in mullions extending over several storeys, each section is jointed to the next in a manner which allows each to move without influencing the other (page 175, A,F,H,). Methods of attachment designed to allow for differential movement of the structure and framing are shown at A to D. Fixing devices must, in addition, be capable of adjustment in any direction to provide for inaccuracies in the structural surfaces to which the framing is attached. Bolt holes should be slotted and packing pieces used to provide for movement and adjustment. Plastic washers should be interposed between adjacent surfaces to allow adequate tension in the bolts combined with sufficient reduction in friction to permit differential movement (page 175, A to E). Movement between members must be allowed for by sufficient tolerance in the joints or by the use of split members. Details of typical spigotted joints between members are shown on page 175, F. Details of typical split member construction are shown at G, H. The latter method permits erection of the walling in large pre-assembled units.

Differential movement between panels and framing is accommodated by sufficient tolerance to permit free movement at the edges of the panels, which necessitates either flexible weatherproofing at the joints or drainage of the joints. Glazed panels must be detailed with care. Contraction of the frame rather than expansion of the glass is likely to be the cause of breakage. Clear glass should have an edge clearance of $\frac{1}{8}$ in. for widths up to 30 in. and $\frac{3}{16}$ in. for widths over 30 in. Opaque and heat absorbing glass should have $\frac{1}{4}$ in. clearance, irrespective of its dimensions. Only two setting blocks (lead or hardwood) should be used to obtain the correct bottom clearance and up to $\frac{1}{8}$ in. face clearance should be allowed between glass and frame and glass and bead. Internal stresses may be set up by differential expansion due to differences in temperature at the edges and centre of a glass panel (particularly in coloured, opaque or heat-resisting glass) caused by the shading of the edges by frame or beads. To prevent this it is recommended that the maximum edge cover should be not more than $\frac{3}{8}$ in. In this connection it should be noted that edges of the glass must be smooth and free from shelling, chipping or grazing (a particular problem with wired glass, which should not be used in coloured form and only in transparent or translucent forms if well ventilated at the rear to assist in cooling, see page 179, E). The temperature difference between the edges and centre of a glass panel will be less if the frame

---

[1] See Table 18.

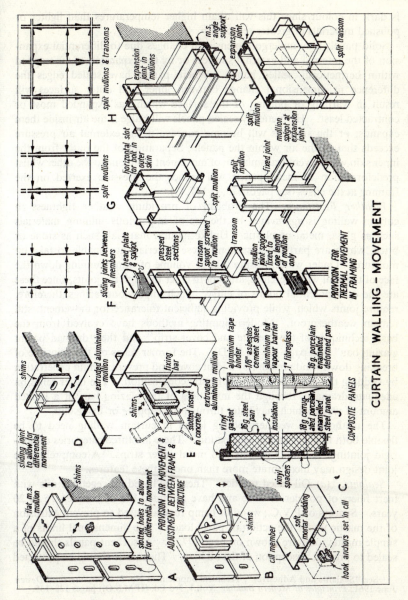

CURTAIN WALLING – MOVEMENT

is dark in colour since this will attain higher temperatures than lighter or polished materials of greater reflectivity.

Solid panels may undergo dimensional changes due to differential expansion of the internal and external surfaces or by the expansion of air trapped within hermetically sealed panels. Where panels have sealed edges the difference in dimensional change between inner and outer surfaces will result in warping or bulging of the surface which has expanded most or contracted least. Hermetically sealed panels will bulge if the air inside them expands, or the surfaces will become concave if the external air pressure exceeds that of the air within the panel. Separation of the outer from the inner skin will prevent transmission of movement from one to the other whilst predeformation of metal panels will reduce the pressure exerted on the framing at the edges (see pages 175, J; 177, G).

Weather Resistance. The problem of providing weather tightness in curtain walling is aggravated by the use of impervious infilling materials such as glass, metal or plastic. Unlike natural materials such as stone or brick, which are partially absorbent, these materials are unable to take up moisture. Under wind pressure a large volume of water running down the face of the wall will, therefore, attempt to enter through the joints, since these are the only potential points of entry. Such impervious facings, therefore, require joints which, while providing sufficient tolerance for movement, still remain weatherproof. Modern jointing methods have evolved from the basic techniques of the "rebate and cover strip" and the "drained patent glazing bar" (see page 177 A, B, D). The former relies on the principle of breaking down wind pressure by a joint cover and preventing rain penetration by bedding the panel in a suitable mastic composition. The latter relies on adequate drainage, through the interstices of the glazing bar, of a limited amount of water which may enter through the capping or fixing clip.

The methods of weatherproofing joints in curtain walling need to be flexible both in effect and in application. There are three categories of non-rigid jointing: sealants,[1] gaskets and metal cover strips. A comprehensive joint design may incorporate more than one of these features.

Sealants. (*a*) Oil-based mastics. These are based on vegetable oils with inert fillers of powder or fibre and have a limited life of between 15 to 20 years. Spacers of P.V.C., wood or hemp rope are used to prevent extrusion of the mastic under the action of panel loads. The dimensional limits of a simple mastic joint are shown on page 177, F. Absorbent panels should be sealed to prevent absorption of the oil base. The mastic should be protected

---

[1] See "Sealants and Adhesives", Technical Supplement No. 3, to *Architectural Design*, June 1961; *Principles of Modern Building*, Vol. 1, 3rd Ed. (H.M.S.O.) pages 128–135.

from dust, sunlight and air as far as possible (see this page B, C) and the joints should allow for replacement of the mastic without dismantling the cladding.

(b) Synthetic rubber. Sealants based on synthetic rubber compositions have good weathering properties, are chemically inert and are not affected

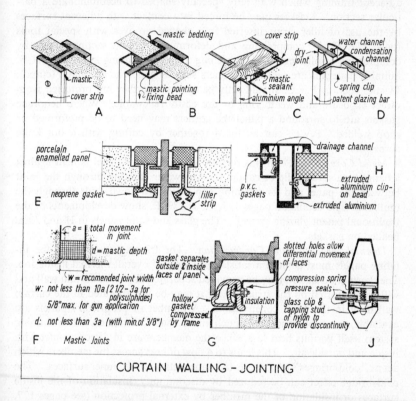

CURTAIN WALLING – JOINTING

by acids, alkalis, vegetable oils or ultra-violet light. They may be used between absorbent surfaces without staining, since they do not contain oil. Two types of synthetic rubber are in use: Thiokol and Butyl. Thiokol has excellent weathering and adhesive properties, but it is expensive and joints should be designed to use the minimum amount whilst ensuring at least $\frac{1}{8}$ in. of the sealant between the surfaces being joined. Butyl has not the adhesive properties of Thiokol but exhibits similar weathering characteristics. It is a one-part compound and is available in strip form for easy placing. Although Butyl has not the adhesion of Thiokol, it is nearly as cheap as oil-based mastic and has a superior bond.

Gaskets. These are generally specially shaped solid or hollow strips which grip the panel and establish a seal by their close fit between the panel and the adjacent framing which is usually specially shaped to accommodate a particular section. Gaskets may be forced into contact with adjacent surfaces by the use of filler strips inserted into shaped grooves with special tools (page 177, E), by compressing and deforming a hollow section (G) or by compressing a solid gasket by tightening a cover moulding against it, (H,J). Suitable materials are synthetic rubbers such as neoprene and butyl (cured). Plastics such as P.V.C. should only be used where they are protected from direct exposure and weathering or are easily renewable. Where neoprene gaskets are to surround a panel the corners may need to be preformed or shop welded. P.V.C. can be fused together by cutting with a hot knife across the mitre.

Metal Cover Strips. In this method of jointing the panel is held against a flange by a sprung clip or capping. Any water entering through the joint between the panel and its retaining clip is drained downwards through the mullion. The details on pages 177, H, J; 179, E, show developments of the traditional patent glazing system. The glass and solid panels in H and J are bedded on gaskets.

Thermal Insulation and Condensation. The framing system and the infilling panels must achieve a satisfactory level of overall thermal insulation. The thermal insulation may be provided separately from the curtain wall and will be supported on the structure, or it may be incorporated in the curtain wall itself in the panel construction. A number of proprietary panels are available, none of which are much more than 2 in. thick. The framing system itself permits heat loss, since the members are in direct contact with inside and outside air. This leads to a flow of heat across the members which act as "cold bridges" and results in condensation on the inner surfaces. The cold bridge effect can be reduced by discontinuity, insulation of the inside surfaces or insulation of the member by external protection (see pages 177, J; 179, A, B). Few proprietary systems of curtain walling in Great Britain incorporate any such refinements.

The problem of interstitial condensation needs particular attention in curtain walling systems which are infilled with well insulated panels having impervious external facing materials. In well heated buildings the internal relative humidity is generally higher than that of the external atmosphere. This results in a vapour pressure differential between inside and outside.

Since most insulating materials are porous, it is possible for moisture laden internal air to penetrate the interstices, where condensation will occur if the temperature gradient through the thickness of the panel is steep enough to fall below the dewpoint temperature of the air in the panel. In homogenous porous materials such as brick, the condensate will evaporate to the atmos-

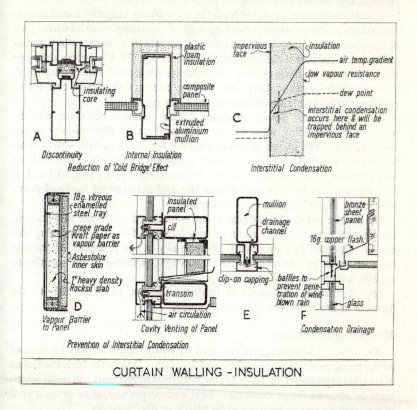

A Discontinuity

B Internal Insulation

plastic foam insulation
composite panel
extruded aluminium mullion
insulating core

Reduction of 'Cold Bridge' Effect

C
impervious face
insulation
air. temp. gradient
low vapour resistance
dew point
interstitial condensation occurs here & will be trapped behind an impervious face

Interstitial Condensation

D Vapour Barrier to Panel
18 g. vitreous enamelled steel tray
crepe grade Kraft paper as vapour barrier
Asbestolux inner skin
1" heavy density Rocksil slab

Cavity Venting of Panel
insulated panel
cill
transom
air circulation

Prevention of Interstitial Condensation

E
mullion
drainage channel
clip-on capping
baffles to prevent penetration of wind blown rain

F Condensation Drainage
bronze sheet panel
16 g. copper flash.
glass

CURTAIN WALLING – INSULATION

phere, but where an impervious external skin prevents evaporation the trapped moisture can do damage to the back of such materials as stove enamelled steel, or painted glass (see this page, C). Furthermore, insulating materials become less effective when their conductivity is increased by dampness. A vapour barrier placed on the room side of an insulated panel will help to reduce the passage of moisture-laden air from the room into the insulation. Such a vapour barrier may be formed of well lapped and sealed aluminium foil, bitumen-coated paper or two coats of aluminium primer finished with two coats of oil paint on plaster. It is, however, difficult to maintain a vapour seal at the joints between panel and framing elements, and some residual vapour will penetrate into the panel unless careful end sealing is achieved or hermetically sealed panels are used, pages 175, J; 179,D.

Where insulation is separated from the outer facing, either by use of double skin construction or where a back-up wall of insulating material forms part of the construction, condensation on the inner face of an impervious external panel can be reduced if the cavity is vented (see page 179, E). Proper drainage should be provided to carry away any condensation moisture which may form. In high buildings particularly, any drainage openings should be detailed to prevent rain being blown up into the cavity as shown at F.

Sound Insulation. Sound insulation against airborne noise can only be achieved by providing walls of adequate mass or by discontinuity in the construction. The panels generally available for use in curtain wall systems are usually very light and discontinuity is difficult to achieve. The back-up wall required by fire regulations can contribute mass to a panel wall and, if discontinuity can be achieved between this and the external facing element, reasonable sound reduction can be expected.

The problem of structure-borne sound is increased by the use of a framing system which has elements common to a number of rooms. In theory this can be alleviated by introducing discontinuity at the junctions of framing members and by cushioning the anchorages, although few proprietary systems incorporate such devices.

Fire Resistance. Reference is made in Chapter 10, page 503, to the problem of fire resistance in curtain walling.

Materials of Construction

Aluminium. Aluminium is favoured by many manufacturers because of its lightness, moderate cost and ease of forming. Due to the high coefficient of thermal expansion (see Table 18) large thermal movements will occur which must be allowed for in detailing. Steel anchorages should be given a coat of protective paint or be isolated by plastic or fibre washers.

Steel. Mild steel, either hot rolled or cold formed, is used for framing elements and in sheet form for panels. Hollow sections are usually built up. Despite the disadvantages of potential corrosion, mild steel is cheap and strong, and is widely used for curtain walling construction.

Stainless Steel. Unlike carbon steel, stainless steel is corrosion resistant, although having a higher coefficient of expansion. The material is expensive and narrow strips are cheaper per square foot than wider and squarer sheets, so that it is cheaper to build up facings to panels from a number of interlocking strips. The material may be used for framing, or more usually for pressed cover sections to aluminium or mild steel cores (see also page 164).

Bronze. Bronze is expensive but has excellent weathering qualities (page 164). It is used for panels and pressed cover sections to steel cores.

Timber. Where building regulations permit, timber may be used for framing and panelling. The material is cheap and has the advantages of being non-corrosive, easily shaped and of low thermal transmittance. Careful detailing is necessary to allow for moisture movement by including sufficient tolerances between panels and framing. Flexibility is achieved by loose tongueing and interlocking sections (page 182, C).

Glass. If correctly used this is an excellent panel material since it is comparatively cheap, weather resistant and corrosion resistant. Coloured wired glass should not be used since it is susceptible to thermal breakage. Transparent or translucent glass placed in front of a coloured surface with a cavity between should be removable to permit dust and condensation staining to be cleaned off the rear surface.

Asbestos. Asbestos silica, an asbestos composite is frequently used as an insulating core in composite panel construction. It may be stove enamelled. Asbestos cement has low thermal movement, is non-combustible and is comparatively light and it is cheap. It has, however, a high moisture movement and gets more brittle with age. Specially densified sheets are stronger and may be integrally coloured and polished. A wide range of colours is obtained by applying coloured skins during manufacture, some of which are suitable for external use. Chlorinated rubber paints and silicone paints reduce water absorption and repel surface water.

Plastics. As described on page 164, certain groups of plastics are suitable for external use. Plastic infill panels may be cellular or the material may be used as an external or internal lining bonded to other materials in composite panel construction.[1]

INFILLING PANELS

Most materials used in the forms of cladding described in the previous section may be employed in the construction of infilling panels.

The technical problems of weather exclusion, thermal and sound insulation,

---

[1] For a full discussion of all aspects of curtain wall design see *Building Research Station Digests* Nos. 98, 99, "Light Claddings"; "The Glass Curtain Wall", by Thomas A. Markus in *The Architect's Journal*, in a number of articles commencing November 7 1957, and terminating January 23, 1958; "Light Cladding" by R. Michael Rostron in the same journal in a series commencing February 25, 1960, and terminating October 13, 1960, from which much information in this section has been drawn.

7

condensation and fire resistance associated with infilling panels are identical
with those encountered in curtain walling.   Brick and block infilling panels
are considered under "Panel Walls".   Lightweight infilling panels present
the same problems of edge jointing as heavy panels but are even more liable
to thermal or moisture movement and need careful design at the junctions
with the structure, particularly at head and jambs.

Metal-framed Infilling Panels.   Complete storey height infillings, sometimes
referred to as "window walls", are constructed in a similar manner to curtain

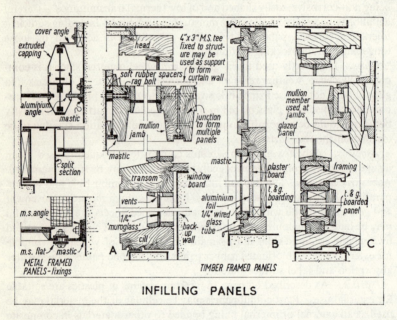

INFILLING   PANELS

walling systems, the vertical framing elements being so fixed at the base and
head as to allow for thermal movement (page 175 F).   Methods of providing
suitable fixings at jambs to allow for movement are illustrated on this page.
Spandrel height panels may be screwed or clipped to metal angle framing
fixed to the floor slabs or between columns.

Concrete Infilling Panels.   This term is usually applied to the forms of
horizontal cladding which span between columns and which are described on
page 169.

Timber-framed Infilling Panels.   It has been common practice for many
years to infill between brick walls with timber-framed walling based on

traditional stud walling technique, the timber being cut and assembled on site.

Modern trends towards prefabrication have brought about the introduction of pre-assembled frames which can be erected as units and finished on site or are already finished before erection. It is common practice to construct the panel with a frame of rebated sections, similar to a large timber window frame with all necessary mullions and transomes, and to infill this with glazing, openable sashes and fixed panels in the manner of curtain wall technique. The junctions of head, sill and jamb with the structure are usually designed to allow sufficient erection tolerances. Typical details of this type of infilling panel are shown on page 182, A, B.

Proprietary curtain wall systems provide a further method of timber infill panel walling. These consist of various sections forming the main frame into which are fitted various types of panels. A typical example is shown on page 182, C.

In all methods of installing panels or frames (including window frames between structural elements) it is an advantage to form a rebate to reduce the risk of wind blown rain entering the joint directly. This may be provided by shaping the basic structural material such as brick or concrete, or by forming the rebate with a facing element as shown on page 136.

WEATHER RESISTANCE

The external walls of a building, whether of loadbearing or panel construction, are required to provide adequate resistance to rain and wind penetration. The actual degree of resistance required in any particular wall will depend largely upon its height and upon the locality and exposure.

Wind force and rainfall vary considerably throughout the British Isles so that a form of construction adequate for one locality may not be satisfactory in another. Within any locality there can also be variations of exposure. For example, a site near the coast is likely to present greater problems of rain exclusion than one a mile or two inland. Such factors must be borne in mind. Reference to variations in wind pressure for variations of locality and height has already been made in the section on "Loading" earlier in this chapter. Variations in rainfall can be seen from maps of average rainfall over the British Isles.[1]

Generally speaking the problem of wind penetration rarely presents difficulties. Tests by the Building Research Station on solid and cavity walls have shown that, providing these are plastered internally, there is a

[1] See *Principles of Modern Building*, Vol. 1, 3rd Ed. (H.M.S.O.), page 32.

negligible penetration of wind.   The possibility of wind penetration might arise with some types of modern walling of dry construction consisting of external cladding or sheathing and dry internal linings on some form of frame.   Here, some barrier may be required similar to the layer of building paper or bituminous felt normally placed under timber weatherboarding on a timber-framed wall.   Wind, of course, has considerable influence on rain penetration, forcing the water through pores and cracks which otherwise it might not penetrate.   This is an important fact to be considered in the design of the types of walling systems mentioned above, especially curtain walling.   Reference has already been made to this on page 180.

Rain penetration through solid walls can be resisted in two ways.   Either by the absorption or by the shedding of the water falling on the surface of the wall.   In the first case the water will be absorbed by the walling material and held, as in a sponge, until dry weather conditions permit it to evaporate.   In the second case the use of an impermeable walling material, or an impermeable facing, will force the water to run down the wall face without entering the wall thickness.   Both methods present difficulties.   The alternative to either is to provide an outer surface which is isolated from the inner surface by a continuous gap or cavity.   The outer surface or skin may be non-loadbearing in the form of traditional tile or slate hanging or as large suspended cladding slabs, or it may be loadbearing or self-supporting as in the case of the cavity wall.

Solid Masonry Walls

If water is to be prevented from getting to the inside of a wall by means of absorption it is essential that the mortar and the walling units should have similar absorptive qualities.   Strong dense mortars should be avoided in order to ensure sufficient porosity in the joint and to reduce shrinkage so that cracking between mortar and units is kept to a minimum.   Penetration more often occurs through cracks between the mortar and units than through the units themselves.   The use of insufficiently cured concrete blocks increases the risk of cracks at the joints since drying shrinkage will continue after the blocks have been built into the wall.   Complete curing of such blocks before use is essential.   The units should have an absorption similar to that of a normal facing brick.

Water will enter the pores of blocks and mortar and be held in the body of the wall.   Success by this method, therefore, presupposes adequate absorptive capacity of the wall and the absence of prolonged and very heavy rainfall.   In such circumstances a 9 in. wall is sufficient in very sheltered positions, but for all normal exposures at least $13\frac{1}{2}$ in. thickness is required.   On exposed sites in districts of heavy, prolonged rainfall excessively thick walls would be required. Table 15 indicates the suitability of brick walls under different conditions of exposure.[1] The thick, heavy wall essential in most cases for the success of this method is one of the reasons which has brought about the more general use of cavity wall construction.

The difficulties in producing a barrier to water penetration by means of an impermeable wall of small bonded units are considerable and are centred round the joints. Impervious units, such as engineering bricks, are usually smooth-faced and do not assist adhesion between block and mortar. The dense mortars required to provide impermeability in the joints undergo a large initial shrinkage. There is, therefore, a marked tendency for cracks to

---

Table 15. Suitability of masonry walls for various exposures

R denotes recommended.   N denotes not recommended.

Construction	Exposure		
	Sheltered	Moderate	Severe
Unrendered 4½ in. wall	N	N	N
Unrendered 9 in. solid wall	R	N	N
Unrendered 13½ in. solid wall	R	R	N
Rendered solid walls	R	R	N
Walls covered externally with slate-hanging or tile-hanging	R	R	R
Hollow walls	R	R	R

---

develop at the joints and for rain to penetrate these joints by capillary attraction. Since rain will not be absorbed by the impervious walling units it will stream down the face of the wall and rapidly enter any such cracks. Apart from the danger of complete penetration of water through cracks to the inner face of the wall there is the danger of water remaining in the centre of the wall, because in fine weather it is unable easily to evaporate through the dense face. Ultimately it will penetrate to the inner face. In frosty weather this trapped water may freeze and cause disintegration of the wall. In order to minimize these dangers a high standard of workmanship is essential to ensure that all joints are flushed up solid. In order to reduce shrinkage, workability in the mortar should be obtained by the use of a care-

[1] From Code of Practice 121.101 (1951), "Brickwork". A similar Table in C.P. 121.202 (1951), "Masonry-Rubble Walls", relates to rubble walls. (Reference to the latter Code should be made for all aspects of the constructional design of rubble walls.)

fully graded sand or by the addition of a small proportion of lime or other plasticizer. This is preferable to the use of a high proportion of cement. The mix should be no wetter than that required to permit the joints to be thoroughly filled and consolidated.[1]

When the ends of cross walls are exposed on elevation some positive weatherproofing is required, particularly when the infilling wall units are of an impervious nature. In such cases the area of wall face exposed is small in relation to the amount of water likely to fall on it, so that the normal process of absorption and subsequent evaporation is limited. Painting of the reveals or the use of impervious facing bricks alone at the wall ends will not necessarily prevent water penetration. This is because the joints will still be exposed and water may pass through cracks by capillary attraction. A number of alternative methods of dealing with the problem are shown on page 136. On the same page are shown methods of dealing with cross walls which terminate in returned ends for reason of stability, or which may be completely covered by the outer skin of a cavity panel wall.

In addition to the possibility of water penetration at the ends of cross walls that of heat loss also arises. This is particularly so in the case of dense concrete walls. It can cause condensation on the inner wall faces near the external walls and is avoided by the use of thermal insulation. Depending upon the relationship of the infilling panels and the wall ends, the insulation may be applied to the inner faces or to the external face of the cross wall as shown on page 136.

Monolithic Concrete Walls

A well graded and carefully mixed and placed cement concrete wall can be impervious to water. Small areas of such walls can be quite waterproof, but with larger areas problems of cracking arise due to shrinkage and thermal movements and to possible settlement. The dense monolithic nature of the wall tends to produce a few large cracks, possibly penetrating its full thickness, rather than many fine ones. These, together with the considerable volume of water streaming down the impermeable face of the wall, can result in serious water penetration. Precautions against such cracking are taken by controlling shrinkage and moisture movement by steel reinforcement, by allowing for thermal movement by means of expansion joints and by the careful detailing and execution of construction joints.

Walls constructed with no-fines concrete do not, by their nature, resist water penetration by shedding the water off the surface in the manner of

---

[1] See *Principles of Modern Building*, Vol. I, 3rd Ed. (H.M.S.O.), Table 11.4, for suitable mixes for normal brick- and blockwork.

dense concrete walls. The omission of the fine stuff from the aggregate results in the formation of relatively large spaces round the pieces of aggregate. Thus although water enters the surface of the wall it is unable to pass through it by capillary attraction. It tends, as in traditional "dry" walling in various parts of the country, to fall within the wall and run out at a lower level. Damp-proof courses must, therefore, be placed over all lintels to openings, except immediately under an eaves, and be laid to conduct moisture to the outer face as in the case of cavity walls. These, together with the damp-proof course at ground level, should be turned up vertically at least 3 in. on the inside face of the wall.

Such walls must be finished externally with a rendering in order to prevent water being forced through by wind pressure. The rendering must be of a suitable porous type with, preferably, a rough surface. No-fines concrete walls 8 to 9 in. thick, rendered and satisfactorily detailed at openings, are quite resistant to moisture penetration.

Renderings, used as a means of reducing water penetration through any type of solid wall, can act either as an impervious or as an absorbent skin. Practical difficulties in attaining a surface free of cracks have brought about the general use of absorbent types of renderings rather than those of an impermeable nature. This matter is discussed in *Advanced Building Construction (Components, Services and Finishes)*. Adequate protection in the form of weatherings and damp-proof courses is essential (see page 167).

CAVITY WALLS

Cavity construction overcomes the problems inherent in both absorbent and impermeable solid wall construction. Provided that all details are well designed, particularly around openings, and the work carefully executed, it has proved to be the most reliable method of avoiding moisture penetration through walls.

The successful functioning of a cavity wall depends on the cavity being continuous, without bridging of any kind capable of transferring moisture to the inner leaf. There should be no projections on the inside of the outer leaf extending into the cavity as these can collect mortar droppings, and water trickling down the inside face may drop from one projection to another and splash across to the inner leaf. For this reason the use of brick bonds necessitating snap headers are undesirable.

Horizontal damp-proof courses must be provided over all openings and vertical damp-proof courses at all points of contact between inner and outer leaves. All such points of contact should be minimized. Where possible it is preferable to so detail around openings that the cavity is not closed by an

external sill nor at the jambs by returning one leaf on to the other. The
risk of mortar droppings forming a bridge at the base of the cavity can be
minimized by extending the cavity several courses below the horizontal
damp-proof course, and by bedding a number of bricks in sand at the quoins
to permit raking of the cavity on completion of the wall. After this the
bricks are finally bedded in mortar.

Methods of damp-proofing round openings and details of the construction
of cavity walls are given in *Elementary Building Construction*.

In addition to protection against lateral penetration of rain a wall must
be protected at its base against ground moisture. This can enter and rise
by capillary attraction. Protection is also necessary in the case of a basement
wall against subsoil water entering under pressure. The function and the
provision of horizontal and vertical damp-proof courses are discussed in
Elementary Building Construction. Protection against subsoil water by
means of damp-proof tanking is discussed later.

RISING DAMP IN EXISTING WALLS

The commonest cause of rising damp in existing walls is the absence of a
damp-proof course. In some cases this can be cured by forming a narrow
external trench or dry area against the base of the wall. This will permit
the damp to evaporate outwards before it rises to a level where it can penetrate to the inside of the building. When the wall is thick, evaporation from
the inside of the wall may be assisted by inserting porous high capillary tubes
along the base of the wall. These are tubes about 2 in. diameter made of
high-capillary earthenware inserted in holes formed in the wall and sloping
upwards slightly from the outside face. They should penetrate about two-
thirds the thickness of the wall and must be bedded in a weak mortar in
order to provide sufficient capillarity. This is used very dry to minimize
shrinkage and breaking away from the surrounding wall. The spacing of
the tubes depends upon the degree of dampness in the wall but will usually
be in the region of 18 to 36 in. apart. The functioning of the system depends
on the fact that evaporation of the moisture through the tube causes a fall in
temperature and an increase in weight of the air in the tube. This damp
air slips out from the bottom of the tube and is replaced by fresh air: thus a
continuous circulation of air is set up and evaporation is continuous. This
method can also be used without cutting a trench as an alternative to
inserting a normal damp-proof course above ground line.[1]

The traditional method of inserting a damp-proof course in an existing

---

[1] See *Stones of Britain*, by B. C. G. Shore, F.A.M.S., L.R.I.B.A. (Leonard Hill Ltd.),
pages 235–237.

wall is to cut out at intervals short sections of the wall at the appropriate level on the lines of normal underpinning work and rebuild them to incorporate a damp-proof course of engineering bricks or other suitable material. This is a lengthy and expensive operation, and in recent years a method has been developed which involves sawing either by hand or power-driven saw a narrow slot in a mortar bed joint into which is driven a metal damp-proof membrane. By this method the work can be carried out much faster and at less than half the cost of the traditional method. It is, however, only suitable for walls in which the courses are reasonably straight and in which the walling is sound. Unsound brickwork and loose rubble in the core of thick stone walls will fall and block the slot.[1]

Silicone water-repellent has been used successfully to form a water barrier at the base of a wall. Holes penetrating well into the thickness of the wall are drilled about 2 in. apart in a mortar joint and a silicone-rubber latex solution is introduced through them until the full thickness of the wall is saturated and a damp-proof barrier formed. This method is particularly suitable for walls the nature of which would make difficult the insertion of a damp-proof course.

An electrical method of drying out damp walls and maintaining them in a dry state is based on the phenomenon of electro-osmosis. The principle of this is that if an electric current is passed between two electrodes buried in a capillary material any free water in the material will flow towards the cathode or negative electrode. In practice, a number of positive electrodes, consisting of spirals of copper wire, are embedded in holes drilled to a depth of about two-thirds of the wall thickness. These are connected by a copper wire embedded in a deep chase in the wall. Negative electrodes connected by insulated cable are buried in the soil at or below foundation level. The leads connecting the wall and soil electrodes are connected to accessible junction boxes so that an electric current can be applied if required. This is seldom necessary because by short circuiting the electrodes sufficient current to operate the system is obtained due to the potential difference naturally existing between a damp wall and the soil on which it rests and from which derives its dampness.[2] One particular advantage of the system is that it is not necessary to fix the wall electrodes below the floor because the wall below the electrodes will be dry down to the soil electrodes at the foundation level.

Waterproof renderings, or corrugated bituminized fibre-based lathing for

---

[1] See *Building Research Station Digest* No. 107, for a full description of this method. See also Digest No. 41, for a general discussion on "The Treatment of Damp Walls".
[2] A patented system, the Ernst Damp-Proofing System, based on electro-osmosis, is installed in Great Britain by Messrs. Silicaseal Ltd. of Newcastle upon Tyne.

plaster, may be applied to the internal face of damp walls to protect finishes. These methods will not, however, dry out the wall.

WATERPROOFING OF BASEMENTS

When walls and floor form a basement below ground level, the penetration of moisture through the sides of the wall as well as through the floor is commonly prevented by the application of an unbroken membrane or coating of suitable impermeable material over the whole of the walls and floor. When the basement is below the level of subsoil water, the latter will be forced through the walls and floor under pressure and special precautions must be taken, either by completely enclosing the basement in a waterproof "tank" of impermeable material or by the use of high-grade dense concrete, with or without an integral waterproofer, for walls and floor. Prestressed concrete can also be used for this purpose.

WATERPROOF TANKING

This is most commonly carried out in asphalt although alternatives to this are asphaltic bitumen on a fabric base applied in three layers with all joints lapped and sealed, or tough plastic sheeting similarly sealed at all joints. This has the advantages of flexibility and rapid installation. Asphalt in tanking work is laid in three coats to a total thickness of not less than $1\frac{1}{8}$ in. on horizontal surfaces and not less than $\frac{3}{4}$ in. on vertical faces. All internal angles are reinforced by means of a fillet 2 in. on the face, formed in two coats. All joints in the coats must be broken by at least 6 in. in horizontal work and 3 in. in vertical work. The asphalt membrane may be placed either on the outside or the inside face of the structure. When placed on the inside it may be necessary to provide "loading" walls and floor of sufficient strength to prevent the asphalt being forced off the structure by the pressure of water.

External Tanking. The advantages of placing the asphalt on the outside face as shown on pages 191, 199 are: (i) the structure itself provides the necessary resistance against the pressure of water on the asphalt; (ii) the asphalt keeps the water out of the structure. Faults due to poor workmanship or to settlement are, however, difficult to locate and remedy, because the point at which the water enters the internal face may be a considerable distance away from the fault in the asphalt. In spite of this the advantages of the external membrane are such that it is usual to adopt this method in all new buildings.

The asphalt to the floor is laid on a 3 to 4 in. blinding layer of concrete and is usually protected immediately by a 2 in. fine concrete screed. The concrete floor slab which is then laid must either be thick and heavy enough to resist the upward pressure of any subsoil water or be suitably reinforced to fulfil the same function. The vertical asphalt to the walls should be protected externally by a protective skin. This is usually $4\frac{1}{2}$ in. of brickwork, but the requirements of the job may necessitate the use of thin *in situ* reinforced concrete or precast concrete poling boards (see page 103). The asphalt may be applied either direct to the retaining wall or to the protective skin, according to the circumstances of the job. When working space is

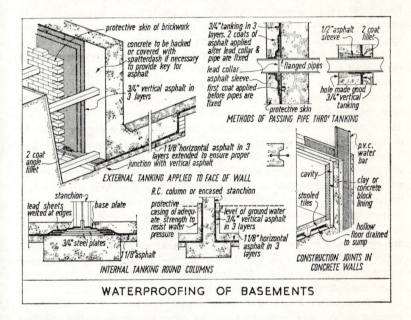

protective skin of brickwork
concrete to be hacked or covered with spatterdash if necessary to provide key for asphalt
3/4" vertical asphalt in 3 layers

3/4" tanking in 3 layers. 2 coats of asphalt applied after lead collar & pipe are fixed
lead collar
asphalt sleeve
first coat applied before pipes are fixed
protective skin
flanged pipes

1/2" asphalt sleeve
2 coat fillet
hole made good
3/4" vertical tanking

METHODS OF PASSING PIPE THRO' TANKING

2 coat angle fillet
11/8" horizontal asphalt in 3 layers extended to ensure proper junction with vertical asphalt

EXTERNAL TANKING APPLIED TO FACE OF WALL

R.C. column or encased stanchion

stanchion
lead sheets welted at edges
base plate
3/4" steel plates
1/8" asphalt

INTERNAL TANKING ROUND COLUMNS

protective casing of adequate strength to resist water pressure
level of ground water
3/4" vertical asphalt in 3 layers
11/8" horizontal asphalt in 3 layers

p.v.c. water bar
cavity
clay or concrete block lining
stooled tiles
hollow floor drained to sump

CONSTRUCTION JOINTS IN CONCRETE WALLS

WATERPROOFING OF BASEMENTS

available behind the wall the wall is first built and the asphalt then applied direct to the face of the wall which, if of brickwork, should have the joints raked out to a depth of half-an-inch to form a key. If of concrete, it should be treated in some way to give a rough surface for the same purpose, (see this page). Where possible the excavation on the outside of the wall should be sloped back to avoid the use of timbering, but if strutting is essential this must be arranged so that the position of the struts can be changed to permit the asphalt to be applied at the strut points. The protective skin would most suitably be of $4\frac{1}{2}$ in. brickwork built up as the asphalting is carried out, so that the struts may be repositioned to bear on the brick skin and thus avoid possible damage to the asphalt.   When no space at the back of the wall is available, for example in underpinning work or on a confined site where the basement extends to the boundary of the site, the asphalt is applied to the protective skin.   In these circumstances temporary support to the soil face behind the protective skin must be maintained until the new retaining wall has been constructed, and the asphalt work must be carried out in short lifts as each section of the wall rises (see page 532).   In the case of a reinforced concrete wall which is cast direct against the asphalt, care must be taken that the asphalt is not damaged or pierced by reinforcing bars or tamping rods.   In some circumstances when the basement wall is of concrete, even when working space is available behind the wall, it may be cheaper to build up the brick skin as a thin, self-supporting wall, stiffened by piers at intervals, to which the asphalt can be applied.   The concrete wall can then be cast between the asphalted skin and inside formwork.   The pits for column foundations and retaining wall bases are covered with a blinding layer of concrete and the sides lined with $4\frac{1}{2}$ in. brickwork built up off the edge of the blinding layer. The whole is then tanked with asphalt, the upper edges being joined to the asphalt layer in the floor (see page 199).

Internal Tanking.   Application of the asphalt to the inside face of the structure is largely confined to existing buildings where it would normally be required as a damp-proofing measure rather than as a tanking against water under pressure.   When used as tanking, apart from the disadvantages of not protecting the structure from water and of requiring loading walls and floor to protect and hold the asphalt in position against the pressure of water, there are problems involved in waterproofing round columns.   If the internal tanking is carried over the top of the column foundation slab, the column will pierce the asphalt skin .   It is thus necessary to form a "pipe" of asphalt round the column rising from the horizontal layer to some distance above the highest surface level of the subsoil water, page 191.   A reinforced concrete casing will then be required round the sleeve to prevent it being forced off the column face.   As in the case of the walls and floor, the column or steel stanchion is permanently, or at least periodically saturated.   An alternative method which may be used for steel stanchions in a new building is to sandwich two or three lead sheets between steel base plates, large enough to project at least 9 in. beyond the plates all round.   The edges of the lead sheets are welted all the way round and the exposed faces painted with bitumen, after which the asphalt is worked between them up to the edges of the base plates and to the base of the stanchion.   This is illustrated on page 191 and can make a reasonably watertight junction provided the water pressure is not excessive. However, neither of these methods is really satisfactory and in most cases where practicable it is better to drop the asphalt skin completely under the foundation slab. This necessitates lining and tanking the pits in exactly the same way as described above.

Although asphalt is not likely to be over-stressed under a foundation slab, the pressure on the asphalt due to heavy loads over confined areas should be considered and be limited to six to eight tons per square foot.[1]

Service pipes and drainpipes must often pass through asphalt tanking and some provision must be made to prevent water entering at these points. The usual method when the water pressure is not high is to form an asphalt sleeve round the pipe about 12 in. long and extending an equal distance on both sides of the line of the asphalt tanking. This sleeve is applied before passing the pipe through the wall after it has been thoroughly cleaned, scored and painted with a coat of bitumen. The asphalt tanking is then worked up to the sleeve and the joint is reinforced with a fillet. When the water pressure is high, and is likely to force water between the sleeve and the surface of the pipe, a metal collar is incorporated at the junction of the pipe and the tanking to form a seal. The collar may be formed by an $\frac{1}{8}$ to $\frac{1}{4}$ in. plate welded on the pipe or by a lead sheet sandwiched between a flanged pipe joint. The collar should project a minimum distance of 6 in. all round the pipe and both faces should be painted with bitumen before the asphalt is worked round it, (see page 191). Waterproofing round pavement lights is shown on page 199.

WATERPROOF STRUCTURE

High-grade thoroughly consolidated concrete can be highly impervious to moisture, but in practice it is not easy to obtain an impervious structure owing to the difficulty of working round strutting and forming proper construction joints, which are usually weak points. A number of precautions are generally taken to overcome this weakness. P.V.C. or copper water-bars may be incorporated at the joints (see page 191). When long lengths are being cast it is preferable to leave a gap of 18 to 24 in. between adjacent sections and to fill these later after the edge faces have been prepared in the manner described on pp. 103–4. This minimizes the extent of shrinkage. Vibration should be used in order to obtain maximum density of concrete and an integral waterproofer may be incorporated with the mix, although it is inadvisable to rely on this in the absence of first quality concrete.[2] When

---

[1] Natural Rock Asphalt and asphalt complying with B.S. 1097 with a 50/50 mixture of Trinidad Epure and Residual Bitumen have been tested satisfactorily to 12 tons per square foot.

[2] See Ministry of Works Advisory Leaflet, No. 51, "Watertight Basements, Part 1".

dependence is on the impermeability of the concrete rather than on water-proof tanking, the possibility of damage and inconvenience through leakage may be overcome by constructing a hollow floor consisting of a concrete topping over special half-round or stooled flat tiles, and building up a lining of clay or concrete blocks 2 to 3 in. thick and 2 in. in front of the face of the basement walls (page 191).   Should any leaks occur the water will drain into the hollow floor from which it will run into a sump constructed for the purpose and fitted with a float controlled electric pump which will come into operation when the sump fills.   In some circumstances, this method, even allowing for the cost of periodic pumping, can be cheaper than full waterproof tanking.

The prestressing of concrete, because it maintains the whole of the concrete in compression, prevents cracks occurring under load and also has the effect of closing up shrinkage cracks at working joints.   Since high-quality concrete must be used for prestressed concrete work and prestressing overcomes the weakness at construction joints, it is possible to obtain a waterproof construction with greater certainty than with ordinary reinforced concrete. However, prestressed concrete is not likely to be used solely on this account but where for structural reasons it appears appropriate, advantage can be taken of its impermeable qualities.

RETAINING WALLS

The function of a retaining wall is to resist the lateral thrust of a mass of earth on one side and sometimes the pressure of subsoil water.   In many cases the wall may also be required to support vertical loads from a building above.

STABILITY

A retaining wall must be designed so that (i) it does not overturn and does not slide, (ii) the materials of which it is constructed are not overstressed, (iii) the soil on which it rests is not overstressed and circular slip is avoided on clay soil.

The pressure on the back of the wall is called "active" pressure and tends to overturn the wall and push it forward.   The force exerted by the earth on the front of the wall in resisting movement of the wall under the active pressure is called the "passive" earth resistance (page 195).   The actual thrust of retained earth on a wall and its direction and point of application can only be determined approximately.   There are several theories for assessing the active pressure and the passive resistance which are explained in detail in most textbooks on the theory of structures.   Active water pressure is avoided by the provision of a vertical rubble drainage layer, or drainage counterforts, discharging through weep holes in the wall or, if the wall encloses a basement, through lateral drainpipes at the back of the wall as shown on this page, which conduct the moisture to a main drain. In the case of clay soils, this will prevent saturation leading to increased pressure due to the reduction in the shear strength of the soil arising from the increase in moisture content. An impermeable covering to the retained soil is also useful for this purpose.

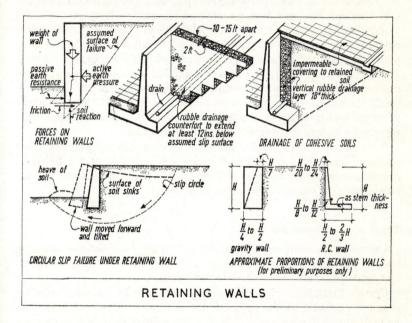

RETAINING WALLS

The tendency of the wall to slide is resisted by friction on the underside of the base and by the passive earth resistance at the front of the wall. When the frictional resistance is insufficient, the passive earth resistance must be used to increase the total resistance to sliding to the required amount. This may necessitate the provision of vertical ribs on the base of the wall to increase the passive resistance (see page 197).

Overturning will occur (i) if the line of the resultant pressure falls outside the base of the wall, or (ii) if the eccentricity of the resultant is such that the maximum pressure at the toe is great enough to cause settlement leading to rotation of the wall. As the resultant will normally pass through the base at some eccentricity and, in fact, in reinforced concrete retaining walls will usually fall beyond the middle third of the base, a triangular distribution of pressure on the soil must be assumed as in the case of normal eccentrically loaded walls (see page 195).

In addition to possible movement due to sliding and overturning, when on clay soil the wall may also move because of the tendency of a mass of clay to slip and carry the wall with it. This movement, which can occur under any foundation on clay, is described in Chapter 3 and occurs on a circular arc. Because clay soils have no angle of repose, any bank of clay has a tendency to slip in this manner. The safe angle of slope is a function of the height and it is possible for the height of a retained mass of clay soil to be such that the arc of circular slip is situated well below the base of the wall. The strength and stability of a retaining wall has no bearing upon such soil movement beneath it and no variations in the detailed design of the wall would affect its overall stability in this respect (see page 195). When this type of failure appears likely, sheet piles may be used, taken to a depth below the slip circle sufficient to prevent movement taking place.

In basement retaining walls, sliding or rotation can be overcome when necessary by making the active pressures on each side of the basement counteract each other through the floors. The weight of the structure over often assists the weight of the wall in resisting overturning.

Types of Retaining Wall

There are two main types of retaining wall (i) the gravity or mass retaining wall, constructed of brickwork, masonry or mass concrete, (ii) cantilever or L-shaped walls constructed of reinforced concrete.

Gravity Retaining Walls. In building work gravity retaining walls are commonly used for heights up to 6 ft and depend on mass for their strength and stability. They are designed so that the width is such that the resultant of lateral earth pressure and the weight of the wall falls in such a position that the maximum compressive stress at the toe does not exceed the maximum safe bearing capacity of the soil, nor the permissible bearing stress of the material of which the wall is constructed. An endeavour is usually made to keep the resultant within the middle third of the base so that no tensile stresses are set up at the back of the wall at its bearing on the soil or in any of the lower joints. This would result in high compressive stresses at the front of the wall. A width of base between one-quarter and one-half of the height is usually satisfactory. For high walls the rectangular section is uneconomic in design, since the material at the front of the wall operates against the resultant passing within the middle third and also adds to the load imposed on the soil.   The front face, therefore, may usefully be sloped back, page 195.[1]

Cantilever Retaining Walls.   In the cantilever retaining wall this variation in shape is carried further so that full benefit may be derived from the advantages which arise in doing so.   This is particularly necessary in high retaining walls where the size of a gravity wall would be excessive.   As the resultant of the lateral pressure and weight of wall falls well outside the thickness of the wall, or vertical stem, high tensile stresses are induced and it is necessary to use reinforced concrete so that the stem can act as a vertical cantilever.   These walls are more economical in the use of materials, occupy less space and weigh less than gravity walls.

Different forms of reinforced concrete walls are illustrated on this page. That shown in (*a*) is most commonly used in building structures where it is not possible to excavate behind the stem of the wall.   When some excavation

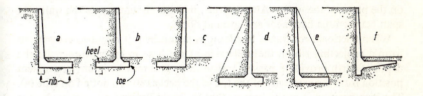

TYPICAL REINFORCED CONCRETE RETAINING WALLS

can be carried out behind the wall, advantage should be taken of this to form a base projecting partly in front and partly behind the stem as shown in (b) so that the weight of the soil on the heel, or back portion of the base, can assist in counterbalancing the overturning tendency.   The most economical arrangement is usually that in which the length of the heel is approximately twice that of the toe.   The form shown in (c) has the whole of the base under the retained soil which, because of the increased stability given by the weight of the retained soil, may be shorter than in type (a).   The inherent economy of types (b) and (c) may, however, be counterbalanced by the cost of excavation when the soil must be removed in order to construct the base slab, and type (c) may not be a suitable form when the stem carries superimposed loads from a structure above, since these would be concentrated on the toe. When the height of the wall is over 25 ft, and the thickness of the wall might

---

[1] It should be noted that L.C.C. By-law 5.14 limits the difference in height of the ground levels on either side of a normal wall to four times the thickness of the wall at the higher level unless the wall is adequately buttressed.

be excessive, it is usually cheaper to use a counterfort retaining wall as shown in (d) and (e), in which vertical ribs called "counterforts" act as vertical cantilevers. Type (e) with the counterforts at the front of the stem is also called a "buttressed retaining wall". The pressure of the soil on the wall is transferred to the counterforts by the wall slab which spans horizontally between them. Similarly, the base slab is designed to span between the counterforts. In very tall counterfort walls it is cheaper to use horizontal secondary beams spanning between the counterforts with the slab spanning vertically between them. If the spacing of these beams is varied down the height of the wall, the bending moments in each span of the slab can be kept the same so that the same thickness of slab can be maintained throughout the full height of the wall. In the case of deep basements formed as cellular rafts, the cross walls or cross frames can act as the buttress counterforts, and in normal single-storey basements columns from the superstructure above can sometimes be used in a similar way, if suitably spaced and running down on the plane of the wall. Alternatively, in some circumstances the wall may span between the basement and ground floor.

When frictional resistance to sliding is insufficient, it may be necessary to form a projecting rib on the underside of the base in order to increase the depth of earth providing passive resistance. This may be in any convenient position from the extremity of the toe to the heel as shown dotted on type (a). The best position is at the heel so that the great bearing pressure under the toe of the base can prevent the spewing of the soil in front of the rib. A rib is usually essential with the type of wall shown in (a) when the vertical load is small compared with the lateral thrust of the earth. This sometimes occurs in a building with a high basement retaining wall such as the multi-storey wall illustrated on page 199. The construction of the base at an angle assists in increasing the resistance to sliding and at the same time will result in a more even distribution of pressure on the soil. The sloping up of the base in this way is most useful when incorporated with a projecting rib under the stem of the wall (page 197 f).

When the base of a cantilever retaining wall projects entirely in front of the stem as a toe, the main reinforcement is arranged vertically on the tension side of the stem, that is, nearest the retained earth, and is carried round on the under side of the base slab. Shear stresses are not often so great as to require the provision of shear reinforcement. If any part of the base projects under the retained soil, the downward pressure of the soil will set up a reverse bending moment and the tension side of the slab under the soil will be at the top where the horizontal reinforcement must be placed (page 199).

In the counterfort wall the counterforts are designed as vertical cantilevers

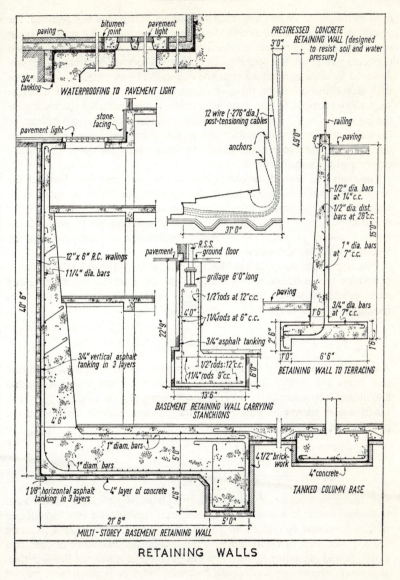

WATERPROOFING TO PAVEMENT LIGHT

paving · bitumen joint · pavement light

3/4" tanking

stone facing

pavement light

12"x 6" R.C. walings

11/4" dia. bars

40' 6"

3/4" vertical asphalt tanking in 3 layers

4' 6"

PRESTRESSED CONCRETE RETAINING WALL (designed to resist soil and water pressure)

3'0"

12 wire (·276"dia.) post-tensioning cables

anchors

43'0"

31' 0"

pavement

R.S.S. ground floor

grillage 8'0" long

1/2" rods at 12" c.c.

11/4" rods at 6" c.c.

3/4" asphalt tanking

1/2" rods 12" c.c.

11/4" rods 9" c.c.

4'0"

22'9"

6'0"

13'6"

BASEMENT RETAINING WALL CARRYING STANCHIONS

railing

9" paving

1/2" dia. bars at 14" c.c.

1/2" dia. dist. bars at 26" c.c.

1" dia. bars at 7" c.c.

paving

3/4" dia. bars at 7" c.c.

15'0"

1'6"

2'6"

1'0" · 6'6" · 1'6"

RETAINING WALL TO TERRACING

1" diam. bars

1" diam. bars

1 1/8" horizontal asphalt tanking in 3 layers

4" layer of concrete

5'0"

9'4"

21' 6"

5'0"

MULTI-STOREY BASEMENT RETAINING WALL

4 1/2" brick work

4" concrete

TANKED COLUMN BASE

RETAINING WALLS

fixed at the base. When they are on the same, side as the soil retained, the compressive edges are stiffened by the stem slab but there is no such stiffening when they act as buttresses on the front of the stem, so the edges may need thickening to resist the tendency to buckle. The stem and base slabs are designed as slabs continuous over the counterfort or buttress supports, the base slab distributing the pressure on to the soil. The disposition of the steel reinforcement in the base will depend on whether counterforts or buttresses are used. In the first case there will be tension at the bottom of the slab between the counterforts due to the downward pressure of the soil it carries. In the second case there will be tension at the top due to the upward pressure of the subsoil below.

The stem and base of the cantilever retaining wall may be tapered as the bending moments reduce, but it is often cheaper not to do so in order to simplify shuttering and the placing of the concrete.

The approximate proportions of the type of wall commonly used in basements is shown on page 195. Typical applications of reinforced concrete retaining walls are shown on page 199.

Prestressing can be applied to high retaining walls and permits the thickness to be kept to a minimum. Set backs, at suitable intervals on the base and stem, provide positions for the anchorage of the post-tensioning cables as indicated on page 199.

PARTITIONS

A partition is an internal wall other than a party, division or separating wall (see pages 147, 488). Its primary function is to divide the space within a building into rooms. It may be loadbearing or non-loadbearing. The functional requirements which a normal partition should satisfy are the provision of adequate

>Strength and stability;
>Sound insulation;
>Fire resistance.

A reasonable degree of sound insulation is usually required between the individual rooms in a building and in some circumstances a very high degree of insulation may be required. The main problem in such cases is to attain the required level of insulation with the lightest possible form of construction. Sound insulation is discussed in Chapter 9 of *Advanced Building Construction* (*Components, Services and Finishes*). Partitions which must provide fire protection, such as those round escape stairs and along escape routes within buildings, must have a minimum standard of fire resistance according to the class of building of which they form part. The standards required can usually be attained with the use of normal partition construction (see Chapter 10).

The thickness of a loadbearing brick or block partition is calculated in the same way as that for a loadbearing wall.[1] Loadbearing partitions are generally used only in one- or two-storey buildings with external loadbearing walls. Bricks and clay and concrete blocks and some types of plaster slabs are suitable for loadbearing partitions. This chapter is concerned with non-loadbearing partitions constructed on the site with normal building materials.

The numerous proprietory systems of demountable partitions which are used in certain types of building, such as offices, to provide an easy means of changing the room layout, are not considered here.

In non-loadbearing partitions the compressive strength is not important provided the material is capable of bearing its own weight at the base. Thus they can be of lighter construction than loadbearing partitions. Transverse strength against lateral pressure, however, is important. Since this type of partition, in order to obtain a structure of minimum weight, is thin relative to its height, it must be considered, for the purpose of stability, as a slab spanning between supports which provide adequate restraint at the edges. Thickness as well as edge restraint is also important in relation to transverse strength. The L.C.C. By-laws require a non-loadbearing partition built of bricks or blocks which is adequately restrained laterally on all four edges, and otherwise restrained or buttressed, to have a thickness of at least one-fortieth of its height or length, whichever is less. This thickness may include $\frac{1}{2}$ in. of cement rendering on each face.[2] This particular rule in the L.C.C. area is meant to apply only to bricks and blocks. Limits usually accepted elsewhere for blocks and other materials are given on page 202.

Edge isolation should be provided when structural movements are likely to produce cracks in the partition. Fibre-board, cork or other similar material is used for a resilient material and some degree of fixity may be obtained by sinking the edges into a chase sunk in the structure against which the partition butts, or in timber members fixed to the structure.

Partitions may be constructed of bricks or blocks of various types, of slabs of different materials or as a framework covered with some form of facing. Bricks are now generally used only for loadbearing partitions, the design and detailing of which are similar to those for normal brick walls already

---

[1] When the thickness is not determined by calculation the L.C.C. By-laws lay down a minimum thickness of "not less than one-half the required thickness of an external or party wall of the same height and twice the length"—By-law 5.10 (2).
[2] L.C.C. By-law 5.10 (4).

Table 16. Block

Type of Partition	Strength and Stability			Movements

Block

Thickness of Block in inches	Clay or Concrete Blocks—H or L not to exceed in feet	Plaster Blocks— L 20 ft max. H not to exceed in feet
2	8	9
2½	10	9
3	12	12
4	—	15
4¼	15	—
5	—	20
6	20	20

Provide lateral rigidity—see text.

Movements (Block):
Clay blocks: Thermal and moisture movement negligible.
Concrete blocks: To be fully matured to avoid shrinkage cracking and reasonably dry when used. Use weak mortars. Shrinkage joints not exceeding 20 ft apart.
Plaster blocks: Thermal and moisture movement negligible. Provide edge isolation where movement of surrounding structure is likely to affect partition. Expanded metal or wire netting face reinforcement above openings.

Glass Block

Maximum height   20 ft.
Maximum area   120 sq. ft.
Provide lateral rigidity—see text.

Movements:
Max. length of panel—20 ft.
Edge isolation at top and vertical edges of panels and openings with ½ in. clearance.
Support coated with bitumen emulsion before bedding bottom blocks. Build in every 3rd–5th course 2½ in. wide open mesh non-rusting reinforcement with ends built in to structure.

Slab

Wood wool:
H'ts not exceeding 12 ft—2 in. slabs
   ,,   ,,   ,,   16 ft—3 in. ,,
,, greater than 16 ft and lengths greater than 20 ft—provide intermediate vertical and horizontal support.
Compressed Straw: H'ts not exceeding 9 ft—timber coupling strips at vertical joints fixed to slab edges.
H'ts greater than 9 ft—full height timber studs at slab width spacing.
H'ts over standard max. length of 12 ft—intermediate horizontal supports required.
Plasterboard Core: Max. length of panel 20 ft.
H'ts not exceeding 12 ft—horizontal joints staggered when h't exceeds standard length.
H'ts greater than 12 ft—horizontal stiffeners at 10 ft intervals.
Cellular Plasterboard: No limit on length. H'ts over standard max. length of 12 ft—intermediate horizontal supports required.

Movements:
Wood wool: Max. length of panel 20 ft. Edge isolation or partial isolation by very weak mortar or mastic joint. Face reinforcement of exp. metal or wire netting at changes of longitudinal or transverse section (e.g. over door openings) to extend 12 in. on each side of point of change. Carry up door frames where possible.
Compressed straw: Thermal and moisture movement negligible in normal conditions.

Plasterboard and Fibre Reinforced Plaster: Negligible thermal and moisture movement.
Edge isolation where movement of surrounding partition is likely to affect partition.
Face reinforcement above all openings.

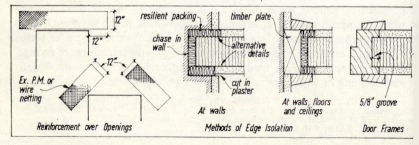

Reinforcement over Openings   12"   resilient packing   timber plate   chase in wall   alternative details   cut in plaster   Ex. P.M. or wire netting   At walls   At walls, floors and ceilings   5/8" groove   Methods of Edge Isolation   Door Frames

and Slab Partitions

Mortar and Jointing	Openings	Fixings
Clay and concrete: Cement, lime, sand 1:1:6 for 2 in. blocks, 1:2:9 for thicker blocks. *Plaster:* 1 part retarded h.h. plaster to 2 sand. Joints as thin as possible.	Thin partitions: carry up door frames and anchor to ceiling. Use grooved frames. Carry blocks on door frame. Thick partitions: tie frames to partition with metal ties or use grooved frames. Use reinforced blocks or R.C. lintels over all openings. For openings wider than 6 ft in plaster block partitions use R.C. lintels with min. bearing of 8 in. at each side.	Lightweight fittings and fixtures— Nail fixing to lightweight aggregate blocks. Nail fixing to timber strips nailed on vertical edge of plaster blocks: ⅞ in. at 30 in. c/c (1½ in. at 15 in. c/c for medium weight fixtures). Toggle bolts or similar fixing to hollow clay and concrete blocks. Heavy fittings (W.C. tanks, L.B's): Bolt through to steel or timber back plate for thinner partitions.
Fairly dry, fatty mortar. Suitable mix: cement, lime, sand 1:1:4. Joints about ¼ in. thick.	Carry out door frames and secure to structure above or at sides, or secure frame by 3/16 in. perforated M.S. strips fixed to top of frame and running vertically or horizontally through joints to structure. Secure frames to partition by exp. metal ties in every 3rd or 5th course depending on size of opening.	Fixings cannot easily be arranged. Fittings and fixtures should be kept clear of this type of partition.
Wood wool: Slabs laid horizontally; vertical joints broken bonded. Cement, sand 1:3 with up to ¼ part hydrated lime, or Retarded h.h. plaster, sand 1:2. Mortar fairly wet. Joints as thin as possible. *Compressed straw:* Built up dry. *Fibre reinforced plaster:* Panels bedded in 1:3 cement and sand mortar. Joint in neat h.h. plaster.	*Wood wool:* Use grooved frames. For openings up to 5 ft wide use single 2 ft deep slab as lintel with 4 in. min. bearings. Over 5 ft wide use timber lintel with 6–9 in. bearings. For very wide openings use separate supporting frame to avoid excessive load on slabs. *Compressed straw:* Carry up door frames and anchor to ceiling. Use grooved frames. *Plasterboard Core and Cellular Plasterboard:* If h't not great partition may carry over door openings but better to carry up frames and anchor to ceiling. Use frames rebated for plasterboard core or grooved for cellular units.	*Wood wool:* Lightweight fittings and fixtures—Use special nailing slabs with timber fillets let into centre or cement dovetailed timber blocks into slabs at suitable centres. Heavy fittings—Fix pipes by bolting through to timber or steel back plate. Use independent framing for W.C. flushing tanks and L.B's. *Compressed straw:* Nail fixing for light trim only. Nails driven at angle and adjacent nails opposed to form "dovetail" grip. Lightweight fittings and fixtures—Use 1¾ in. screws dipped in cold adhesive. Heavy fittings—W.C. tanks and L.B's bolted through to timber or steel back plate. *Plasterboard Core and Cellular Plasterboard:* Lightweight fittings and fixtures—Fix to ⅝ in. splayed timber grounds secured to plasterboard core before plastering and to cellular units by toggle or similar bolts. Heavy fittings—Should not be fixed to plasterboard core partitions. Use bolts passing through cellular units to timber or steel back plates.

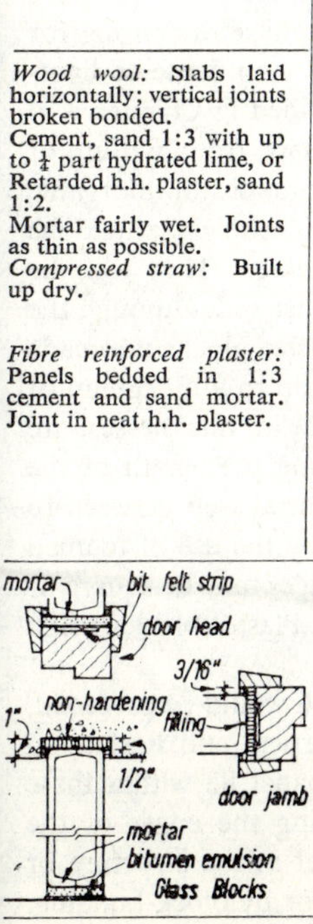

mortar — bit. felt strip
door head
3/16"
non-hardening filling
1"
1/2"
door jamb
mortar
bitumen emulsion
Glass Blocks

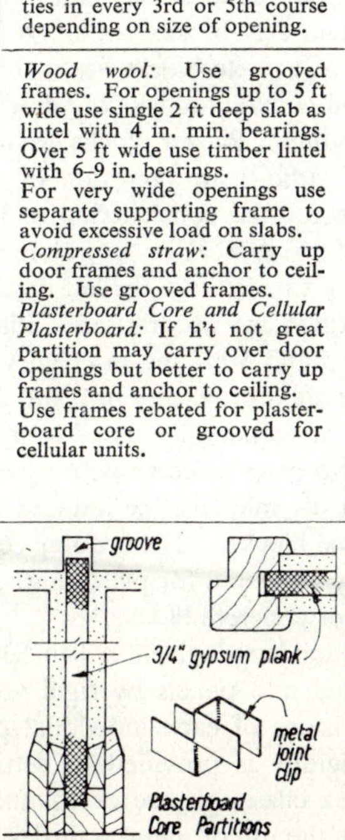

groove
3/4" gypsum plank
metal joint clip
Plasterboard Core Partitions

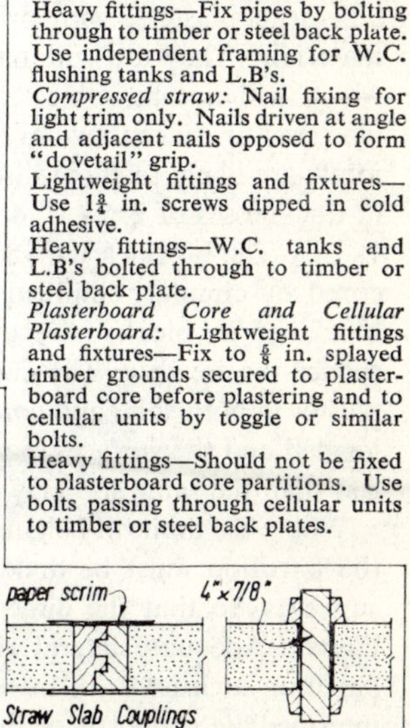

paper scrim
4" x 7/8"
Straw Slab Couplings

described. Blocks are larger and sometimes lighter than bricks and can, therefore, be more quickly laid, although the size must be limited to that capable of being handled and laid by one man. Light materials can be made up into large units or slabs which, although requiring two men to handle, need far less jointing.

The design and construction of partitions is covered by Code of Practice 122 (1952), "Walls and Partitions of Blocks and Slabs", and the tabulated information given on pages 202 and 203, together with that in the remainder of the text, is based on this Code.

BLOCK PARTITIONS

Partition blocks may be of clay, concrete or plaster. Hollow glass blocks are also used but their characteristics have little in common with the other types of blocks and they are discussed separately. Hollow clay blocks are made from clay or diatomaceous earth. The latter produces blocks about half the weight of similar blocks made of clay; they are easily cut but have less resistance to crushing than clay blocks, although sufficiently strong for non-loadbearing partitions. Concrete blocks are made with dense or lightweight aggregates. Clay and concrete blocks are described in Chapter 7 of *Elementary Building Construction*. Plaster blocks are made from gypsum or anhydrite plasters, with or without an aggregate of organic or inorganic material. They are suitable for the construction of lightweight partitions which will not be subjected to vertical or lateral loading. They may be plastered or, since they have a smooth face, be left unplastered, although the joints are likely to show through any decorations. Plaster blocks are made in thicknesses of 2, $2\frac{1}{2}$, 3, 4, 5 and 6 in. and in heights up to a maximum of 18 in. The blocks are made solid or, except in 2 and $2\frac{1}{2}$ in. thicknesses, are cored by circular, elliptical or rectangular cores running the length of the block. 6 in. blocks have two rows of cores with a central web between to reduce the weight. The density may also be reduced by the use of foamed plaster in both solid and cored blocks. The bedding edges may be square or joggled and the surfaces may be scored for plastering. Plaster blocks weigh less than the same size clay or concrete blocks.

Where the limits of height and length given in Table 16 would be exceeded, the partition must be divided into panels by rigid vertical and horizontal supports, so that the dimensions of each individual panel lie within these limits. Adequate lateral rigidity is provided by setting the edges of the partition at least 2 in. into a chase, groove or channel in the structure or intermediate supports, or by the use of metal wall ties or by block bonding, when this is appropriate, to the structure.[1] Block bonding, however, should not be used in the case of plaster or diatomaceous earth block partitions.

Building blocks vary in the ease with which they may be chased and cut and this should be borne in mind in choosing the blocks and the thickness of partition. Vertical chases cannot readily be formed in solid dense concrete blocks or hollow clay or concrete blocks. Special conduit blocks already grooved are available for bonding in with normal blocks. Lightweight aggregate blocks cut fairly easily. Horizontal chases should not exceed one-sixth of the thickness of the block in depth and vertical chases one-quarter. Plaster blocks can be cut easily, but horizontal chases in solid blocks should be limited in depth to one-quarter of the thickness of the block and in cored blocks to two-thirds of the thickness of the solid shell. Cored blocks less than 4 in. thick should not be chased. The depth of vertical chases in either type of block should be limited to one-third of the thickness of the block.

HOLLOW GLASS BLOCK PARTITIONS

Hollow glass blocks are used where light transmission through a partition is required. They are hollow translucent glass units manufactured by welding together the rims of two glass coffers. They are covered by B.S. 1207 (1953). The blocks are made in two sizes, $5\frac{3}{4}$ in. and $7\frac{3}{4}$ in. square, with radius corner blocks to match. Louvred ventilator blocks are also available in sizes to match the standard blocks. A non-standard rectangular block 8 in. × $4\frac{7}{8}$ in. is also available. All the blocks are $3\frac{1}{8}$ in. thick. Different surface patterns are produced by pressing flutes on the inner and outer surfaces at various spacings, or on the inside face only to give a smooth external surface. The jointing edges are painted and sanded to form a key for mortar.

When the dimensions of a partition are greater than those given in Table 16, vertical or horizontal intermediate supports of adequate strength and rigidity must generally be used. As at junctions with the main structure a $\frac{1}{2}$ in. clearance must be provided at all junctions with intermediate supports. Lateral restraint at the edges can be provided by building the edges of the panel into a groove or channel formed in the structure or intermediate supports $4\frac{1}{4}$ in. wide and not less than 1 in. deep; this will allow $\frac{3}{16}$ in. clearance at each face and $\frac{1}{2}$ in. clearance at the end.

---

[1] In the case of a loadbearing partition flanked by masonry walls, block bonding is preferable as it gives a better distribution of load.

SLAB PARTITIONS

Wood wool, compressed straw, plaster-board and cored plaster-board slabs can be used for the construction of non-loadbearing partitions.

Wood Wool Slabs.   These are described in Chapter 8 of *Advanced Building Construction* (*Components, Services and Finishes*).   Heavy duty slabs 2 in. or more in thickness are suitable for partitions.   They are usually plastered.

Edge joints should usually be designed to allow longitudinal movement while giving support against lateral movement.   This can be done by sinking the top and vertical edges into chases or grooves in the structure or intermediate supports.   When the panels are short the edges may be restrained by expanded metal reinforcement on each face of the partition.   It is carried over the joint and securely fixed on each side.   Plaster finish may be made discontinuous by a cut through the full depth of the plaster at the junction of adjacent surfaces or, if left continuous, the joints should be reinforced with scrim or metal mesh not less than 4 in. wide.

Holes and chases can be made easily in wood wool slabs with normal woodworking tools.   The depth of chases should not exceed one-third of the thickness of the slab and these should be covered over with light metal reinforcing strips before plastering is carried out.

Compressed Straw Slabs.   These are made from straw by heat and pressure and are described in Chapter 8 of *Advanced Building Construction* (*Components, Services and Finishes*).

For heights up to 9 ft the vertical butt joints between the slabs may be secured by timber coupling pieces slightly less in width than the thickness of the slab, nailed or screwed to the vertical edges of the slabs and grooved to key with each other.   The coupling pieces are secured at floor level to a 2 in. wide batten fixed to the floor and to the ceiling if this is of timber, or to a similar batten if not.   The coupling pieces may be covered over by a cover strip or by a 5 in. wide Kraft paper scrim glued to the slabs on each side. This allows for any slight movement of the timber.   Similar coupling members should be used at the junction of the partition with the structure. Alternatively, lateral restraint should be provided by sinking the edges of the slabs into grooves or channels in the structure, or formed in timber edge members.   For heights over 9 ft, 4 in. timber studs should be used running from floor to ceiling and spaced to take the 4 ft wide slabs. The minimum thickness of the studs should be $\frac{7}{8}$ in., with the slabs held by fixing beads. Alternatively, thicker posts grooved to take the slabs can be used.

Plaster-board.   Plaster-board is described in Chapter 8 of *Advanced Building Construction* (*Components, Services and Finishes*), and is used in two ways in the construction of partitions: (i) as a solid core to an applied plaster skin on each side, (ii) as a facing or skin on each side of a cellular core to form a self-supporting unit. In the first method ¾ in. gypsum planks, fixed vertically to avoid horizontal joints, are fitted between top and bottom grooves or between channels of timber or metal fixed to the floor and ceiling. The grooves may be formed *in situ* in concrete floors and ceilings, in which case the top groove must be sufficiently deep to permit the top edge to be pushed up and the bottom edge of the plank then dropped into the floor groove. Adjacent planks are held in the same plane by metal joint clips. Temporary bracing is required until the first undercoat of the three-coat ⅝ in. plaster on each side has been applied. The finished 2 in. partition weighs approximately 14 lb per sq. ft. In the second method the partition is built up from 3 or 4 ft wide panels consisting of two sheets of ⅜ or ½ in. plasterboard fixed to a square cellular core made of fibrous material, finishing 2¼ or 2½ in. overall. The approximate weights are 4¼ lb and 5¼ lb per square foot respectively, and heights of panels range from 6 to 12 ft. This form of partition is fully illustrated in *Elementary Building Construction*.

Another type of cellular plaster partition is made of gypsum plaster reinforced with fibre and consists of two ⅝ in. thick faces bonded to a core of hexagonal ribs. The vertical edges are rebated and thickened so that when erected against each other integral vertical stiffeners are formed. The joints are covered with scrim and plaster placed in recesses on the face edges. Panels are 2–6 in. thick, 2 ft wide and in lengths up to 10 ft. Partitions 4 in. thick and over can be used as loadbearing partitions. The panels are bedded in mortar and tied to the structure with metal ties. With the thinner panels, generally used for non-loadbearing partitions, the construction of frames to openings should be as described in Table 16. Frames and heavy fittings may be fixed to dovetail timber blocks set in plaster within the cellular core, and lighter fittings can be fixed with toggle or similar bolts. Conduit may be chased in the face or passed through the core.

Timber Stud Partitions

Timber-framed partitions have largely been superseded for general use by the types of partition already described, but they are light and can, if required, support considerable loads which can be distributed directly to end bearings if the partition is trussed. It is a dry construction and a wide variety of facings can be applied, the spacing of the studs being varied to suit standard sizes of sheets.

The framing consists of uprights or studs fixed between a timber plate and head, usually the same section as the studs, which are fixed to floor and ceiling. The studs are nailed to the head and plate and the latter are nailed direct to wood floors and ceilings or to fixing blocks let into concrete floors. Nailed joints at all points in the frame usually give sufficient rigidity together with the use of nogging pieces. These are short lengths of timber nailed tightly between the studs to stiffen them. The noggings may be fixed in herringbone fashion but are usually fixed horizontally and spaced at centres at which they can act as cross fixings to any sheet coverings which may be used to face the partitions. The size of the studs will depend upon their height and spacing, and the latter depends upon the type of facing to be used. Table 17 indicates the appropriate sizes for the members of a framed partition based on a stud spacing of 18 in. centre to centre. The same table shows the centres at which studs and noggings should be fixed for a number of facings in

Table 17. Sizes for Members in Timber Partitions

Height up to		Studs at 18 in. centres in.	Plate and head in.	Noggings	
Lath and plaster	Other facings			Main in.	Intermediate in.
7 ft 6 in.	8 ft 6 in.	3 × 1¼	3 × 1¼ or 2	3 × 2	3 × 1¼
10 ft 6 in.	12 ft 0 in.	4 × 1½	4 × 1½ or 2	4 × 2	4 × 1½
14 ft 0 in.	16 ft 0 in.	5 × 2	5 × 2	5 × 2	5 × 2
17 ft 0 in.	20 ft 0 in.	6 × 2	6 × 2 or 3	6 × 2	6 × 2

Spacings for Studs and Noggings

Facing	Maximum centres of supports	
	Studs, in.	Noggings, ft.
Plaster-board	12–24	4
Fibre-board	12–18	4
Hardboard	15–20	4
Asbestos wallboard	16	4
"Plastic" Sheet	25 max.	4
Plywood	12–48	3–6
Wood wool slab	18–24	None

general use. When 1¼ or 1½ in. studs are used, those providing support to the meeting edges of facings sheets usually need to be wider to provide space for the fixing of two edges.

Openings may be simply formed by nailing head timbers between normal studs on each side of the opening, but a better way is to double-stud the sides of the opening with the inner studs cut short to form bearings for the head timber. Alternatively, the opening can be framed more rigidly if 3 or 4 in. thick posts are used to form the opening, with the same size timber for the head-piece which is jointed rigidly to the posts with wedged mortise and tenon joints. Fixings for skirtings, trims and fittings can be easily made by means of fixing studs and noggings framed into the partition at the appropriate points. The open structure of the partition makes it an easy matter to accommodate conduits and cables freely within it.

Sheet and board coverings suitable for facing framed partitions are described in Chapter 8 of *Advanced Building Construction* (*Component, Services and Finishes*).

5
Multi-Storey Structures

The virtue of the loadbearing wall is that it is capable of fulfilling at one and the same time the dual functions of loadbearing and of space enclosure and division. In many circumstances, therefore, it is for this reason a most economical form of construction. Nevertheless, it suffers certain inherent disadvantages. As a loadbearing element it can become thick and heavy at the base of a very tall building although, unless the building is exceptionally tall, with modern materials and methods of design the wall will not be unduly thick, even in brickwork. This is probably in many cases less of a disadvantage than the fact that loadbearing wall construction is restrictive when an open plan is required (see page 117). As an enclosing element, adequate weather resistance and thermal insulation in particular can be obtained only with a considerable thickness of wall, or by the application of cavities and lightweight materials and linings.

By relieving the wall of its load bearing function it is possible to fulfil the enclosing functions by forms of construction more suited to the purpose than heavy loadbearing walls, and to provide a structure lighter in weight and, often, more quickly erected. The alternative to the loadbearing wall is, therefore, a system which allocates the loadbearing and space enclosing functions to two separate elements: the structural frame to fulfil the former, and light but efficient panels or claddings to fulfil the latter. The advantages of the framed structure are (i) saving in floor space, (ii) flexibility in plan and building operations, (iii) reduction in dead weight. Such a system is now used for many multi-storey buildings, but the point made in the opening paragraph must be stressed here: that in certain circumstances loadbearing wall construction will prove cheaper in terms of overall cost than a framed structure. This is particularly so in the case of individual small-scale and domestic buildings, although in the case of large programmes involving one basic type of small-scale building, permitting bulk ordering of materials and the use of a prefabricated system to reduce site labour, a framed structure may often prove more economical than one based on the loadbearing wall. In the case of taller buildings with suitable plan forms, such as some types of flat blocks, the wall used as a loadbearing element can again produce a cheaper structure than a frame. This has been more fully discussed in terms of brick and plain concrete walls on pages 117 and 138. See also page 269.

The cost of the structural frame of a building is generally a small proportion only of the total building cost and varies on average from 20 to 40% of the total cost. Small economies in the structure will, therefore, have a slight effect only on the total cost. Nevertheless, since the cost of the structural frame is usually the largest single item in the total cost, it should be kept to a minimum, although it must always be borne in mind that the cheapest structure may not necessarily produce the cheapest building. For example, reduction in the cost of the structure at the expense of increased depth of beams will lead to an increase in the cost of finishings, particularly external claddings, due to the increased overall height of the building. As another example, in some proprietary forms of prefabricated steel building frames beams of rather wide span are closely spaced and the resulting light load carried by the wide span beams produces beams which are slightly wasteful in steel (see page 215). The extra cost is, however, more than balanced by ease of erection, economy in roof cladding and simplification of services.

The frame, therefore, must be considered not alone but in relation to the other elements of the building. A comparative analysis of different ways of constructing a simple two-storey office building made by Stillman and Eastwick-Field[1] emphasizes this point very clearly and at the same time shows the economic advantages of loadbearing wall construction over framed construction for small buildings. In the first scheme external loadbearing cavity walls are used, "punctured" at intervals for normal windows; in an alternative scheme a structural frame is used with solid and glazed infilling panels. Although the cost of the frame in the alternative scheme is shown as little more than half that of the loadbearing walls, since the frame cannot enclose space, the cost of the infilling panels must be added to this to make it comparable in functional terms with the wall construction, so that the total cost of the frame and infilling panels is shown to be rather more than one-and-a-half times the total cost of the walls together with the windows.

The high cost of the glazed infilling panels in this particular example could be reduced by replacing them with cavity wall panel construction, but in a small building such as this the final result would be quite illogical since the cavity wall itself is capable of carrying the floor and roof loads without the frame. The justification of a framed structure in circumstances such as these rests on the advantages given by a frame in other directions, such as the large areas of glazing which are necessary in some building types.

[1] *Architects' Journal*, October 25, 1956, and January 24 and April 25, 1957.

CHOICE OF APPROPRIATE STRUCTURE

Although the frame must be considered in relation to the other elements of the building it is, nevertheless, necessary to consider it separately in broad terms at the outset of a scheme in order to establish a basis from which to begin. There is no simple formula by means of which the most appropriate framing for a particular building may be selected, and because there are so many variable factors affecting the choice and economy of a structural frame these can be discussed only in general terms.

1. Site

The available site, its cost, the nature of the subsoil and planning restrictions on the height of buildings in the particular area must all be considered. When the cost of the land is low and a large area is available, the automatic choice of a multi-storey structure is illogical. Apart from increased construction costs, such things as the extra cost of external walling due to the increased ratio of external wall to floor area in a tall building, with its repercussions on the heating of the building in terms of greater heat loss, make the serious consideration of a low structure essential. But where the cost of land is high, as in central city areas, a multi-storey structure must invariably be used in order to reduce to a minimum the required area of site to economize on its cost.

The height of a tall structure may be limited by economics or by height regulations. Construction costs increase with building height and additional storeys lead to increased column, foundation and wind-bracing costs, so that for each particular job there is an economical height limit at which the structure may be stopped, even though it may be lower than that permitted by regulations. The economical height may be determined by assessing the return on investment, this being calculated with regard to the area of the building, land costs, the number of floors and the cost per unit volume or area, as well as many other factors. This, of course, necessitates the use of some form of cost analysis and cost planning. Above the economical limit there are diminishing returns on the money invested in the building. If the maximum height should be limited by height regulations rather than by the cost of construction, it may be necessary to place the maximum number of storeys within the permitted height and this will have a profound influence upon the choice of a type of floor to give the thinnest possible construction. In commercial buildings the rental value of any extra floors gained in this way must be capitalized before comparing the cost of a selected floor with that of alternative floor systems.

The type of soil on which the structure is to rest will influence its design, above as well as below ground. For example, in the case of soil with a low bearing capacity and high compressibility, on which differential settlement might occur, a low structure imposing minimum point loads on the soil through simple foundations would be most suitable, but if the location of the site made it necessary to build high over a small area, expensive foundations such as piles or caissons taken to a firm stratum might be required. In this case it might prove cheaper to increase the span of beams in the frame in order to restrict the number of columns and thus the number of expensive foundations. The relationship between soil, foundations and superstructure is considered in more detail in Chapter 3.

2. Type and Use of Building

An analysis of the problem on the basis of the site considerations—a balancing of costs and use requirements as they arise from site conditions—will usually give in broad terms an indication of the most suitable kind of structure, and this will lead to a final choice from a few alternative systems within the broad lines suggested. This choice will be influenced by the nature and use of the building and the architect's conception of the finished building. Plan forms requiring a repeating unit both horizontally and vertically, and in which room widths may be multiples of the structural unit, lead logically to the use of a simple skeleton frame. The intensity and nature of the superimposed loading[1] must be considered so that a suitable type of floor structure can be selected and the most economic span chosen for the particular floor type. When a square structural grid can be adopted, or at least one in which the larger side of each bay does not exceed one-and-a-quarter times the length of the shorter side, the use of a two-way continuously reinforced floor slab with four-edge support becomes economically possible, as it can result in a thinner and lighter slab when load and span conditions are suitable. Certain building types, such as flats, may be more cheaply constructed in loadbearing wall construction, or box frame, than as a frame. The standard of natural lighting required from outer walls will influence the height from floor to ceiling according to the depth of the rooms on plan. All these factors will involve the consideration of column centres, wall spacings, storey heights and infillings and claddings and of the implications of the provision of mechanical services, especially heating and air-conditioning with the ducts involved. Should the solution suggested by these considerations

---

[1] See Table 20 for minimum imposed loads to be assumed on floors and Table 2 for permitted reductions which may be made in the design of columns, walls and piers.

8

be at variance with that suggested by site considerations, then a review of both must be made in order to arrive at a final satisfactory solution.

3. Span and Spacing of Beams

Span: The column spacing which determines the span of the beams is, perhaps, the most important factor influencing the cost of the structural framework. Generally, the cheapest frame will be that with the closest column spacing and, therefore, the lowest dead weight. Apart from frames with exceptionally tall columns, that is in those of normal storey height, a column costs less than a beam. Although in practice the selection of the most economic structure may not always be possible, because of the space requirements of the building, it is desirable to bear in mind this economic factor as a "yardstick" by means of which can be assessed the cost consequences of adopting a particular solution.

Spacing: The spacing of the beams is dependent upon a number of factors:

  (i) The economic span of floor slab;
  (ii) The economic loading of beams;
  (iii) The economic loading of columns.

In the case of a building not requiring wide span beams the economic span of the floor slab will be a decisive factor in fixing the spacing of the main floor beams. For multi-storey buildings such as flats, offices and other types with light and medium loading this will be from 10 to 15 ft, to give a floor slab in the region of 5 to 6 in. thick. Greater spacing will necessitate the use of a thicker floor, of tee, hollow beam or other type. A detailed consideration of floor construction will be found in Chapter 6.

In establishing the spacing of beams in a structural frame another important influence, apart from the requirements of planning, is the relationship between load and span of beams. Since both the bending moment and, especially, the deflection of a uniformly loaded beam are more rapidly increased by an increase in span than by an increase in the load per foot run, it is generally uneconomical to carry light loads over long spans. This can be seen from the expressions for bending moment and deflection:

$$\text{BM} = \frac{wl^2}{8} \quad \text{and} \quad d = \text{constant } (c) \times \frac{wl^4}{\text{EI}}$$

The bending moment increases with the square of the span l, and the deflection with fourth power, but both only directly with the load per foot run, w. If the span of a beam is doubled the deflection will be sixteen times as great but if the load per foot run is doubled the deflection will be only twice as great.

In other words, an increase in span necessitates a much greater increase in the "I" value of the beam in order to keep deflection within acceptable limits, compared with that necessitated by a proportionate increase in the load per foot run. This being so, when beam spans must be large it will usually be cheaper to space the beams further apart, particularly when floor loading is light or medium, so that the load per foot run on the beams is increased. The savings in cost due to a smaller number of beams will be greater than the increase in cost due to the wider floor slabs and the increase in size of the remaining beams and columns due to the greater load they carry.

Heavy loading on wide span beams also has economic repercussions on the columns of a frame. Variations in loading cause only relatively small variations in column sizes since the decisive factor in most columns is strength against buckling, so that where beam spans are great an increase of the unit load on the beams obtained by spacing the beams at wider intervals has the effect of imposing greater loads on fewer columns without necessitating a great increase in their size. This is particularly beneficial where the column heights are great and the greater tendency to buckle, because of the greater slenderness ratio, results in large column sizes.

It will be appreciated from what has already been said that for a given span of floor slab, which will establish the load per foot run on the supporting beams, there will be an economic span for the beams. For types of buildings with light to medium floor loads and normal concrete floors used at their economic span this will be from 14 to 20 ft.

When the column centres have been tentatively established, studies of typical bays are made for comparative purposes in terms of construction and costs. An analysis will be made of the various possible framings in structural steel or reinforced concrete or in both, some of which will prove to be more economic than the others. Wherever possible the frame should be based on a uniform "grid", a term derived from the pattern of beams at each floor level. The term "grid spacing" is applied to the set out of the columns of the frame which determines the grid. The following are some of the advantages of a uniform grid:

(a) Loads are transmitted evenly to the foundations, thus minimizing relative settlement and standardizing the sizes of foundation slabs.

(b) It produces regularity in beam depths and column sizes and in the position of columns and beams relative to walls. This is valuable for architectural reasons.

(c) In reinforced concrete work the regular floor spans minimize the variations in rod sizes.

(*d*) It permits greater re-use of formwork, both in precast and *in situ* concrete construction.

The imposed loads on building frames are transmitted through successive units or stages to the foundations, that is, for example, from floor slab to beam and from beam to column, and the total cost of the structure is made up of the cost of each successive stage. Generally, to achieve maximum economy the number of stages by which the load is carried should be kept to a minimum, although since they are interdependent and modifications to one will affect the others, the introduction of an extra stage may in some circumstances be justified. For example, the introduction of secondary beams may result in a saving of so much dead weight in the floor slabs as to make it economically advantageous to do so.

As a general principle loads should not be transferred horizontally if it is possible to carry them axially downwards from the point of application. Thus setbacks on section resulting in columns bearing on beams should be avoided where possible, as this necessitates the use of heavy or deep beams and increases the cost of the structural frame, as does the introduction of wide span beams on lower floors, carrying a number of columns in a closely spaced grid above (page 232 D, E, G).

4. Wind Pressure

Another factor to be considered in the selection of the most appropriate structural frame is the need for the structure to be able to resist wind pressure. This is a most important consideration in the case of very tall buildings as far as both foundations and superstructure are concerned. The recommendations of C.P. 3 (Ch. V) concerning wind pressure on buildings as a whole and upon claddings, and the design of buildings and their parts to resist the pressure of wind, are described in Chapter 4. They apply to framed structures as well as to loadbearing wall structures.

A structural frame may be considered as acting under pressure of wind either as a cantilever in which the floors remain plane or as a portal frame in which the floors bend. In analysing the structure in terms of wind resistance the height-to-width ratio is extremely important in deciding in which of these ways the structure is likely to react. A very tall, slender building will act more nearly as a cantilever while a short, squat structure will act as a portal frame. In practice most buildings act partially in both ways. In multi-storey buildings any tendency to uplift at the foundations will usually be more than counter-balanced by the total weight of the building, which will keep the resultant pressure within the middle third of the base. In whichever way a particular structure may behave it will move under wind pressure, in the same way that a beam or cantilever deflects under load, and in the case of tall buildings particularly, where the movement could be large, this must be limited if it is not to result in cracks in finishes and discomfort to occupants of upper floors. In heavy structures with heavy, stiff claddings, wind forces are not likely to produce much lateral deflection, but in framed structures with light curtain walls the basic structure required by dead and imposed loads may have to be strengthened or stiffened in order to limit lateral movement, or side-sway. A maximum permissible deflection at the top may be fixed and the bending moments produced by this may be calculated and the structure designed accordingly. In the United States a maximum deflection of $0 \cdot 002$ times the height of the building is used as a limit for buildings having a rigid outer skin, and $0 \cdot 001$ times the height for buildings with curtain walls which provide little rigidity to assist in reducing the deflection. The necessary stiffness or wind-bracing can be obtained in a number of ways, used either separately or in combination:

(a) by the use of deep girders producing very stiff joints with the columns (steel and reinforced concrete);

(b) by the use of brackets or gussets on beams to produce stiff joints (steel);

(c) by the use of diagonal or "K" bracing in the vertical plane (steel and precast concrete);

(d) by using the floor slabs to transfer the wind loads to cross walls or frames. This necessitates an increased thickness of floor slab on the lower floors.

(e) by constructing solid walls in suitable positions within the frame or by using stair wells or lift shafts, if these are constructed in monolithic reinforced concrete, running the full height of the building so that they act as large, stiff annular columns to which wind loading is transmitted by the floors or the frame (see page 266). Solid walls, called shear walls, may be introduced in panels of the frame to fulfil the same function as diagonal braces and act as stiffeners to the frame.

The method of windbracing to be adopted must be considered at the beginning of the design stage because it will have a bearing upon floor thicknesses and floor types, beam depths and column sizes and the introduction or not of stiffening walls.

CHOICE OF MATERIAL FOR THE STRUCTURE

The materials most suitable for the construction of multi-storey structural frames are steel and reinforced concrete. Timber, apart from its use in domestic type buildings up to about three storeys high, and the aluminium alloys, by reason of their particular characteristics, are not suitable for this purpose. A comparison of the characteristics of these four structural materials is given in Chapter 9.

The principal factors influencing the choice between steel and concrete are

    (i) the availability of materials and labour;
    (ii) cost;
    (iii) speed of erection;
    (iv) possibility or otherwise of standardizing the sizes of the structural members;
    (v) size and nature of site;
    (vi) fire resistance required.

With these in mind the two materials may be compared in order better to understand the consequences of the choice of one or the other.

Site Considerations.   Both steel and cement are made under factory conditions and both are subject to British Standards. The strength of steel is controlled and established during manufacture, but that of concrete is often dependent upon strict supervision on a building site. On a large contract effective supervision and the use of carefully controlled batching plant is likely to lead to better quality concrete than on a small contract. Doubt regarding the possibility of obtaining first class supervision for a particular job might lead to the choice of steel.

The fabrication of the individual members of a steel frame is carried out "off-site" in the steel contractor's shop and erection only is necessary on the site itself. The erection of the steel is carried out by skilled labour, quickly and accurately within small tolerances. Completion at an early stage in the building programme permits the laying of floors and roofs and the rapid sealing-in of the whole structure to permit other trades to follow on continuously without interruption through adverse weather. The fixing of lower floors can, of course, be commenced before the frame has been completed up to roof level and while the upper members are being fixed in position. The obstruction of floor space by the vertical struts for *in situ* cast floors may be avoided by the use of telescopic shutter supports off the beams or by the use of precast concrete or steel deck floors.

In *in situ* cast concrete structures all work, except possibly the cutting and bending of reinforcing bars, is carried out on the site, the erection of formwork and placing of reinforcement by skilled and unskilled labour and the making and placing of concrete by semi-skilled or unskilled labour. The proportion of site work to prefabricated work is greater in the case of *in situ* concrete and building operations are complicated by formwork and centering, which has to be in position for a considerable time to allow the concrete to set before the frame can take up loads and subsequent lifts be commenced. Much site space is needed for the storage and mixing of materials, although in some districts this problem can be overcome when the site is restricted in area by the use of "truck-mixed" concrete. The type of formwork used and the nature and size of the building will, of course, have an effect upon the actual method of work and the speed at which it progresses.

Cost and Speed of Erection. With a repetitive skeleton frame and the employment of a suitable contractor, reinforced concrete is likely to be from 20 to 25% cheaper in cost but, if *in situ*, generally longer in construction than steel, although construction can be rapid with careful and detailed planning of the site work, good site organization and properly trained operatives and good supervision.

To some extent cost and speed of erection are dependent upon the availability of materials and labour. When materials are scarce prices rise and delivery periods become extended. When they are abundant prices and delivery periods fall.

On expensive sites speed of erection to permit early occupation of the completed building is a most important consideration and is sometimes the decisive factor in the choice of the framing material.

The use of precast concrete framing members for multi-storey structures helps to overcome some of the disadvantages of *in situ* work and reference should be made to page 270 where this is discussed.

Design Considerations. *In situ* reinforced concrete often allows greater flexibility in design because of its monolithic nature and because it is not confined to standard sections. There is, however, an economic limit set to this flexibility by the increased costs of formwork for excessive changes of section and, generally, reinforced concrete can be used most economically when the structure is designed to permit the maximum re-use of a minimum amount of formwork. This fact is not only of vital importance to the structural engineer but also to the architect designing in reinforced concrete, for it imposes on him a strict discipline in terms of form and detail of which he must be aware during the design period of any project. When the plan for some reason or other must be irregular, reinforced concrete may prove to be cheaper in cost and quicker in construction since a large number of complicated connections might be necessary in a steel frame. Sometimes it is desirable to extend a framed building. When the frame is of steel the problem is relatively simple, the new members being bolted or riveted to the existing after they have been exposed by the removal of any fire-resisting casing. With reinforced concrete it is necessary to expose sufficient of the reinforcement in the existing members to obtain a satisfactory bond with the new work or, alternatively, sufficient to permit the welding on of extension bars to provide the necessary bond.

In choosing between steel and concrete it must be borne in mind that each material should be used in the way which best exploits its particular potentialities. Solutions which are favourable to steel are not necessarily so to concrete, and if comparisons are to be realistic it is important that they should be made on the basis of the cost of a building as a whole based on the structural solution most favourable to each material.

Fire Resistance. Reinforced concrete itself, with normal cover to the reinforcement, provides a substantial degree of fire resistance which can be varied by variations in cover thickness and other means. Steel, because of its behaviour under the action of fire (see page 478), requires a protective cover varying in nature and thickness according to the standard of fire resistance required. The material commonly used for this purpose in the past and still very widely used at present is concrete, poured round the steel members within a timber formwork. Although support for this formwork can be obtained from the structural frame itself the process slows down the progress of work. Regulations now permit the use of sprayed asbestos and hollow protection in the form of various combinations of renderings or plaster on metal lathing, or plaster or asbestos board, by means of which fire protection periods of up to four hours can be attained. These methods have the advantage of reducing the weight of the casing and speeding up the progress of work, but are not all necessarily cheaper than, nor even as cheap as the concrete casing. (See also page 246.)

MOVEMENT CONTROL

Generally. All buildings move to some extent after construction. Within limits this movement can be accommodated by the fabric of the building without damage to structure or finishes. When greater movement is anticipated provision must be made for it to take place freely without damage to the building.

Apart from overturning forces and possible overstressing of materials movement is caused by settlement, changes in moisture content and changes in temperature. Space does not permit a full discussion of the nature and effects of these movements. Reference should be made to other sources which deal with these in detail.[1]

---

[1] See *Principles of Modern Building,* Vol. 1 (H.M.S.O.) and *Building Research Station Digest* No. 12.

Settlement Movement. The problems of settlement, particularly differential settlement, are discussed in Chapter 3 and the means by which this can be minimized are described. Proper foundation design, relative to the nature of the structure, will usually keep these movements within acceptable limits, but in some cases it will be cheaper to provide for movement in the structure. This is done on subsidence sites as described on page 85. Settlement joints are often provided at the junction of parts of a building which vary considerably in height or in loading, and this can probably best be done by providing in the structure a flexible or hinged bay at the junctions (see page 60 (A) and (A) below). Claddings and windows in such bays must be designed to permit free movement.

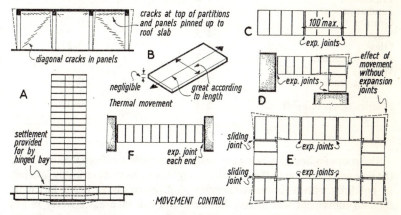

MOVEMENT CONTROL

Moisture Movement. The magnitude of moisture movement in a structural frame is likely to be small. It is primarily in walls and claddings that provision must be made for this and reference should be made to page 148 where this is discussed.

Thermal Movement. This is caused by variations in the temperature of the structure and its parts. The magnitude of the movement will depend upon (i) the variation in temperature, and (ii) the coefficient of thermal expansion of the materials of which the building is constructed. In Britain the seasonal variation, between a cold winter night and a hot summer day, may be as great as 90°F. Some indication of the coefficient of thermal expansion of some common building materials is given in Table 18, together with the increase in a length of 100 ft for a 50°F rise in temperature. The coefficient values shown are average figures only. Considerable variations occur between samples of any material.

Table 18.   Approximate thermal movement of various building materials

Material	Linear coefficient of thermal expansion per °F × 10⁻⁶	Increase in a length of 100 ft for a 50°F rise in temperature (inches)
Concrete	6·7	0·40
Steel	6·5	0·39
Aluminium and alloys	12·7	0·76
Brickwork	3·4	0·21
Limestone	3·2	0·19
Sandstone	6·5	0·39
Granite	5·25	0·32
Slate	4·5	0·27
Glass	4·5	0·27
Asbestos cement	4·7	0·28
Wood:		
along grain	3·1	0·19
across grain	23·5	1·40
Plastics (glass reinf'd)	5·3	0·32

The roof of a building, being exposed fully to radiation from the sun during the day and radiation to the cold sky at night, will be most seriously affected. In buildings with a simple rectangular plan, up to about 100 ft in length, thermal movement will usually be small and can take place freely in any direction.   Precautions against the effect of such movements on walls and partitions (page 221 (B)) must, however, be taken.[1]   (*See* p. 470.)

When the length of the building exceeds much more than 100 ft expansion joints are usually provided, placed at intervals not greater than 100 ft or at other suitable positions not exceeding this distance apart.   These subdivide the length of the building so that the amount of movement is limited, and they provide space for expansion so that damage to the structure is avoided. (page 221 (C)).   The actual spacing and widths of the joints can be calculated from the coefficients of expansion and a selected rise of temperature.   When the form of the building is such that expansion at some points is restrained, movement will be greater at the unrestrained areas.   This can be limited by the provision of expansion joints at the points of restraint as shown on page

---

[1] See *Building Research Station Digest* No. 12, "The Design of Flat Concrete Roofs in Relation to Thermal Effects", for a detailed consideration of this.

221 (D, E).   The design of the end joints in (E) must permit a sliding action. Expansion joints should similarly be placed where sudden changes occur in plan (F), and where floors and roofs are weakened by large openings in the structure.

Expansion joints should not be limited to the roof slab.   They should also be formed in the external walls extending some distance down and inwards to enable the stresses set up by expansion to be distributed.   It is common practice to carry expansion joints through the whole of the structure from top to bottom, particularly in monolithic reinforced concrete buildings.   In a framed building the simplest method is probably to use double columns and beams as shown on page 224 (L), but when double members are undesirable the joint may be formed in the centre of a bay with cantilevering floor slabs or beams or on the line of a column with sliding bearings to the floor structure as shown at L.   In suitable steel-framed structures joints are sometimes provided in the roof and top storey only, reliance being placed on the flexibility of the top floor stanchions.

Typical details of expansion joints are shown on page 224.   As it is often difficult to remove the shutter board forming a narrow gap between two *in situ* cast concrete members bitumen-impregnated soft fibreboard is frequently used for this purpose and left permanently in position (H, R).   With wider gaps the board may be withdrawn and the space filled with non-extruding resilient filling (N), or left open as circumstances require. Waterproof resilient filling or crimped 16 oz copper strip is used to form a flexible weather-resisting barrier in joints in external walls and columns (A and J).   Expansion joints in floors should be detailed in the same way to prevent water used for cleaning passing to the ceiling below (M, N).   Alternatively a grease seal may be used (O).   Where a sliding joint is required as in (E), page 221, this can be detailed for floor slabs as shown at (O), for walls as (E) and for roof slabs in principle as (S).

For further consideration of expansion joints in walls and roofs reference should be made to pages 149 and 469 respectively.[1]

THE STEEL FRAME

The majority of multi-storey steel frames erected up to the present time have been, and still are, designed and constructed on the same general principles as the first multi-storey frames erected over fifty years ago.   They are

---

[1] For a comprehensive treatment of the subject of expansion joints see *Joints de Dilatation dans la Construction en béton et en béton armé*, by Adolf Kleinlogel, Editions Eyrolles.

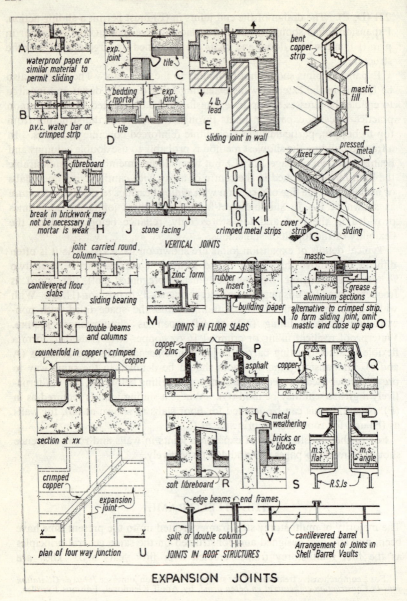

A waterproof paper or similar material to permit sliding

B p.v.c. water bar or crimped strip

C exp. joint / tile

D bedding mortar / exp. joint / tile

E 4 lb. lead / sliding joint in wall

F bent copper strip / mastic fill

H fibreboard / break in brickwork may not be necessary if mortar is weak

J stone facing

K crimped metal strips

G fixed / pressed metal / cover strip / sliding

VERTICAL JOINTS

L joint carried round column / cantilevered floor slabs / sliding bearing / double beams and columns

M zinc form

N rubber insert / building paper

O mastic / grease / aluminium sections / alternative to crimped strip. To form sliding joint, omit mastic and close up gap

JOINTS IN FLOOR SLABS

P counterfold in copper / crimped copper / copper or zinc / asphalt

Q copper

section at xx

R soft fibreboard

S metal weathering / bricks or blocks

T m.s. flat / m.s. angle / R.S.Js

U crimped copper / expansion joint / x x / plan of four way junction

V edge beams / end frames / split or double column / JOINTS IN ROOF STRUCTURES / cantilevered barrel / Arrangement of Joints in Shell Barrel Vaults

EXPANSION JOINTS

designed on the assumption that the beams are simply supported at their junctions with stanchions, connections are made by means of rivets and bolts and fire-resisting casing is in the form of 2 in. or so of concrete.

Certain definite advances in many directions have been made as a result of research carried out in the period between the two world wars and subsequent to the last, which lead to a more rational design approach and to economies in the use of steel. As yet, they are being put into practice very slowly and before discussing them it is proposed as a basis to examine in some detail what might be called the "classic" steel frame still largely adopted.

The frame consists of horizontal beams in both directions and vertical columns called stanchions, usually all of standard rolled sections of various sizes, joined together by rivets or bolts with plates and angles, to form a stiff, stable skeleton capable of transmitting its own dead weight and all other loads to the foundations, to which the feet of the stanchions are bolted. All the steel members are commonly encased with 1 to $2\frac{1}{2}$ in. of concrete, the thickness depending on the degree of fire resistance required. The beams carry one of the many types of *in situ*, precast concrete or steel floors described in Chapter 6.

BASIC ELEMENTS OF CONSTRUCTION

The multi-storey steel frame is built up of hot-rolled mild steel units standardized in shape and dimensions and known as British Standard Sections.[1] There are joist, channel, angle and tee sections and of these the I section, commonly called a "rolled steel joist" (R.S.J.), is the basis of the frame for both beams and stanchions (see page 226). Where necessary these can be strengthened by the addition of plates riveted to the flanges. The beams and stanchions are connected by means of steel angle cleats riveted or bolted to each member. When the largest standard R.S.J. section, 24 in. by $7\frac{1}{2}$ in., is insufficient for the purpose, even when plated, it is necessary to build up girders from steel plates and angles riveted together to form a plate girder, or from angles, tees or channels to form an open web lattice girder.

In addition to British Standard sections covered by B.S. 4 and 4A[2] some steel firms roll sections covered by B.S. 2566 called "broad flange beams" which have certain advantages over the standard sections. They have the bearing capacity of a compound member without the disadvantages of riveting and are, therefore, useful for beams and stanchions, particularly the latter, where plating would otherwise be required. Broad flange beams are rolled in sections from 6 in. by 6 in. up to 12 in. by 12 in. and thereafter in a

[1] See page 252 for a description of cold-formed steel sections and their uses.
[2] From January 1963 these will be replaced by revised B.S. 4: 1962 which is based purely on Universal sections.

12 in. width with depths from 14 in. up to 24 in.   The full range is given in B.S. 2566 (page 236).

More recently a wide range of non-standard sections known as "Universal" sections has become available.   Joist and broad flange sections are produced,

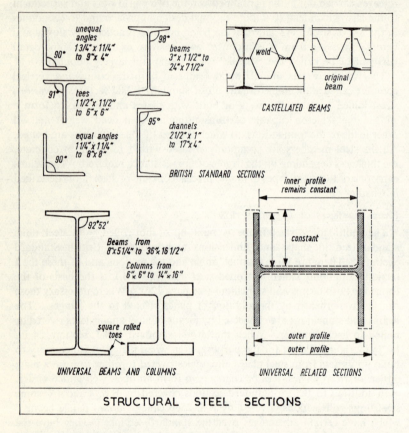

unequal
angles
1 3/4" x 1 1/4"
to 9"x 4"

98°

beams
3"x 1 1/2" to
24"x 7 1/2"

weld

original
beam

CASTELLATED BEAMS

tees
1 1/2"x 1 1/2"
to 6"x 6"

95°

channels
2 1/2"x 1"
to 17"x 4"

equal angles
1 1/4"x 1 1/4"
to 8"x 8"

BRITISH STANDARD SECTIONS

inner profile
remains constant

constant

92°52'

Beams from
8"x 5 1/4" to 36"x16 1/2"

Columns from
6"x 6" to 14"x 16"

square rolled
toes

outer profile

outer profile

UNIVERSAL BEAMS AND COLUMNS

UNIVERSAL RELATED SECTIONS

STRUCTURAL   STEEL   SECTIONS

both in related "families" of different weights, the use of which eliminates a great deal of plating and compounding for heavily loaded beams, and riveted-on flange plates to stanchions (see above).   Also available are very deep plate girders made up of a web plate welded between flanges made of heavy tee sections cut from a large "Universal" beam section.

A form of deep beam cut from a standard R.S.J. section is known as the "castellated" beam and this also has the advantage of eliminating plating and riveting. This is shown on page 226. The web of an R.S.J. is cut along its length on a castellated line by a flame cutter and the two halves are then placed "point" to "point" and welded at the junctions to produce an open web beam of the same weight as the original section but with a depth one-and-a-half times that of the original and, therefore, having a greater moment of inertia.

High-tensile steel can be used for the sections instead of mild steel. It is more costly but its high yield point permits greater working stresses, usually 50% more than for mild steel, resulting in a saving in weight which can offset the extra cost of the material. Deflection criteria may limit the development of the maximum stresses since its elastic modulus is approximately the same as that of mild steel, although methods have been devised to overcome this disadvantage (see page 247). Even so an ultimate saving in weight of 8 to 10% is possible. Although not widely used for complete frames, it is useful where a local reduction in size of beam or stanchion is essential and this in turn leads to a reduction in the amount of casing and to a saving in height and floor space.

The number of standard and non-standard sections now available to the designer is large and necessarily so if design is not to be limited. Nevertheless, the cheapest frame is not necessarily that which contains least material, although weight can be a useful, broad guide, and it is usually more economical to standardize the size of sections to some extent on any particular job rather than to relate the size of every member exactly to the calculations. Any saving effected by using the minimum size in every case may be outweighed by the cost of excessive "firring" and packing out in order to obtain some degree of uniformity in the finished overall beam and stanchion sizes, and by the cost of making more complicated connections. It must also be borne in mind that the material is cheaper than labour, that sections held in stock are cheaper and more readily available than others, and that it is cheaper to buy a large number of members of the same size than to buy a few lengths of a number of different size sections. A regular grid layout for the frame assists such a standardization by equalizing the loading on different parts.

Rivets and bolts are manufactured from mild steel, the quality of which is laid down in B.S. 15:1961.

Rivets are formed with different shapes of head. The snap head, which is almost semicircular in section, is used for the great majority of structural work, but where the projection of the head is inconvenient, a countersunk head is used to give a flush finish. Other shapes of head are seldom used.

Bolts are of three types: (i) "turned and fitted" bolts, (ii) "black" bolts and (iii) high strength friction grip bolts, each with hexagonal heads and nuts. Tapered washers are used to provide a flat bearing on bevelled surfaces. Turned bolts, as the name suggests, are turned to be parallel throughout the length of the barrel and must fit tightly into their holes. The working stresses permitted in turned and fitted bolts are the same as those for rivets but they are more expensive than rivets.

Black bolts are not turned to a precise diameter throughout and, therefore, cannot be a tight fit in their holes. As a consequence, the allowable stress in shear is not so high as for rivets and turned bolts and they may be used only for the end connections of secondary floor beams or for other connections where dead bearings are formed by seating brackets which resist the whole of the shear forces involved.

Friction grip bolts, also called torque or, more correctly, torque-controlled bolts, are used instead of rivets and turned bolts. They are made from steel with a greater yield point than mild steel and are placed in holes large enough to permit a push-fit, making assembly easy. The nut is tightened to a predetermined amount by a torque-controlled spanner or a pneumatic impact wrench which presses together the surfaces in contact to such an extent that they become capable of transmitting a moment from one to the other by friction. Torque bolts can of course be useful when site welding is impracticable.

FRAME LAYOUT

Planning requirements permitting, economy in the steel frame is obtained by the adoption of a regular and reasonably close spacing of stanchions as indicated on page 229. Short span beams are more economical per unit of length than long span beams.

For normal conditions of loading the cheapest beam will be the deepest available R.S.J. section giving the required strength. Although this may be in excess of the strength required it can still be cheaper than a shallower but heavier section. Take as an example a beam spanning 16 ft carrying a total distributed load of 17 tons. The shallowest R.S.J. suitable is a 10 × 6 weighing 40 lb per foot run which will carry 17·1 tons, but a 13 × 5 R.S.J. will carry 18·1 tons over the same span yet weighs only 35 lb per foot run, resulting in a saving of 80 lb of steel on the beam. As indicated earlier such savings must be balanced against increased costs which may arise in other parts of the building due to increased overall floor heights. The savings on the frame are likely to be greater than the increases in other directions in the case of large buildings of the warehouse class, where the area of external walls and internal walls and partitions is small relative to the total floor area.

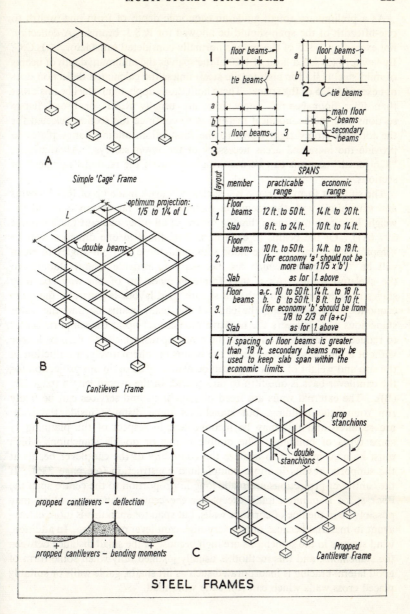

A

Simple 'Cage' Frame

B

Cantilever Frame

optimum projection:
1/5 to 1/4 of L

double beams

propped cantilevers - deflection

propped cantilevers - bending moments

C   Propped Cantilever Frame

prop stanchions

double stanchions

1   floor beams

tie beams

2   floor beams

a
b   tie beams

3   floor beams

a
b
c

4   main floor beams
secondary beams

layout	member	SPANS	
		practicable range	economic range
1.	Floor beams	12 ft. to 50 ft.	14 ft. to 20 ft.
	Slab	8 ft. to 24 ft.	10 ft. to 14 ft.
2.	Floor beams	10 ft. to 50 ft. (for economy 'a' should not be more than 1 1/5 x 'b')	14 ft. to 18 ft.
	Slab	as for 1. above	
3.	Floor beams	a.c. 10 to 50 ft. b. 6 to 50 ft. (for economy 'b' should be from 1/8 to 2/3 of (a+c)	14 ft. to 16 ft. 8 ft. to 10 ft.
	Slab	as for 1. above	
4	if spacing of floor beams is greater than 18 ft. secondary beams may be used to keep slab span within the economic limits.		

STEEL FRAMES

As a preliminary rough guide an economic depth of from one-twelfth to one-fifteenth of the span should be allowed for R.S.J. beams. A deflection not exceeding 1/325 of the span is normally considered satisfactory. L.C.C. By-law 6.14 (3) sets a limit of 1/20 of the span as the minimum depth of beams of mild steel (1/13 for high-tensile steel) unless the calculated deflection does not exceed 1/325 of the span. These limitations apply to all steel beams other than filler floor beams. Stanchions are usually R.S.J. or broad flange sections and the economical method is to continue the section selected for the topmost storey right down to the foundation, adding flange plates to provide the increased areas necessary at the lower storeys. Alternatively, "Universal" sections can be used, making use of the related "families" of sections.

The simplest form of frame is a skeleton "cage" made up of R.S.J. beams and stanchions with the members standardized as far as possible and the weight kept to a minimum, having regard to all other relevant factors (page 299 (A)). Of the beams at each floor level those in one direction will be "floor" beams carrying the floor slabs and those at right-angles to them will be "tie" beams which are necessary to provide lateral stability to the skeleton frame. As a steel frame is made up of one-way spanning stages a rectangular rather than a square, grid layout is generally the most economic. By projecting the ends of the main beams beyond the outer stanchions as cantilevers the negative moment set up at the supports serves to reduce the positive moment in the centre spans, which can then be longer without an increase in the size of the beams or, alternatively, a reduction in the size and weight of the beams can be made. The optimum projection for the cantilever bays is one-fifth to one-quarter of the overall length (page 229 (B)). The external walls are freed of stanchions and services can be freely run round the building, but stanchions some distance inside the walls are required and this may be inconvenient in respect of the planning of some types of building. The double beams or double stanchions which must be used in order to achieve the continuity of the cantilever beams at the supports, results in more complicated construction (see page 236). If the cantilever projections are made long in proportion to the centre span the floor space is uninterrupted except for the central stanchions which may possibly be in the line of corridor walls, but span for span this is more extravagant in material because of the very high cantilever moments. In addition, wind stresses in the stanchions are high because of the small distance between the stanchions, and this method is usually justified only when some form of good lateral bracing is incorporated such as lift shafts, gable walls or suitably placed cross walls which can resist the wind load.

The outer end of the cantilevers may be simply supported by props or struts in the plane of the walls to give what is known as propped cantilever construction as shown on page 229 (C). In this, the centre span is small as before but the negative bending moments over the supporting stanchions and the deflection of the cantilevers are smaller (C). The props are designed with free or hinged ends at the floor levels. Their function is to provide end support to the cantilevers, to transmit to the frame the wind load at each floor level and to transmit their proportion of the vertical load to the foundations. They can be comparatively small in cross section as they provide no rigidity to the frame against lateral wind pressure and, as a consequence of this, they will transmit no turning force to the foundations due to wind pressure.

If it is not desired to cantilever out at all floors, it may still sometimes be necessary to set in the outer stanchions at the lower floors either for architectural reasons or in order to simplify the problems of foundations adjacent to a building line. This may necessitate heavy compound or plate cantilever girders, particularly if headroom requirements prevent the use of the most economic depth (page 232 (D)).

Certain types of buildings require wide span beams throughout; others, based generally on a close, regular grid, require a variation of that grid to permit the provision of large, unobstructed floors at certain levels, such as ballrooms and restaurant areas in hotels, or the provision of wide shopfronts. These will require stronger beams (page 232 (E)) in the form of some type of girder.

GIRDERS

Compound Girders. Spans greater than the economic limits suggested earlier require the use of the deeper, heavier R.S.J. sections, and when the loads are heavy it is necessary to increase the flange area by the addition of plates riveted to the top and bottom flanges forming a "compound girder". One, two or three R.S.J.'s, or pairs of channels, may be compounded in this manner (page 233).

For heavier loads and for spans in the region of 50 to 120 ft, where a section larger than that obtainable from standard sections of R.S.J.'s would be required, it is necessary to use plate girders or trussed girders built up of smaller standard sections (page 232). The weight of steel in relation to the cube of the building is increased in such cases, resulting in an increase in cost. This may be minimized if ample depth can be allowed for the girders. The increased depth of lever arm results in a decrease in flange stresses, and this in a considerable reduction in the weight of the flanges, at the expense of a slight increase only in the weight of the thin web of a plate girder or the thin braces of a trussed girder.

Plate Girders. A riveted plate girder consists of a web plate connected to flange plates by means of angles and rivets to form a large I section, the thick-

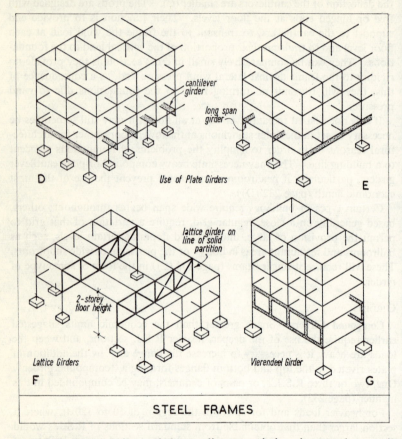

cantilever girder

long span girder

D

Use of Plate Girders

E

lattice girder on line of solid partition

2-storey floor height

Lattice Girders

F

Vierendeel Girder

G

STEEL FRAMES

ness of the flanges being varied according to variations in stress by curtailment of the flange plates as the stresses reduce. The webs are strengthened against buckling by stiffeners of tees or angles cut to fit between the flange angles and riveted to the web (see page 233). In order to take up the thickness of the longitudinal angles the stiffeners are joggled over the vertical legs of the angles or, alternatively, a packing piece, the same thickness as the angle

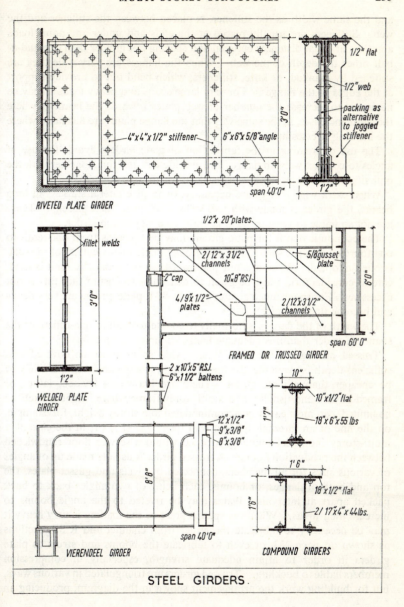

RIVETED PLATE GIRDER

1/2" flat
1/2" web
packing as alternative to joggled stiffener

4"x 4"x 1/2" stiffener
6"x 6"x 5/8"angle
3'0"
span 40'0"
1'2"

1/2"x 20"plates
2/12"x 3 1/2" channels
5/8"gusset plate
2"cap
10"x 8"R.S.J.
4/9"x 1/2" plates
2/12"x 3 1/2" channels
6'0"
span 60'0"

FRAMED OR TRUSSED GIRDER

fillet welds
3'0"
1'2"

WELDED PLATE GIRDER

2 x 10"x5" R.S.J.
6"x 1 1/2" battens

10"
10"x1/2" flat
18"x 6"x 55 lbs
1'7"

12"x 1/2"
9"x 3/8"
8"x 3/8"
8'8"
span 40'0"

VIERENDEEL GIRDER

1'6"
18"x1/2" flat
2/ 17"x4"x 44 lbs.
1'6"

COMPOUND GIRDERS

STEEL GIRDERS.

and the same width as the stiffener, is placed between the stiffener and the web. Stiffeners are usually placed at the ends and under any point loads and then at equal distances between at a spacing not greater than one-and-a-half times the depth of the web. When the flanges are very wide they are stiffened by cranked, or knee, stiffeners, which bend out to provide support at the edges of the flanges. For very large spans and heavy loads it may be necessary to increase the number of web plates towards the bearings where the shear increases, in the same way that the flange plates are increased where the bending stresses increase.

The use of welding in the fabrication of plate girders avoids the use of angles to connect webs to flanges and as stiffeners and this, together with the omission of rivets, results in smaller dead weight (see page 233).

When extra wide flanges are necessary, or to give lateral stiffness in long beams, the girder is made with two webs to form a "box girder". These are not so liable to twist or bend laterally as a single-web girder.

The economic depth for plate girders may be taken as from one-tenth to one-fourteenth of the span. For stiffer box girders one-twentieth of the span is often adopted. When a depth shallower than the economic limit is used, careful consideration must be given to deflection to ensure that this is not excessive. For spans much greater than 60–70 ft plate girders are very heavy and become uneconomic.

The width of the flanges is normally from one-fortieth to one-fiftieth of the span. If wider than this adequate flange stiffening is necessary.

Trussed or Framed Girders. Where wide spans must be covered and sufficient depth is available, the use of a deep, triangulated beam is likely to be cheaper than a plate girder. These are known as trussed, lattice or framed girders and usually, in a multi-storey frame where height is likely to be limited, can most easily be accommodated in a storey height, for example, on the line of an internal dividing wall (page 232 (F)) or, in the case of a multi-storey industrial building, exposed within a service floor sandwiched between the production floors.   A trussed girder is usually made up of angles of various sizes for all members, connected by rivets and gusset plates, the top and bottom flanges, or booms, each being of two angles back to back packed apart at intervals. Plates may be riveted to the angle booms to increase their areas. When the span is great or the loading is very heavy it may be necessary to fabricate the girder from channel and R.S.J. sections as shown on page 233, or even to fabricate the booms and struts as plate girders in order to attain adequate strength, especially in compression members liable to buckling.   Trussed girders are triangulated in various ways, but for building work the arrangement shown in the diagram, producing an

"N" girder, is most common. The struts or compression members are vertical and the sloping ties, lying in the plane of diagonal tension, are in tension.

The economic depth of trussed girders is from one-sixth to one-tenth of the span.

Lightweight lattice girders prefabricated in standard depths and lengths from hot- and cold-rolled sections are widely used for roof and floor framing in structures where the loading is relatively light (see Chapters 6 and 9).

Space Frames. These are described on page 429. Although more commonly applied to roof construction, the space frame can with advantage be applied to multi-storey frame construction. A light, rigid member with considerable stiffness results from forming a three-dimensional frame, and triangular section frames can show substantial savings over conventional girders—some have quoted savings as much as 20%. Used for floor framing, wide spans can economically be covered giving an open floor through which all services can be freely run.

Vierendeel Girders. A Vierendeel girder may be used as an alternative to a floor height trussed girder when the diagonal ties of the latter would cross door or window openings, or for some other reason would be inconvenient (page 232 (G)). The Vierendeel girder has no diagonal members, the shear normally carried by these members being transferred to the bearings by the stiffness of the chords and vertical members and by the rigid joints connecting them (page 233).

In such circumstances the chords would lie in the planes of the floors and the vertical members would appear as columns. These girders are expensive in steel and more costly than a trussed girder, and although the necessary rigidity at the joints can be attained by riveting, large gusset plates are necessary in order to accommodate the required number of rivets and the result is rather cumbersome. The rigid joints are more easily and more economically attained by welding.

STANCHIONS

R.S.J. and Compound Stanchions. The R.S.J. and broad flange sections, used alone or plated as necessary, are commonly used for the stanchions. They are very suitable for making riveted connections and for the continuous stanchions of multi-storey frames in which the same size section can be used as the "core" through a number of storeys with flange plates added as necessary. This simplifies the joints, or splices, in the lengths of the stanchions. The use of broad flange "Universal" sections eliminates, to a large extent, the

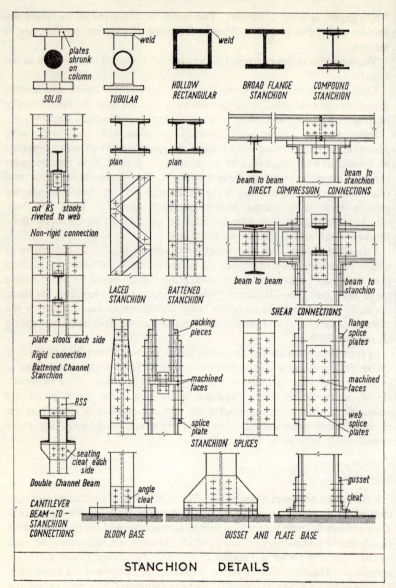

SOLID

TUBULAR

HOLLOW RECTANGULAR

BROAD FLANGE STANCHION

COMPOUND STANCHION

plates shrunk on column

weld

weld

plan

plan

cut RS stools riveted to web

Non-rigid connection

plate stools each side

Rigid connection
Battened Channel Stanchion

LACED STANCHION

BATTENED STANCHION

beam to beam

beam to stanchion

DIRECT COMPRESSION CONNECTIONS

beam to beam

beam to stanchion

SHEAR CONNECTIONS

RSS

seating cleat each side

Double Channel Beam

CANTILEVER BEAM-TO-STANCHION CONNECTIONS

packing pieces

machined faces

splice plate

STANCHION SPLICES

flange splice plates

machined faces

web splice plates

angle cleat

BLOOM BASE

GUSSET AND PLATE BASE

gusset

cleat

STANCHION DETAILS

need of plating on the lower storeys, as they are produced in varying weights for each basic size.

Rolled steel and compound stanchions are usually positioned with the web in line with the main beams which they support so that the beam is connected to the stanchion flange. This is because smaller bending stresses due to the eccentric bearing will be set up in the stanchion than if the beam is connected to the web. In the case of riveted joints, regulations require a minimum eccentricity of 2 in. to be assumed at the beam connection and when the beam is connected to the stanchion web rather than the flange, greater bending stresses always result, in spite of the smaller total lever arm, due to the small value of the minimum section modulus (see below). With broad flange sections the difference is less marked and with direct welded joints a connection to the web will, in fact, produce less bending stresses in the stanchion because of the extremely small eccentricity at the joint.

EFFECT OF BEAM CONNECTIONS ON STANCHION STRESSES							
Riveted Connections				Direct Welded Connections			
12"x6"x54 lb. R.S.S.		10"x8"x55 lb. R.S.S.		12"x6"x54 lb. R.S.S.		10"x8"x55 lb. R.S.S.	
8" e 2"	$e=2$"	7" e 2"	$e=2$"	6" e	$e=25$"	5" e	$e=.2$"
$Z = 62.6$	$Z = 9.4$	$Z = 57.7$	$Z = 13.7$	$Z = 62.6$	$Z = 9.4$	$Z = 57.7$	$Z = 13.7$
Relative stress in stanchion $f = M/Z = We/Z$							
$\frac{Wx8}{62.6} = .128$	$\frac{Wx2}{9.4} = .213$	$\frac{Wx7}{57.7} = .121$	$\frac{Wx2}{13.7} = .146$	$\frac{Wx6}{62.6} = .096$	$\frac{Wx.25}{9.4} = .027$	$\frac{Wx5}{57.7} = .087$	$\frac{Wx.2}{13.7} = .015$

As most stanchions fail by buckling in the direction of the least dimension, and since strength in this respect depends upon the value of $\frac{l}{r}$ (effective length divided by the least radius of gyration), those sections with the widest flanges are most efficient for use as stanchions since they give closer values for the radius of gyration in the direction of both principal axes. This is shown clearly on the graph on page 238. The use of flange plates further reduces this inequality and with broad flange beams of equal dimensions in both directions, it is possible by this means to obtain a section differing little in its resistance to buckling about both axes.

Circular Stanchions or Columns. Solid and hollow circular columns have the same r value in all directions and occupy less floor space than any other equally strong stanchion under axial load, but they present difficulties in making connections to them and in a multi-storey frame vertical continuity suffers. In addition, the solid steel column is heavy and expensive.

In terms of efficiency, that is in terms of strength to weight ratio, as distinct from size, the solid circular column is less efficient than an R.S.J. section with a wide flange. For example, a 4 in. diameter solid steel column, weighing 42·7 lb per foot run, has an *r* value of 1·00 in. while a 6 × 6 × 25 lb broad flange section has a greater minimum *r* value of 1·51 in. Where the effective length of a stanchion can be reduced by adequate restraint in the direction of least *r*, the efficiency of the R.S.J. section will be further enhanced.

The caps and bases of solid circular columns are of thick steel plate bored to fit over the ends of the column, which are turned to produce a small shoulder. The plates are "shrunk" on to the column by being heated and

Load carrying capacity related to Radius of Gyration and Slenderness Ratio.

1·6·3 shows in each case the ratio of minimum to maximum radius of gyration.

In shorter stanchions, strength is to some extent proportional to weight. With increase in height, strength reduces more rapidly in in sections having a high ratio of minimum to maximum radius of gyration.

EFFECT OF WIDE FLANGES ON STANCHION STRENGTH

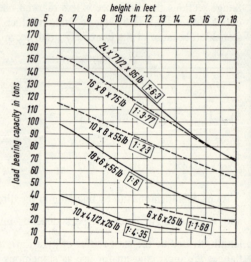

then forced on to the turned ends where they cool and shrink thus tightly gripping the column.

A hollow circular column has a greater *r* value than a solid circular column of the same diameter, that for the former being approximately 0·35 × mean diameter and for the latter 0·25 × O/A diameter. The tube section, with its smaller area of material and load-carrying capacity but greater *r* value, has advantages, therefore, in cases where buckling rather than direct stress will be the critical factor.

Cap and base plates and connecting cleats are normally welded to hollow circular columns. Tubular columns have been used in Great Britain for two-storey frames where the total height of column can be in one length to preserve continuity. Where the advantages justify it, multi-storey structural frames can be fabricated from welded tubing.[1]

Hollow Rectangular Stanchions. A hollow square section made from two angles or two channels welded toe to toe permits connections to be made to it more easily than to circular columns, and has an equal r value about both normal axes slightly greater than that for a hollow circular column of the same dimensions, that for the former being $0 \cdot 41 \times$ mean breadth. As with hollow circular columns this section is particularly useful for long, slender but lightly loaded stanchions and will show an economy in material over the R.S.J. section. Connecting cleats are normally welded to the stanchion.

Lattice or Braced Stanchions. Stanchions formed from pairs of R.S.J. sections or channels braced together by diagonal or horizontal plates are called respectively laced and battened stanchions, and are used in cases where very tall but relatively lightly loaded stanchions are necessary, requiring a maximum r value in both directions, or in cases where the load is too great for even the largest rolled section (see page 236). These sections can easily be arranged to give equal r values about each axis by adjusting the distance between the pair of basic members. For heavy R.S.J. sections the distance between webs will be about three-quarters of the depth of the joist, and for channel sections placed back to back the distances between webs will be about half to two-thirds of the depth of the channel according to the particular section used. Limits on the spacing of lacing bars and battens are laid down in B.S. 449.

CONNECTIONS

Connections between the members of a steel frame are made by means of rivets and bolts with angles and cleats, or by means of welding.

Rivets and bolts are described on pages 227 and 228. A welded joint is one in which the adjacent members are joined by the fusion of the steel at their point of contact. Additional metal at the joint is deposited in the process from steel welding rods. Welded connections are discussed in more detail under "Welded Construction' on page 248.

Connections between the different members of a steel frame can be classified as follows:

(i) compression connections, in which the load is carried directly from one member to another and the connection serves mainly to fix the two parts together;

See *Acier*, No. 6, June 1956, for an eight-storey example in Paris.

(ii) shear connections, in which the joint elements are stressed in shear;

(iii) tension connections, in which the joint elements are stressed in tension.

Compression connections are the most economical, but where these are not suitable shear connections are preferable to tension connections which, generally, are adopted in special cases only.

Connections are detailed so that fabrication is as simple as possible having regard to erection problems. For example, when the flange width of a beam is greater than the web depth of the supporting stanchion the beam flanges must be side notched in order to effect a web connection. Such notching could be avoided by increasing the depth of the stanchion section which might produce an economy in the frame, especially if a number of similar beam connections were involved.

Stanchion Bases. The foot of a stanchion must be expanded by means of a base plate large enough to reduce the pressure on the foundation to the safe bearing pressure of the concrete. The base plate itself will act as an inverted cantilever beam and is designed accordingly.

There are two types of bases: (i) the gusseted base and (ii) the slab or bloom base.

Gusseted Base: This consists of a thin plate of steel stiffened by gusset plates and angles which act as ribs (see page 236). If the ends of the stanchion and gusset plates are machined for bearing, all the parts work in combination to transmit the forces to the base plate, but if the ends are not machined, the fastenings connecting them must be capable of transmitting the whole load to the base plate. This, of course, is likely to result in larger gusset plates. The size of the base plate depends on the safe bearing pressure which the concrete can resist. The breadth of the base generally varies from two to three times the breadth of the column, and the height of the gusset plates from one-and-a-half to three times the breadth of the column. Gusseted bases are commonly used, but when the stanchion is heavily loaded the use of a slab base may prove advantageous.

Slab or Bloom Base: This consists of a base plate thick enough to resist the moments caused by the bearing pressure without the assistance or stiffening effect of gusset plates. It is fixed to the foot of the stanchion by a pair of angle cleats (see page 236). Both the end of the stanchion and the upper face of the base plate must be machined true so that they are in close contact one with the other. The fastenings are designed to secure the slab to the stanchion and to resist all forces other than the direct load. This base requires less labour in fabrication than the gusseted base and there is a saving in depth of the cover necessary to give a clear floor compared with that required when there are large gusset plates, but it sometimes requires more material, particularly in the case of large bases. When the area of the base plate is large relative to the area of the stanchion, it may be cheaper to use a gusseted base in order to reduce the thickness of the slab or bloom plate.

The underside of base plates and slabs need not be machined when the base will be grouted to a concrete foundation, provided the underside is true and parallel with the upper face. A bloom base is always used for solid circular columns.

A stanchion base is secured to its foundations usually by four holding-down bolts which are grouted into the concrete. Levelling up of the base is done by means of steel wedges before grouting up with a fairly dry cement and sand mix. When bending moments will be transferred to the foundation the base must be sufficiently strong and rigid and the holding-down bolts must be well tied to the foundation block (see page 242 and also 453).

Stanchion Caps. A cap must be provided to the stanchion if the beams rest on top of it. The cap plate is secured to the stanchion by a pair of angles and rivets; no gusset plates are used, the top of the stanchion and the angles being machined true before being fixed to the cap plate so that the load is transmitted directly through the plate to the end of the stanchion (see page 236).

Stanchion Splices. Joints in the length of stanchions, generally termed splices, are necessary for erection and fabrication purposes because it is difficult and expensive to handle lengths much greater than about 35 ft (see page 236). Stanchions should be fabricated in lengths as long as possible and the limit of 35 ft for an individual length results in stanchion lengths of two to three storeys in height, depending on the floor-to-floor height of the structure. The joints should be made as near as possible to the beam level, but in order that splice plates shall not obstruct beam connections they are usually placed about 12 to 18 in. above floor level. Any change in the depth of the root joist section is made at these points, and where the whole of the end of the upper length does not bear on the lower length a horizontal seating plate of the same overall size as the lower stanchion must be placed between the two lengths. Packing plates will be necessary between the upper smaller section and the splice plates as shown on page 236. The use of "Universal" sections reduces the need for seating plates. When the same root section runs through adjacent lengths of stanchion, the ends of each may be machined and bear directly one on the other, and transmission of load will be by direct compression so that the splice plates serve only to secure the two lengths. If the ends are not machined and are not in full

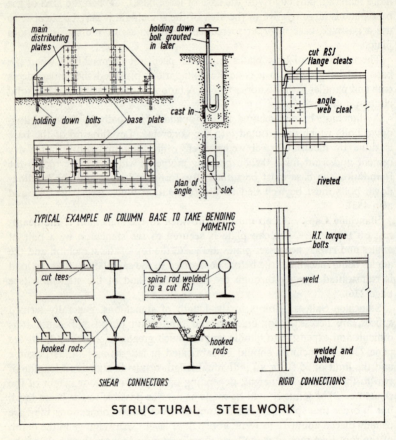

main distributing plates

holding down bolts   base plate

holding down bolt grouted in later

cast in

plan of angle   slot

TYPICAL EXAMPLE OF COLUMN BASE TO TAKE BENDING MOMENTS

cut RSJ flange cleats

angle web cleat

riveted

H.T. torque bolts

weld

welded and bolted

cut tees

spiral rod welded to a cut RSJ

hooked rods

hooked rods

SHEAR   CONNECTORS   *RIGID   CONNECTIONS*

STRUCTURAL   STEELWORK

contact the splice plates and rivets must be sufficient to transmit the entire load.

Beam to Stanchion Connections

Direct compression connections are only possible where the beam rests on top of the stanchion. This is normally not possible at lower beams where loads have to be transmitted by shear connections as shown on page 236. In order to facilitate erection these joints are provided with seating cleats or stools riveted to the stanchion in the shop, so that when the beam is hoisted into position it can bear on the stool while being fixed. Load transmission from beam to stool is by direct compression and through the stool to the stanchion by the rivets in shear. Angle cleats are also provided to the web or top flange of the beam to prevent canting of beam. It is simpler to have these connected to the web and it also leaves the top flange clear at the junction with the stanchion, but sometimes it is not possible to arrange this and flange cleats must be used. A top flange cleat produces a stiffer joint than web cleats.

Bearings for cantilever beams passing through a double member stanchion can be provided by a stool formed from a piece of R.S.J. section fixed between the stanchion members on which the beam rests and to which it is fixed by stool cleats as shown on page 236. Greater rigidity at the connection may be provided by plate stools connected to the flanges of the stanchion members and secured to the bottom flange of the beam with angle cleats. The use of top plates and cleats fixed after the erection of the beam further increases the rigidity of the connection when bending moments have to be transmitted. Where the beam itself is a double member, stools are fixed to the flanges of the stanchion to take the beam members (see page 236).

The maximum stress permitted in stanchions depends on the ratio of effective length to radius of gyration. The former varies with the number and disposition of the beams connected to the stanchion, as this affects the degree of fixity and restraint given to the stanchion. The restraint given by various arrangements is indicated in Appendix D, of B.S. 449.

Beam-to-Beam Connections. The direct compression connection, in which one beam bears directly on the top flange of the other, is the most economical, but in multi-storey frames this is generally not suitable because of the considerable depth of the pair of beams one on top of the other. Shear connections are therefore usual with web connected to web. The angle cleats are riveted to the web of the secondary joists in the shop and the connection is completed on the site by bolting to the main beam (see page 236).

When the main beam is much deeper than the secondary beam, for example in the case of a deep R.S.J. or a plate girder, erection is facilitated by using stools made up of plates and angles or of a piece of cut R.S.J. section. These have the added advantage of forming stiffeners at the point of application of the load which is desirable in deep beams. Where the flanges of both beams are to be level, that of the secondary beam must be notched to clear the flange of the main beam.

Tension joints are generally avoided but may have to be used when the secondary beam must pass under the main beam. The connection depends entirely upon the nuts of the bolts by which the secondary beam is hung from the other. Direct connection of flange to flange should be avoided whenever possible, the better method being to hang from the flange of the main beam by means of angles and gusset plates.

WIND BRACING

Adequate lateral resistance against wind pressure may be provided in a number of ways. In many cases where the beams are reasonably deep and satisfactory connections to the stanchions can be made, special bracing is not necessary. Connections can be made by means of angle cleats of sufficient size and rivets in sufficient numbers. The cleats must be stiff enough to transmit moments without excessive distortion and often would become uneconomically thick, especially when the stanchion is narrow and necessitates the use of long cleats to accommodate the required number of rivets. The thickness of the cleats can be reduced by the use of plate or gusset stiffeners, or by the use of T's cut from R.S.J. sections instead of angles as shown on page 242. The use of web cleats gives only a small additional resistance because of the small lever arm for their moment of resistance. A more satisfactory method is to weld a steel fixing plate on to the end of the beam with sufficient projection above and below the beam to accommodate the required number of rivets. This takes advantage of the stiff joint given by welding but avoids actual welding on to site. Increased stiffness is obtained by the use of torque bolts instead of rivets (see page 242).

Very tall structures with small base areas usually require special measures. These may take the form of (*a*) X or K braces in the frame panels; (*b*) knee braces, or gussets; (*c*) rigid frames; (*d*) shear walls. (*a*) is often not practicable when large unobstructed spaces are required; (*b*) is used to make beam to stanchion connections capable of transmitting the forces and moments set up by the lateral pressure of the wind when the type of joints described above would not be strong enough.

Considerable resistance to wind pressure and sway can be given by wall panels and floor slabs and by making use of these elements, special forms of bracing can sometimes be avoided. The use of light, steel deck floors eliminates this possibility and, in fact, may necessitate the incorporation of bracing devices solely on account of their use.

Research has shown that even lightweight wall panels and $4\frac{1}{2}$ in. brick panels with door openings in them increase to a considerable degree the stiffness of the structural frame.[1] Hitherto, no account has been taken of this in respect of normal brick-panel walls, but substantial solid internal walls, known as shear walls, have been used for this purpose, built in the panels of the steel frame to prevent "racking" under the pressure of the wind. Such walls would be situated at suitable points on plan, where they would not form an obstruction to open space, such as along the central "service" core of an office block or similar building.

Floors, if adequately designed, can act as deep horizontal beams between cross or end walls, between strong braced frames or, when bracing is not practicable, between rigid frames designed to take all the wind load. This relieves the intermediate frames of the effect of side-sway. At present, however, membrane action of floors and walls is usually disregarded with steel frame structures.

COMPOSITE CONSTRUCTION

In reinforced concrete structures it has been usual to keep in mind the interaction of the different parts during the design stage, but in the case of steel structures it has been usual to design a frame in complete isolation from the rest of the structure, leading to an analysis of its behaviour which is now known to be false, at least in the case of building frames. Considerable data is now available regarding the composite action of the various parts of a building structure, and B.S. 449 permits allowance to be made for concrete casing on beams and stanchions.

Due to its early failure under the action of fire, structural steel members in multi-storey frames must be adequately protected from the effect of fire, and this is fully discussed in Chapter 10. Solid concrete casing is common and, while it is used primarily for the fire protection of the steel,[2] B.S. 449

---

[1] See *Principles of Modern Building*, Vol. 1, 3rd Ed. H.M.S.O., pages 13, 14.

[2] The L.C.C. By-laws lay down certain minimum thicknesses of solid casing to steel-work in external and party walls, and to steelwork exposed to the weather, which may be greater than that required for fire protection. By-law 6.02 requires that, subject to the provisions of Part 9 (Fire Resisting Construction), the steelwork shall be solidly encased in brickwork or concrete or similar material at least 2 in. thick all round. Provided that where the casing is exposed to the weather it shall be

   (i) of concrete not less than 3 in. thick; or
   (ii) of brickwork or stone or similar material, properly secured, if the steel is protected from the effects of corrosion by:

     (a) 2 in. of concrete on the flange faces, $1\frac{1}{2}$ in. on the flange edges and 1 in. on all projecting rivet heads, bolts or splice plates so that the total thickness of encase-ment to the column or beam is not less than 4 in.;

or,
     (b) such material as the District Surveyor may approve as being suitable, having regard to the particular circumstances of the case, and the thickness of the brick-work, stone or similar material, is not less than 4 in.

Where the structural steelwork may be adversely affected by moisture from the adjoining earth, it shall be solidly encased with concrete at least 4 in. thick.

9

and the L.C.C. By-laws do permit allowance to be made for the stiffening effect of the casing on beams and stanchions resulting in higher permissible stresses for the steel. B.S. 449, in addition, permits some of the stanchion load to be carried by the concrete, with a limit on the total axial load carried of twice that permitted on the uncased section. In the case of both beams and stanchions these allowances do not apply to sections greater than 30 in. × 18 in. or to box sections.[1] In a multi-storey steel-frame building, having solid concrete casing to the members, a saving in steel can, therefore, be effected by taking the casing into account, even allowing for the somewhat heavier reinforcement required. This results in smaller overall sections and, therefore, a saving in the concrete casing content. In the case of stanchions, the more lightly loaded a stanchion is, the greater will be the benefits deriving from this procedure. Composite stanchions can also be formed with the concrete placed internally, relative to the steel. Multi-storey stanchions of two opposing channels have been used, the channels being filled with concrete vibrated after erection, designed to carry 28% of the load, and showing a saving of 50% of steel compared with normal stanchions.

It should be noted here that asbestos spray and hollow casings of various types are now permitted as fire protection, the use of which considerably reduces the dead load on the frame. B.S. 449 lays down conditions in which the frictional resistance between the top flange of a steel beam and the floor slab it supports may be considered sufficient to provide adequate lateral restraint to the beam. As this restraint is more often than not available in practice solid concrete beam casing is not essential for this purpose and light-weight hollow protection can be used with economic advantage. In some circumstances hollow casings to the stanchions may show economies, but in others it may be more advantageous to use concrete casings to carry some of the stanchion load.

Some types of hollow casings, although having the advantage of dry construction, offer little cost advantage over solid concrete even taking into account the savings in the cost of foundations, since these are usually small relative to the total cost of the frame. Others, as shewn by investigations into the use of vermiculite-gypsum plaster on metal lathing,[2] appear to be more promising from the economic point of view.

Concrete floor slabs may be used to act together with the steel supporting

---

[1] B.S. 449:1959, Clauses 21; 30.   L.C.C. By-laws 6.11 (5); 15 (3).
[2] See "Lightweight Fire Protection and the Structural Engineer" by A. R. Mackay, A.M.I.Struct.E., in *The Structural Engineer*, January, 1960, and "Report on Lightweight Fire Protection for Structural Steelwork" by Frederick Snow and Partners, Consulting Engineers, London.

beams.   A concrete slab adequately bonded to a steel beam will act in the same way as in a reinforced concrete T-beam.   This is particularly useful when the steel is encased, as the lever arm of the composite section will be greater by about half the thickness of the slab.   The concrete casing by itself does not, however, provide sufficient bond between the steel and concrete to transmit the steel stresses, and this is essential if composite action is to be achieved.   The greatest shear stress is at the neutral axis, which is always near the top of the combined section, so that a satisfactory bond can be obtained by welding shear connectors to the top flange of the R.S.J. in the form of angles, channels, spiral wire or hooked rods, as shown on page 242.   As the compressive stress is taken primarily by the concrete, the top flange is under little stress and the steel element can consist only of the lower flange and the web of an R.S.J., with the shear connectors welded to the top edge of the web.   Spiral wire or hook rods are most suitable for this purpose. The problem of tension arising in the top of the member and compression in the bottom over the supports in continuous composite beams may be dealt with as follows:

(1) The concrete may be reinforced longitudinally with rods;
(2) The R.S.J. may be strengthened by welding on top flange plates, ignoring the concrete entirely, as well as plates on the bottom flange to strengthen that.

Although the construction of this type of beam results in a reduction in the amount of steel used, the method entails a considerable amount of fabrication, and it is probably most useful in cases where labour is cheap and steel is scarce.

Concrete is also used to stiffen high-tensile steel beams in order to permit them to be stressed to their working limit.   In normal building structures these beams cannot always be stressed to their limit because the amount of deflection might be unacceptable, high-tensile steel having an elastic modulus approximately equal to that of mild steel.   In this system the beam is deflected to the same extent that it would be under full working load and the concrete is cast as a casing round the tension flange.   After this has set, the deflecting force is removed, and as the beam reverts to its original unstressed state, it compresses the concrete.   Under working load the tensile stresses in the bottom flange are resisted by the compressive stresses in the concrete casing and this has the effect of reducing the deflection of the beam, thus permitting the high-tensile steel beam to be stressed to its limit so that its high strength may be fully utilized.

Prestressing may be applied to mild steel beams in order to allow the use of reduced cross sections resulting in savings in weight and cost. The post-tensioning cables may be passed through a box tension flange with anchor plates at the ends, or they may be external to the beam at the sides or below the tension flange. In the latter case the beam may be bent up so that the cable is straight or the cable may be strutted off the tension flange to form a trussed beam. Depth/span ratios in the region of one-thirtieth to one thirty-fifth can be attained.[1] Typical applications are shown below.

Welded Construction

Substantial savings in the weight of steel arise when joints are welded and allowances made in the design of the frame for the effects of rigid connections. These savings are stated in some quarters to be as high as 20 to 25%

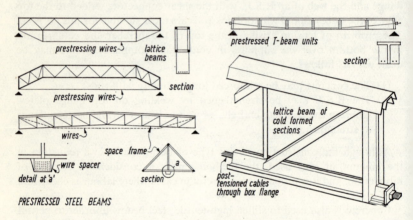

PRESTRESSED STEEL BEAMS

of the weight of a comparable frame in riveted construction. The economies are due to (*a*) the elimination of rivet holes; (*b*) simpler connections with no rivet or bolt heads or, in many cases, angle cleats; (*c*) the possibility of developing fully rigid end connections leading to the use of lighter members; (*d*) in the case of built-up members, such as plate girders, the use of single plates, welded directly one to the other without the addition of angles. Although not normally possible with multi-storey frames, where the frame is exposed the appearance is enhanced by the cleaner and neater joints, and less maintenance costs are involved in re-painting, because of the smaller sections and the absence of gusseted connections.

The use of welding permits the better use of tubular and cold-rolled steel

[1] See *The Structural Engineer*, November 1950, February 1954 and February 1955, for papers on the subject of prestressed steel beams and girders.

sections, both of which, when used in appropriate circumstances, tend towards further reductions in weight. Flexibility in design arises from the fact that built-up sections may easily be fabricated, thus freeing the designer from the restrictions of the standard rolled sections. In addition, the material in such members may be proportioned to the moments it is called upon to resist in the different parts, thus producing maximum structural efficiency; greatest advantage may be taken of this in single-storey frames rather than in multi-storey frames.

Methods of Welding. Two methods are normally employed in structural work: (i) oxy-acetylene welding, (ii) metal arc welding. In the former, the flame from an oxy-acetylene torch heats the two surfaces to be joined at their point of contact, and molten metal from a steel filler rod held in the flame at the same time fuses into the two surfaces. In the second process, an electric current passes through the metal filler rod, which acts as an electrode, and the material to be joined. An arc is produced, which heats and melts the surfaces and the end of the filler rod.

Types of Welds. There are two types of weld: a butt weld and a fillet weld. The fillet weld is that in which the two surfaces joined are basically at right-angles one to the other, the butt weld is that in which the two surfaces to be joined butt against each other. There are varieties of each of these and some are shown on page 250. The strength of a weld is based upon its area, made up of the effective length and the throat thickness.[1]

Types of Welded Connections. Varying degrees of rigidity may be produced in welded joints according to their design, but unless especially designed to produce full fixity, a welded joint will generally possess no more rigidity than a normal riveted connection. Welded joints may be in the form of direct or indirect connections. A direct connection is one in which the members are in direct contact one with the other and are joined to each other directly by welds without the use of cleats or plates (page 250 (A)). In the case of beams, particularly, this necessitates accurate cutting to length and complicates the erection process, so that more often than not an indirect connection is used, involving flange and web cleats (B, D), which overcomes these disadvantages. Stanchion bases and caps, and stanchion splices, may be formed with direct or indirect connections (E, F).

It will be noticed that in the splices, angle cleats are welded to the foot of the upper stanchion length to enable this to be bolted on site to the lower stanchion length and held in position while the necessary site welds are executed.

---

[1] General requirements and permissible stresses for welded construction are laid down in B.S. 449. For details of methods and forms of joints see also B.S. 693 and B.S. 1856.

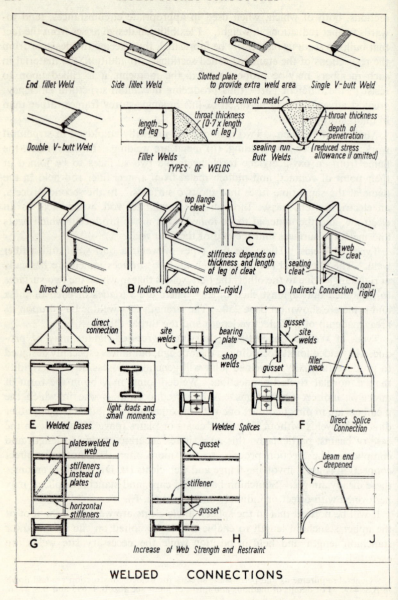

End fillet Weld   Side fillet Weld   Slotted plate to provide extra weld area   Single V-butt Weld

Double V-butt Weld

reinforcement metal

throat thickness (0·7 x length of leg)

length of leg

Fillet Welds

throat thickness

depth of penetration

sealing run

Butt Welds

(reduced stress allowance if omitted)

TYPES OF WELDS

A Direct Connection

B Indirect Connection (semi-rigid)

top flange cleat

C

stiffness depends on thickness and length of leg of cleat

D Indirect Connection (non-rigid)

web cleat

seating cleat

E Welded Bases

direct connection

light loads and small moments

site welds

bearing plate

shop welds

gusset site welds

gusset

Welded Splices

F

Direct Splice Connection

filler piece

G

plates welded to web

stiffeners instead of plates

horizontal stiffeners

H

gusset

stiffener

gusset

J

beam end deepened

Increase of Web Strength and Restraint

WELDED CONNECTIONS

Indirect beam to stanchion, and beam to beam connections may be made in a number of ways. A non-rigid connection may be made by the use of web cleats, fillet welded at the toes to each of the members, with a space between the members themselves (D). To facilitate erection, it is an advantage if a seating cleat is incorporated in the joint. Very often cleats are shop-welded to the various members and the site joints made with bolts.

Semi-rigid joints between beams and stanchions can be obtained by the use of flange cleats fillet welded at the toes, one acting as a seating cleat, the other as a top cleat, with a space between the end of the beam and the stanchion flange (B). The rigidity of such a joint varies mainly with the type of tension flange connection, that is, with the top cleat, the stiffness of which varies with the thickness and length of the legs of the angle. The stiffness increases with the increase of thickness and with the decrease in length of the vertical leg (C). By means of such variations it is possible to attain either a very rigid joint or a flexible joint.

In fully rigid connections it may be necessary to increase the shear strength of the stanchion web. This may be accomplished in a number of ways. (1) By welding on rectangular plates to the web of the stanchion. In addition to these, horizontal stiffeners at the level of the beam flanges will usually be required (G). (2) By means of a triangulated system of stiffeners which may be designed to act either in conjunction with the stanchion web, or entirely alone. The use of gussets or brackets at the junction of the beam and stanchion, or deepening the end of the beam, has the effect of reducing the shear stress at the connection and is a method which may be adopted as an alternative to (1) or (2), (H, J). It also increases restraint at the joint.

SEMI-RIGID AND FULLY RIGID FRAMING

The majority of steel frames have been designed on what is known as the simple design method, in which all the beams are assumed to be simply supported at the connections with the stanchions, in disregard of the obvious and proved partial fixity existing at the ends of beams with riveted connections. B.S. 449 permits the alternative methods of simple, semi-rigid and fully rigid design. In the semi-rigid method, in certain conditions of end fixity, beams with riveted connections may be designed as partially fixed at the ends and can achieve a saving in steel of from 2 to 5%. An approximate allowance in design may be made for the end restraint of beam to stanchion connections where the beam is efficiently connected to a stanchion, efficiency of the connection being based on the thickness of the top cleat which varies from $\frac{3}{8}$ to $\frac{5}{8}$ in. according to the weight of the beam section and the type of beam.

The fully rigid method in which the interaction of beams and stanchions is calculated for all conditions of loading gives greatest rigidity and greatest saving in steel, but is not so readily applied to multi-storey as to single-storey frames, because of the large number of joints. The full development of fully rigid multi-storey frames probably depends upon the extensive use of welding as a joining technique, and perhaps on the use of friction grip, or torque, bolts (see page 228).

COLD-FORMED STEEL SECTIONS

These are made from light-gauge steel strip, 0·04–0·15 in. thick (20 B.G.–8 B.G.) and occasionally as thick as $\frac{3}{16}$ in., cold formed to shape in a rolling mill or press-brake and are known as Cold-Rolled and Pressed-Steel Sections.

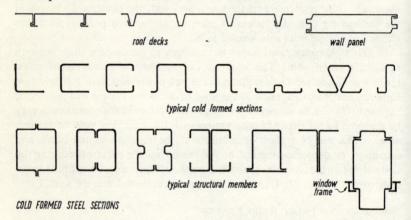

roof decks   wall panel

typical cold formed sections

typical structural members   window frame

COLD FORMED STEEL SECTIONS

Considerable development has taken place in the production of floor and roof units and metal trim, and also in the field of structural members. Pressed-steel sections are largely used for flooring and roofing units and wall panels, and for metal trim such as skirtings and sub-frames, the lengths of which are limited by the maximum width of the press-brake (page 337 and above). The press-brake is a machine which has a long horizontal former rising and falling with a pressure of 150 tons. This former presses the steel strip into a suitable shaped horizontal bed to form folds by means of which simple sections are shaped, usually up to 10 ft. long, although a few machines can produce lengths up to nearly 20 ft. The limitations of pressed-steel sections are explained in *Advanced Building Construction* (*Components, Services and Finishes*).

For structural members of greater length, cold-rolled sections are used.

These are formed into the required shape by passing metal strip between six to fifteen progressive sets of forming spindles or rollers, each pair of which adds successively to the shaping of the strip, the final pair producing the finished section. The basic sections rolled are plain angles and channels, lipped channels, and zeds (see page 252). Outwardly lipped channels are commonly called top-hat sections. The length is limited only by considerations of transport. The maximum width of strip which can be formed is $22\frac{3}{4}$ in. and the minimum width, $\frac{1}{4}$ in. The final cross-section must lie within an area of 20 in. $\times$ $5\frac{1}{4}$ in. There is virtually no limit to the shape that can be rolled so that the designer can choose a shape best fitted for any particular purpose although, as the manufacture of the rollers for sections outside the basic range is expensive, the economic advantage of choosing such a section must be considered carefully if the quantity required is small.[1] Where possible the section should be made to fulfil more than one function by shaping it, for example, to avoid the casings often necessary with hot-rolled sections and to permit the direct attachment of claddings and windows. In addition to this, the strength of individual members may readily be varied by varying the gauge of the steel while maintaining the same overall sizes. These possibilities can lead to increased efficiency in the structure and to substantial economies in the weight of steel used.

Cold-rolled sections are most efficiently used with structures of moderate loads and span, in which circumstances they can be cheaper than hot-rolled members. Erection of the structure is often cheaper and easier because of its light weight and rigidity. Cold-rolled sections are used for roof trusses, lattice beams and rigid frames, where they are probably used to greatest advantage, but they have been used for two-storey frames throughout, and for three-storey frames in which the bottom storey lengths are in hot-rolled sections in order to keep the overall size the same as the cold-rolled lengths above. As an alternative to the use of hot-rolled sections, a heavier section with the same overall size can be obtained by spot welding cold-rolled reinforcing sections on the inside.

Channels placed back to back and box sections are suited to axial load, the latter having considerable torsional strength. There appears to be little economic advantage in using cold-rolled sections for columns as far as cost of material and fabrication are concerned, but there are considerable savings in erection costs, which may be 10 to 15% cheaper than with hot-rolled sections. When fire-resisting casing is not required external columns can, as mentioned above, be shaped to act as window mullions to accommodate

---

[1] Up to 5,000 ft may need to be run off before the cost of setting up the machine is covered, depending on the complexity of the section to be rolled.

9*

windows by direct fixing as shown on page 252. I-section beams formed from channels placed back to back are only likely to be economic for light loads over short spans, where the smaller R.S.J. sections might not be used to their limits. The wider choice of section possible with cold-rolled sections gives them an advantage in these circumstances. Greater savings over hot-rolled work are found by using cold-rolled lattice beams over intermediate spans with light loadings, although, as indicated above, the most economic field is in roof structures where the advantages of the low dead/live load ratio and ease of handling and erection show most clearly (see Chapter 9, page 443).

Connections are made by various types of welds, self-tapping screws, bolts, cold rivets and hot rivets, and sections can be formed to push-fit into each other, thus avoiding the use of gusset plates. For example, top-hat flange sections can be used for beams into which the bracing members fit, so that the node connection is direct.

Structural considerations are similar to those in the design of light alloy structures. The design of thin wall structures requires special consideration, due to the possibility of local instability, and, as in aluminium sections, lips to the edges are provided to give increased stiffness to the section.[1] The need for protection from corrosion is important, because there is not so much margin for wastage of metal as in hot-rolled sections. Phosphating followed by paint dipping and stoving is usually adopted for internal work and where the structure is to be exposed to the weather, hot-dip galvanizing can be used. Mild-steel strip is widely used in the production of cold-rolled sections but high-tensile steel with rust-inhibiting qualities is likely to be used to an increasing extent because of its structural advantages.

THE REINFORCED CONCRETE STRUCTURE

Reinforced concrete, because of its particular characteristics, can be formed into walls as well as into beams and columns to form a skeleton frame, and floor slabs can be designed without projecting beams to carry them. A reinforced concrete structure may, therefore, consist solely of slab floors and columns or may be a combination of columns, beams and loadbearing walls, each being used to fulfil most satisfactorily the functions required at various points. For example, staircases and lift shafts often must be enclosed in solid walls, and it is logical to make these of reinforced concrete capable of both enclosing the areas and carrying the floor loads, rather than to surround the areas with beams and columns and then enclose with non-loadbearing

[1] The design of cold-rolled steel structures is covered by Addendum No. 1 (1961) to B.S. 449—"The Use of Cold-Formed Steel Sections in Building".

panel infillings.   Such enclosures, being monolithic in form, result in very broad annular columns running right through the building which can be used to provide resistance to wind pressure on the structure.

Greater flexibility in planning and design is possible with reinforced concrete than with steel.

Cross wall construction in concrete, known as "box frame", is dealt with in this chapter rather than in that on "Walls and Piers" because of its total monolithic character enabling the walls and floor slabs to act together.   For ease of reference reinforced concrete floors have been considered in a separate chapter, although they do, in fact, form an integral part of most reinforced concrete frames.

At the beginning of its structural life reinforced concrete is fluid or plastic in character and this gives rise to two important factors concerning the nature of the structures for which it is used:

(a) the ease with which a monolithic structure may be obtained, producing a rigid form of construction with the economies inherent in this form (page 256), and

(b) the ease with which almost any desired shape may be formed either for economic, structural or aesthetic reasons.   For example, the material may be disposed in accordance with the distribution of stresses in the structural members, placing most where the stresses will be at a maximum and reducing it where they will be at a minimum.

These two factors together, monolithy, giving particular distributions of stresses, and variation in the disposition of material according to the stress distribution, produce characteristic concrete forms which are most obvious, as far as building structures are concerned, in single-storey structures. Nevertheless, these characteristic forms do find a place in multi-storey frames, and it should be made clear at this point that the designer's freedom to cast concrete in almost any shape is limited by the cost of the formwork or shuttering into which the concrete must be poured.   This forms a large proportion of the total cost of a reinforced concrete structure as can be seen from the following approximate percentage break-down:

Concrete	40%	Materials	28%
		Labour	12%
Shuttering, including erection and stripping	32%	Materials	12%
		Labour	20%
Reinforcement	28%	Materials	20%
		Labour	8%

Shuttering costs for beams alone may be as high as 40% of the total cost of the beam. It will be seen that the percentage labour content in shuttering is far greater than that in steel fixing or concreting, so that economies in shuttering will have a significant effect in reducing the cost of the concrete work. Such economies are the outcome of simple structural forms repeated a number of times, making the construction of the shutters a simple matter and enabling them to be used repeatedly to the maximum extent. Complicated shapes, particularly if curved, appearing only once in a structure lead to high shuttering costs.

Up to comparatively recent times multi-storey reinforced concrete frames have always been erected as *in situ* cast structures for which all the constituent concrete materials have been brought to the site, mixed and placed in formwork erected in the position the concrete will finally occupy in the completed structure. Such frames are invariably of monolithic construction by which full continuity throughout columns, beams and slabs is attained. The advantages of monolithic or fully continuous construction are:

(*a*) Reduced deflections in the members.

(*b*) Reduced bending moments distributed more uniformly throughout the structure than in discontinuous structures. The reduced moments result in lighter members. The greater uniformity in distribution will, in members of uniform section sized to the maximum bending moment, have the effect of involving less waste of material at the points which are less highly stressed.

(*c*) In the case of beams there is a less rapid increase in dead weight with increase in span because, due to the stress distribution, a great deal of the extra material is required over the supports which will take its weight directly. It will not, therefore, increase the bending moments as it would if placed at the centre of the span. This is particularly important in long span construction where the superimposed loading is light and, for economy, a low dead/live load ratio is required, and in cases where the structural depth is limited.

Against these advantages must be placed the following disadvantages:

(*a*) The adverse effect of differential foundation settlement, which has been described on page 59.

(*b*) Adverse effect of temperature movement. Movement due to temperature changes has a similar effect upon a continuous structure to that of foundation movement, and close attention is necessary at the design stage to the maximum possible movement and the use of expansion joints at appropriate points to prevent accumulative movement throughout the whole structure.

For a number of reasons, discussed more fully on page 270, the technique of building up the frame with precast elements has developed in recent years. The structural members are cast either off-site or on a casting area, or bed, on the actual building site, and after maturing are erected with the aid of cranes. Certain difficulties are encountered, especially in obtaining satisfactory monolithic joints between the different members, but these can be overcome in various ways as described later. The completion of a frame can be effected more quickly than by *in situ* casting methods, thus bringing about in this respect a more favourable comparison with steel.

Since the end of World War II the application of another technique, that of prestressing, has rapidly developed in this country. Concrete, being weak in tension, cracks around the steel reinforcement at a low stress. In practice these cracks are usually limited to about one-hundredth of an inch, which prevents the steel being stressed to its maximum, but prestressing, by preventing the development of tensile stresses in the concrete when under load, enables the high-tensile strength of modern steel and the great compressive strength of modern high-quality concrete to be fully and effectively used. This results in members, particularly beams, of smaller cross-section and less dead weight than in reinforced concrete and involves the use of far less weight of steel.

In multi-storey frames the application of prestressing is largely confined to freely supported members, particularly floor slabs (see Chapter 6) and precast beams. It is reasonably easy to arrange for the prestressing of beams cast monolithic with the columns, but considerable complications arise in design and construction when it is applied to the complete monolithic structure. Prestressing is more fully discussed on page 281.

CHOICE OF STRUCTURE

The choice of a particular reinforced concrete structural system as most suitable in any given case will depend largely upon the nature and purpose of the building. For example, the structure of a building to accommodate heavy, evenly distributed loads might most economically be developed as flat slab construction, whereas one in which considerable concentrated loads caused by machinery would occur could most economically be formed with a beam and column system in which the various elements could be designed more easily with regard to the local loading at any point. In the case of flats requiring a high degree of fire resistance and a measure of sound insulation in the separating walls, a box-frame structure is suitable and can be economic, whereas for an office block, requiring large areas which can freely be divided up in different ways by non-loadbearing partitions, this would be unacceptable.

Linked with these considerations will be that of resistance to wind. A box-frame structure provides ample resistance in a transverse direction but will require stiffening longitudinally by lift or stair enclosures or by solid walls. The frames to heavily loaded structures may have beams sufficiently deep to provide the necessary rigidity at the joints with the columns without any other form of bracing. In other cases, where solid walls must be provided on plan for functional reasons, perhaps fire division walls, it may be economical to transfer the wind loads to these entirely by the floor slabs so that the columns may be relieved of lateral pressure. When a precast concrete frame appears to be suitable the decision must be made whether to use diagonal bracing within the frame or solid walls at suitable points to provide wind bracing.

As pointed out in Chapter 3, the choice of structure is closely linked with the soil conditions on the site and the economic design of the foundations, and the consideration of both must take place at the same time.

The most economic structure is not always that in which the amounts of steel, concrete and shuttering are all kept to a minimum, and the most economical beam is not necessarily one in which the "economic percentage" of steel is provided, that is the amount of reinforcement which permits the safe working stresses in the steel and concrete to develop at the same time. In fact, it is normally only in slabs and sometimes in rectangular beams that this is possible. For economy of shuttering it may be desirable to maintain a constant depth for a continuous beam, although the bending moments vary considerably at different points, rather than attempt to reduce the amount of concrete. In order to standardize shuttering in this way to reduce its cost, considerable variations in the concrete mix and steel content, as a means of standardizing the size of beams and columns, can often be justified. In some circumstances it may be necessary to increase the steel content in order to restrict the depth of the beam for reasons of headroom, or in order to keep floor to floor heights to a minimum, and the extra cost may well be counterbalanced by savings in other directions.

THE MATERIALS OF REINFORCED CONCRETE

Concrete itself has great compressive strength but is weak in tension, its strength in this respect being about one-tenth only of its compressive strength. C.P. 114:1957 gives the crushing strengths required for nominal mixes and the permitted working stresses in respect of these strengths. In structural members in which both compressive and tensile stresses occur under load, the full compressive strength of the material cannot, therefore, fully be developed, and in order to overcome this deficiency a material, strong in tension, is introduced in the tensile zones to reinforce the concrete at those points. Steel is used for this purpose at the present time but some investigations have been made into the use of glass fibre. So far, however, the problems of obtaining a reliable bond and uniform strength, and the overcoming of brittleness have not been solved. Experiments are also in progress with cables of glass fibre for prestressing.

Reinforcement. Steel is used, either as mild steel or high-tensile steel bars or wires, because it can easily be produced in forms suitable for the purpose, and it possesses to a large degree characteristics which are essential in any material to be used for reinforcement. Assuming adequate tensile strength these are:

(a) a surface which will satisfactorily bond with the concrete so that when the steel is stressed it will act together with and not pull away from the concrete,

(b) a coefficient of lineal expansion much the same as that of concrete, so that under changes of temperature undesirable stresses will not be set up,

(c) a relatively small elongation under stress to avoid excessive deflection.

Steel reinforcement is obtainable in a variety of forms of bars and fabric.

Bars. Circular section rolled mild steel bars or rods are most commonly used for all forms of reinforced work. High-tensile steel rods can also be used. Due to the higher working stress, less steel will be required to provide the same strength as mild steel, but in developing its full strength it stretches more than mild steel and the cracks in the concrete around it will be larger. This might be undesirable in circumstances where corrosive fumes, for example, could attack the steel. The problem of the formation of large cracks is closely linked with that of bond between the steel and concrete. The better the bond the less risk there is of large, concentrated cracks developing, and as a means of increasing bond and limiting cracking to fine, well distributed cracks, *deformed bars* can be used. The greater bond stress obtainable makes it possible to stress the steel to higher limits and thus develop its strength to a maximum. Greatest advantage is obtained when a large number of small diameter bars are used rather than a few larger bars, because the surface area in contact with the concrete is thereby increased. The use of these bars eliminates the necessity of end hooks, thus economizing in steel and simplifying work on the job.

Deformed bars are produced in a number of ways. Firstly, as high-tensile steel bars rolled with projecting ribs, or corrugations along the length or, secondly, from mild steel bars which are cold-worked to increase the ultimate tensile strength and raise or eliminate the yield-point of the steel, the amount of increase depending upon the nature of the basic steel and the amount of cold-working. Both stretching and twisting are used as methods of cold-working and may be applied to circular ribbed bars or to square bars which become deformed by the twisting process and thus afford better bond. Some examples are shown below.

The importance of eliminating the yield-point lies in the fact that when mild or high-tensile steels are used for reinforcement, both of which have yield-points, the bond between reinforcement and concrete begins to break down when this stress is reached, so that in practice design is based on this value. The use of cold-worked mild steel or the new high yield-point steel recently introduced makes it possible to work to much higher stresses,

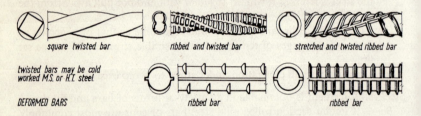

square twisted bar   ribbed and twisted bar   stretched and twisted ribbed bar

twisted bars may be cold worked M.S. or H.T. steel.

DEFORMED BARS   ribbed bar   ribbed bar

particularly if deformed bars are used, and in this respect Dr Hajnal Kónyi quotes tests which show that within certain limits such steel used as reinforcement can be stressed to its ultimate strength.[1]

Although used widely in the U.S.A. and in Europe, deformed reinforcement has not been greatly used in Great Britain, although in the future its advantages, particularly in the realm of cold-worked bars, may make it competitive with prestressing in many applications.

Fabric. The use of this form of reinforcement is an economic way of reinforcing large areas such as floor and roof slabs. It is produced in two main forms: as a mesh of wire or rods electrically welded at the points of crossing or as expanded steel sheets.

Mesh fabric is manufactured either from hard (cold) drawn steel wire or from small cold twisted steel bars, both of which, due to drawing or cold-working, have greater strength than mild steel, that of the wire being con-

[1] *New Ways of Building*, Ed. Eric de Maré (Architectural Press, 1958).

siderably greater. It is supplied as square or rectangular mesh in pieces or in rolls and its use avoids the necessity of tying together separate bars.

Expanded metal fabric of steel sheets slit and stretched to form a diamond-shaped mesh is supplied in pieces and for reinforcing purposes has a mesh of 3 in. or more.

Aggregates. Various materials are employed as aggregate, the selection depending upon the purpose for which the concrete is used. They may be divided into (i) heavy, (ii) lightweight aggregates.

Heavy Aggregates. These include the natural sands and gravels and crushed stones covered by B.S. 882, and crushed brick. These are normally used where strength and durability are required, although many lightweight aggregates are now being used for structural concrete.

Lightweight Aggregates. These have been used for many years for reinforced concrete floor, roof and wall slabs, and are being increasingly used for general reinforced concrete construction. Satisfactory materials are foamed slag, expanded or sintered clay or shale, and sintered fly ash. Pumice and expanded slate are also satisfactory, but are not generally available in Great Britain. These aggregates can be used with the addition of sand to provide a satisfactory grading to give the necessary strength and impermeability, the resulting concrete weighing from 100 to 120 lb per cu. ft with 28 day crushing strengths up to more than 4,000 lb per sq. in. (see Table 10). The modulus of elasticity of these concretes is less than that of gravel concrete so that deflection in beams and slabs tends to be higher. Depths of members, therefore, need to be greater. Multi-storey structures have been constructed in lightweight reinforced concrete in the U.S.A. for many years and are being built in Great Britain, making use of both *in situ* and precast-concrete.[1]

Fire Resistance. When a high degree of fire resistance is required, the type of aggregate used is important as this largely affects the behaviour of concrete under the action of fire. The classification of aggregates in respect of fire resistance is given on page 478 and it will be seen that one natural stone, limestone, is included in the non-spalling types. C.P. 114 permits a reduction in the size of reinforced concrete members made with limestone as the coarse aggregate. For example, for fire-resistance periods of four hours and two hours, columns may be reduced from 18 in. and 12 in. to 12 in. and 9 in. minimum overall size respectively.

Size of Aggregate. This should be as large as possible consistent with ease of placing round reinforcement. C.P. 114 prohibits sizes greater than

[1] See "The Use of Lightweight Concrete for Reinforced Concrete Construction", by A. Short, M.Sc., A.M.I.Struct.E., in *The Reinforced Concrete Review*, March 18, 1959.

one-quarter of the minimum thickness of the member. For heavily reinforced members the nominal maximum size is usually limited to $\frac{1}{4}$ in. less than the minimum space between the bars or $\frac{1}{4}$ in. less than the minimum cover to the bars, whichever is the smaller size. For general purposes $\frac{3}{4}$ in. is usually satisfactory and normally used, and for members such as the ribs and the topping of hollow block floors $\frac{3}{8}$ in, is normal. Where the reinforcement is widely spaced, as in solid slabs, the aggregate size may be as great, or even greater than, the minimum depth of cover to the steel, provided that the aggregate is not of a porous nature.

IN SITU CAST CONCRETE STRUCTURES

THE SKELETON FRAME

For small span structures a rectangular grid layout, similar to that for a steel frame, with one-way spanning floor slabs, can be satisfactory, but with large spans or heavy loading a square grid with two-way spanning slabs is more economical because of the resulting reduction in thickness and dead weight of the slab. Codes of Practice restrict the thickness of floor slabs to a fraction of the span[1] as a precaution against excessive deflection so that there is a limit to the possible reduction in dead weight of slab for any given span. Up to the point at which deflection ceases to be the factor governing slab thickness, no advantage, therefore, is gained by using a two-way spanning slab in place of a one-way span, because the thickness of slab and, consequently, its dead weight, must be the same in both, and there will be little difference in the amount of steel required. After this point has been reached advantage can be taken of the economies resulting from the use of a two-way spanning slab on a square grid.

In the case of one-way spanning slab construction the transverse, or tie-beams, necessary in a steel frame to provide lateral rigidity to the frame are not essential to an in situ cast reinforced concrete frame, since each floor is cast as the frame rises and can provide rigidity to the frame. Where such transverse beams are omitted, lateral stiffness against wind pressure must, of course, be provided by the floor slab which should be made strong enough to fulfil this function. Page 263 shows ways of framing in this manner. (A) shows the floor beams running parallel with the main external walls resulting in a flat ceiling for the length of the structure, an advantage in certain types of buildings, such as offices, where movable partitioning is likely to be changed in position from time to time. With no transverse beam projections such partitioning can be standardized to the floor to ceiling height

---

[1] See Chapter 6, footnote on page 301.

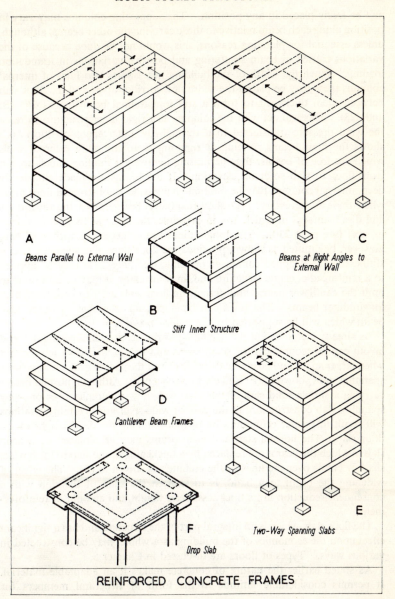

A

Beams Parallel to External Wall

B

Stiff Inner Structure

C

Beams at Right Angles to External Wall

D

Cantilever Beam Frames

E

Two-Way Spanning Slabs

F

Drop Slab

REINFORCED CONCRETE FRAMES

and be freely placed in any position. The supporting columns may vary in position along each beam relative to those carrying the other beams, although, unless essential for planning reasons, this would not be done because of the variations caused in beam shuttering and possible variations in foundation loading. When the width of the building necessitates two lines of internal columns these may be placed the width of a corridor apart and the floor slab between them thickened to form a stiff longitudinal beam (pages 263 (B) and 328). This will act with the columns as a rigid inner structure to resist the wind pressure transferred to it through the outer spans of floor. (C) shows the floor beams running at right-angles to the main external walls which are free of beams, thus permitting lightweight infilling panels to run from floor to slab soffit on elevation. If the beams are made sufficiently deep, internal columns may be omitted giving wide, unobstructed floor areas where these are necessary. (D) shows cantilever beam frames, the advantages and disadvantages of which are, in principle, the same as those constructed in steel (see page 230). The longitudinal beams necessary with steel can, however, be omitted as shown, provided the floor slabs give adequate lateral stiffness. The propped cantilever principle (see page 231) may be applied to a reinforced concrete structure and, in some cases, it may be economic to omit the cantilever beams and design the floor slab itself to cantilever over longitudinal beams. The soffit can be sloped up to a shallow outer edge beam which will be supported by the outer "props".

As already mentioned at the beginning of this section, the rectangular grid layout can be economical for small spans and lightly loaded structures, but when larger spans and heavy loads are involved the square grid with two-way spanning slabs shown in (E) is likely to be cheaper. Although normal beams carrying a simple solid slab of this type will show economies over one-way spanning slab construction, in the case of wide-span grids certain variations will result in greater economies by further reducing the dead weight of the floor slab. The normal slab and deep beams may be replaced by a drop slab in which the beams are replaced by a thickening of the slab to form wide, shallow bands over the lines of the columns as shown in (F). The effect of widening the beam to a band, is to shorten the span of the slab with a consequent reduction in its thickness, dead weight and amount of reinforcement.

The floor slab, which is an integral part of the structure and has a significant effect upon the economics of the building as a whole, may be constructed in various ways. Types of floors are discussed in Chapter 6.

As stated earlier the nature of concrete makes it an adaptable material. It permits considerable latitude in the form of structural members for

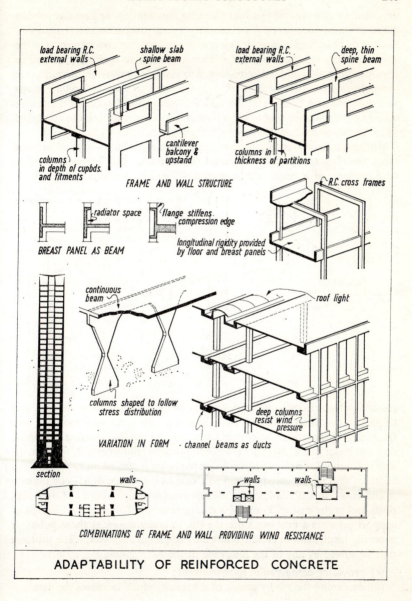

load bearing R.C. external walls
shallow slab spine beam
cantilever balcony & upstand
columns in depth of cupbds. and fitments

FRAME AND WALL STRUCTURE

load bearing R.C. external walls
deep, thin spine beam
columns in thickness of partitions

radiator space
flange stiffens compression edge

BREAST PANEL AS BEAM

R.C. cross frames
longitudinal rigidity provided by floor and breast panels

continuous beam
roof light
columns shaped to follow stress distribution

VARIATION IN FORM · channel beams as ducts

deep columns resist wind pressure

section

walls

walls
walls

COMBINATIONS OF FRAME AND WALL PROVIDING WIND RESISTANCE

ADAPTABILITY OF REINFORCED CONCRETE

structural or other reasons such as planning and lighting, and readily permits the interaction of beams and floor slabs to produce more economical members. The use of beam and column framing with load-bearing concrete walls in the same structure is logical when the latter can fulfil an enclosing, as well as structural, function and is often adopted to provide or assist in the resistance to wind pressure. This adaptability is illustrated on page 265, which shows how columns and beams may be varied in shape for functional reasons or reasons of appearance, and how frame and loadbearing wall can be combined where desirable for functional or other reasons.

Where the floor slab is cast monolithic with a beam, as is usual in most cases, the T-beam is commonly used (see below). The necessary tension reinforcement in a beam can be accommodated in a relatively thin rib of

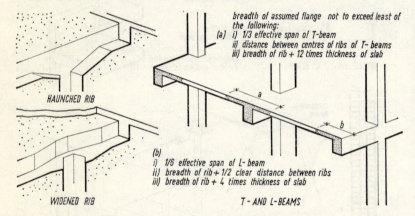

breadth of assumed flange not to exceed least of the following:
(a) i) 1/3 effective span of T-beam
    ii) distance between centres of ribs of T-beams
    iii) breadth of rib + 12 times thickness of slab

HAUNCHED RIB

(b)
i) 1/6 effective span of L-beam
ii) breadth of rib + 1/2 clear distance between ribs
iii) breadth of rib + 4 times thickness of slab

WIDENED RIB   T- AND L-BEAMS

concrete which needs to be only wide enough to accommodate the steel and to provide for shear stresses. By combining such a rib with the floor slab the necessary resistance in compression may be obtained with a minimum depth of beam and without the use of compression reinforcement. Where the slab is on one side only of the rib beam the beam is termed an L-beam. The width of slab which may be assumed to act as the flange of a T- or L-beam is laid down in C.P. 114:1957. Beams are normally continuous over supports and in the case of T- or L-beams the reversal of stresses at the point of support presents a problem since the rib, in compression at those points, is generally insufficient in area to resist the compressive stresses. The problem may be solved by any of the following methods:

(a) providing compression reinforcement;
(b) deepening the rib by means of a haunch, which increases the area;

(*c*) widening the rib for its full depth;

(*d*) widening the bottom of the rib only to provide a lower flange.

For most building frames compression reinforcement is invariably used and is generally no dearer than the provision of haunches, which is the most common alternative. However, in heavily loaded frames, where shear stresses are likely to be high at the supports, haunches may be preferable. The flaring or widening of the rib and the provision of a lower flange are rarely used as they complicate the shuttering (see page 266).

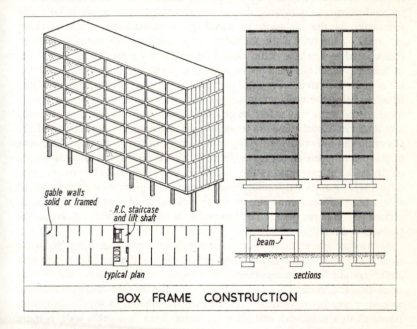

gable walls
solid or framed

R.C. staircase
and lift shaft

typical plan

beam

sections

BOX   FRAME   CONSTRUCTION

THE BOX FRAME

This is a form of cross-wall construction in which the walls are of normal dense concrete, and with the floors form box-like cells (as shown above). As in the case of brick or block cross-wall construction, it is suited to those building types in which separating walls occur at regular intervals and are required to have a high degree of fire resistance and sound insulation. The most common building type in this category for which it is suitable is the multi-storey flat or maisonette block.   The advantages listed on page 135 in respect of brick and block cross-wall construction apply also to the box frame.

In concrete walls of normal domestic scale—about 8 ft high and 4 in. thick, failure is almost wholly related to the strength of the concrete and very little to the slenderness of the wall.   Reinforcement, therefore, may be nominal in amount or may be omitted altogether provided that the concrete is sufficiently strong to resist the stresses set up under load.   For multi-storey blocks in the region of ten or eleven storeys high the mix would be designed to give a strength of around 2,250 lb per sq. in. at 28 days, although for the two lowest storeys a stronger mix might be necessary as well as the inclusion of reinforcement.   Cracking due to the shrinkage of concrete is normally overcome by the inclusion of shrinkage reinforcement.   Such cracking generally occurs only if the shrinkage is resisted by some restraint, such as that offered by changes in the plane of a wall or by a previously poured lift of concrete which has been permitted to take up its shrinkage before the next lift is poured on to it.   Provided that concreting can proceed without undue delay and that the walls are in simple, straight lengths, shrinkage reinforcement in the walls may safely be omitted.   Although the junctions of walls and floors in a box frame are monolithic, if the walls are not reinforced the structure can only provide rigidity in the length of the building to the extent of the precompression set up in the walls by the floor loads and self-weight of the walls, as explained in the case of normal cross-wall construction (see page 137).   Additional stability must normally be given by staircase and lift shafts of reinforced concrete, or by the inclusion of longitudinal walls at certain points in the plan.   The box-walls themselves provide rigidity in the transverse direction.

Many box frames have been constructed with the end, or gable, walls similar in form to the internal cross walls.   The solid external concrete wall suffers certain disadvantages (pages 127, 186) and to it must be applied thermal insulation and, generally, some external facing for the sake of appearance and to ensure weather resistance.   As both can be applied as satisfactorily to a frame as to a solid wall and since the latter, used as a gable wall, is more expensive than the frame, it appears logical to use a frame in this position.[1] With regard to thermal insulation it is desirable to apply insulation to the exposed ends of the box walls as heat losses at these points can be high, leading to condensation on the internal faces of the walls adjacent to the exposed ends (see pages 136, 186).

---

[1] Mr P. Dunican, of Ove Arup & Partners, gives the cost of mounting and demounting the shuttering for the gable walls of the flats at Roseberry Avenue, London, as about six times the cost of that for the internal walls—*Architects' Journal*, 3.4.53, page 497.

Creasy[1] gives graphs showing that for low blocks the box frame is not so economical as either a reinforced concrete frame or brick cross-wall construction (see page 138). In high blocks, however, it is cheaper than the frame when plan requirements permit the walls to be spaced 17 ft or more apart but less economic when the walls must be placed closer together (see below). It should be noted that the optimum spacing of the walls is 17–18 ft with the cost curve rising a little more rapidly with a decrease than with an increase in the spacing. It should also be noted that the graphs show the relative costs of the structural frames only, and disregard the effect of other elements which have a bearing upon the total cost of the building as a whole. For example, the cost of infilling panels of bricks or blocks at the separating wall position, to provide the necessary degree of fire resistance and sound insulation, must be added to the cost of the reinforced concrete frame to make it comparable with the box frame.

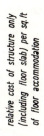
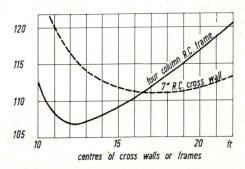

BOX FRAME – RELATIVE COST OF STRUCTURE

based on ten-storey construction with 9ft storey height and 30 ft depth of building

In its simplest and most economic form all the box walls run in a straight, unbroken line from back to front of the building and are supported directly by a strip foundation. They may, however, be pierced by openings or be in completely separate sections on the same line, or staggered relative to each other provided that each section is in the same position throughout the height of the building. If the upper floors are to be supported on columns at ground level the necessity of beams and the disposition of the columns will depend upon the arrangement of the walls above. Straight, unbroken box walls can act as deep beams spanning between the supporting columns with any necessary reinforcement placed in the tension and shear zones. If the walls are broken extra columns must be introduced to enable each wall section to act as a beam or, alternatively, a separate beam must be introduced

[1] See "Economics of Framed Structures", by Leonard R. Creasy, B.Sc. (Eng.), M.I.C.E., page 256, *Proceedings of the Institution of Civil Engineers*, Vol. 12, March 1959.

to pick up the sections and transfer the loads to the columns. These variations are shown on page 267.

EXTERNAL REINFORCED CONCRETE LOADBEARING WALL CONSTRUCTION

The reinforced concrete loadbearing wall used as the enclosing wall to a building is the alternative to its use as a dividing element in the box frame, see page 265. The wall areas over openings act as beams and those areas between openings as columns, thus no projections occur internally. These openings may be wide, since with normal sill heights there is ample depth of wall between window head and sill above to act as a deep, thin beam and the wide, narrow window is a characteristic of this form of construction. Alternatively, the whole height of the wall may be regarded as a beam pierced by any necessary openings for windows.

Sufficient width of wall must, of course, be left between openings to act as columns taking all the vertical loads. The problems of appearance and thermal insulation are the same as with the plain concrete wall, but the danger of cracking due to possible unequal settlement is reduced because reinforcement is present to resist any tensile stresses set up.

PRECAST CONCRETE STRUCTURES

A precast concrete component may be defined as a component cast in formwork in a position other than that which it will finally occupy in the completed structure and which, after removal from the forms and maturing, requires to be placed and fixed in position.

The technique of precasting concrete for structural purposes was originally applied to the manufacture of floor and roof slabs, but the process has now developed to such an extent that whole building structures can be erected from factory produced precast components involving columns, beams, floor and roof slabs and external panels and cladding.

In terms of site work the great advantage of the precast structure is that the speed and simplicity of erection compares favourably with that for a steel frame and this, allied to the cheapness of concrete, makes it an extremely valuable method of construction. In addition to the saving of time and labour on the site factory production makes possible a closer control of the concrete than is often possible on the site, particularly in the case of small jobs, and leads to a saving in materials and an improvement in quality. Formwork and its support is greatly reduced, the site is less obstructed and, in cases where the concrete is to be exposed, the production of satisfactory surface finishes is facilitated (see "Claddings", Chapter 4). The difficulties arising from the shrinkage of fresh concrete are eliminated because all maturing takes place before the components are built into the structure.

The principle disadvantage is that the continuity and rigidity of structure attained in an *in situ* cast frame are more difficult to achieve in the precast structure, and special consideration must be given at the design stage to methods for overcoming this difficulty.

Precast concrete itself tends to be more expensive than *in situ* concrete because of factory overheads and transport costs, but against this must be put, in terms of the structure as a whole, the savings in time and labour on the site, so that the costs of precast and *in situ* structures, are generally about the same, unless the units are precast a considerable distance away from the site making transport costs high. A regular layout and simplicity in jointing are essential.

THE PRECAST SKELETON FRAME

The precast concrete structural frame has developed as a result of attempts to link the advantages of the steel frame with the economy of the concrete frame. A precast frame will generally be cheaper than a steel frame encased in concrete and comparable in cost with an uncased steel frame. In multi-storey buildings a steel frame must be encased with some appropriate fire-resisting material and in most cases concrete is used to obtain sufficient protection. The amount of concrete necessary is usually almost as much as that required for a comparable frame constructed of reinforced concrete, and the concrete frame would show a saving in cost, in some cases as much as 30%, over that of the encased steel frame. In addition to this, the process of casing the steel does away with much of the saving in time associated with steel construction. The *in situ* concrete frame, however, does involve a considerable time lag between the pouring of the concrete and the removal of all shuttering and temporary supports, resulting in a delay in the re-use of shuttering and in the obstruction of working areas for long periods. Shuttering can be complicated in the case of slabs and beams. By applying the technique of precasting the disadvantages of *in situ* work can be avoided and benefit derived from some advantages linked with the steel frame.

The frame may be (i) partially or (ii) wholly precast. In the first method only the horizontal members are precast, the columns being cast *in situ* with continuity simply achieved in the normal way as each section of the column is cast. The factors in favour of casting the columns *in situ* are, firstly, the simplicity of achieving continuity by this means and, secondly, the fact that solely from the point of view of shuttering there is little in favour of pre-casting. This is because column shuttering is simple in form, takes up little space, requires relatively little labour to erect and strip and involves a negligible wastage in re-use. In contrast, in the case of beams and slabs, bending stresses are set up in the shuttering while the concrete is wet, necessitating heavy forms and a considerable amount of propping. This is avoided when the shuttering is supported by the ground or a production bench and the formwork can be lighter and cheaper. Floor areas are obstructed by props for considerable periods while the concrete attains sufficient strength to support its own self-weight. Considerable wastage in horizontal shuttering occurs in stripping and re-erecting,[1] and this work takes longer than in the case of columns. These disadvantages are avoided when the horizontal members are precast, so that the arguments in favour of this are considerable.

Nevertheless, arguments in favour of *in situ* cast columns based only on shuttering disregard questions of quality of concrete and of time and labour spent on the site and there is now a wide use of wholly precast frames, especially with the development of multi-storey columns precast up to five storeys in height, which minimize site labour in erection. The attainment of satisfactory continuity at the column connections necessitates either the exposure of relatively long lengths of reinforcing rod at each joint in order to obtain sufficient bond length, the welding of the rods or the use of some form of connecting plate. The section of column left open for the jointing of the rods must then be boxed in and concreted solid *in situ*. While such a joint is being made and until the concrete has gained sufficient strength, the upper section of column must be adequately supported and held fixed in position, and a number of methods of jointing have been evolved to permit the self-weight of the upper section to be transferred to the lower section while the joint is being made so that bracing only is required to hold it in a vertical position (page 274 (B)).

As with normal *in situ* work, precast work should be designed to produce the maximum repetitive use of a minimum amount of shuttering. Individual components should be simple in form and they should be as large as methods of transport and erection will permit in order to reduce the number of joints in the structure. As far as transport is concerned the limit on the size of a factory cast component is in the region of 60 to 70 ft by 8 ft overall. For multi-storey work a crane is invariably employed for erection purposes and, whereas a 5 cwt component is about the heaviest which can be manhandled,

---

[1] It has been shown that average comparable figures for the re-use of horizontal timber shuttering are 4 to 6 times for *in situ* work and 20 times for precast work, although with the use of plywood for shutters, re-use is considerably greater in both cases. For large precast contracts the use of steel forms can be economic and results in more than 100 times re-use.

when a crane is to be used on a job the size and weight should be related to the capacity of the crane likely to be used, since it will most economically be employed when hoisting at its maximum capacity. Individual joints can as easily be made in the case of heavy as in the case of light components when the units are supported by crane, but with smaller, lighter units more joints must be made and the crane must make a greater number of lifts at greater cost.

Precasting can, of course, be carried out on the site and some large contracting firms do, in fact, carry out much of their casting work in this way, although other comparable firms make a practice of carrying out all such work in a factory, even though this may involve transport over long distances.

Site casting does reduce the amount of handling and avoids transport costs but a large amount of site space is required for the casting beds. Provided that the quality of control and supervision usually available in the factory, and similar means of efficient vibrating and cleaning of shutters are available on the site, good results are possible. When structural components must be of such a size as to prohibit transport from a factory there is no alternative to site casting. Precasting of facing material or of components requiring a high degree of surface finish is probably best carried out under factory conditions.

Methods of Fabrication. Precast frames can be fabricated in a number of different ways:

(a) from individual beams and columns, the columns sometimes being cast in more than one storey height;

(b) from "frames" composed of column sections and beam lengths forming a single cast unit;

(c) from precast units acting as permanent structural shuttering to cast *in situ* concrete to form a composite structure.

Precast Beams and Columns. Details of this method are shown on page 274. As in the case of a steel stanchion a precast concrete column must be connected by some means to the foundation slab, and methods of accomplishing this are shown at (A). Column joints, usually of such a nature as to ensure continuity, must be made at each floor level in the case of storey height columns or at less frequent intervals if multi-storey height columns are used, and various methods of forming these joints are shown at (B). With multi-storey height columns provision must be made for the connection of the beams at the intermediate levels and this is accomplished either by

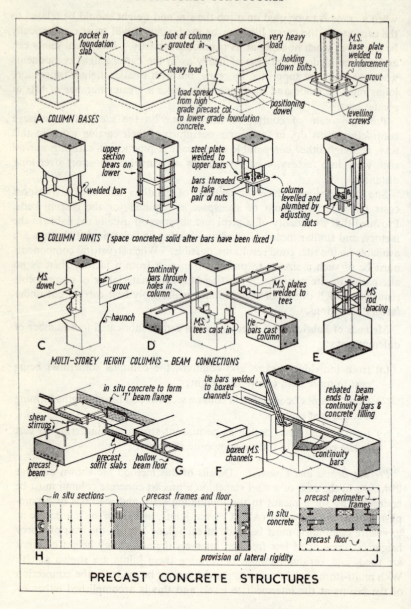

A COLUMN BASES

pocket in foundation slab

heavy load

foot of column grouted in

very heavy load

holding down bolts

load spread from high grade precast col. to lower grade foundation concrete.

positioning dowel

M.S. base plate welded to reinforcement

grout

levelling screws

B COLUMN JOINTS (space concreted solid after bars have been fixed)

upper section bears on lower

welded bars

steel plate welded to upper bars

bars threaded to take pair of nuts

column levelled and plumbed by adjusting nuts

MULTI-STOREY HEIGHT COLUMNS - BEAM CONNECTIONS

M.S. dowel

grout

haunch

continuity bars through holes in column

M.S. plates welded to tees

M.S. tees cast in

tie bars cast in column

MS rod bracing

C   D   E

in situ concrete to form 'T' beam flange

shear stirrups

precast beam

precast soffit slabs

hollow beam floor

G

tie bars welded to boxed channels

rebated beam ends to take continuity bars & concrete filling

boxed M.S. channels

continuity bars

F

in situ sections

precast frames and floor

precast perimeter frames

in situ concrete

precast floor

H   provision of lateral rigidity   J

PRECAST CONCRETE STRUCTURES

providing haunches as a seating for the beams or projecting steel sections (C, D), or by wholly or partially omitting the concrete at the appropriate points according to the number and disposition of beams to be connected. The exposed reinforcing rods are stiffened against bending under the weight of the upper column lengths during erection by welding mild steel rod bracing to the main rods (E). Alternatively, at such points the reinforcing rods are replaced by a length of R.S.J. section or by a boxed channel section formed of two R.S. channels welded edge to edge (F).

Connections between beams and columns can be made in various ways according to the degree of rigidity and continuity required. (F) shows a method commonly adopted in which the beam ends are boxed or rebated so that the *in situ* concrete filling makes the whole joint monolithic. Continuity rods are placed between the beam ends to transfer the negative bending moment over the column. In the case of three-way connections or corner columns the continuity rods for the centre or corner beams are usually cast in the column and bent up out of the way until the beams are in position. When the columns can be haunched to provide the beam seating, a simple connection can be made using a mild-steel dowel to provide a positive beam fixing within the small beam rebate which is filled with *in situ* concrete (C). Site welded steel bearings and continuity bars passing through holes in the column are shown at (D). The bars bond with the *in situ* topping to the beams. Sometimes, in the case of secondary beams where great rigidity is not required, the beam may be connected by means of steel brackets connected to the column by high-tensile steel bolts. Beam to beam connections may similarly be made or, more commonly, by means of rebates formed in the main beam to accommodate the ends of the secondary beams.

To ensure a full bearing of beam on column, or on another beam, steel bearing plates can be cast in to the underside of the beam ends and on the column bearing surfaces. Beams may be quite independent of the floor or roof slab which they support or, more generally, they may be designed to act integrally with the slab in the form of T- or L-beams. This necessitates some form of shear connector and *in situ* concrete to enable beam and slab to act together. The connectors are usually in the form of bent steel rod stirrups projecting from the top of the beam (page 274 (D, G)). In addition, or instead, castellations at regular intervals are sometimes formed along the length of the beam similar to those shown in the illustration on page 327. *In situ* concrete is required at the beam position to integrate the beam and the precast floor or roof elements which are usually notched or troughed at the ends to receive it (see page 322). When the slab elements run parallel with the beam, sufficient width of *in situ* concrete must be allowed to provide the flange to the beam (page 274 (G)).   As shown in this illustration precast soffit elements can be incorporated to avoid the use of normal shuttering.

A structure of precast beam and column units can be given lateral rigidity by making certain parts of *in situ* construction to which the precast portions are securely tied.   Less rigidity is then required at the joints between the precast units and construction is simpler.   The *in situ* work can be in the form of end and intermediate bays of the building constructed with cross walls running the width of the structure, as shown at (H).   To these the precast portions between may be tied at each floor level by tensioned cables passing through ducts in the floor slabs, the floors thus forming wind girders spanning between the *in situ* blocks.   In building types with a central core of services, stairs and lifts, the whole core can be of *in situ* cast reinforced concrete and precast concrete members can be used on the outside walls as shown at (J).   These can be tied back to the *in situ* core by cables as described above, or by bolting the precast floor slabs to the precast perimeter frames and the core.

Lateral rigidity may also be obtained by the use of diagonal braces placed in the vertical plane at various points in the structure, similar to the arrangement in a steel frame.

Precast Frame Units.   These can be formed in various ways but each type consists essentially of a pair or more of columns linked by a beam and so formed that beam and column connections do not occur at the same point, thus overcoming the difficulties of assembly which arise when they do coincide.   A pair of columns linked by a beam is easier to brace temporarily while the joints are being made than separate columns.   Such units are, therefore, easier and quicker to erect than separate beam and column units.   These units are suited to a layout in which there are no lateral beams, the floor and roof slabs spanning directly between lines of support running parallel to each other.   Page 277 shows two types of such units.   In (A) the column joint is located at the top of the beam and in (B) at the points of contraflexure in the columns where the bending moment is at a minimum.   When the perimeter columns of a building are closely spaced to act as window mullions, frame units can be formed of two columns, a head beam and a sill beam. The method of linking the units varies according to the treatment of the elevation.   In (C), page 277, the head and sill beams will be hidden by cladding and the columns will be exposed.   The head beam, that is the floor beam, can project on each side and meet its neighbour at the centre of the adjacent bay without detriment to appearance.   The sill beam acts as a brace to the frame and may or may not provide support to cladding.   When the whole of the frame is to be exposed on elevation care is needed in the arrangement

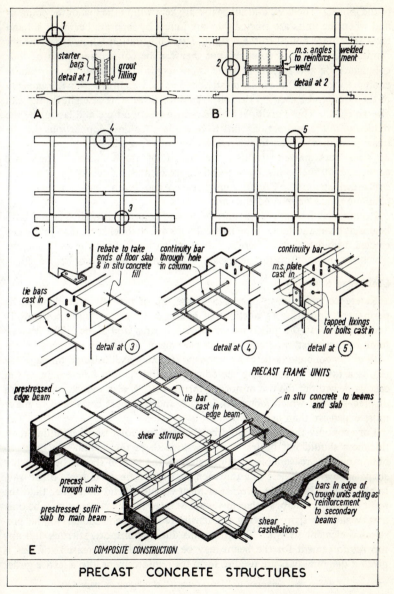

A

starter bars

detail at 1

grout filling

B

m.s. angles to reinforce-weld

welded ment

detail at 2

2

C

4

3

D

5

rebate to take ends of floor slab & in situ concrete fill

continuity bar through hole in column

continuity bar

tie bars cast in

m.s. plate cast in

tapped fixings for bolts cast in

detail at ③

detail at ④

detail at ⑤

PRECAST FRAME UNITS

prestressed edge beam

tie bar cast in edge beam

in situ concrete to beams and slab

shear stirrups

precast trough units

prestressed soffit slab to main beam

shear castellations

bars in edge of trough units acting as reinforcement to secondary beams

E

COMPOSITE CONSTRUCTION

PRECAST CONCRETE STRUCTURES

of the joints.   The head and sill beams are kept within the line of the columns and when the units are erected they are joined by separate beams at sill and head which are bolted to them (D).   These illustrations show storey height frames with a pair of columns, but they can be constructed three or four columns wide and with only a top beam, provided the beam is substantial enough to withstand the hoisting stresses and the weight is within the capacity of the crane to be used on the job.   Two- or three-storey height frames can also be used.   These multiple frames reduce erection time and labour by the reduction in the number of joints to be made.   Column connections may be made by plates welded to the reinforcing rods (page 274 (B)), or by means of steel bars passed through the height of the columns.   These are connected at the joints by screwed couplers and tightened by a torque-controlled spanner.   Connections between the beam ends are made by coupling plates or rebated ends and dowels.

Rectangular frames may be formed of half-columns at each side and half-beams at head and foot.   The half-columns are channel shaped so that when erected a void is formed between them which is filled with *in situ* concrete, which can be reinforced if necessary.   The half-beams are bolted together.

COMPOSITE STRUCTURE

Reference is made on page 276 to the use of precast soffit elements as permanent shuttering to portions of *in situ* cast work required to form T- and L-beams at the junctions of precast beams and slabs.   The use of reinforced precast concrete units as permanent shuttering, designed to act with *in situ* concrete to form a composite structure as illustrated on page 277 (E), is a means of obtaining the continuity and rigidity inherent in *in situ* cast work without the use of normal formwork.   It also reduces the amount of precast work which factory overheads and transport costs tend to make more expensive than *in situ* work.[1]

For economy the units should be shallow, but for ease of handling their thickness should not be less than one-fortieth of the length.   In order to obtain units of reasonable length, therefore, the section should be of such a shape as to give stiffness to a thin member or be stiffened in some other way. In the case of beams the precast element should extend no higher than the soffit of the floor slab, so that in some instances the precast unit may be only a very shallow strip carrying the tensile reinforcement similar to the pre-stressed element shown.   To stiffen this during transport, stirrups and any top reinforcement for the beam may be introduced.   Increased stiffness is given if diagonal bars are used to form the reinforcement into a lattice girder

---

[1] See also reference to "ferro-cement" shuttering on page 430.

similar to the elements of this type used for floor slab construction described on page 323.   Satisfactory bond between the precast units and the *in situ* cast concrete is essential in order to transfer shear stress, and although research has shown that a roughened surface on the precast unit is adequate, this does assume good site supervision and workmanship in forming the junction between the two.   A definite mechanical bond is usually ensured in practice by means of projecting wire stirrups or castellations.   When composite beams or slabs are continuous the negative moments over the supports must be resisted by reinforcement placed in the *in situ* cast concrete.   Page 277 (E) shows a wide shallow beam in which the lower part only of the tensile zone is a precast prestressed slab, the web and compression zone being of *in situ* cast concrete.   The side shuttering of the beam is formed by the edges of the precast trough units forming the lower part of the floor slab.   The trough units are referred to in connection with floors on page 324.

The combination of precast and *in situ* cast concrete is particularly economical when allied to prestressing in the range of 20–30 ft spans, for which normal prestressed concrete is not generally economical.   In a normal prestressed concrete beam the concrete throughout is of high quality, but in a composite beam the lower precast and prestressed section only need be of high quality concrete, thus effecting an economy due to the smaller volume of high quality prestressed concrete to be manufactured and transported to the site.

Precast units and *in situ* concrete may be combined in columns as well as in beams and slabs.   By using a precast concrete casing with an *in situ* cast core, time and labour can be saved by the elimination of normal shuttering and a good finish is obtained when the surface of the columns is to be exposed. It also permits the construction of the next floor to proceed more quickly while still maintaining full monolithic junctions with the floors and beams above and below.

PRECAST WALL STRUCTURE

In this form of construction the loadbearing elements are large storey-height precast wall panels, used with precast floor and roof units as shown on page 280.   Window openings may be cast in the external panels which are finished with an exposed aggregate or tooled or profiled surface and incorporate thermal insulation, usually in the form of lightweight concrete backing.   Internal panels can be made smooth enough to make plastering unnecessary.   Various methods of fixing the wall panels together may be adopted, one of which is to join them by means of horizontal steel plates welded to reinforcing bars projecting in rebates in the bottom corners of each panel. This method of joining is similar to that used for precast concrete columns shown on page 274 (B). To provide lateral rigidity the crosswall panels can be tied together by *in situ* reinforced concrete beams which may be formed within the floor thickness between adjacent floor panels, the edges of which can be rebated to form a trough for this purpose as at (A) below.

Although overall rigidity in this type of construction can, when necessary, be provided by *in situ* cast lift and stairwells, this has the disadvantage of mixing precast and *in situ* work on the site. Fully precast construction uses bathrooms precast as reinforced concrete boxes complete with floor and ceiling and lift and stairwells precast in storey or half-storey heights, which when erected on each other form structural "columns" running the

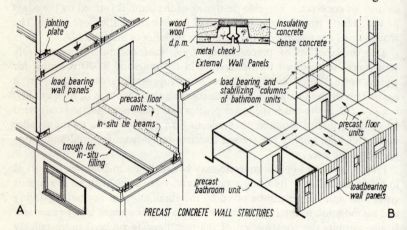

PRECAST CONCRETE WALL STRUCTURES

full height of the building. A number of these vertical units along the centre of the block forms a structural spine to the remainder of the structure which is fabricated from large precast floor panels and storey height loadbearing wall panels as shown at (B) above.

LAYOUT OF REINFORCEMENT

In detailing the reinforcement in a member, the arrangement of the bars should be as simple as possible with sufficient space left between the bars for each to be surrounded by concrete. The minimum distance between bars must be greater than the maximum size of aggregate used. The space needed between the bars, together with the thickness of external cover, is often a governing factor in determining the size of a member.

The minimum number of different bar sizes should be used, and the use of the largest size consistent with good design will reduce the number of bars to be bent and placed.

Bars must be extended beyond any section sufficiently far to enable the required grip to be developed. Hooked bar ends occurring in a tensile zone may cause cracking, and to avoid this the hooks should be omitted and the bars made longer to allow for the loss of the hooks. Alternatively the bars should be bent into a compression zone. Tension bars continuous round a re-entrant angle, as in a cranked slab, should have a radius large enough to reduce the outward pressure of the steel to that which the concrete can resist in shear and tension. If this is not possible the tension bars should be linked by stirrups to compression bars, or better, the bars should be separate and should extend beyond the intersection sufficient for bond (page 282).

Binders must be provided to avoid the possibility of buckling of the compression reinforcement and the bursting out of the concrete. To make the reinforcement stiff during concreting, and to hold stirrups in position, bars in the corners of beams are provided and the stirrups are continued round the tension side. At all points of intersection the bars must be wired together to prevent displacement during concreting.

Some typical details of reinforcement layout are shown on page 282.

PRESTRESSED CONCRETE

Reference has already been made to the technique of prestressing concrete and it is proposed here to discuss in more detail the principles involved and its application in practice. Prestressing is the process of imparting to a structural member a compressive stress in those zones which, under working loads, would normally be subject to tensile stresses. It is, in fact, a process of precompressing by means of which the tensile stresses produced by the applied load are counteracted by the compressive stresses set up before the application of the load. This can very simply be seen in the process of removing a row of books from a bookshelf. The row of books in itself has no tensile strength and unless supported by a shelf would fall apart, but by applying pressure by a hand at each end the row may be made to act as a beam and be lifted off the shelf. The pressure of the hands sets up a compressive stress which overcomes the tensile stress which the weight of the books would set up and which would cause the books to part from each other. Although particularly advantageous in concrete work for reasons given below, prestressing is also used in steel and timber construction (see pages 247, 447).

Normal reinforced concrete is not able to benefit fully from the high-quality concrete and high-tensile steel now available because of the low straining capacity of concrete in tension, which results in cracks appearing in the concrete around the reinforcement at loads well below the normal design load. While generally not dangerous these cracks in practice are usually limited to about one-hundredth of an inch in width, thus limiting

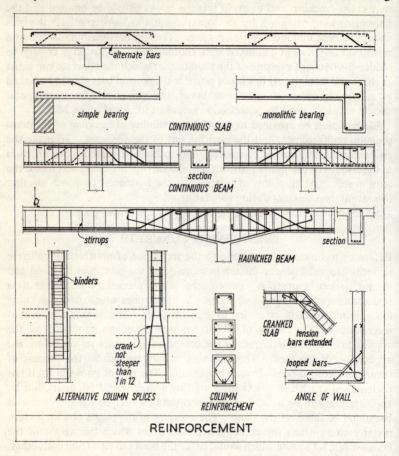

the stresses which may be applied to the reinforcement, so that neither the qualities of modern high-strength concrete nor of high-strength steel may be fully developed.[1] In a prestressed member, however, the concrete

---

[1] The use of special types of reinforcement in normal reinforced concrete to give increased bond and to limit cracking to fine, well distributed cracks is discussed on page 259.

is at all times under compression so that there is a complete absence of cracks. In the event of an overload, provided that this is within the elastic limit, the cracks formed will close again after removal of the load without harm to the structure. The high compressive strength obtainable in present day concrete can, therefore, be fully used, while at the same time the high-tensile qualities of modern steel may also be fully utilized because the steel is not used as normal reinforcement to take the tensile stresses which the concrete is unable to resist, but, as will be seen later, is used solely as a means of producing the compressive stress in the concrete.[1]

Reduction in the depth of beams and slabs, thus producing higher stresses, is therefore possible without giving rise to crack formation, and depth/span ratios of 1:20 for beams and 1:40 for slabs are common, although for beams much smaller ratios are possible depending upon loading conditions. The applied compressive stress, in addition to cancelling out the tensile stresses due to bending, considerably reduces those tensile stresses caused by shear so that the webs of prestressed beams can be much thinner than in normal reinforced concrete beams, resulting in I- and box-sections as typical prestressed concrete forms. The smaller sections thus possible produce considerable savings in steel and concrete. They result in dead weights of up to 50% less than with normal reinforced concrete, and because the high grade steel used can be stressed to its limit, a saving in the weight of steel of one-tenth to one-fifth can be shown over that of normal reinforcement. Although high-tensile steel is more expensive than mild steel there is a saving in cost because of the small amount required. The decrease in the dead/live load ratio considerably reduces costs over medium and long spans, increases maximum spans, and makes prestressed concrete much more suitable for wide span members carrying light loads than normal reinforced concrete. The lightness of prestressed work, due to reduced depth and web thickness and to the reduced amount of steel, and the longer spans economically possible, results in lower column and foundation costs.

In its application to building work prestressed concrete is mostly used for beam and slab members in precast construction. When applied to complete monolithic structures, prestressing presents complications in design and construction. For wide spans, freely supported beams are generally considered preferable to continuous beams in order to avoid similar complications (see page 292). For spans below 20 ft, normal reinforced concrete construction is generally cheaper than prestressed concrete. Between 20 and 30 ft,

---

[1] Concrete with a 28 day crushing strength of 6,000 lb per sq. in. is generally used, although for pretensioned work 4,500 lb per sq. in. concrete is sometimes used. Steel wire with ultimate tensile strengths up to 150 tons per sq. in., and high-tensile bars with ultimate strengths up to 72 tons per sq. in. are used.

prestressed work may or may not prove more economical according to the particular job, having regard to such factors as the reduction in size and numbers of columns and foundations likely to result from the use of pre-stressed work. In this range the composite form of construction described on page 278 is likely to be the cheapest. For spans greater than 30 ft, pre-stressed work will usually show economic advantages over reinforced con-crete, especially when the imposed loading is light, as in roof construction. Creasy[1] shows that for multi-storey frames as conventionally planned, pre-stressed concrete is not, in most cases, likely to be cheaper than reinforced concrete.

Columns, being compression members, are normally not prestressed. However, in tall columns particularly, where bending stresses may be high due to wind pressure or an eccentric load such as applied by a travelling crane, prestressing can usefully be applied. Tensile stresses in walls, even loadbearing walls, are normally not such as to justify prestressing, but in tall retaining walls where bending stresses may be high, prestressing can be economical. As indicated in Chapter 4, when applied to retaining walls, prestressing, by preventing crack formation, has advantages in terms of the water resistance of the wall (see page 194).

PRINCIPLES OF PRESTRESSING

The prestress, or precompression, may be induced in a beam entirely with-out the use of steel by means of external jacks, in the same manner that hand pressure is applied to a row of books, provided that sufficiently solid abut-ments are available as in the case of a bridge, see page 285 (A). The prin-ciples of prestressing can usefully be considered on the basis of this method. The pressure will be of a uniform intensity over the whole section if applied on the neutral axis of the beam, and if of equal intensity to the tensile stresses induced by the imposed load will cancel them out. As will be seen, this results in a final compressive stress in the upper fibres, assuming a beam of uniform cross-section, of twice that set up by the imposed load. This precompression of the compression zone is neither necessary nor does it make maximum use of the concrete in carrying its load, since, in terms of the final compressive stress, which must not exceed the maximum permissible strength of the concrete, that induced by the imposed load is only one half of this maximum. For greatest efficiency it is necessary to apply the prestress in the tensile zone only. The distribution of the prestress across the section depends upon the point of application of the pressure (page 285 (B)),

---

[1] See "Economics of Framed Structures", by Leonard R. Creasy, B.Sc. (Eng.), M.I.C.E.—*Proceedings of the Institution of Civil Engineers*, Vol. 12, March 1959.

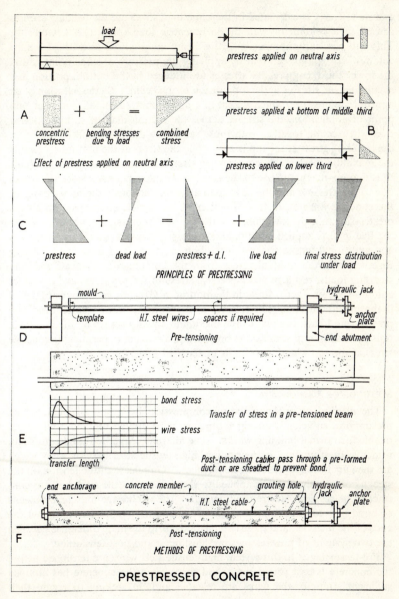

A
concentric
prestress + bending stresses
due to load = combined
stress

Effect of prestress applied on neutral axis

prestress applied on neutral axis

prestress applied at bottom of middle third

prestress applied on lower third

B

C
prestress + dead load = prestress + d.l. + live load = final stress distribution
under load

PRINCIPLES OF PRESTRESSING

mould
template   H.T. steel wires   spacers if required
hydraulic jack
anchor plate
end abutment

D
Pre-tensioning

bond stress
wire stress

Transfer of stress in a pre-tensioned beam

E
transfer length

Post-tensioning cables pass through a pre-formed
duct or are sheathed to prevent bond.

end anchorage   concrete member   grouting hole   hydraulic jack
H.T. steel cable   anchor plate

F
Post-tensioning

METHODS OF PRESTRESSING

PRESTRESSED CONCRETE

10*

and its intensity is calculated in the same manner as are the bending stresses caused in a column or wall by an eccentric load (page 112, Chapter 4). This will be clearly appreciated if the beam is visualized as a "horizontal" column. It will be seen that by applying the pressure at some point within the lower third, compressive stresses are induced in the bottom portion and smaller tensile stresses in the top portion of the beam. By the selection of an appropriate pressure, which is kept to a minimum to economize in steel, and point of application, the stresses across the section may be so apportioned that when acting together with those set up by the dead load of the beam the resulting stress at the top is zero while the stress at the bottom represents the maximum permissible compressive stress of the concrete (page 285 (C)), thus making maximum use of the strength of the concrete. Since the forces due to prestressing and the dead load act simultaneously the upper fibres of the concrete are not, in fact, subjected to the tensile stresses set up by the prestressing, nor the lower fibres to the excess compression indicated. When the live load is applied additional compressive stresses are set up in the top and additional tensile stresses in the bottom fibres, and these forces, acting together with the residual forces from the combination of dead and prestressing loads, result in a compressive stress in the top fibres and a smaller compressive, or a zero, stress in the bottom. Greatest economy is obtained if the maximum compressive stress in the bottom fibres, due to dead and prestressing loads, is equal to the maximum stresses set up by the live load, thus producing zero stress at the bottom and a maximum permissible concrete stress at the top when the beam is under load (page 285 (C)).

METHODS OF PRESTRESSING

The method of applying the precompression by means of jacks, which presupposes sufficiently strong abutments, is of limited use and rarely practicable for normal building works. The alternative method used consists in principle of stretching, or tensioning, high-tensile steel bars or wires which are then anchored to the concrete member. On release of the tension on the steel a compressive force is applied to the concrete as the steel seeks to contract to its original, unstretched, length. The anchorage may be by means of bond between steel and concrete or by external mechanical means at the ends of the member, and these two methods form the main difference between the two systems of prestressing: pre-tensioning and post-tensioning.

Pre-tensioning. In this system high-tensile steel wires are tensioned before the concrete is cast round them, and then, when the concrete has attained sufficient strength, the wires are released and, in seeking to regain their original length, but being bonded to the concrete, induce in the concrete the required compressive force. Based on Hooke's law that within the elastic limit stress is proportional to strain, the amount of elongation required in the steel wires (both in pre- and post-tensioning) to produce a particular compressive force in the concrete can be easily calculated (see page 290 for the effect of certain stress losses). As strong abutments are required between which to stretch the wires pre-tensioning is invariably applied to precast units and is usually carried out in a factory, although a prestressing bed set up on a site as a means of avoiding factory overheads might prove more economical for a very large contract. Factory production is generally preferable since the need for close control of the concrete preparation and its placing and of the stressing of the steel is more likely to be satisfied under factory conditions than on the site.

Although pre-tensioning can be applied to individual members formed and stressed in their own moulds, the most usual method is that known as the "long line" system in which the wires are stretched within continuous moulds between anchorages 400 ft or more apart. The wires pass through templates at each end which position them correctly and the ends are gripped in anchor plates. Spacers are placed at various intervals along the mould according to the required lengths of units. The anchor plates are then jacked away the calculated distance to stretch the wires, the concrete is poured and after it has hardened sufficiently the wires are released and are cut between each unit (page 285 (D)).

At the extreme ends of pre-tensioned members the bond between steel and concrete is not fully developed, and for a short length, varying from 80 to 120 times the diameter of the wire according to the quality of the concrete and the roughness of the surface, the wires contract considerably in their length with a consequent loss of stress in the wires, the stress at the cut end being zero. At the same time this contraction is accompanied by a lateral swelling which forms a cone-like anchor (page 285 (E)). The length in which this occurs is termed the transfer length and requires reinforcement for shear in the form of stirrups. The lateral swelling of the released wires tends, of course, to occur throughout their length, thus further increasing the bond between wires and concrete. Small diameter wires are used so that the greatest surface area is obtained to increase the bond, and the usual diameters lie between 0·08 in. and 0·2 in. These wires have ultimate tensile strengths ranging from 100 tons per sq. in. for the larger diameters to 150 tons per sq. in. for the smaller. It is essential that the wires be thoroughly degreased and allowed to rust slightly in order to produce a satisfactory surface. Careful control of the concrete mix and vibration are used to produce high quality concrete, and some form of curing is normally applied to accelerate the hardening.

Post-tensioning. In this system the concrete is cast and permitted to harden before the steel is stressed. The steel, which is usually in the form of high-tensile steel cable or bar, if placed in position before concreting, is prevented from bonding with the concrete either by being sheathed with thin sheet steel or tarred paper or by being coated with bitumen. Alternatively, the prestressing steel can be introduced after the concrete has set by casting in bars or duct-tubes at the appropriate positions which are extracted before the steel is inserted. It is also possible to place the wires outside the concrete and protect them. The cable or bar is anchored at one end of the concrete unit and stressed by jacking against the other end to which it is then also anchored (page 285 (F)). The steel is subsequently grouted under pressure through holes at the ends of the unit to protect it from rust and to provide bond as an additional safeguard.

There are a number of methods of anchoring and jacking the prestressing steel, some of which are illustrated on page 289.

The Freyssinet system uses a cable of eight to eighteen wires positioned round a central open spring forming a hollow core, and an anchorage device cast into the end concrete member consisting of a concrete cylinder with a central conical hole and a conical concrete plug grooved on the outside to take the cable wires which are laid between the cone and the cylinder. The special double-acting Freyssinet jack incorporates a stressing piston and a wedging piston. The wires, led through grooves spaced round the head of the jack, are wedged to the stressing piston which is operated until the required extension of the wires is obtained. Then the wedging piston is used to force the plug into the concrete cylinder to anchor the wires. The wires are then released, the cable grouted through the conical plug, the wires cut flush and the face of the anchorage protected with a pat of mortar.

The Magnel-Blaton system differs from the Freyssinet system in the form of anchorage used and in the manner of stressing the wires. The wires are stressed in pairs by a normal single-acting jack bearing on the anchorage and are secured by steel wedges to grooved steel plates, each of which anchors eight wires. These plates are arranged in layers, the number depending upon the size of the cable, and bear on a steel distribution plate. The wires in the cable are held about $\frac{3}{16}$ in. apart throughout their length by spacer grilles.

The Gifford-Udall system and the *P.S.C. system* both stress the wires one at a time. They are anchored individually, in the former system by means of a pair of conical half-wedges driven into a steel barrel accommodated in an anchor plate. In the latter, by a single-piece split sleeve driven into

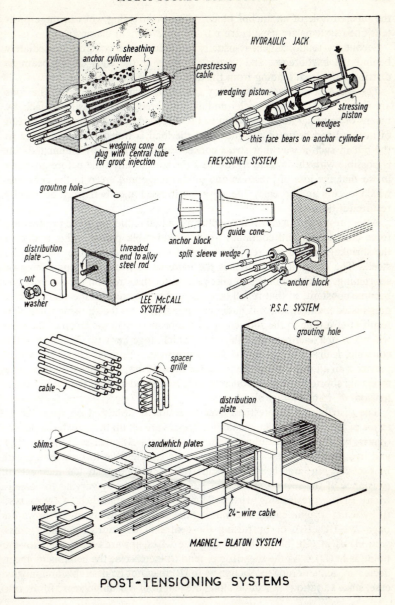

sheathing
anchor cylinder
prestressing cable
HYDRAULIC JACK
wedging piston
stressing piston
wedges
this face bears on anchor cylinder
wedging cone or plug with central tube for grout injection
FREYSSINET SYSTEM

grouting hole
anchor block
guide cone
split sleeve wedge
anchor block
distribution plate
nut
washer
threaded end to alloy steel rod
LEE McCALL SYSTEM
P.S.C. SYSTEM

grouting hole
cable
spacer grille
distribution plate
shims
sandwhich plates
wedges
24-wire cable
MAGNEL-BLATON SYSTEM

POST-TENSIONING SYSTEMS

the tapered hole of an anchor block. The prestressing wires in these post-tensioned systems are usually from $0 \cdot 2$ to $0 \cdot 276$ in. in diameter.

Secondary reinforcement is usually required in the concrete immediately behind the anchorages, and vertical stirrups at the ends of the beam to distribute the local loading from the anchorage of the cables.

The Lee-McCall system uses alloy steel rods instead of cables. The rods are from $\frac{1}{2}$ to $1\frac{1}{8}$ in. in diameter and are anchored, after stressing by jack, by means of a special nut screwed on to the threaded end of the rod, the thread of nut and rod being so designed that the load is transferred by degrees to the nut in such a way that stress concentrations are largely eliminated. It is possible with this system to re-stress the rods at any time before grouting in, so that the loss of prestress due to shrinkage and creep in the concrete, which occurs in the early life of a prestressed member, may be wholly restored if desired.

After prestressing a concrete member a gradual reduction in the prestressing force commences and continues for a considerable period. This is due to the shrinkage of the concrete, the creep of the concrete and the creep of the steel. The creep of a material is the increase in strain, i.e. lengthening or shortening, which continues to take place after the stress on the material has become constant, so that it will be evident that the creep in the concrete of a prestressed member which is under compression from the stressing wires, will result after a time in the shortening of the beam, whilst the creep of the steel will result in a lengthening of the wires, which, together with shrinkage of the concrete, leads to a loss in the initial prestress. In determining the initial prestress an allowance must be made for these losses, together with those due to elastic shortening of the concrete as it is stressed and, in the case of post-tensioning, to anchorage slip.

The distribution of prestress over a section is discussed on page 286 in terms of the point at which maximum stresses are set up by the external loads, that is, the point of maximum bending moment. At other sections the dead and live load moments will be less and the stresses due to prestressing will be excessive, in large beams particularly. A reduction in the moment of resistance of the section at these points can be made by varying the eccentricity of the prestressing wires. This can be accomplished in two ways: (i) by using straight cables and varying the section of the beam as shown on page 291 (A), (B), or by raising the centre of a beam of constant cross section, as in (C), or (ii) by curving the wires upwards from their lowest point as in (D). As the shear forces tend to increase as the bending moment decreases, reduction of the section as in (B) may not be desirable and, in any case, since variations in section along the length of a beam increase formwork costs, a constant cross section is preferable except for very large spans.   The curving upwards of the prestressing cable gives a vertical component which helps to resist the shear forces in the beam and enables high shear loads to be taken.

Pre-tensioning is most suitable for the production of large numbers of similar units, particularly if they are of a cross-section too small satisfactorily

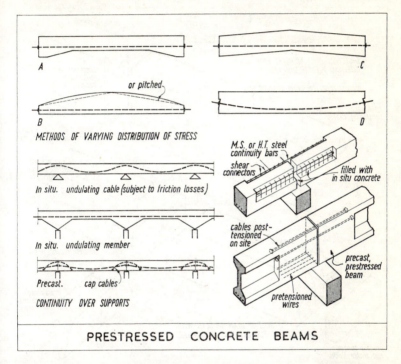

A

or pitched

B

METHODS OF VARYING DISTRIBUTION OF STRESS

C

D

In situ. undulating cable (subject to friction losses)

In situ. undulating member

Precast.   cap cables

CONTINUITY OVER SUPPORTS

M.S. or H.T. steel continuity bars

shear connectors

filled with in situ concrete

cables post-tensioned on site

precast, prestressed beam

pretensioned wires

PRESTRESSED   CONCRETE   BEAMS

to accommodate the relatively large post-tensioning cables.   In pre-tensioning the wires must be straight so that shear-resistance from curved-up wires is not obtainable.   Generally speaking, the method is not suited to prestressing on the site.   Beams range generally from 15 to 75 ft in length, the maximum length depending upon transport and handling.   Beams up to 100 ft or more can be made as "specials".

Post-tensioning is invariably used for prestressing on the site and for large members.   In most cases it is not economical for members less than 30 ft long because the cost of the anchorages relative to the length is high, while the cost of jacking is the same as for a long beam. It may be cheaper to use reinforced concrete for a large number of small units if, for some reason, pre-tensioning is not suitable. The general range of spans is 50 ft upwards. Post-tensioning has the advantage, particularly with members carrying heavy shear loads, that the cables can be curved upwards to provide added shear resistance.

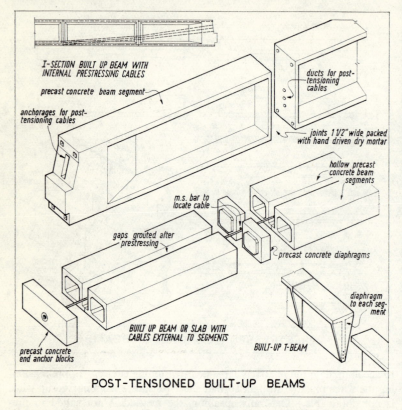

I-SECTION BUILT UP BEAM WITH
INTERNAL PRESTRESSING CABLES

precast concrete beam segment

ducts for post-
tensioning
cables

anchorages for post-
tensioning cables

joints 1 1/2" wide packed
with hand driven dry mortar

hollow precast
concrete beam
segments

m.s. bar to
locate cable

gaps grouted after
prestressing

precast concrete diaphragms

diaphragm
to each seg-
ment

precast concrete
end anchor blocks

BUILT UP BEAM OR SLAB WITH
CABLES EXTERNAL TO SEGMENTS

BUILT-UP T-BEAM

POST-TENSIONED BUILT-UP BEAMS

When continuity over supports is essential the necessary stressing in the zones of negative moment can be effected in a number of ways, illustrated on page 291. In *in situ* cast members either the cable must be undulating, which gives rise to friction losses, or the member itself must be "undulating" in form to vary the point of maximum prestress. Precast members can be prestressed in the normal way and continuity be provided over the supports by cap cables, curved in the case of rectangular sections or straight in the case of I-sections, or by continuity bars set in *in situ* filling in rebates in the beams ends.

By the use of post-tensioning it is possible to build up a beam from a number of precast concrete units or segments placed end to end like the row of books mentioned earlier. These units can be produced on the site, but being small are often manufactured in a factory to benefit from the advantages of factory production. Holes for the cables can be formed through the units by light steel tubing or duct-tube, and the units are assembled by being placed end to end with stiff mortar in the joints, the whole being post-tensioned (page 292). Alternatively, when the members are wide, or in slab form, the cables may be placed in gaps between the precast units as shown on the same page. These methods reduce site work and avoid expensive formwork. Assembly may be on the site or in the factory; if assembled on the site the costs of transport of a large beam can be eliminated while gaining the advantages of factory production (see also page 451).

6
Floor Structures

The term "floor" in this chapter refers to the structural part of a horizontal supporting element as distinct from the wearing surface.

FUNCTIONAL REQUIREMENTS

The main function of a floor is to provide support for the occupants, furniture and equipment of a building. To perform this function and, in addition, others which will vary according to the situation of the floor in the building and the nature of the building itself, the floor must satisfy a number of requirements in its design and construction. These may be defined as the provision of adequate

> Strength and stability;
> Fire resistance;
> Sound insulation;
> Damp resistance;
> Thermal insulation.

Thermal insulation is normally not required in upper floors unless in relation to certain forms of floor or ceiling heating but some regard must be paid to it in ground and basement floors. This is especially so in the case of suspended and ventilated timber floors where the heat losses can be considerable, and in solid floors embodying heating pipes or cables where the heat losses at the edges of the floor slab can be high.

Sound insulation need not normally be considered in ground or basement floors since contact with the mass of the earth damps out sound vibrations to a great extent. It is, however, an important consideration in the design of upper floors.

The problems of thermal and sound insulation are considered in *Advanced Building Construction* (*Components, Services and Finishes*).

Fire resistance is important in respect of upper floors which are often required to act as highly resistant fire barriers between the different levels of a building. The degree of resistance necessary in any particular case depends on a number of factors which are discussed in Chapter 10.

GROUND AND BASEMENT FLOORS

Problems of strength and stability are usually minor ones at ground and basement levels since full support from the ground is generally available at all points. The major problem is damp exclusion.

In most buildings without basements the ground floors are of solid construction, of concrete on hardcore, resting directly on the ground. They are invariably so in the case of basement floors and in floors taking heavy loads or traffic. Sometimes for small scale work on steeply sloping sites the use of a suspended timber floor with some form of applied thermal insulation will prove more economic than a solid floor laid direct on "cut and fill". Solid concrete and suspended timber ground floors for small scale work are discussed in *Elementary Building Construction*.

Solid concrete floors of any type are basically constructed as described in the above. The thickness of the slab will vary according to the loading which the floor is to carry and the bearing capacity of the ground. When the latter is uneven or when the ground is weak or made-up, the slab is reinforced over the whole of its area with mesh reinforcement. Reinforcement is also required when a basement floor must resist the upward pressure of subsoil water (see page 191).

Where a variety of floor finishes of different thicknesses are used each will require a different sub-floor level obtained either by varying the thickness of the screed or by varying the level of the slab. The former method, unless the variation is great, is usual and the most economic.

A floor slab designed to transmit the whole of the building load to the soil becomes a "raft" foundation.

Protection against damp penetration is commonly provided by a damp-proof membrane on top of the slab or sandwiched between two layers of concrete. This links at the edges with the horizontal damp-proof course in the walls (see *Elementary Building Construction*) or with the vertical damp-proof course in surrounding retaining walls.

Problems arising in damp-proofing against subsoil water under pressure are the same as those arising in the damp-proofing of retaining walls under the same conditions and are discussed under "Waterproofing of Basements", page 190.

UPPER FLOORS

The simple timber floor used in domestic work is discussed in *Elementary Building Construction* and in this chapter floors appropriate to multi-storey and heavily loaded buildings will be considered.

It will be seen in the next section that in these types of buildings the floors are main structural elements closely related to the general structure of the building and they must be considered at the design stage in relation to it.

CHOICE OF FLOOR

The main factors influencing the choice of floor type, together with some indication of the manner in which each may be relevant, are discussed below. Reference should also be made to "Choice of Appropriate Structure" in Chapter 5 and to pages 257 and 262.

Nature of the Building Structure. With a steel frame, providing in itself all the necessary lateral rigidity, a precast concrete floor or a cellular steel floor laid quickly on the steel beams but contributing little to the rigidity of the frame could be suitable. With an *in situ* reinforced concrete frame an *in situ* concrete floor cast in with the frame and designed to provide lateral rigidity would be logical and would permit the omission of tie beams parallel to the floor span.

In a reinforced concrete frame with beams on all four sides of the floor panels the latter may be designed as two-way reinforced slabs to minimize thickness and weight. With a steel frame, for which a rectangular grid layout is generally more economical than a square layout, one-way spanning floor construction will usually prove more suitable, particularly over short spans.

The height of the structural frame will also have a bearing upon the choice of floor type. Creasy[1] states that "where the columns are carrying five or more storeys they have a relatively greater influence on the cost of the framework, and a hollow-slab form of construction compares favourably with the solid slab from the reduction in dead weight to be carried by the columns. For buildings of less height this advantage is offset by an increase in the construction costs and the solid slab becomes more economical".

Loading. Flat slab construction is economical for heavy uniformly distributed loading, which with normal beam and slab construction might require very deep beams. Because of the smaller overall thickness the total floor to floor height is reduced, and this in turn will effect overall economies by a reduced height of structural frame and reduced area of external cladding. Where heavy concentrated loads must be carried a diagonal beam floor might be selected because such loads are dispersed throughout all the members of the grid.

Span. This may sometimes be fixed by plan requirements but very often

[1] "Economics of Framed Structures", paper by Leonard R. Creasy, B.Sc., M.I.C.E., in *Proceedings of the Institution of Civil Engineers*, Vol. 12 March 1959.

may be varied to fall within the economic ranges of the various types of floor systems, some indication of which is given in the Table below. With increase in the span and in the load there will normally be an increase in the thickness and weight of the floor. Any increase in the weight of the floor will impose a greater load upon the structural frame and the foundations, with a consequent increase in the cost of these elements. The desirability of reducing the dead weight of the floor to a minimum, for reasons of structural economy, has resulted in a large variety of floor systems now available. Each system is most economical over a limited range of spans and loading, having regard solely to the relationship between weight of floor, the distance it will span and the load it will carry.[1] But other factors are also involved. For example, weight may be reduced simply by an increase in the

Table 19. Economic Range of Spans for Floors Systems

Span range	Loading		
	Up to 40 lb/sq. ft	40–80 lb/sq. ft	Over 80 lb/sq. ft
Up to 10 ft	Timber	Timber	R.C. Slab
10 to 20 ft	Timber (16 ft max.)	R.C. Slab	Beams and R.C. Slab
20 to 30 ft	Double Timber Floor (above 16 ft)	Beams and R.C. Slab	Special Floor types

depth of the floor. But such an increase may increase the total height of the structure, the area of external cladding and the cubic contents of the building, while the total floor area remains the same. Thus possible economies effected in the structural frame and foundations by a reduction in floor weight must be related to the extra cost of the greater height and the greater area of external facing and a balance struck between the two.

Degree of Fire Resistance Required. This is frequently a determining factor in the choice of a floor. Many buildings, because of their high fire load, must be divided into fire-tight compartments by walls and floors. These must have a degree of fire resistance sufficient to withstand the complete burn-out of the contents of any compartment and prevent the spread

---

[1] See "Floor Assemblies", by John Voelcker, *Architectural Design*, February 1956, for comparative table of different proprietary systems.

of fire to other parts of the building. The considerations involved in respect of forms of construction and the nature of the materials used with regard to their action under fire are discussed in Chapter 10.

Provision of Services. The large number of services and extensive equipment required in many types of buildings necessitates early consideration of the means of housing them both vertically and horizontally. Horizontal runs can often conveniently be accommodated in the topping or screed to the floor but if the services are extensive this can result in a screed 3 to 6 in. thick, adding to the depth and weight of the floor. A common alternative is to run the services below the floor slab and beams and to conceal them by a suspended ceiling. Where a suspended ceiling is not required for some reason other than the concealment of services, they may often economically be run freely in the floor depth by the choice of an appropriate type of floor.

In extreme cases, such as laboratories and industrial processing plants, the number of services and the amount of room required for their distribution may necessitate a considerable depth of space below the floor. This depth may be used to advantage in the adoption of a deep, light supporting structure to the floor. When plant is involved, the depth required may be so great as to result in what is, in fact, a service floor sandwiched between the production or processing floors.

Degree of Sound Insulation Required. Weight of structure is important in connection with insulation against airborne sound. The greater the weight the greater the insulation provided. The degree of insulation provided by a boarded timber floor may be acceptable in the first floor of a house but is inadequate in most other buildings. Many types of light concrete floors can provide insulation against airborne sound sufficient for some buildings, but for others their inherent insulation value must be increased by the provision of a suspended ceiling underneath or a floating floor on top. A solid concrete floor of sufficient thickness and weight can give a reasonable degree of insulation against airborne sound but has little effect on impact sound. Apart from the increase they make in airborne insulation, floating floors are widely used to reduce the transmission of impact sound. For a detailed consideration of sound insulation see *Advanced Building Construction* (*Components, Services and Finishes*).

Cost, Speed of Erection, Adaptability. Consideration of cost must enter into the choice of the floor, but not solely in terms of the floor itself. As with all other building elements the effect of each type of floor upon the remainder of the building must be examined and the economic consequences assessed and compared. One aspect of this has been considered briefly under "Span", page 296. Speed of erection may be an over-riding factor in some circumstances and in others adaptability to non-rectangular panels which, due to site or other limitations, are sometimes unavoidable.

A floor is required to be strong enough to bear its own self-weight and the dead weight of any floor and ceiling finishes together with the superimposed live loads which it is required to carry without deflecting to such an extent as to cause damage to ceiling finishes, particularly if these are of plaster. In framed buildings the floors are sometimes designed to act as horizontal "struts" capable of transferring wind pressure to the vertical members of the frame and providing lateral rigidity to the frame. They also serve to provide lateral restraint to loadbearing walls (see Chapter 4).

Loading. The dead load is usually based on the weights of materials specified in B.S. 648. Code of Practice 3 (Ch. V) requires the dead load of any partitions not definitely located in the design of the building to be allowed for as a uniformly distributed load per sq. ft of floor of not less than 10% of the dead weight per ft run of the partitions. If the floor is to be used for office purposes this load must be not less than 20 lb per sq. ft.[1]

A floor is usually designed on the basis of an average superimposed loading per sq. ft except in the case of large pieces of equipment in fixed positions when sections of a floor are designed for the individual loads. The minimum imposed loads to be assumed are laid down in Code of Practice 3 (Ch. V), the Model Building Byelaws and in the L.C.C. By-laws. The load requirements are similar and the Table from the Code of Practice is reproduced on page 300.[2]

The average imposed load per sq. ft of floor area will vary not only with the type of building but also with the area of floor being considered. As there is a greater risk of a small area being heavily loaded than a large area, minimum loads are laid down for slabs of less than 8 ft span and for beams supporting less than 64 sq. ft of floor. These loadings are given in columns 4 and 5 of the Table. In garages there is a particular danger of small areas

[1] Similar provisions are laid down in the L.C.C. By-laws, Part II, and the Model Building Byelaws, 2nd Schedule.
[2] The descriptions of types of floor in Column 2 of this Table include those for public buildings. These are not included in the L.C.C. Table because, under the discretionary powers conferred on the District Surveyor by the London Building Acts (Amendment) Act, 1939, Part 3, Section 26, in respect of public buildings, all matters connected with the construction of such buildings must be approved by the District Surveyor. Although these loadings would generally apply, in some circumstances the District Surveyor might require other loadings to be assumed for design purposes.
It should be noted that the L.C.C. now grant a waiver to permit a floor loading on the upper (bedroom) floors of maisonettes of not less than 30 lb per sq. ft. Other authorities probably make similar relaxations in respect of this type of floor.

Table 20.   Superimposed Loading on Floors

In this Table a reference to a floor includes a reference to any part of that floor to be used as a corridor, and "slabs" includes boarding and beams or ribs spaced not further apart than three feet between centres, and "beams" means all other beams and ribs.

"Fixed seating" implies that the removal of the seating and the use of the space for other purposes is improbable.

Floor		Minimum imposed loads		
			Slabs	*Beams*
Loading Class No.	Types of Floors	Pounds per square foot of floor area	Pounds per foot width of slab uniformly distributed over span	Pounds uniformly distributed over the span of the beam
(1)	(2)	(3)	(4)	(5)
30	Floors in dwelling-houses of not more than two storeys designed for one occupation	30	240	1,920
40	Floors (other than those of Class 30) for residential purposes including dwelling houses of more than one occupation, tenements, hospital wards, bedrooms and private sitting rooms in hotels and dormitories	40	320	2,560
50	Office floors above the entrance floor; floors of light workrooms without storage	50	400	3,200
60	Floors of banking halls; office entrance floors and office floors below entrance floor; floors of class-rooms in schools	60	480	3,840
80	Shop floors used for the display and sale of merchandise; workrooms generally; garages for vehicles not exceeding 2¼ tons gross weight; places of assembly with fixed seating; churches and chapels; restaurants; circulation space in machinery halls, power stations, etc., where not occupied by plant or equipment	80	640	5,120
100	Floors of warehouses, workshops, factories and other buildings or parts of buildings of similar category for light-weight loads; office floors for storage and filing purposes; places of assembly without fixed seating (public rooms in hotels, dance halls, etc.)	100	800	6,400
150	Floors of warehouses, workshops, factories and other buildings or parts of buildings of similar category for medium-weight loads; floors of garages for vehicles not exceeding 4 tons gross weight	150	For garage floors only, $1 \cdot 5 \times$ maximum wheel load, but not less than 2,000 lb. considered to be distributed over a floor area 2 ft 6 in square.	
200	Floors of warehouses, workshops, factories and other buildings or parts of buildings of similar category for heavy-weight loads; floors of book stores and stationery stores; roofs and pavement lights over basements projecting under the public footpath	200	—	—

being excessively loaded so that special provision is made for this against Class 150 buildings.[1]

It should be noted that beams, ribs and joists spaced not further apart than 3 ft between centres may be calculated at slab loadings.

In the case of a single span of a beam supporting not less than 500 sq. ft of floor at one general level, the imposed load may be reduced by 5% for each 500 sq. ft supported, up to a maximum reduction of 25%.

In order to minimize the cracking of plaster ceilings the deflection of floor slabs and beams is limited. In regulations this is covered by laying down a fraction of the span as the maximum permitted deflection in the case of steel and timber, and in the case of reinforced concrete by laying down maximum values of the ratio of span to depth of slab.[2]

MOVEMENT CONTROL

Settlement Movement. When settlement joints are provided in the structure, as described in the previous chapter, the junctions of the floor slabs must be designed to permit relative movement by rotation. These would be detailed as pivoted joints.

Thermal Movement. Typical details of expansion joints in floors are shown on page 224 and reference is made to these under the section on movement control in the previous chapter (page 223).

UPPER FLOOR CONSTRUCTION

These floors may be constructed of timber, reinforced concrete or steel. The choice of a particular type will depend largely upon the factors already discussed.

[1] C.P. 3 (Ch. V.) Amendment No. 1, 1958, includes further loading provisions for garages and parking floors.
[2] Steel beams—L.C.C. By-laws and B.S. 449:1959, 1/325.
Timber beams and joists—L.C.C. By-laws, 1/333. C.P. 112:1952, 1/300.
R.C. slabs—C.P. 114:1957, Table 13:

Beams	Max. value of span to O/A depth	Slabs	Max. value of span to O/A depth
Simply supported	20	Spanning in one direction, simply supported	30
Continuous	25	Ditto ditto, continuous	35
Cantilever	10	Spanning in two directions, simply supported	35
		Ditto ditto, continuous	40
		Cantilever	12

TIMBER FLOORS

The timber floor has the advantages of light self-weight and of being a dry form of construction. It is simple to construct and this, together with the savings effected in the supporting structure because of its light weight, make it economical particularly where the imposed loads are small.

In itself it is a combustible form of construction and has a low fire resistance which depends on the thickness of the boarding, size of joists and, especially, on the nature and thickness of the lining (see page 507).

There is scope, however, for the use of the timber floor in many types of building higher than two storeys, where the means of escape is good and the building is divided by fire-stop walls into sections of limited area or cubical content (see page 507).

Single Floors

These are described in *Elementary Building Construction*. For economic reasons the clear span of softwood joists is usually limited to about 16 ft which will require, for domestic loading with joists at 16 in. centres, 9 in. × 2 in. or $2\frac{1}{2}$ in. joists.[1] For heavier loadings and greater spans the required size of timber soon falls outside the range of stock sizes and becomes uneconomical.

It is common practice to use single timber floors as the intermediate floors in multi-storey maisonette blocks, with reinforced concrete floors between the maisonettes, as shown on page 136. This results in a considerable economy in the cost of each maisonette and is possible because the floors within the dwellings are not required to provide so high a degree of fire resistance as the separating floors and the required degree of sound insulation may be lower than that desirable in the separating floors.

The 16 ft span falls close to the economic spacing for cross walls (see Chapter 4) and the joists usually span between these walls. If they are built-in the ends should be creosoted or protected in some other way. In order to maintain the minimum of 4 in. of solid incombustible material between the ends of joists on opposite sides of a 9 in. wall as required by the Model Building Byelaws[2] the bearing of the joist must be limited to about $2\frac{1}{4}$ in. This will be ample for normal softwoods and domestic floor loading. The L.C.C. By-laws prohibit the building-in of timbers to the required thickness of a party wall[3] and the ends of joists must be carried on steel hangers or brackets giving a bearing of at least $1\frac{1}{2}$ in. as shown on page 303. Although

---

[1] 9 in. × 2 in.: 15 ft 8 in. clear span. 9 in. × $2\frac{1}{2}$ in.: 16 ft 9 in. clear span. *M.o.W. Economy Memorandum* No. 4, "Use of Timber in all Building Work" (H.M.S.O.)
[2] Byelaw 42.   [3] By-law 5.27.

separating walls between flats and maisonettes are not subject to the provisions relating to party walls (see page 147), most District Surveyors do not permit timber joists to be built into them.

Should the floors be required to provide lateral support to the walls for design purposes, the ends of the joists must be secured to the wall by metal ties. (See Chapter 4, page 134.)

In narrow frontage maisonettes where the staircase must be planned parallel to the cross walls it may be more economical to run the timber joists parallel to the walls and bear them on precast concrete beams accommodated in the depth of the timber floor. These beams, in addition to carrying the floor joists, may serve to stiffen the wall.

To take advantage of the crane now normal on most multi-storey jobs the timber floors can be prefabricated in sections in the workshop and be lifted

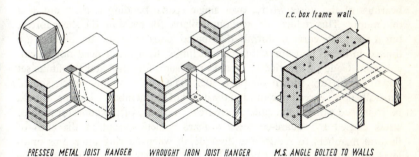

PRESSED METAL JOIST HANGER   WROUGHT IRON JOIST HANGER   M.S. ANGLE BOLTED TO WALLS

into position by the crane. Experience has shown that when this is done it is better to prefabricate the joists only as units and to fix the boarding in the normal way after the building is covered in, or, at least, after the reinforced concrete floor above has been completed. Otherwise in wet weather the panels become wet and the boards swell and rise.

Partition Support. When a timber or other lightweight non-loadbearing partition bears on a timber floor the joists of which run parallel with the partition the joists are commonly doubled up under the partition, a pair being spiked together if the ceiling is of plasterboard or similar sheet lining. If the ceiling is plaster on lathing, they are blocked apart about 2 in., the distance blocks being kept about ¾ in. up from the underside so that the plaster key is not broken for too great a distance. If the partition runs at right angles to the joists, a 3-in. deep timber sole piece, the same width as the partition, is used to span over the joists.

This procedure was generally quite satisfactory for floor construction based on rule-of-thumb joist sizes (see *Elementary Building Construction*) which gave ample margin of strength and stiffness.   At present, when joist depths are kept to a minimum by calculation or by reference to Tables of limiting spans referred to in Byelaws,[1] a check should be made to ensure that excessive deflection will not occur under the extra weight of any partition carried by the floor.

Notching.   Timber is easily cut and drilled for pipes and conduits but this must be done with care.   Notching near the centre of the span should be avoided, particularly if a number of adjacent joists are notched in line, since this cuts through the fibres at the point where, in uniformly loaded joists, they are most heavily stressed in bending.   If a pipe or conduit must pass across joists in this region it should pass through holes drilled at the centre of the depth, that is on the neutral axis.   Notching should be done near the bearings of the joists where, over single spans, bending stresses are at a minimum.   This reduces the section available for resisting the shear forces, but if the joists carry uniformly distributed loads only and the notches are limited in depth and are within certain limits, their effect need not be calculated.   Code of Practice 112 makes provision for this[2] and the limits set down therein are shown on page 305.   The depth of any notch should generally never exceed one-third of the depth of the member.   Notches should be U-shaped rather than square-cornered.   Because of the concentration of stress caused by square-cornered notches sometimes cut at the ends of flexural members to reduce the floor depth when bearing on beams or to level up the top surfaces, Code of Practice 112[3] requires a reduction in the basic stress to be made in calculating the shear strength of members cut in this way.

Lateral Support.   Stiffening is required when joists are long or deep in order to avoid winding or buckling at the top or compression zone.   Code of Practice 112,[4] makes certain recommendations in respect of this which are shown on page 305.   This stiffening is provided by normal herring-bone or solid strutting.   Should the joists be slightly in-winding when laid solid strutting is difficult to fit.   It is used mainly for heavy floors with a bolt passing through the centres of the joists close to the strutting.   On completion of the strutting the whole is screwed up very tightly to give a rigid result (see page 305).

It is common practice to space timber floor joists at 16 in. centres requiring

---

[1] *Ministry of Works Economy Memorandum* No. 4, "Use of Timber in all Building Work" (H.M.S.O.).
[2] Clause 0.310 (e).   [3] Clause 0.307 (a) (iii).   [4] Clause 0.310 (d).

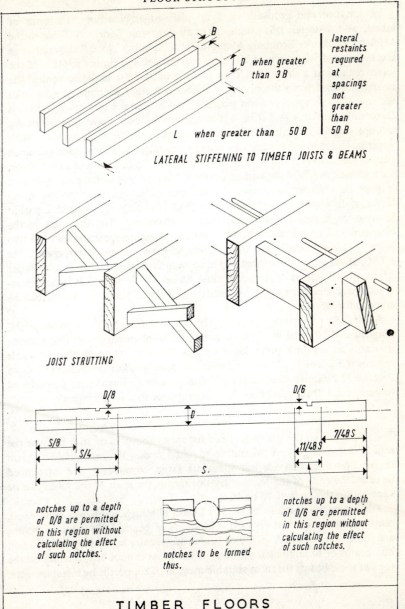

LATERAL STIFFENING TO TIMBER JOISTS & BEAMS

B

D when greater than 3 B

L when greater than 50 B

lateral restraints required at spacings not greater than 50 B

JOIST STRUTTING

D/8

D/6

D

S/8

S/4

7/48 S

11/48 S

S

notches up to a depth of D/8 are permitted in this region without calculating the effect of such notches.

notches to be formed thus.

notches up to a depth of D/6 are permitted in this region without calculating the effect of such notches.

TIMBER FLOORS

¾ in. tongued and grooved, or ⅞ in. plain-edge, boarding. In terms of labour and materials this usually gives an economic floor. A Table in the Ministry of Works Economy Memorandum "Timber No. 2" shows that as the spacing of joists in a small house is increased the timber content of the joists reduces at a slower rate than the rate of increase in the content of the boards. Apart from the saving in timber a further economy results from the use of 16 in. spacing when plaster board is used for the ceiling. This is commonly available in 8 ft by 4 ft boards and as both these dimensions are multiples of 16 in., labour in cutting is reduced and waste avoided. With wider spacings of joists noggings would be required entailing extra labour in cutting and fixing and a further increase in the timber content of the floor.

In situations where the cost of labour is high relative to the cost of timber, it may be cheaper to reduce the amount of labour involved by using larger, widely spaced joists spanned by thick boarding. This produces what in America is called plank and beam construction. The thickness of the boards would be calculated in the usual way as beams spanning between two joists. This gives a board of sufficient stiffness for most purposes. The L.C.C. By-laws lay down that the maximum fibre stress shall be 800 lb per sq. in. for all classes of timber because timber for floor boards is not stress-graded, and that an extra ⅛ in. over the calculated board thickness shall be allowed for wear.[1]

Apart from preventing the passage of dust and draughts through the joints, tongued and grooved boarding is preferable to plain-edge boarding because it is able to transmit point loads on one board to adjacent boards. This reduces the intensity of load on individual boards. For this reason Code of Practice 112 requires that each individual plain-edge board shall be designed to carry the full superimposed load appropriate to a foot width.[2]

Double Floors

The single joisted floor is rarely used for spans above 15 or 16 ft because the rapidly increasing depth of timber required makes it uneconomic. When timber floors are suitable but spans are large, cross-beams are introduced to carry the ends of the joists. By this means the span of the joists can be kept within the limit of 15 or 16 ft.

The beams are normally of steel or timber although, as already mentioned, reinforced concrete can be used. Methods of bearing the joists on beams are shown on page 307. Timber beams are usually in the form of plywood box beams or of laminated timber. If the joists cannot bear directly on the tops of these beams the most suitable method of support is by metal hangers.

---

[1] By-law 8.02 (4).   [2] Clause 0.314 (a).

REINFORCED CONCRETE FLOORS

The concrete floor has the advantage of strength and good fire resistance. Its use is now normal in most forms of multi-storey building, particularly because of the requirements in respect of fire resistance which apply to such structures.

The choice of a concrete floor can be made from a wide variety of types including *in situ* solid concrete floors, *in situ* hollow block floors and precast floors of numerous forms.

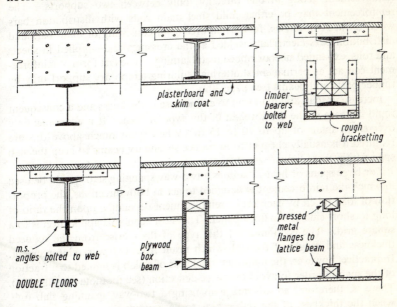

plasterboard and skim coat

timber bearers bolted to web

rough bracketting

m.s. angles bolted to web

plywood box beam

pressed metal flanges to lattice beam

DOUBLE FLOORS

In situ Floors

The *in situ* concrete floor is a wet form of construction incapable of bearing loads until quite set and requiring shuttering which must be left in position with all the supporting props until the concrete has gained sufficient strength. This, with ordinary Portland Cement and normal temperatures, is usually a matter of three days at least, followed by a further four or more days of strutting by a reduced number of props.[1]

Solid Concrete Floor Slab. This type is commonly used when the slab is to act as a membrane supported on columns without beams, as in the flat

See Table on page 563.

slab and flat plate floors which are described later, or where a high degree of lateral rigidity is required to be provided by the floor. In buildings up to four storeys in height in its simplest form it may often prove more economic than hollow block construction. It gives maximum freedom in design on plan and section since it can easily be made to cover irregular plan shapes and can easily be varied in thickness at different points according to variations in load or span. It is a heavy floor but highly fire resistant.

The simplest form of solid floor is the one-way spanning slab with the reinforcement acting in one direction only between two supports. The reinforcement may be either mild steel main rods with distribution bars wired on at right-angles, fabric reinforcement, consisting of main bars and distribution bars electrically welded at the crossings and supplied in sheets and rolls, expanded steel or ribbed metal lathing. The last form of reinforcement can act as permanent shuttering requiring temporary support only by timber posts and beams (see page 309).

Increase in span and load lead to an increase in thickness and a consequent rapid increase in the dead weight of this type of floor. It is economic only over small spans of up to 10 to 15 ft. When spans much above this are required it is usually cheaper to introduce secondary beams to keep the slab span within these limits.

For large spans or heavy loadings a two-way spanning slab should be used in which the reinforcement is designed to act in both directions, the proportion of load taken by each set of reinforcement depending upon the ratio of long to short side of the floor panel. The most economic application is to a square grid. The economies of this type of floor arise from the reduced thickness and weight of the slab which result from two-way reinforcement. In practice, however, the minimum thickness of a slab is limited to a fraction of the span in order to avoid excessive deflection (see footnote on page 301). There is, therefore, an advantage in using a two-way spanning slab only when the thickness of the slab ceases to be governed by considerations of deflection.

Normal *in situ* solid floor slabs are not generally prestressed, this being applied most economically to rib or beam members.

Flat Plate Floor. In its commonest form this *in situ* concrete floor consists of a solid reinforced slab resting directly on reinforced concrete columns with which it is monolithic. There are no projecting main or secondary beams, the slab acting as an elastic diaphragm bearing on point supports.

The slab, or plate, is reinforced at the bottom in each direction over the whole of its area with concentrations of reinforcement along the lines of the column grid. These form wide "column bands" within the plate thickness.

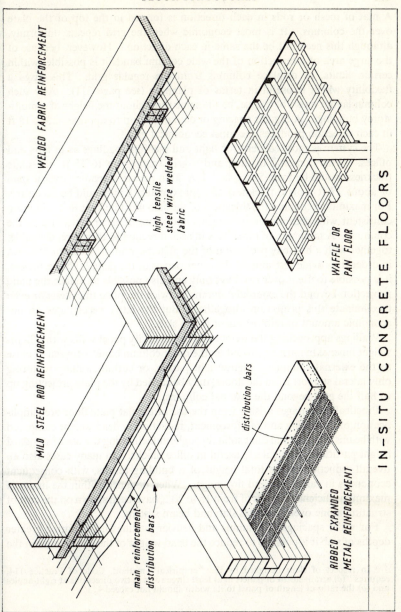

WELDED FABRIC REINFORCEMENT

high tensile steel wire welded fabric

WAFFLE OR PAN FLOOR

MILD STEEL ROD REINFORCEMENT

main reinforcement
distribution bars

distribution bars

RIBBED EXPANDED METAL REINFORCEMENT

IN-SITU CONCRETE FLOORS

A mat of mesh or rods in each direction is formed in the top of the plate over the columns. It is most economic when the grid repeats uniformly, although this need not be the same in each direction. However, because of the large area of intersection of the wide column bands it is possible, within certain limits, to displace columns from the regular grid. This gives a flexibility which is useful in terms of planning (see page 311). Any such column layout must, of course, be the same throughout the height of a multi-storey building. A regular spacing of columns of up to approximately 18 ft in each direction produces the most economical grid.

The system is most efficient for light and medium loadings as in flats and offices. With domestic loading and a grid spacing up to 15 ft, the plate thickness would be from 5 to 6 in. For 80 lb per sq. ft loading over a span of about 17 ft a plate thickness of approximately 8 in. would be necessary. For maximum economy the thickness of the slab must be kept to a minimum consistent with deflection requirements and those of shear resistance at the columns. A minimum of three bays in each direction is, therefore, desirable, together with a half-bay projection of the plate beyond the external columns in order to provide restraint on the outer panels of the plate.[1] Nevertheless, it is possible to use it over two bays only and also possible to reduce the plate projection beyond the external columns to twice the plate thickness, or even to eliminate this projection altogether. But the latter necessitates an uneconomic amount of reinforcement in the slab.

Wallings approaching the weight of normal cavity panel walls with a lightweight inner skin must be carried on the outer column bands between or close to the external columns. Lightweight panels, or curtain walling requiring only lateral support from the floors, may be carried by the plate projecting up to half the grid beyond the external columns.

Practical advantages arising from the use of the flat plate floor are simplification of shuttering and reinforcement, reduction in dead weight compared with beams and slab and a flat soffit throughout facilitating the use of standard height partitions, particularly useful in office blocks. In many cases also an overall reduction in the total height of a building results, with consequent economies in carcassing and finishings. When designed within the limits of maximum efficiency savings of from 15 to 20% have been shown on the cost of structure alone over a normal slab and beam system.

For wider spacings of columns and heavier loadings necessitating greater depths of slab it is possible to reduce the dead weight of the panel between the

[1] In respect of slabs designed by the "empirical" method, Code of Practice 114, requires "(a) arrangement of panels in at least three rows in two directions at right-angles and (b) the ratio of length of panel to its width should not exceed 4:3".

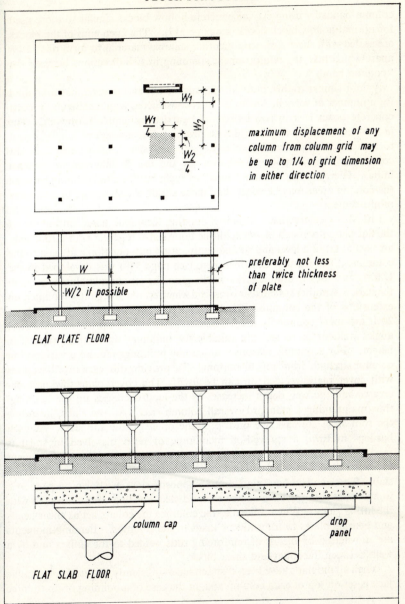

maximum displacement of any
column from column grid may
be up to 1/4 of grid dimension
in either direction

preferably not less
than twice thickness
of plate

W/2 if possible

FLAT PLATE FLOOR

column cap

drop
panel

FLAT SLAB FLOOR

FLAT PLATE & FLAT SLAB FLOORS

column bands by using clay or concrete hollow blocks similar to those used for normal hollow block floors (see page 317). The open ends of the blocks are sealed with sheet steel strip or other suitable material to form ribs 12 in. apart which take the reinforcement spanning in two directions between the "column bands".

A floor similar to this, but with ribs spaced about 3 ft apart, has been used for a number of years in America. It is constructed with rectangular precast concrete boxes cast in two halves, and carried on simple formwork. The *in situ* concrete ribs vary in width according to the amount of reinforcement to be accommodated and shear stresses to be resisted, particularly over the columns. This variation is achieved by the use of different size precast units. There are no "column bands" as such, but the ribs spanning between the column areas may be wider than those within the slab area, to take extra reinforcement.

Lift-Slab Construction. This is a building technique based on the use of the flat plate floor slab in which all the floor slabs, together with a roof slab, are cast at ground level and subsequently raised into position and fixed to the columns. The method described here (see page 313) was developed in the U.S.A. and uses hydraulic jacks working on the structural columns to raise the slabs. Another system uses overhead winch cranes on a gantry mounted on extensions of the columns. Steel or concrete columns on a grid of about 20 ft are most commonly used. Box columns, made up of two mild steel angles welded toe to toe, are suitable for buildings up to three storeys in height. For economic reasons multi-storey buildings require a variation in column strength from top to bottom. To provide this variation I-sections with cover plates welded on can be used. The cover plate thickness decreases and the web depth increases as the load decreases up the building, thus maintaining a standard overall column size. All the slabs, including the roof slab, are cast one on top of the other on the site slab. As each hardens in turn, a sprayed-on membrane of resin dissolved in spirit is used as a curing membrane and to prevent adhesion. As the reinforcement for each slab is laid, steel collars threaded on the columns are cast in with the slab. These collars have slots on two opposite sides as shown on page 313, to accommodate the ends of two screwed steel hoisting rods connected with the lifting jacks. When welded to the columns the collars act as shear heads and bearing plates to transmit the loads to the columns. Bending moments are transferred by means of reinforcing rods welded to the collars and by a weld between the collar and shear block.

When all the slabs have been cast and have sufficiently matured, a hydraulic jack is set on top of each column and, in the case of a building of up to three

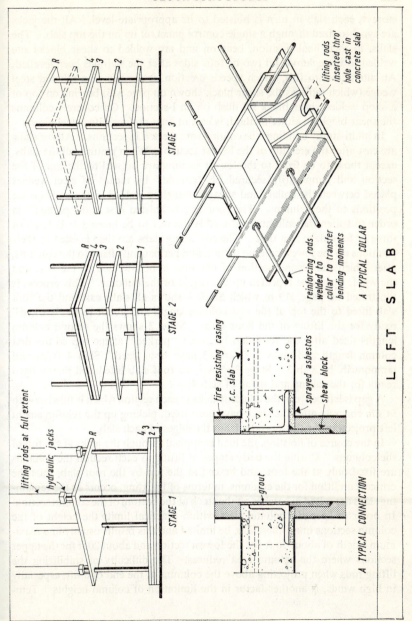

STAGE 1

STAGE 2

STAGE 3

lifting rods at full extent

hydraulic jacks

lifting rods inserted thro' hole cast in concrete slab

reinforcing rods welded to collar to transfer bending moments

A TYPICAL COLLAR

fire resisting casing

r.c. slab

sprayed asbestos

shear block

grout

A TYPICAL CONNECTION

LIFT SLAB

storeys, each slab in turn is hoisted to its appropriate level. All the jacks are synchronized through a single control panel set up on the top slab. The slabs, in their final position, bear on and are welded to shear blocks site welded to the columns on two or four sides after the slab has been levelled. An alternative to this, which speeds erection, is the use of a rebated steel wedge (which replaces the shear block shown on page 313) bearing on top of a shop welded shear block set flush on an I-section. On concrete columns the shear block, in either method, is cast in on a prefabricated steel insert.

In multi-storey buildings the columns are erected in sections. All the slabs are cast after the erection of the lowest section. When mature, all the slabs, except those to be fixed to the lowest section, are hoisted to the top of the section and temporarily secured or "parked" by means of steel wedges placed between the collars and shear plates shop welded in the appropriate positions to the columns. The roof slab is hoisted first and "parked" in order to stiffen the columns and enable the rest to be hoisted in batches of three or four slabs at a time. The remaining slabs are then hoisted to their positions up the lowest column section and permanently fixed to the columns, after which the second section of columns is butt-welded to the first and the whole operation repeated up the height of the building. This process is illustrated on page 313 in which Stage 1 shows all slabs cast and the roof slab lifted to the top of the first column length and about to be "parked" ready for the lifting of the floor slabs. Stage 2 shows the second column lengths fixed after the roof slab has been "parked" at the top of the first column length and slabs 1, 2 and 3 have been fixed. Slab 4 is carried temporarily by slab 3. Stage 3 shows the roof slab lifted and finally fixed ready for the raising and fixing of slab 4.

A gap is left between the adjacent slabs in each section which is filled in with *in situ* concrete after the slabs have been fixed, picking up the reinforcement left projecting for this purpose from the edges of each slab.

In the course of hoisting, the load is applied through the jacks at the top of the columns. During the early stages of lifting in each section the columns are fixed only at the foot, and braced at the top by the roof slab, thus the critical condition for the columns, in terms of buckling, occurs as the remaining slabs are raised in batches off the stack at the bottom of the column section. In order to keep the column sizes within practical limits the height of the column sections must, therefore, be limited and this results usually in a maximum length of about 30 ft for the lowest section and about 20 ft for the upper sections where the column area reduces. The difficulty of stabilizing the lifting rods when projecting above the columns at the end of a lift, especially in high winds, is another factor in the limitation of column heights. Temporary bracing during erection is provided by guy wires or by angles at the tops of the columns, and permanent stability by *in situ* concrete elements such as stair and lift wells, or by steel framed elements with adequate diagonal bracing.

The advantages claimed for this system are that it eliminates elaborate formwork and the hoisting of materials to great heights, and that it enables concrete placing and the fixing of reinforcement to be carried out at ground level. Electrical and other services can be positioned and fixed in the slabs at ground level before pouring and lifting the slabs. These factors taken together produce a simple economical system, particularly if the building is designed specifically for this form of construction. Where span and loading make it advisable a rectangular grid floor, the forms described under "Flat Plate Floor" or ribbed slabs with broad slab-depth beams may be used instead of the solid flat plate.

Flat Slab Floor. This is another form of *in situ* solid concrete floor without projecting beams and is termed coloquially "mushroom construction" because of the expanded column heads which are part of its design (see page 311). Code of Practice 114:1957 now provides for the design of flat plate floors but uses the term "flat slab" to describe both plate and "mushroom" construction. For sake of distinction the term is used here in its original, limited sense.

As in the flat plate floor, the slab is reinforced in both directions with "column bands" running on the lines of the column grid, the slab acting as an elastic diaphragm supported directly on the heads of the columns.

The system is designed for heavy evenly distributed superimposed loads and is economical for loadings of 100 lb. per sq. ft or more and in cases where there is little solid partitioning on, or large openings in, the slab. It is, therefore, suitable for such building types as warehouses and others with heavy imposed loadings and large imperforate, undivided areas of floor.

For maximum efficiency the columns should be on a regular grid of about 20 to 25 ft in approximately square bays. In order to provide adequate resistance to the compression stresses in the bottom of the slab over the points of support, and to increase the resistance to shear and punching stresses at these points, the heads of the columns are expanded to give the typical "mushroom" cap. This will be square or circular depending upon the shape of the column. In some circumstances it is necessary to thicken the slab over this cap to form what is termed a drop panel. The main advantages over normal beam and slab floors, as with flat plate floors, are the reduction in floor to floor height due to the elimination of beams and simpler formwork, advantages which must be balanced against its relatively great weight. For grid spacings of 20 to 25 ft and for loadings of 100 lb per sq. ft and over, the slab thickness will be from 9 to 12 in.

As with flat plate floors, not less than three bays in each direction are desirable, with half-bays cantilevering beyond the outer column bands to obtain restraint on the outer panels.

In situ Tee-beam or Ribbed Floor. This is illustrated on page 317 and consists of a series of tee-beams cast monolithically side by side to produce a relatively thin slab with ribs on the underside. The basis of the tee-beam is described on page 266, and by applying the principles to slab construction a floor lighter than a solid slab results.

It is an expensive floor to construct with normal shuttering and proprietary steel forms, hired by the general contractor or used by the makers as sub-contractors, are generally employed. These forms produce ribs at 2 ft centres 3½ or 4 in. wide at the bottom and slightly wider at the top. The depth is adjusted according to the load and span. The thickness of the top slab is 2 to 3 in. reinforced with rods or mesh.

Hardwood fillets can be embedded in the bottom of the ribs, or be attached to the bottom of prefabricated "beams" of lattice reinforcement, to provide a fixing for lathing or battens. The underside may then be enclosed with a ceiling and the resulting voids between the ribs can accommodate services and recessed lighting fittings.

This type of floor, being cast monolithic with the main supporting beams, may be used to stiffen the structural frame in buildings up to three or four storeys high. Because of its low dead weight it can economically be used for spans up to 30 ft. It can be prestressed by means of post-tensioned cables run in holes formed at the bottom of the ribs or by means of precast pre-tensioned "planks" bonded to the bottom of the ribs as shown on page 317. To cover spans up to 45 ft for light loads this would require a floor depth in the region of 18 in. overall. For spans less than 30 ft normal reinforced concrete is cheaper.

In situ Hollow Block Floor. Based on the tee-beam principle this type of floor is lighter than the simple solid slab floor, and as it provides a flat soffit the applied ceiling required with an *in situ* tee-beam floor is not necessary (see page 317). Like the solid concrete floor, in most forms it requires shuttering over its whole area. On this the blocks are laid end to end in parallel rows, about 3 or 4 in. apart, according to the width of rib required. Reinforcement is laid in these spaces and concrete poured between and over the blocks to form a series of tee-beams. The hollow blocks are of clay, similar to those used for partitions, or of concrete, and are 12 in. long and 10 or 12 in. wide with depths from 3 to 8 in. When shear requirements at

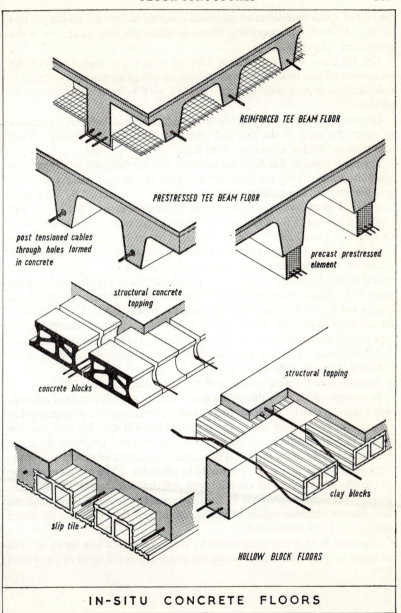

REINFORCED TEE BEAM FLOOR

PRESTRESSED TEE BEAM FLOOR

post tensioned cables
through holes formed
in concrete

precast prestressed
element

structural concrete
topping

concrete blocks

structural topping

clay blocks

slip tile

HOLLOW BLOCK FLOORS

IN-SITU CONCRETE FLOORS

11*

the end of spans necessitate an increased concrete section the blocks are laid to stop short of the supporting beams to allow for this, as shown in the illustration on page 332.

The thickness of the structural topping is not less than 1 in. for the shallowest of this type of floor and increases for greater depths. The thin slab and the blocks only may be punched with holes for the passage of services.

Clay slip tiles, grooved like the blocks, can be laid between the blocks to cover the soffit of the ribs and give a uniform key for plaster. They also increase the fire resistance of the floor.

The main types of this floor are patented and are designed and erected by specialist firms. They are normally designed as one-way reinforced floors and the majority are most suitable for spans up to about 22 ft. They can be adapted to two-way reinforcement by closing the ends of the blocks and spacing them out to form ribs at right-angles to the normal ribs as described under "Flat Plate Floor". One type makes use of hollow precast concrete blocks, the blocks being made in such a way that in addition to the parallel spaces forming the ribs of the tee-beams, in this case 18 in. apart, narrower lateral spaces 18 in. apart are formed at right-angles to the ribs as shown on page 317. These take lateral reinforcement. The bottom edges of the blocks are lipped, the lips touching when the blocks are laid in position to form a soffit to the ribs, thus reducing shuttering problems. This particular type is most economical for superimposed loadings of 80 lb per sq. ft or more.

A composite form of the *in situ* hollow block floor is described under "Precast Ribs and Fillers" on page 323.

All these floors are monolithic with the supporting beams.

Rectangular Grid or Waffle Slab Floor. This is a development of the two-way spanning slab in which the two sets of reinforcement are concentrated in ribs, as shown on page 309. The restricted span of the slab over the ribs results in a considerable reduction in its thickness, and consequently in the total dead weight of the floor. It is most economic over relatively wide spans where the weight of a solid slab would be excessive. The optimum spacing of the ribs is controlled by the minimum practical thickness of the slab they carry. The latter is governed by fire-resistance requirements, depth required for effective accommodation of reinforcement and the maximum permitted depth/span ratio for the slab.

The floor is normally constructed by means of square box forms or pans of metal or glass-fibre reinforced plastic which are in the form of deep trays with projecting horizontal edges or lips. The pans are laid on temporary skeleton formwork with the edges touching to form the soffits of the ribs. The depth of the pans will vary according to the required depth of the ribs.

The metal or plastic pans can be re-used a great number of times but, as an alternative, stout, stiffened cardboard boxes can be used as expendable forms.

In situ **Diagonal Beam Floor.** This type of floor, like the rectangular grid floor, is a single layer grid construction. It consists of two intersecting

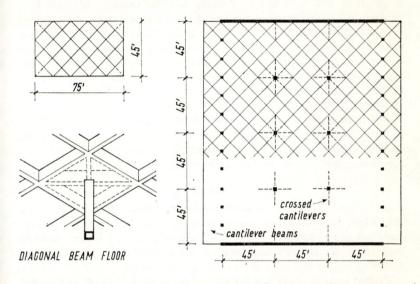

DIAGONAL BEAM FLOOR

sets of parallel beams equally spaced and set at 45° to the boundary supports as shown above. The beams are basically all of the same depth and cross-section and are rigidly connected at their intersections and to continuous edge beams. The support and end restraint provided by the shorter and stiffer corner beams to those of longer span, together with bottom slabs provided in the corners to resist uplift due to the negative bending moments in these areas, results in a considerable reduction in the bending moments in the longer beams compared with those in a normal slab and beam floor of the same span. Thus a depth/span ratio of 1:30 is possible. In addition to the bottom slabs the short beams across the corners are sometimes, for greater efficiency, made slightly deeper and wider than the other beams.

For greatest efficiency the grid layout should give a sub-division of three panels along the shorter side of the structural bay.   Where internal columns are necessary these are preferably located on the intersection of the beams. Crossed cantilevers, springing from the heads of the columns within the thickness of the floor, may be necessary if the layout results in beams of excessive length as shown on page 319.   Cantilever beams are also required if the columns are located within a panel instead of at an intersection of beams (page 319).   Ideally, this type of floor should be square on plan, or sub-divided into squares, to give maximum efficiency.

The floor slab need not be integral with the beams.   Although it is generally of *in situ* concrete it may be of precast concrete units, of corrugated asbestos-cement sheets with a topping, or of timber joists with boarding, since the beam structure is designed independent of the slab.

This floor is most economic when used to carry heavy superimposed loads, particularly concentrated loads, over spans of 50 ft or more.   In Great Britain it is very generally called the "Diagrid" floor, although this particular name is, in fact, the trade name of Truscon Ltd.

Prestressing can be applied to this type of floor because of its beam structure.   When prestressed the beams are generally precast in panel lengths, supported on temporary runners and props, and post-tensioned together as shown in the roof example on page 462.

Precast Floors

Most types of *in situ* concrete floor require shuttering over the whole of their area which must be kept in position for a considerable period until the concrete has gained sufficient strength.   The floor must be kept free of traffic and the props underneath take up space and interfere with other work, all of which reduce the rate of progress of the job as a whole.

Precast concrete floors have been developed in order to reduce or eliminate shuttering and to save site work and the use of wet concrete as far as possible, these being factors which lead to speedier erection.

The large variety of precast floor systems can be divided into two basic categories:

(1) Precast beams placed close together.

(2) Precast ribs or beams with filler blocks or slabs between.

Those in the first category can be erected rapidly and almost immediately form a working platform as the non-structural top screed may be laid afterwards.   Many of those in the second category require an *in situ* structural topping of concrete to be placed before they can take their working load.   Prestressing is applied to floors in both categories.   Because maximum economy in precast work results from a maximum repetition of standard units, the precast floor is not suited to irregular plan shapes requiring a large number of special size units to cover the varying spans of floor. Nor is it so well suited to circumstances where monolithy is required in the structure because of the difficulty of providing an efficient rigid junction between the floor and the supporting beams or walls, although continuity over supports in adjacent floor panels themselves may be obtained easily.

Precast Beams. These are illustrated on page 322. They provide the simplest form of precast concrete floor and are widely used because of the speed with which they can be erected and used as a working platform. The floor consists of a number of beams placed side by side and, to a very large extent, spanning between supports independent of each other. The cross-section varies with the individual maker, some having a closed soffit, others an open soffit requiring an applied ceiling. All are designed to produce a more or less hollow floor to reduce the dead weight.

Solid Beams. In this type some form of I-section is normal. The beams are laid with edges touching or, in some cases, overlapping slightly, so that the bottom flanges form a flat soffit. If continuity over supports is required portions of the top flanges must be removed to allow the insertion of reinforcement and *in situ* concrete.

Hollow and Channel Beams. The solid units are relatively narrow and heavy, and developments in the form of channel and hollow beam sections of greater unit width, and much the same weight, enable floor areas to be laid more quickly. Widths of the units vary from about $11\frac{1}{2}$ to $16\frac{1}{2}$ in. and depths according to span and load. Each beam is reinforced in the bottom corners and in some types in the top corners also. The sides are splayed or shaped to form a narrow space between the beams. This is filled with grout to assist the units to act together in some measure, the adjacent faces of the beams being grooved to provide mechanical bond. The grout is normally taken up to finish flush with the top of the beams, a structural concrete topping being used only when extra strength is required for heavy loads over long spans. Continuity over supports is obtained by the insertion of rods in the joints prior to grouting (page 322, top).

In all types of precast beam floors the units are made to the correct lengths between bearings with the ends designed to suit the type of bearing. Notches, holes and fixings for applied ceiling and floor finishes can be incorporated. The underside of the units can be left smooth or keyed for plaster in types having a flat soffit forming a continuous ceiling.

The beams are delivered to the site, hoisted and placed in position on their supports and the joints grouted up. A minimum of *in situ* filling is required

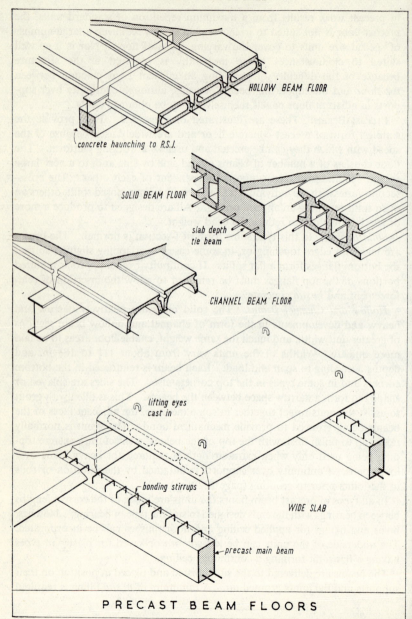

HOLLOW BEAM FLOOR

concrete haunching to R.S.J.

SOLID BEAM FLOOR

slab depth
tie beam

CHANNEL BEAM FLOOR

lifting eyes cast in

bonding stirrups

WIDE SLAB

precast main beam

PRECAST BEAM FLOORS

and no temporary shuttering or supports.   Spans up to approximately 20 ft are possible although the economic limits for most types are 12 to 16 ft.

Precast Ribs and Fillers.   This type of floor consists basically of precast reinforced concrete ribs spanning between the main supports and carrying hollow blocks or slabs to fill the spaces between the ribs similar to the example shown on page 330.   In most systems a flush soffit is produced. The *in situ* topping may be simply a screed or may be structural, to act with the ribs, depending on the load range for which the system is designed.

The ribs, which are placed at centre spacings ranging from about 10 to 24 in., are manufactured in the required lengths for each job.   In the case of heavy floors they may be pierced at intervals to permit the passage of lateral distribution rods.

The fillers may be hollow clay tiles or pots, hollow precast concrete blocks or wood wool or lightweight concrete slabs.   The pots or blocks are usually rebated at the bottom edges and sit on projecting flanges or lips at the bottom of the ribs so that a flush soffit results (page 328).   In those systems designed as a composite construction with a structural topping, the filler blocks are shallower in depth than the ribs so that the latter project above the fillers and bond with the topping when this is cast.   The sides of the ribs are usually grooved to provide mechanical bond.   In systems with lightweight slabs resting on the tops of the ribs, bond is obtained by means of steel stirrups or dowels left projecting from the top of each rib.

No shuttering is required for this type of floor, although in those systems with structural toppings a few props may be necessary under the ribs until the *in situ* concrete has matured.   Continuity over supports is obtained by means of rods placed between the ribs.

In one form of rib and filler floor the precast rib is reduced to a thin reinforced concrete plank which forms the soffit of an *in situ* tee-beam rib. This floor is, in fact, an *in situ* hollow block floor of composite form combining the advantages of monolithic construction with those of the precast rib and filler floor.   The widths of the planks can be varied to suit grid requirements. To suit heavy load or wide span requirements the depth of the ribs may be increased by the use of deeper filler blocks and the thickening of the structural topping.   The reinforcement is in lattice form expanded from cold rolled steel strip or formed of welded rods which projects from the plank.   Its particular form provides good bond between the plank and the *in situ* concrete and stiffens the plank during handling and erection.   The top boom can serve as compression reinforcement when required and additional tensile reinforcement can be introduced in the form of high-tensile or cold-twisted steel bars.

Precast reinforced panels.   These are used as permanent shuttering to form composite slabs, and for reasons of economy should be as thin as possible. To overcome difficulties in handling thin flat slabs of any length, wide but shallow trough sections are used. These are very rigid, particularly if the bottom lip is carried round the four edges and incorporates continuous rod reinforcement. They can be as thin as 1 in. in thickness and are able to carry the live loads during the casting of the *in situ* concrete. The depth and shape of these units may be such as to produce small tee-beams to the slab or deeper main beams as illustrated on page 277.

Prestressed Floors. Prestressing is now applied to many types of precast floors. This is advantageous where wide spans are involved because it reduces the thickness and dead weight and increases the economic span of the floor.

Pre-tensioning is most commonly adopted so that no stressing is carried out on site and it is applied to all the precast floors so far described—solid, hollow and channel beams and rib and filler types.

In some systems prestressing is carried out by post-tensioning. If applied to the beam units in the factory these are, in practice, so far as hoisting and placing in position is concerned, no different to other units. If carried out on site special anchor and end blocks at the bearings are necessary. The cables may be placed between hollow beam units and grouted up after tensioning. This method which is shown on page 325, is economical for long spans up to 40 ft and for heavier loads up to 2 cwt per sq. ft or more.

The economic advantage of combining prestressed precast elements with *in situ* concrete has been discussed in Chapter 5 (page 279). Many types of prestressed floor are based on composite construction of this nature, two of which are illustrated on page 325. Some forms use thin prestressed precast elements called "planks". One, a rib and filler floor, uses prestressed planks of clay or concrete supporting filler blocks of the same material. *In situ* concrete is cast between and over the fillers to form a rib having the prestressed plank as the tension zone. The planks are grooved to accommodate the tensioning wires and these grooves are filled with mortar after tensioning and before the jacks are released in order to bond the wires to the planks. Steel stirrups bedded in the top of the planks provide mechanical bond with the *in situ* filling. The planks require temporary support by props until the concrete has matured.

Another form uses prestressed concrete planks placed close together side by side without filler blocks to form a permanent shuttering. The edges are grooved to provide a dovetail key for the *in situ* concrete structural topping in addition to the natural bond between the rough top of the plank and the topping. The planks are 14 in. wide by 2 or 2½ in. deep in lengths

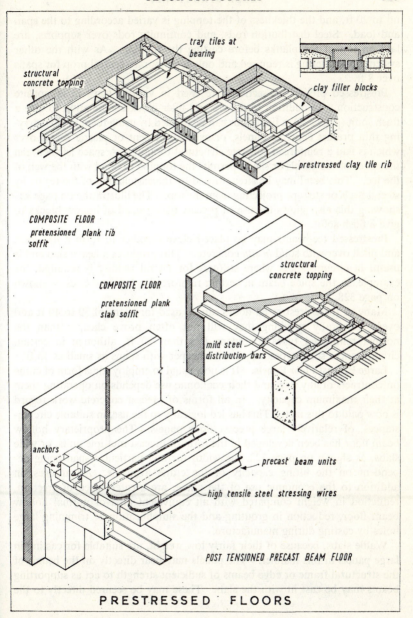

structural concrete topping

tray tiles at bearing

clay filler blocks

prestressed clay tile rib

COMPOSITE FLOOR
pretensioned plank rib soffit

COMPOSITE FLOOR
pretensioned plank slab soffit

structural concrete topping

mild steel distribution bars

anchors

precast beam units

high tensile steel stressing wires

POST TENSIONED PRECAST BEAM FLOOR

PRESTRESSED FLOORS

up to 20 ft, and the thickness of the topping is varied according to the span and load. Steel distribution rods, and continuity rods over supports, are laid on top of the planks before casting the topping. As with the other system no shuttering is required and only a temporary central prop for spans over 8 ft.

Prestressed precast tee-sections are used in various ways in composite construction. In addition to the rib and filler block combination to give a flush soffit (page 328), a light floor can be formed by using them as ribs carrying thin precast concrete panels, or asbestos-cement or plastic sheets over which is laid a reinforced concrete structural topping. A space left between the edges of the panels or sheets permits the topping to bond with the web of the tee. This bond may be strengthened by the castellation of the tee or by steel dowels or stirrups projecting from the top. The illustration on page 327 showing this also shows the use of precast tiles instead of hollow blocks to give a flush soffit.

Prestressed tee-beams may be placed close together to form a flat soffit and filled over with solid *in situ* concrete. This produces a heavy slab and is useful in circumstances where stiffness for lateral rigidity is required, for example, in the spine beam in certain reinforced concrete frames as shown on page 328.

Many of these prestressed floors can be used for spans of 30 to 40 ft and over. Generally speaking they will not often prove cheaper than the normal reinforced types for spans less than 20 ft, although in certain circumstances some types may prove cheaper with spans as small as 15 ft.

Large Precast Floor Panels. It is now usual to employ some form of crane on contracts of any size, and their economic use depends on operating them at their maximum capacity. In all forms of precast concrete work regard is now paid to this fact. This has led logically to the use, in suitable circumstances, of relatively large precast floor panels. The proprietary hollow beam floor has been developed in the form of precast multiple units, or wide slabs, as shown on page 322, the width for any particular span being dependent on the lifting capacity of the crane available. Advantages, in addition to the economic use of the crane, are greater speed of erection, reduction in weight compared with an equivalent area of normal hollow beam floor, reduction in grouting and the simplification of trimming large holes by casting during manufacture.

Waffle slabs, because of their fairly low weight, are suitable for casting in large panels in this manner. The panels may bear directly on the beams of the structural frame or edge beams of sufficient strength to act as supporting beams may be cast in with the slab. These may be secured directly to the

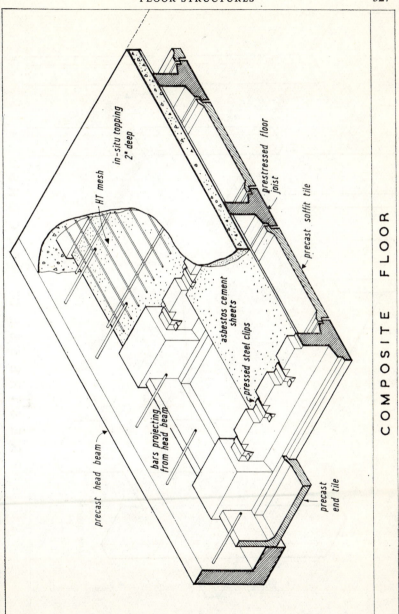

in-situ topping
2" deep

HT mesh

prestressed floor
joist

precast soffit tile

asbestos cement
sheets

pressed steel clips

bars projecting
from head beam

precast head beam

precast
end tile

COMPOSITE FLOOR

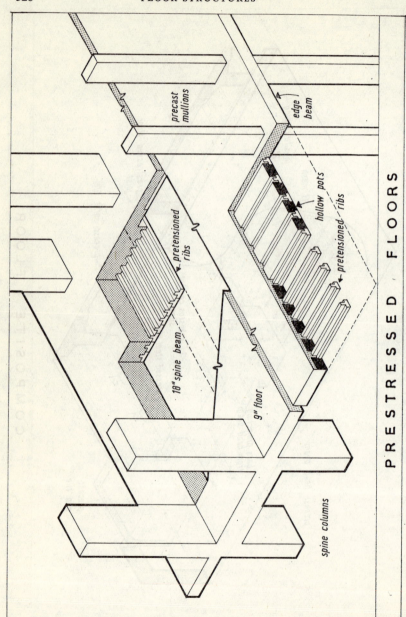

PRESTRESSED FLOORS

precast mullions

edge beam

hollow pots

pretensioned ribs

pretensioned ribs

18" spine beam

9" floor

spine columns

columns by means of metal connectors cast in the beams and shear plates welded to steel stanchions or cast into concrete columns.

Flat plate floors on precast concrete columns on a grid of about 18 ft have been precast in large panels. The column bands are cast as panels spanning between column head plates and the whole of the centre panel is cast in one piece. Rebates in the top edges of the panels form channels or strips about 18 in. wide in which *in situ* concrete is placed to bond with the steel reinforcement left projecting from the edges of each panel. The column head plates need most accurate setting and levelling and it is usually more economical to carry these out as *in situ* work.

OPENINGS AND SERVICES IN CONCRETE FLOORS

Apart from small holes for pipes in solid floors and holes within the width of an individual section of a hollow beam or of a filler block, openings in concrete floors require to be trimmed. Illustrations of methods commonly adopted are given on page 330.

In *in situ* solid concrete and hollow block floors small openings can be trimmed by the use of appropriate reinforcement placed within the thickness of the slab round the opening, but for larger openings such trimmers and trimming beams are too shallow and normal beams have to be formed. In the flat plate and flat slab floors particular care must be taken in deciding the positions of holes, especially when these lie near to columns and column bands. It is essential that early consideration at design stage be given to this matter.

Small holes for services are often cut after the concrete floor has been cast but this is uneconomical and the positions of all such openings should be settled before the concrete is poured. Small vertical holes are formed by means of timber boxes, pieces off cardboard rolls, sheet metal bent to a rectangular or cylindrical shape or gas barrel fixed to the shuttering to give an aperture of the required size. Most formers are left in position except those of timber, which are usually removed.

Openings of limited size can be formed in two ways in precast beam floors. One, by the use of special trimming beams carrying reinforced trimmers. The other, by the use of cranked steel strap hangers bearing on the beams at each side of the opening, one at each end carrying the ends of the trimmed beams.

In the case of rib and filler block floors the necessary blocks are omitted and the shortened ribs carried on special trimmer ribs, the ends of each being supported on mild steel hangers. The trimming ribs can be doubled up on each side of the opening to give additional strength. A certain amount of

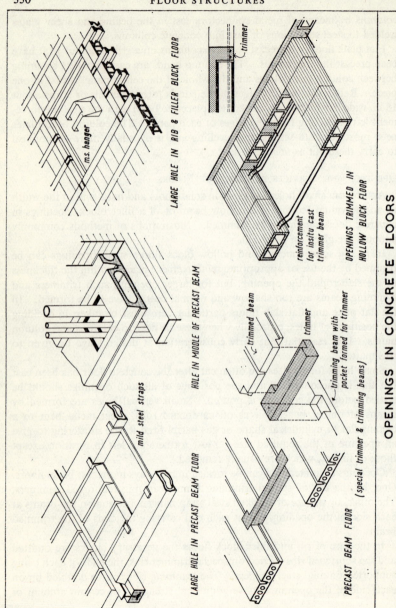

LARGE HOLE IN RIB & FILLER BLOCK FLOOR

m.s. hanger

trimmer

OPENINGS TRIMMED IN HOLLOW BLOCK FLOOR

reinforcement for insitu cast trimmer beam

HOLE IN MIDDLE OF PRECAST BEAM

trimmed beam

trimming beam with pocket formed for trimmer

trimmer

LARGE HOLE IN PRECAST BEAM FLOOR

mild steel straps

PRECAST BEAM FLOOR
(special trimmer & trimming beams)

OPENINGS IN CONCRETE FLOORS

in situ concrete may be necessary to make out openings to sizes not falling within the limits of the precast beams or filler blocks.

Limited openings in the prestressed plank floor can be trimmed within the thickness of the floor by special detailing and the use of cut planks to form trimmers. Holes can be formed in casting, making use of specially wide planks where necessary. Small holes can be cut on site provided they are near to joints.

The method of running pipes and conduits across the floors will depend to some extent on the type of floor being used.

With *in situ* floors, electric conduits can be cast in the soffit of the slab by laying screwed conduit on the shuttering with all the necessary outlet, junction and draw-in boxes in position. Where conduits cross the blocks of a hollow block floor these must be cut or notched. Alternatively, conduit may be laid on top of the structural slab after it is cast, holes being left at all drops to ceiling points below (see page 332). The top screeding must be thick enough to bring the finished floor level above that of the conduit. It is possible to lay conduit in the concrete topping of a hollow block floor, but since this is structural the conduits should run only parallel to the main reinforcement.

Where pipes for water, heating, gas and drainage services are required they cannot generally be cast in the structural slab because of the large diameter of the pipes and the need for ready access to them for maintenance. They are laid either on top of the slab or fixed to, or suspended from, the soffit. When laid on top of the slab the thickness of the finishing screed may be considerable, especially if some pipes cross each other, so that the layout of the services should be settled early enough to permit the weight of the screed to be taken into consideration in the design of the floor. To reduce the weight of thick screeds lightweight concrete or foamed mortar can be used. Thick screeds are also required where fibre or metal ducting is used on top of the slab for telephone and electric wiring. (See Chapter 5, *Advanced Building Construction* (*Components, Services and Finishes*).) When the form of construction involves ribs or secondary beams on the underside of the floor the pipes may be hung from the slab and concealed by a suspended ceiling at the level of the rib or beam soffit as shown on page 332.

Ducts of various diameters can be formed in floor slabs or screeds by means of expendable fibre or cardboard tubes left in position. Alternatively, pneumatic cores in the form of long, inflatable tubes may be laid in position in an inflated state. The concrete is cast round the tube and, when set, the tubes are deflated and withdrawn. The construction of the wall of the tube is such that when it is deflated the tube twists and pulls away from the

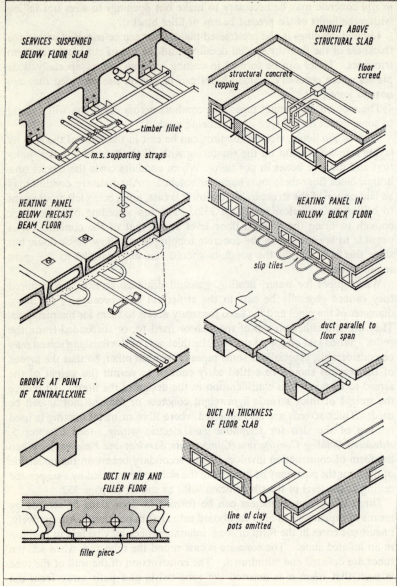

SERVICES SUSPENDED
BELOW FLOOR SLAB

timber fillet

m.s. supporting straps

CONDUIT ABOVE
STRUCTURAL SLAB

structural concrete
topping

floor
screed

HEATING PANEL
BELOW PRECAST
BEAM FLOOR

HEATING PANEL IN
HOLLOW BLOCK FLOOR

slip tiles

GROOVE AT POINT
OF CONTRAFLEXURE

duct parallel to
floor span

DUCT IN THICKNESS
OF FLOOR SLAB

DUCT IN RIB AND
FILLER FLOOR

filler piece

line of clay
pots omitted

SERVICES IN CONCRETE FLOORS

concrete. Pneumatic cores have the advantage that they can be laid in curved lines.

The pipes for floor and ceiling panel heating may be embedded in the floor or screed because they are welded at the connections. In ceiling panels in solid concrete floors the coils are laid on the shuttering and, after testing, the reinforcement is fixed and the concrete cast around and over the pipes so that they are embedded flush with the soffit. In hollow block floors the coils are laid directly on the shuttering with special slip tiles between the pipes to provide a key for the plastering. A $\frac{3}{4}$ in. screed is applied on top of the pipes and on this the normal blocks are laid. In the areas where no heating panels occur deeper blocks are used. Heating panels in precast beam floors are accommodated in recesses formed by the use of shallower but specially strengthened beams, the coils being carried on steel straps and bolt hangers. These methods are illustrated on page 332.

The services in certain types of buildings such as laboratories should, as far as possible, be accessible without the necessity of breaking open a floor screed. It is a simple matter to form ducts in the thickness of most types of one-way spanning floors so long as they run in the direction of the span (see page 332). In a solid *in situ* floor the necessary width of duct is boxed out on the shuttering. In a hollow block floor or precast rib and filler floor, one or more lines of blocks are omitted and in the case of a precast beam floor one or more beam sections are omitted. The service pipes pass through slots in the main supporting beams made, preferably, on the line of the neutral axis. If the latter is too low and the slot is formed at a higher level, compression reinforcement may be required in the "bridge" over the slot. Holes through the webs of steel beams may need strengthening by means of a reinforcing plate welded around the slot. From such ducts lateral branches from the service pipes can be run at right-angles to the span in the thickness of the floor screed or rise directly to fittings when, for example, the ducts are placed relative to a run of laboratory benches.

In solid *in situ* slabs continuous over supporting beams it is possible to form shallow ducts at right-angles to the span on the points of contraflexure. These may be of a depth not exceeding about one-quarter of the thickness of the slab. If a deeper duct, or a complete opening through the floor, is required at any point at right-angles to the span it is necessary to form structural trimming beams on each side of the duct.

FILLER JOIST FLOORS

This type of floor is the forerunner of the modern reinforced concrete floor and consists of small rolled steel joists at fairly close centres, surrounded by

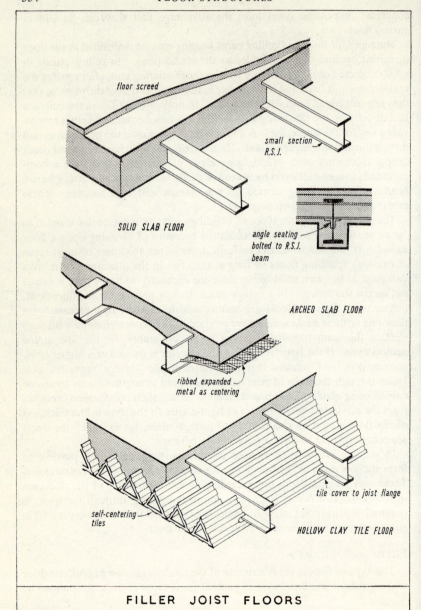

floor screed

small section
R.S.J.

SOLID SLAB FLOOR

angle seating
bolted to R.S.J.
beam

ARCHED SLAB FLOOR

ribbed expanded
metal as centering

tile cover to joist flange

self-centering
tiles

HOLLOW CLAY TILE FLOOR

FILLER JOIST FLOORS

and carrying a concrete slab as shown on page 334. The steel, or filler, joists are cleated direct to the main steel beams or, more commonly, are supported on a continuous steel shelf angle bolted to the web of the main beam, every second or third filler only then being cleated. Where headroom is not restricted it is preferable to run the fillers over the supporting beams, extending over at least three spans. The maximum spacing of the fillers is related to the superimposed loading on the floor and to the thickness of the concrete unless the concrete is reinforced to span as a slab, or function as an arch, between the filler joists.[1] Slabs arched between the filler joists are simply constructed by using ribbed metal lathing curved between the joists and acting as centering and a key for plastering. The thickness of the concrete at the crown must not be less than 2 in. Other methods, designed to eliminate shuttering, use hollow clay blocks or tubes spanning between the bottom flanges of the filler joists. They have lips which protect the underside of the fillers and provide a key for plastering. The minimum thickness of concrete over the blocks is $1\frac{1}{4}$ in. for filler spacings up to 18 in. and 2 in. for greater spacings.[1] One system is illustrated on page 334.

The filler joist floor tends to be heavy and is generally used in cases of severe loading conditions as in factories, loading platforms and colliery buildings where it can be economical. Compared with a solid reinforced concrete floor it has the advantage that holes may be cut subsequent to its completion anywhere between the filler joists. This can prove useful in certain classes of building involving periodic alterations in equipment and services.

LATTICE JOIST FLOOR

Lattice, or open web, joists with flanges of light steel channels, angles and flats, or of cold-pressed sections, and with bent rod, angle or tube lacing to form the web, can be used instead of normal timber joists or R.S.J.'s. Continuous timber nailing fillets can be fixed on the flanges to provide fixing for floor and ceiling finishes. The open lattice web gives complete freedom in running services through the thickness of the floor (see page 336).

For a given floor loading and normal joist spacing, greater spans can be covered than with timber joists of the same depth. For example, with normal domestic loading 9 in. by 2 in. timber joists at 16 in. spacing will span approximately 16 ft, whereas a lattice joist of approximately the same depth would span 28 to 29 ft. Over the 16 ft span a lattice joist about 7 in. deep could be used. When a building programme is sufficiently large the use of

---

[1] B.S. 449:1959 (Section 29); L.C.C. By-law 6.13.

shallow lattice joists at 16 to 18 in. centres can be competitive for domestic work, having regard to the ease with which services can be run through the floor thickness. But, generally speaking, their most economic use is at 24 in. centres using an increased thickness of floor board. For this spacing, 1 in. tongued and grooved boarding is required. Greater spacing of the joists is possible when light concrete slabs are used to span between them as shown below, and a lighter floor is generally obtained than if rolled steel joists are used to carry the slabs. The concrete slabs may be formed from light, precast trough panels or by stretching stout building paper over the joists, stiffened with light mesh reinforcement, to form shuttering for concrete about 2 to 3 in. thick.

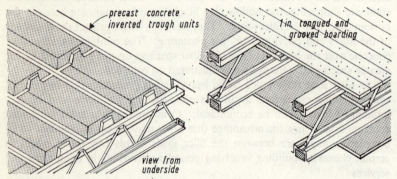

LATTICE BEAMS

Cellular Steel Floor

Steel in the form of cellular units working in conjunction with a concrete topping can be used to form a structural floor slab as illustrated on page 337. The steel cellular units consist of top and bottom ribbed sections spot-welded together at 3 in. intervals along their length, the bottom section varying in depth to suit different spans and loadings. At 2 ft intervals along the top section slots are punched, through which steel strip bonding anchors are fed to provide the bond necessary to permit steel and concrete to function together as a composite loadbearing floor slab. The minimum thickness of concrete topping is 1¾ in. The steel units are fixed to supporting steel beams by welding or, if the beams are of reinforced concrete, to steel plates embedded in the concrete. Alternatively, rapid hammer fixing to concrete may be used.

The continuous cells of the units form a series of ducts at 8 in. centres running parallel to the span. By the use of header ducts laid at right-angles

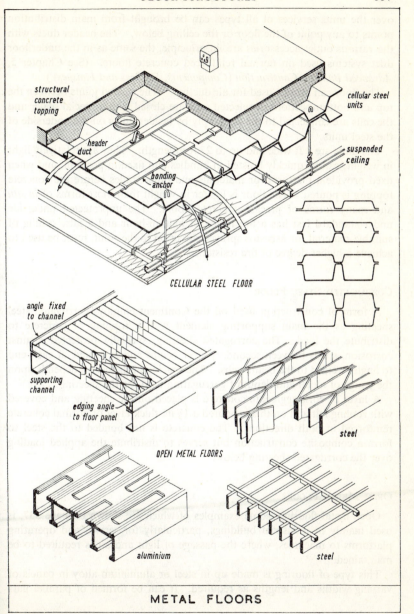

structural concrete topping

cellular steel units

header duct

suspended ceiling

bonding anchor

CELLULAR STEEL FLOOR

angle fixed to channel

supporting channel

edging angle to floor panel

OPEN METAL FLOORS

steel

aluminium

steel

METAL FLOORS

over the units services of all types can be brought from main distribution points to any point of the floor or the ceiling below. The header ducts with the various outlet accessories are, in principle, the same as in the underfloor duct systems used on normal reinforced concrete floors. (See Chapter 5, *Advanced Building Construction* (*Components, Services and Finishes*).)

The floor can also be used for air ducting. The welded joints between the top and bottom sections of selected cells are closed with a special sealer and the cells are connected to the air supply by header ducts on the underside of the steel units.

The units are 2 ft wide and up to 27 ft in length. They are relatively light in weight, can be quickly hoisted in bundles and fixed in position, and when fixed provide a platform for materials and other trades before the concrete topping is poured. The floor is lighter in weight than most forms of *in situ* and many forms of precast concrete floors. The unprotected underside under standard test has a fire rating of half-an-hour and a false ceiling of suitable material, or asbestos sprayed direct on to the soffit, must be used to achieve a higher degree of fire resistance.

CORRUGATED STEEL FLOOR

A form of construction used on the Continent employs corrugated steel sheeting as the main supporting element with a topping of concrete to distribute the load. The corrugated sheeting, specially protected against corrosion, spans between secondary steel beams and is riveted at each end to angles welded to the beam webs. The spacing of the beams depends upon the gauge of metal and depth of corrugation used for the sheeting.

A layer of cork aggregate concrete is placed on the sheeting and covered with roofing felt and on this is poured a $1\frac{1}{2}$ in. thick layer of normal concrete reinforced in both directions. The concrete is not bonded to the steel to form a composite construction but serves to distribute the applied loading over the corrugated sheeting below.

OPEN METAL FLOORS

Open metal flooring, some examples of which are shown on page 337, is used mainly in industrial buildings, particularly for service and operating platforms to machines, where the passage of light and air is required to be maintained.

This type of flooring is made up in steel or aluminium alloy in panels of varying widths and lengths as required. It can be formed of parallel flats spaced apart and braced either by similar flats or by bars intersecting at right-angles at intervals along the length of the panel. The junctions of all members are welded or riveted and depths range from ¾ in. to 2½ in. Clear spans are up to 8 or 9 ft.

Open flooring pressed from 16 gauge mild steel sheet is also available, produced in sections or planks 9 in. wide and in 4 ft 6 in. and 6 ft lengths. The depth is standard at 1½ in. so that variations in loading must be allowed for by variations in the support spacing.

In aluminium alloy this type of floor is also produced as a 6 in. wide ribbed extrusion in depths from ¾ in. to 2 in., with rectangular or square holes punched in the top plate. Clear spans are much the same as for the other types of floors. For all types the supporting structure is formed from various rolled-steel sections to which the floor panels are fixed by means of clips and bolts. An insulated clip and stainless steel or cadmium plated bolts are used with the aluminium extrusions to isolate the two metals and avoid possible electrolytic action.

Perforated cast-iron plates of a similar nature are used externally for walk-ways and for fire escape stairs. It is a heavier form of construction than the steel panels described above, but is used externally because of the greater resistance of cast iron to corrosion (see page 379).

Spring Floors

Gymnasium and dance floors, particularly the latter, should be resilient. This resilience is imparted by the use of a sub-floor of timber bearers, with or without springs or rockers as shown on page 340, on which narrow strip flooring is fixed.

In its most economical form the sub-floor may consist of thin floor battens at 16 in. to 18 in. centres carried on bearers fixed to the main floor in a staggered arrangement. This gives a bearing at every 3 ft to alternate floor battens and at 18 in. to the intermediate battens. Although not producing as much resilience as a floor incorporating springs it is cheaper than a true spring floor.

Another form without springs, developed in Sweden for gymnasium floors, uses bearers made up of timber boards in "sandwich" form in which the boards are blocked apart at staggered intervals. Resilience is given because the blocks carrying the upper board bear on the middle board at a point mid-way between the lower blocks and not directly on them.

Fully resilient floors incorporate special springs or rockers to permit the sub-floor to deflect when in use. In some forms the springs are of a

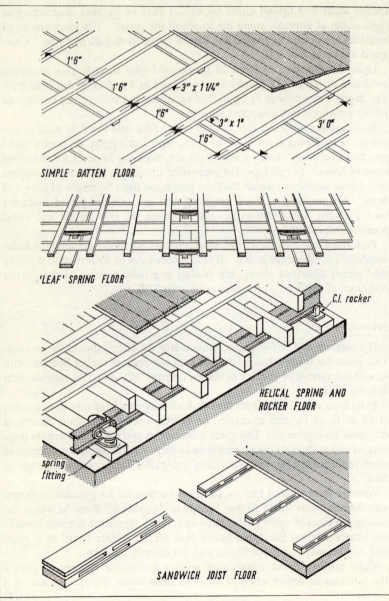

1'6"

1'6"

1'6"   3" x 1 1/4"

1'6"

1'6"   3" x 1"   3' 0"

SIMPLE BATTEN FLOOR

'LEAF' SPRING FLOOR

C.I. rocker

HELICAL SPRING AND
ROCKER FLOOR

spring
fitting

SANDWICH JOIST FLOOR

SPRING FLOORS

leaf type placed at intervals between the joists and continuous parallel wood strips to form "spring joists", on which the strip flooring is laid. Other forms incorporate spring and rocker fitments carrying steel joists on which timber bearers are laid. Others make use of rocking bars only. Illustrations of some of the types available are shown on page 340. Devices can be incorporated to lock the springs when a rigid floor is required.

7

Flues and Chimney Shafts

This chapter is concerned with the construction of flues and chimney shafts. In the first part, flues serving solid-fuel and oil-burning appliances of a domestic scale[1] are discussed and this is followed by a consideration of larger flues and gas flues.

DOMESTIC FLUES

THE PRINCIPLES OF FLUE DESIGN

To ensure the proper functioning of a flue the following factors must be considered in its design:

Size and Shape. Flues to domestic fires should be not less than 12 to 14 ft high measured vertically from the outlet of the appliance or fireplace to the top of the flue terminal. The entry to the flue should be restricted to increase the initial velocity of the gases and a further restriction at the flue terminal is desirable to increase the velocity at the outlet. This reduces the danger of down draughts. The cross-sectional area of a flue for soot producing fuels should not be less than 7 in. diameter. The normal 9 in. × 9 in. brick flue measures $7\frac{1}{2}$ in. × $7\frac{1}{2}$ in. when parged. Table 21 shows required minimum sizes for various appliances.

Flues of circular cross section are most efficient. Where rectangular flues are used the longest side should not be more than one-and-a-half times the shorter (see page 344).

The flue dimensions and chimney heights that satisfy the requirements of a solid-fuel fired boiler are normally more than sufficient when oil firing is used for the same size boiler. Most engineers would use the same size as for solid fuel, particularly for domestic work, where there is always the possibility of installing solid-fuel appliances at some future date.

Flues should be as straight as possible, any bends being near the top rather

---

[1] The traditional open fire described in *Elementary Building Construction* is being widely superceded by improved solid fuel appliances which are referred to in *Advanced Building Construction (Components, Services and Finishes)*. These require careful installation—see C.P. 403 (1952) "Open Fires, Heating Stoves and Cookers Burning Solid Fuel" and "Correct Fixing of Domestic Solid Fuel Appliances" by W. C. Moss, issued by the Coal Utilization Council.

than just above the fireplace. Unavoidable bends should be at an angle of not less than 45° and preferably not less than 60° to the horizontal. Unless lined with concrete or clay liners flues should be parged smooth.

Airtightness. A flue must be airtight in order to maintain the strength of

Table 21. Minimum flue sizes for solid fuel burning appliances

Appliance	4½ in. internal diameter	6 in. internal diameter	9 in. × 9 in. sq. or 7–8 in. internal diameter
Open and closeable fires, openable stoves, cookers	Heat storage cookers only, burning smokeless fuel	Smokeless fuels (up to 25,000 B.Th.U. per hr)	Bituminous fuels (minimum height of flue − 12 ft)
Domestic boilers	Smokeless fuels (up to 25,000 B.Th.U. per hr) Maximum height—30 ft sweeping access every 10 ft	Smokeless fuels (25,000–50,000 B.Th.U. per hr). Sweeping access every 10 ft	Bituminous fuels (all outputs). Smokeless fuels (50,000–100,000 B.Th.U. per hr) —8 in. diam. minimum

Notes: A closed stove should be provided with a flue of the same size as that of a boiler with the same rate of combustion.
Flues with bends making cleaning difficult should have a minimum diameter of 6 in.
Smokeless fuels—include coke, anthracite, dry steam coal, coalite, etc.

the draught at the fireplace. Air may be admitted through faulty pointing, faulty withes and broken parging.

Insulation. Reasonable care must be taken to prevent the flue gases cooling, which might result in downdraught and condensation. This precaution is particularly important where slow burning appliances are used (see page 349).

From the point of view of general heat conservation fireplaces should not

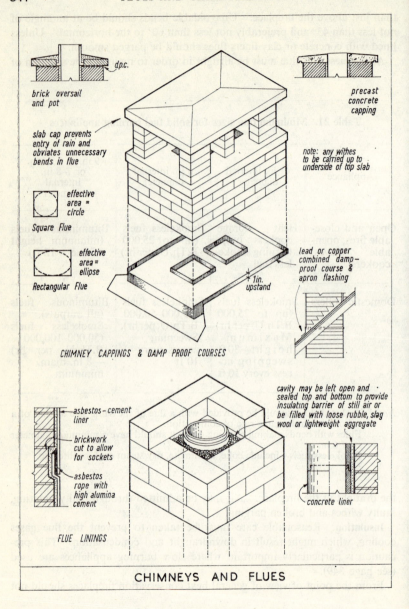

d.p.c.

brick oversail
and pot

precast
concrete
capping

slab cap prevents
entry of rain and
obviates unnecessary
bends in flue

note: any withes
to be carried up to
underside of top slab

effective
area =
circle

Square Flue

effective
area =
ellipse

Rectangular Flue

lead or copper
combined damp-
proof course &
apron flashing

1 in.
upstand

CHIMNEY CAPPINGS & DAMP PROOF COURSES

cavity may be left open and
sealed top and bottom to provide
insulating barrier of still air or
be filled with loose rubble, slag
wool or lightweight aggregate

asbestos-cement
liner

brickwork
cut to allow
for sockets

asbestos
rope with
high alumina
cement

concrete liner

FLUE LININGS

CHIMNEYS AND FLUES

be situated on outside walls, but where this is unavoidable the flues serving them should preferably be constructed with $4\frac{1}{2}$ in. walls and liners (page 344).

The use of 9 in. brickwork in place of $4\frac{1}{2}$ in. does not afford much increase in insulation value and has the disadvantage of offering more surface area to the atmosphere, with consequent cooling of the flue. It also has a high-thermal capacity which requires a longer pre-heating period before the flue is warm enough to encourage the strong up-flow of gases necessary to produce "draught". The greater thickness is, however, desirable for any external walls of flues to prevent damp penetration, as this causes cooling of the interior.

Flues situated internally only need special consideration where they penetrate the roof and become exposed to the weather. It is desirable to use 9 in. brickwork, corbelled out within the roof space if necessary, and to pay particular attention to the arrangement of the damp-proof course and flashings to the stack. A suitable capping should be provided to prevent saturation of the chimney (page 344). A projecting capping, in addition to throwing water clear of the chimney walls, helps to create a zone of low pressure at the flue outlet.

Position of Outlet. For safety in terms of fire, chimneys should have a minimum height of 2 ft 6 in. of $4\frac{1}{2}$ in. brickwork or its equivalent, or 6 in. of stone above the highest point of intersection of the chimney with the roof. The outlet must be at least 3 ft above the same point and should be not less than 7 ft 6 in. from the roof measured horizontally. When the chimney passes through the ridge of a pitched roof the outlet may be not less than 2 ft above the ridge. If the roof covering is of combustible material the outlet should be at least 3 ft above the level of the ridge whatever the position of the stack. These precautions do not, however, necessarily ensure the efficient functioning of a flue, the outlet of which must be positioned outside any potential zones of high wind pressure. The positioning of a flue outlet in a potential suction zone will assist in the removal of the smoke and gases, but should it occur in a high-pressure zone there is every likelihood of the gases being taken down the flue by air moving from this zone to an area of lower pressure within the room. It will be seen from page 346, which shows the extent of these zones, that in cases of flat and low-pitched roofs up to 30°, suitable positions for chimneys are almost anywhere above eaves level. In the case of roofs pitched greater than 30° the ridge position is best unless the chimney is extended above the ridge level from a lower position or is fitted with a cowl. The latter may not be effective unless it takes the outlet out of the high-pressure zone, although there are on the market cowls which are claimed to prevent downdraught even in pressure zones.

CONSTRUCTION OF FLUES FOR SOLID FUELS

Brick Chimneys.   Details of these flues are shown in *Elementary Building Construction.*

The height of the stack above the highest point of intersection with the roof should not exceed six times the least horizontal dimension unless it is designed to withstand the possible maximum wind pressure in the locality.   When oversailing occurs, the total projection of the oversailing brickwork should not exceed the thickness of the wall below with a maximum projection of $2\frac{1}{4}$ in. in each course.

Liners may be cast iron or vinyl-coated asbestos cement pipes (untreated asbestos cement is liable to disintegrate if heavy condensation occurs), or may be made of fireclay, terracotta[1] or acid-resisting refractory concrete.   Where pipes are used the sockets should be uppermost and the joints made with

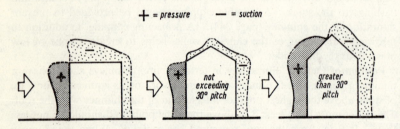

WIND EFFECTS ON BUILDINGS

asbestos rope and high-alumina cement as shown, page 344.   (The rope allows expansion and the cement is acid resistant.)   The space between the lining and the chimney is usually filled with an insulating material such as loose rubble flushed up with concrete or lightweight concrete.

Stone Chimneys.   The temperatures encountered in a domestic flue are not likely to damage a good building stone, except in the immediate vicinity of the fire.   In this position sandstone should be used or protection be given by firebricks.   The walls to flues should be at least 9 in. thick up to roof level, where they can be reduced to 6 in. if stone is used alone.   Where the stone is backed with brick or concrete the minimum thickness of the wall should be 9 in. throughout.   Coursed masonry may be corbelled out to a total projection not exceeding the thickness of the wall below.   Each course may project a distance equal to half the thickness of the wall below it, provided the corbel stone is bonded into the wall a distance equal to twice its projection.

B.S. 1181, "Clay Flue Linings and Chimney Pots Suitable for Open Fires".

Limitations on height of stack and requirements for protection by rendering are the same as for brick chimneys.

If the stone is not lined internally with brick or concrete, it should be protected by liners. Brick may be bonded into the stonework or used as a lining with an insulating air space as shown on page 348.

Concrete Chimneys. Concrete for *in situ* work may be either plain or reinforced, and where in contact with the flue gases should be of an acid-resisting refractory type. Lightweight concrete made with foamed slag or expanded clay aggregates or no-fines concrete can also be used, provided protection is given by flue liners.[1]

The concrete should be at least 4 in. thick and, unless increased to at least 6 in. where penetrating the roof, should be rendered to provide adequate protection against damp penetration. As it is not practical to parge the flue of cast *in situ* chimneys flue liners should be used. Up to a height of seven times its least horizontal dimension the effect of wind pressure on a plain, dense concrete chimney need not be considered. Oversailing projections should form an angle of not less than 60° with the horizontal, unless the projection is reinforced. The height of *in situ* lightweight concrete chimneys should be limited to four times their least horizontal dimension and all oversailing or projecting parts of the chimney should be formed with dense concrete, reinforced as necessary. Damp-proof courses are not generally required at roof level in chimneys of plain dense concrete if the outside is rendered and there are flue liners.

A variety of precast units of dense or lightweight concrete are available for forming chimneys. There are two approaches to the construction of chimneys in this form—one by precast blocks bonded to form the walls and the withes of the chimney; another by forming the internal and external surfaces of the chimney with precast units and filling the intervening cavity with lightweight concrete, page 348. As with *in situ* cast flues of lightweight concrete, flue liners are essential with lightweight concrete blocks.

Metal and Asbestos Cement Flues. These materials have poor thermal insulation value and are not really suitable for external use unless insulated. They should generally be used only for flues within the room containing the appliance. Metal flues can be made of steel or cast iron. Asbestos cement flues are of heavy quality pipes.[2] The pipes should be frequently supported, usually at every joint or at intervals not exceeding sixteen times the internal

---

[1] For suggested mixes and aggregates see Code of Practice 131.101 (1951), "Flues for Domestic Appliances Burning Solid Fuel".

[2] B.S. 41, "Cast Iron Spigot and Socket Flue or Smoke Pipes". B.S. 534, "Steel Spigot and Socket Pipes and Specials for Water, Gas and Sewerage". B.S. 835, "Asbestos Cement Flue Pipes and Fittings (Heavy Quality)".

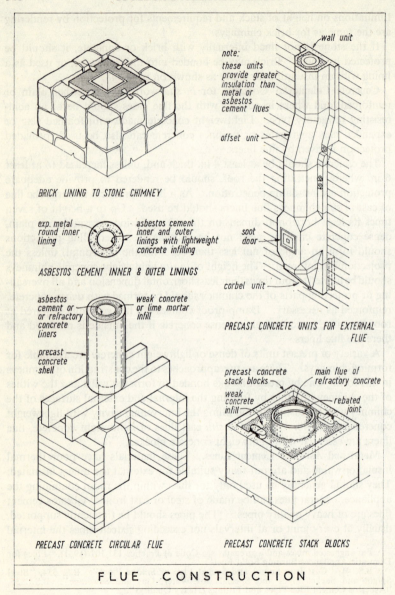

BRICK LINING TO STONE CHIMNEY

exp. metal round inner lining

asbestos cement inner and outer linings with lightweight concrete infilling

ASBESTOS CEMENT INNER & OUTER LININGS

asbestos cement or or refractory concrete liners

weak concrete or lime mortar infill

precast concrete shell

PRECAST CONCRETE CIRCULAR FLUE

note:
these units provide greater insulation than metal or asbestos cement flues

wall unit

offset unit

soot door

corbel unit

PRECAST CONCRETE UNITS FOR EXTERNAL FLUE

precast concrete stack blocks

weak concrete infill

main flue of refractory concrete

rebated joint

PRECAST CONCRETE STACK BLOCKS

FLUE   CONSTRUCTION

diameter. The joints should be airtight and allowance made for the expansion and contraction of the pipes at the joints and at the supports. Asbestos cement flues are not recommended for open fires or appliances using bituminous coal, nor in situations where the internal flue temperature is likely to exceed 500°F, since the material cracks when exposed to high temperatures or to flames impinging on its surface. They should, therefore, be protected from flames by using a 6 ft length of metal flue immediately above the fire.

Greater strength and insulation can be achieved by using asbestos cement

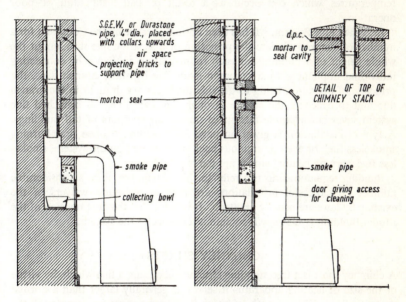

FLUES TO SERVE SLOW COMBUSTION STOVES

pipes concentrically and filling the intervening cavity with lightweight insulating filling (page 348).

Chimneys for Domestic Boilers. Reference has already been made to the need to avoid loss of heat from flue gases. This is particularly important in the case of flues to any form of slow combustion boiler, stove or cooker, for reasons given in *Elementary Building Construction*. These flues should always be constructed with acid-resisting liners such as salt-glazed earthenware or Durastone pipes. Some advantage is gained by sealing the entry and exit joints between the pipe lining and the surrounding brickwork to limit the

12*

cooling effects of leakage from the air space formed between them. Provision should be made for the trapping and removal of the condensate either by a removable vessel or by a container fitted with a drainage pipe. Methods of constructing such flues are shown on page 349.[1]

Oil-fired domestic boilers are now in common use. As with solid-fuel installations the use of linings is desirable to protect the flue from condensation which may occur when the boiler is operating efficiently and the temperature of the flue gas is low. Liners, in addition, combat the effects of high temperatures which can occur as a result of bad installation or poor operation.

Branched Flue System. It has been normal practice on the Continent for a number of years to obviate the provision of a separate flue throughout the whole height of a building for each room heating appliance by connecting individual appliances to a common main flue by short branch flues, the principle of operation being to provide the necessary draught in the branch flue and to evacuate the smoke through the main flue. A branched flue system saves considerable flue space on the upper floors of tall buildings. A typical installation is given on page 351. Although open fires burning smokeless fuel, or even bituminous coal, may be used on the system, smokeless fuel burning heating stoves are the most efficient.

Building regulations do not refer to this system, but since a considerable number of successful installations are now in operation waivers of the existing by-laws are usually granted. It is likely that the next revision of the Model Building Byelaws will contain a reference to the system.

CHIMNEY SHAFTS

A chimney shaft is a free-standing structure enclosing a flue which, by virtue of the size of heating apparatus it serves, is generally larger than a normal domestic flue. This general definition is given more precise meaning in the L.C.C. By-laws.[2]

SIZE OF CHIMNEY SHAFTS

The general considerations involved in flue design have been mentioned under domestic flues. On page 270 of *Advanced Building Construction* (*Components, Services and Finishes*) a formula is given for establishing the

---

[1] A full discussion of this subject is to be found in *Building Research Station Digest* No. 60, "Condensation in Domestic Chimneys".
[2] By-law 1.03: "a construction of solid bricks enclosing a vertical flue exceeding 150 sq. in. in area and extending to a greater height above its topmost lateral support than six times its least horizontal dimension measured at the base, where not supported above the base, or the level of the topmost lateral support".

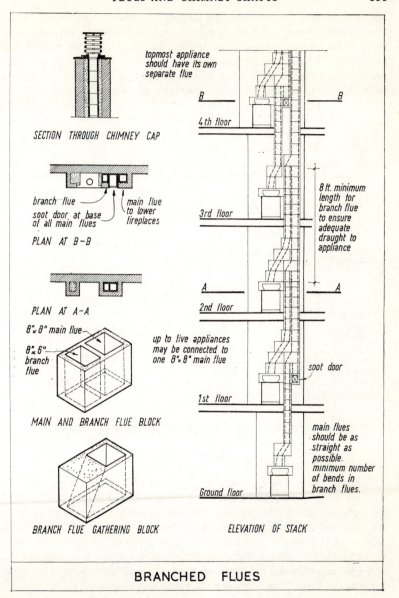

SECTION THROUGH CHIMNEY CAP

branch flue
soot door at base
of all main flues

main flue
to lower
fireplaces

PLAN AT B-B

PLAN AT A-A

8"×8" main flue

8"×6"
branch
flue

MAIN AND BRANCH FLUE BLOCK

BRANCH FLUE GATHERING BLOCK

topmost appliance
should have its own
separate flue

B   B

4th floor

8 ft. minimum
length for
branch flue
to ensure
adequate
draught to
appliance

3rd floor

A   A

2nd floor

up to five appliances
may be connected to
one 8"×8" main flue

soot door

1st floor

main flues
should be as
straight as
possible.
minimum number
of bends in
branch flues.

Ground floor

ELEVATION OF STACK

BRANCHED FLUES

approximate flue area for solid-fuel installations based on the boiler rating·
Table 22 below shows the flue areas required in relation to the volume of
space to be heated, together with approximate sizes of boiler houses and
fuel stores. When planning boiler houses, an adequate air supply must be
provided. A vent or shaft which provides 2 to 2½ sq. ft. of area per million
B.Th.U.'s/hr boiler rating is usually a suitable provision.

Table 22. Boiler House and Chimney Sizes

Additional space is required if hot water supply apparatus is to be installed.   Fuel Store
sizes allow for approximately two weeks' supply.   Sizes shown are approximate only.

Volume of space to be heated (in thousands of cubic feet)	Heating chamber		Fuel store		Internal cross-sectional area of smoke stack in sq. in.					
	Area sq. ft	Height ft	Area sq. ft	Height ft	Height of smoke stack in feet					
					25	50	75	100	125	150
25–50	90	8	15	8	80					
50–100	150	9	20	9	110					
100–250	200	10	40	10	170	120	100			
250–500	250	11	90	11	320	230	190	160	140	130
500–750	320	12	170	12	520	370	300	260	230	210
750–1000	430	13	250	13	770	550	450	390	360	320
1000–1500	520	14	330	14		730	600	520	470	430
1500–2000	540	15	450	15		1080	880	790	710	650
2000–2500	575	16	520	16			1200	1040	920	840

Note: Areas above heavy line should be provided whenever possible.

CONSTRUCTION OF CHIMNEY SHAFTS

Chimney shafts may be constructed of brickwork, concrete or steel.   In
all cases the chimney must be stable enough to resist the overturning effect of
wind pressure from any direction, the various materials must not be overstressed, and the foundations must be designed so that the safe bearing
pressure of the subsoil is not exceeded.   The design of brickwork chimneys,
as with masonry walls, is based on the use of the material in compression
only and such chimneys are, therefore, built with shafts increasing in thickness
towards the base.   The foregoing considerations in relation to brick shafts

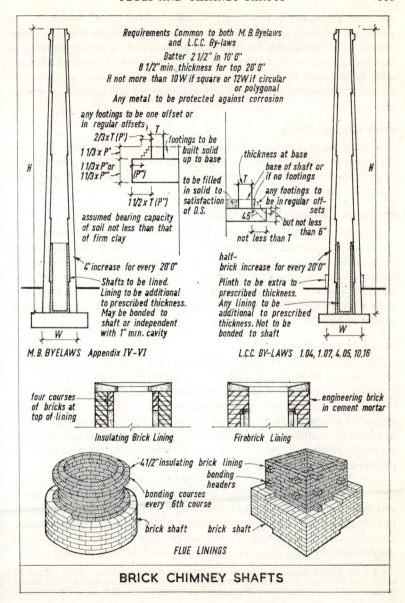

Requirements Common to both M.B.Byelaws
and L.C.C. By-laws

Batter 2 1/2" in 10' 0"
8 1/2" min. thickness for top 20' 0"
H not more than 10W if square or 12W if circular
or polygonal
Any metal to be protected against corrosion

any footings to be one offset or
in regular offsets
2/3 x T (P')
1 1/3 x P'
1 1/3 x P" or
1 1/3 x P'"
T
footings to be
built solid
up to base
(P")
1 1/2 x T (P")

to be filled
in solid to
satisfaction
of D.S.

thickness at base
base of shaft or
if no footings
T
any footings to
be in regular off-
sets
45°
not less than T
but not less
than 6"

assumed bearing capacity
of soil not less than that
of firm clay

4" increase for every 20' 0"

Shafts to be lined.
Lining to be additional
to prescribed thickness.
May be bonded to
shaft or independent
with 1" min. cavity

half-
brick increase for every 20' 0"

Plinth to be extra to
prescribed thickness.
Any lining to be
additional to prescribed
thickness. Not to be
bonded to shaft

H   H

W   W

M.B. BYELAWS Appendix IV-VI   L.C.C. BY-LAWS 1.04, 1.07, 4.05, 10.16

four courses
of bricks at
top of lining

engineering brick
in cement mortar

Insulating Brick Lining   Firebrick Lining

4 1/2" insulating brick lining
bonding
headers

bonding courses
every 6th course

brick shaft   brick shaft

FLUE LININGS

BRICK CHIMNEY SHAFTS

are given expression in the Model Byelaws and the L.C.C. By-laws.[1] No particular reference is made to steel or concrete chimney shafts in either present set of regulations, but the Model Byelaws make a general requirement that the limits of stress of the materials used must not be exceeded when the shaft is subjected to given wind pressures. Steel chimneys are generally classed as temporary structures which are inspected and licensed for certain periods.

Brick Chimney Shafts

A brick shaft tends to fail section by section up its height. Thus, in designing, to check the stability of the whole involves checking the stability of each section. By-law requirements for "uncalculated" brick shafts are shown on page 353.

Reinforced Concrete Chimney Shafts

These are tending to replace brick shafts for very high chimneys since they are of smaller diameter and for heights above about 120 ft they are cheaper than brick. Typical reinforced concrete shafts are shown on page 355. Reduction in thickness may be effected by stepping or tapering but considerable economy in formwork can be achieved by constructing the whole shaft with a constant bore and shell thickness, thus enabling a repeating shutter to be used.

Steel Chimney Shafts

There are two types of steel plate chimney: self-supporting or guyed, both of which may be constructed quickly. These are shown on page 356.

Self-supporting Steel Chimneys have been erected up to 450 ft in height, but a more normal height is in the neighbourhood of 250 ft. The chimney is secured to a concrete base by bolts and may be analysed in a similar manner to a concrete shaft but as the steel shaft weighs far less than a concrete shaft the weight necessary to prevent the whole structure overturning will largely be provided by the concrete base.

Guyed Steel Chimneys are built of $\frac{3}{16}$ in. to $\frac{3}{4}$ in. plate depending on the size. Chimneys up to 100 ft high are guyed at two-thirds of their height, and over 100 ft at ·4 and ·8 of their height. The guys have tightening. bolts in the linkage and terminate at anchor plates buried in concrete blocks. The concrete foundation only needs to be large enough to resist dead weight since the guys resist the overturning effect of wind pressure.

---

[1] L.C.C. By-law 10.16, M.B. Byelaws, Appendix—Clauses IV to VI. It should be noted that these are "prescribed" conditions in respect of brick shafts. The Model Byelaws also make provision for design by calculation in Clauses II to III of the Appendix.

Steel chimneys are cheaper than brick or concrete but are comparatively short lived. Unless lined or clad it is necessary to protect the metal against corrosion due to condensation caused by heat loss from this type of chimney. For this purpose proprietary metal paints are available and P.V.C. coatings.

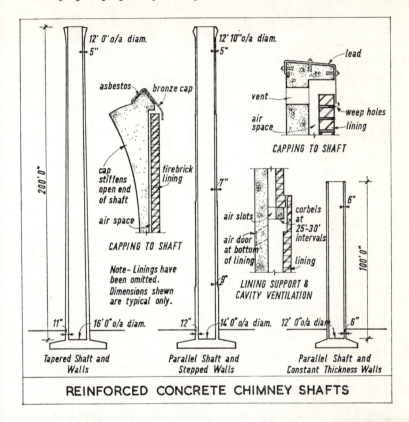

REINFORCED CONCRETE CHIMNEY SHAFTS

Steel construction is also suitable for ejector chimneys. These provide induced draught by means of a small high-pressure blower discharging into a venturi and producing suction. A typical example of an ejector chimney providing a draught equal to a natural draught chimney 200 ft high by 10 ft diameter is shown on page 356.

Flue Linings. Linings assist in raising the insulation value of the walls of the flue and also protect the main structural material from the effects of high

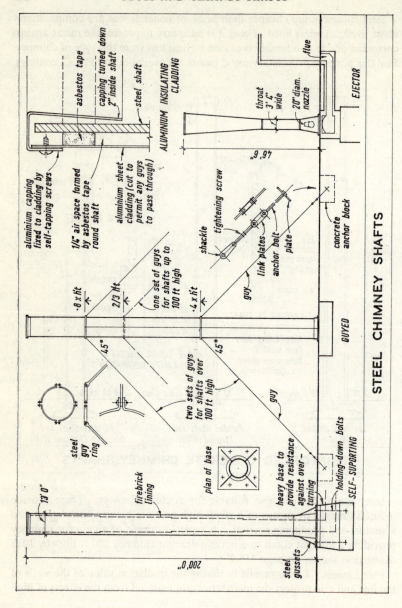

aluminium capping fixed to cladding by self-tapping screws

asbestos tape

capping turned down 2″ inside shaft

steel shaft

1/4″ air space formed by asbestos tape round shaft

aluminium sheet cladding (cut to permit any guys to pass through)

ALUMINIUM INSULATING CLADDING

throat 3′ 4″ wide

20″ diam. nozzle

flue

EJECTOR

·8 x ht

2/3 ht

one set of guys for shafts up to 100 ft high

·4 x ht

45°

45°

steel guy ring

two sets of guys for shafts over 100 ft high

tightening screw

shackle

link plates

anchor bolt

plate

guy

concrete anchor block

GUYED

firebrick lining

13′ 0″

plan of base

heavy base to provide resistance against over-turning

steel gussets

200′0″

holding-down bolts

SELF-SUPPORTING

STEEL CHIMNEY SHAFTS

temperatures, especially near the point of entry of the flue gases. They may be constructed of firebricks or lightweight insulating bricks made from diatomaceous earth known as "moler" bricks. Firebrick linings must be free to move relative to the surrounding brickwork, but moler brick insulating linings with a smaller coefficient of expansion, may be built tight to the inside of the shaft or, where by-laws permit, may be bonded to a brick shaft (page 353) or used as permanent shuttering to concrete.

Linings should be taken to the top of brick and concrete shafts to prevent damage to the walls due to the sudden increase in temperature, which would result if the lining was terminated lower down. They must be protected from weather by extending the capping over in a manner which will allow for thermal movement, pages 353 and 355. "Touch headers" should be built out from firebrick linings at 10 ft intervals.

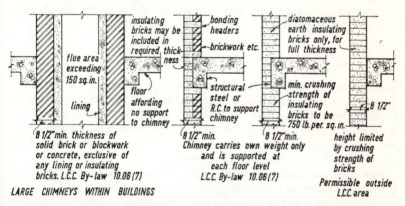

insulating bricks may be included in required thickness

bonding headers

brickwork etc.

diatomaceous earth insulating bricks only, for full thickness

flue area exceeding 150 sq. in.

floor affording no support to chimney

structural steel or R.C. to support chimney

min. crushing strength of insulating bricks to be 750 lb. per. sq. in.

lining

8 1/2"

8 1/2" min. thickness of solid brick or blockwork or concrete, exclusive of any lining or insulating bricks. L.C.C. By-law 10.06 (7)

8 1/2" min. Chimney carries own weight only and is supported at each floor level L.C.C. By-law 10.06 (7)

8 1/2" min.

height limited by crushing strength of bricks

Permissible outside L.C.C. area

LARGE CHIMNEYS WITHIN BUILDINGS

Steel chimneys may be lined with firebrick, usually in 20 ft lengths supported on internal angles with a 1 in. gap between the firebricks and the metal, which is filled with loam. Alternatively, moler bricks or precast moler concrete liners may be used direct against the inside of the shaft, self-supporting without the use of angles. An alternative to lining is an aluminium sheet cladding surrounding the shaft, with an air space between it and the steel (page 356).

LARGE CHIMNEYS WITHIN BUILDINGS

Large chimneys comparable with chimney shafts, that is to say with a flue area exceeding 150 sq. in., may be constructed within a building, provided precautions are taken to protect the building from damage by heat or through the corrosion of any structural steel. By-law requirements for these chimneys are shown above. The general requirements are similar to those for a freestanding shaft but some reduction in the thickness of the shaft may be possible since there are no wind loads to accommodate and the structure of the building may give lateral support at each floor level. In each case the resistance to crushing will remain the main factor governing the thickness of the shaft walls at any given level.

Horizontal Flues. These are often necessary in large installations involving a number of boilers and the cross sectional area is usually made one-and-a-third times the area of the main flue. They are often larger to allow for general access and cleaning. The flue should be kept as short as possible and be well insulated. Brick or concrete construction with insulated lining is commonly used. Steel or cast-iron horizontal flues or "headers" should be insulated to prevent over-heating of the boiler house. Some types of plastic insulation should be separated from the metal by an air space. This is achieved by wrapping the flue in expanded metal before applying the insulating composition.[1]

GAS FLUES

Some gas appliances require no flue provided they are used where ventilation is good. Others with larger heat inputs, or used continuously, must be provided with flues. Code of Practice 331.104, 1947, "Flues for Gas Appliances", gives a list of appliances which should be provided with a flue, based on the gas rate of the appliances, the period of continuous use and the size and standard of ventilation of the room.

Flue Size and Outlet Position. Code 331.104 also gives a Table of desirable flue sizes for various appliances according to heat input.

The positioning of the flue outlet externally should be governed generally by the same considerations as for other flues (see page 345), although when essential, short flues may terminate on an outside wall provided they do not end in a high-pressure zone. Small appliances may discharge into an adequately ventilated roof space.[2]

When no suitable place for the termination of the flue is available or when the provision of a long flue is not practicable a *balanced flue* appliance may be used, the inlet and outlet of which may be positioned almost anywhere on an outside wall. As shown diagrammatically on page 359 these are designed so that the combustion chamber is enclosed and out of contact with the air within a room, the air for combustion being drawn into the

---

[1] For connection of branch flues and the provision of draught stabilizers and explosion doors, see page 270 of *Advanced Building Construction* (*Components, Services and Finishes*).
[2] See Code of Practice 331.104, "Flues for Gas Appliances", and B.S. 766, Part 2.

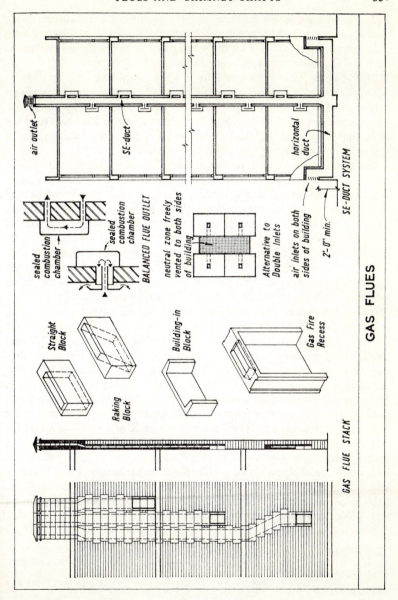

air outlet

SE-duct

horizontal duct

SE-DUCT SYSTEM

sealed combustion chamber

sealed combustion chamber

BALANCED FLUE OUTLET

neutral zone freely vented to both sides of building

Alternative to Double Inlets

air inlets on both sides of building

2'-0" min.

Straight Block

Raking Block

Building-in Block

Gas Fire Recess

GAS FLUE STACK

GAS FLUES

casing from outside the building and the products of combustion being discharged nearby. This ensures that external air pressures affecting both ducts are identical and enables the warm gases to be discharged effectively. Such appliances do not provide any ventilation to a room.

Brick Flues. 9 in. × 9 in. or 9 in. × 4½ in. brick flues may be used for gas appliances. If the flues are parged, aluminous cement mortar is preferable to Portland cement since it resists acid attack better. When condensation is anticipated, asbestos cement flue pipes may be bedded solidly in the brickwork to provide an adequate watertight lining. Alternatively, glazed stoneware or Durastone lining pipes may be used.

Gas fires can be stood in precast concrete fireplace opening units similar to that shown on page 359 to avoid a flue connection.

Asbestos Cement and Metal Flues. Asbestos cement pipes[1] may be used either singly or in groups surrounded by suitable non-combustible material. There is considerable saving in the space required for grouped flues of asbestos cement over normal brickwork and they may be used up to a limit of 100 ft, the weight of the flue pipes being separately supported at each floor level. Individual pipes must be securely fixed, with the sockets upwards, and each joint must be filled with asbestos rope and pointed with plastic asbestos. Suitable terminals are required and need careful design.

Asbestos cement is not resistant to attack by corrosive flue gas condensates. If condensation is anticipated internal protection should be applied in the form of bitumastic paint or brush-on acid-resisting cement finish. Alternatively, asbestos cement pipes with vinyl acetate protection already applied may be used. The height above the appliance at which condensation may occur depends on a number of variable factors. When a very tall flue is being considered the local Gas Board should be consulted in case internal coating of the flue or other precautions may be advisable. Asbestos cement pipes cool very easily and long flues on the outside of a building invariably result in condensation trouble and may even fail to function as a flue. In such circumstances a precast concrete flue, as shown on page 348, would be better. Metal pipes may be used for flues, but preferably only in positions where the flue can be seen and easily replaced if necessary, because of the liability of corrosion. Protected steel or cast-iron pipes and sheet metal with welded or folded seams[2] are suitable.

Precast Concrete Block Flues. Standard precast concrete flue blocks[3] are

---

[1] B.S. 567, "Asbestos Cement Flue Pipes and Fittings for Gas-Fired Appliances".
[2] B.S. 715, "Sheet Metal Cylindrical Flue Pipes, Fittings and Accessories for Gas-Fired Appliances".
[3] B.S. 1289, "Precast Concrete Flue Blocks for Gas Fires (Domestic Type) and Ventilation".

designed to bond in with brickwork. Standard fittings are available for all normal requirements. Blocks having small rectangular flue openings are generally not suitable for flues to water heaters or for flues exceeding about 50 ft in height. In these cases 9 in. × 9 in. flue blocks or tubular flues should be used. A stack built of small aperture blocks is illustrated on page 359.

GAS BOILER FLUES

When gas is used as a fuel a large quantity of water is produced during combustion. Further, the temperature of the gases leaving the boiler is fairly low and the resulting draught weak enough to be easily overcome by adverse wind pressures. Any condensed moisture must be removed from the flue system without entering the boiler by providing means of drainage

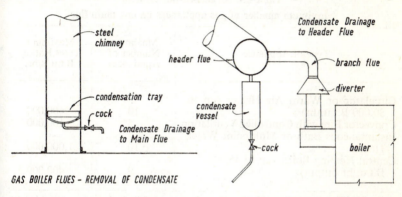

GAS BOILER FLUES - REMOVAL OF CONDENSATE

at the base of the main flue or chimney and, in the case of a number of boilers, an outlet and storage vessel to the header or common flue as shown above. Baffles or draught diverters are either incorporated in the construction of gas boilers or should be provided at each boiler flue outlet to allow free removal of the products of combustion and to divert any down draught away from the combustion chamber. In addition, this "break" in the flue system enables a quantity of air to mix with and dilute the products of combustion thus lessening the risk of condensation in the main flue. Further dilution may be provided by a ventilating grid at the base of the main flue or chimney shaft, situated in the boiler room. It should be as large as practicable up to the area of the main flue.[1]

---

[1] For By-laws and recommendations in respect of gas flues see L.C.C. By-laws, Section 10, particularly By-law 10.11. Model Building Byelaws 105, 106. C.P. 331.104 (1947), "Flues for Gas Appliances". In London there is also control by the London Gas Undertakings (Regulations) Act, 1939.

SHARED FLUE SYSTEMS

Shared flues are a means of reducing the space required by gas flue ducts in tall buildings. There are two basic systems: the branched flue and the SE-duct systems. Although existing building regulations do not refer to either of these systems, installations have been carried out in a number of localities, and following the success of these, waivers are not unreasonably withheld for schemes designed in consultation with Gas Board Engineers and the Local Authorities.[1]

The branched flue system for solid-fuel burning appliances has already been described on page 350 and, in general, all the requirements apply.

Table 23. Branched-flue System
Maximum number of gas appliances on one main flue

Type of Appliance	Maximum Number of Appliances	Maximum Total Rating B.t.u.'s/hr.
Circulator or Warm Air Heater (up to 30,000 B.t.u./hr)	10	400,000
Convector Fire with Controlled Ventilation	5*	100,000
Instantaneous Bath or Multipoint Water Heater	10	1,000,000
Central Heating Boiler (up to 45,000 B.t.u./hr output)	9	400,000

*In the case of the gas fire, this figure may be increased to 6 when the vertical height of the flue between the top appliance and the terminal exceeds 40 ft.

The recommended maximum number of gas appliances which can be vented into one 8 in. × 8 in. main flue is shown in Table 23. The figures in the Table may be increased by 50% if a 12 in. × 8 in. main flue is used. A minimum height of 20 ft from the topmost appliance to the terminal is desirable. To obtain this the top fitting may have to be vented separately.

Gas appliances connected to such a system must be provided with a flame failure device so that there is no possibility of raw gas entering the main flue.

The SE-Duct system consists of a single vertical, rectangular duct open to the atmosphere at top and bottom to which appliances are fitted as required (see page 359). The common duct provides the air for combustion and also

[1] For a full report on existing installations see The Gas Council Research Communication GC72, "Experiences with Branched-Flue and SE-Duct Systems for Venting Gas Appliances".

acts as a flue to remove the products of combustion. Air inlets at the base should be on two faces of the building to avoid suction effects in the duct or one inlet may be provided in any neutral zone such as a ventilated lobby The top of the duct must be positioned to avoid pressure zones.

All appliances must be of the Room Sealed Combustion-Chamber type, which are essentially the same as balanced flue appliances, and must be fitted with a flame failure cut-off device.

The size of the duct is related to the number and types of appliances connected to it. There are four standard units at present available which are set out in Table 24. Larger ducts would have to be especially manufactured or constructed.

Table 24

Unit	Internal dimensions in inches	External dimensions in inches
SE1	8 × 12	10 × 14
SE2	9 × 15½	11 × 17½
SE3	13 × 19	15½ × 21½
SE4	15 × 22	18 × 25

All units are 18 in. high

Table 25 shows appropriate flue areas for some typical single and combined appliances.

Table 25. SE-Duct System—required Area of Duct

Duct Height (ft)	Number of Dwellings Served	Cross Sectional Area of Duct (Sq. ft)		
		Instantaneous Water Heaters (100,000 B.t.u./hr)	Circulators and Space Heaters (30,000 B.t.u./hr)	Instantaneous Water Heaters and Space Heaters
55	6	0·4	0·4	0·7
100	11	0·7	0·7	1·2
140	16	1·0	1·0	1·6
190	22	1·3	1·4	2·1

Note: The flue outlet of the top appliance should be at least 14 ft below the duct terminal.

8
Stairs, Ramps and Ladders

STAIRS

A stair is a number of steps leading from one floor to another, the function of which is to provide means for movement between different levels. This function is twofold: firstly, that of normal, everyday access from floor to floor, and secondly, that of escape from upper floors in the event of fire.

FUNCTIONAL REQUIREMENTS

Strength and Stability. Stairs, like floors, must carry loads; not only the weight of people using them but also the weight of any furniture or equipment being carried up or down them. Timber stairs for domestic work are usually constructed on the basis of accepted sizes for the various parts. In other types of buildings the stair must be designed on the basis of superimposed loads similar to those assumed in the design of floors. These loads, which are given below, are related to the class of building of which the stair is part. The following classes relate to those given in the left-hand column of the Table on page 300 in Chapter 6:

(*a*) for class 30—30 lb per sq. ft
(*b*) for classes 40, 50 or 60—60 lb per sq. ft
(*c*) for other classes—100 lb per sq. ft.

The superficial area on which these loads are assumed to act is measured horizontally. Structurally independent cantilever steps should be designed to carry an alternative minimum load of 300 lb concentrated at the outer end.

Although the strength of balustrades in domestic stairs is not calculated in terms of horizontal pressure, this is sometimes desirable in other stairs, particularly where very large crowds of people are likely to use the stair. B.S. Code of Practice 3, Ch. V (1952) gives as a guide the following loads to be assumed as acting horizontally at handrail level:

(*a*) Light access stairs, gangways and the like—15 lb per ft run;
(*b*) Stairways, landings and balconies, private and domestic—25 lb per ft run;
(*c*) All other stairways, landings and balconies—50 lb per ft run.

It should be noted that the last figure of 50 lb. per ft run is also applied to parapets and handrails to roofs. It is pointed out that where crowds can panic, a force of up to 200 lb per ft run can be exerted.

Fire Protection. Apart from the function of the stair itself as a means of escape in the event of fire, the staircase links the floors throughout a building and can act as a path by which fire can spread from floor to floor. The requirements relating to stairs and staircases in respect of fire protection are discussed in Chapter 10.

Sound Insulation. As a stair links together the various floors in a building it may serve to transmit noise for considerable distances, particularly impact noises, when the walking surfaces are finished with hard material. In some circumstances the only way to prevent this is to make a complete structural break between the stair and the structure of the building (see page 371).

CONSTRUCTION OF STAIRS

Most present-day stairs other than domestic come within the category of geometrical stairs. The stair is often quite detached from its surrounding wall so that it becomes a design element in space. These free-standing stairs can be placed in two broad groups: ramp and ladder or open riser types.

(i) **Ramp Stair.** This can be visualized as a ramp or as the floor flowing from one level to another, a conception which is emphasized when closed or upstand strings are employed to shield the saw-tooth line of the steps. The greatest effect is obtained when a long flight, unbroken by landings, can be employed. Regulations in Britain limiting the maximum number of risers in a straight flight, usually preclude this.

(ii) **Ladder or open riser stair.** This consists of treads only, carried on strings, and in its simplest form is like a ladder spanning between floor slabs. In some forms there may be only one string with the treads cantilevering on one or both sides. Apart from the visual effect upon the stair itself as an element, the absence of risers enhances the actual size of the space within which the stair is situated. In domestic work where, for reasons of economy, circulation areas are reduced to a minimum, this is an advantage.

Timber Stairs

These are commonly used in domestic buildings with either closed or open risers, but by the use of laminated timber strings and treads it is possible to construct timber stairs of considerable span and width suitable for larger buildings in situations where combustible materials may be used.

A simple *dog-leg stair* is described and illustrated in *Elementary Building Construction* which shows the main details of construction. These are similar for all types of simple timber stairs.   For a staircase 3 ft or more wide, it would be necessary to introduce a 4 in. × 3 in. rough carriage under the steps to provide intermediate support.   To form a bearing for this at the top of the lower flight it would be necessary to deepen the landing trimmer or, if this became too deep, to introduce a secondary bearer immediately below it called a *pitching piece*.

Ladder or open riser stairs may be constructed with closed or cut strings. When closed strings are used, page 367, the connection between the ends of the treads and the strings is not so good as in a closed riser stair since there are no wedges or side blocks connecting the two.   The strings should, therefore, be tied together by $\frac{3}{8}$ in. or $\frac{1}{2}$ in. diameter metal rods with sunk and pelleted ends placed under every fourth tread.   Screw fixing between string and tread is not very strong as the screws enter the end grain of the tread.   Glued dowels are better than screws for this purpose.   Cut strings are tied together by the treads which rest upon the string and are screwed and pelleted to it.   It should be borne in mind that the effective depth of a cut string is that of the waist at the narrowest points.   A similar effect to cut strings may be obtained with straight strings by bearing the treads on metal brackets fixed to the tops or sides of the strings, but this needs to be carefully detailed to give a satisfactory appearance.

With open riser stairs, no support is given to the tread by a riser, so that the treads should be at least $1\frac{1}{2}$ to $1\frac{3}{4}$ in. thick.   The treads are generally of hardwood as carpeting is not very satisfactory unless the expensive method of sinking a panel of carpet into the tread is adopted, and even then hardwood is desirable because the nosing is exposed to wear.   As already mentioned, large stairs are possible in timber with the use of laminated strings and treads.   Laminated strings may be cranked to accommodate landings in a similar manner to reinforced concrete.

Reinforced Concrete Stairs

Concrete stairs are widely used in all types of buildings.   They have a high degree of fire resistance, are strong, and make possible a wide variety of forms.   They may be cast *in situ* or be precast as whole flights or in separate parts.   *In situ* cast stairs will first be described.

String Stair (see page 368).   The strings may span between landing trimmers or be cranked to span beyond the landings to take a bearing at the perimeter of the stair.   This type of stair will be thinner than a slab type and therefore somewhat lighter in weight.   With half-space landings the inclined strings, which are reinforced as normal beams, can bear on reinforced concrete trimmers at the landings, and the flight slab will span between the

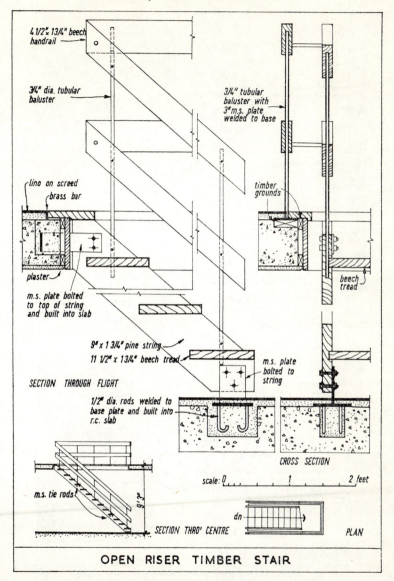

4 1/2" x 1 3/4" beech handrail

3/4" dia. tubular baluster

3/4" tubular baluster with 3" m.s. plate welded to base

lino on screed
brass bar

plaster

m.s. plate bolted to top of string and built into slab

timber grounds

beech tread

SECTION THROUGH FLIGHT

9" x 1 3/4" pine string
11 1/2" x 1 3/4" beech tread

m.s. plate bolted to string

1/2" dia. rods welded to base plate and built into r.c. slab

CROSS SECTION

scale: 0   1   2 feet

m.s. tie rods

9' 2"

SECTION THRO' CENTRE

dn

PLAN

OPEN RISER TIMBER STAIR

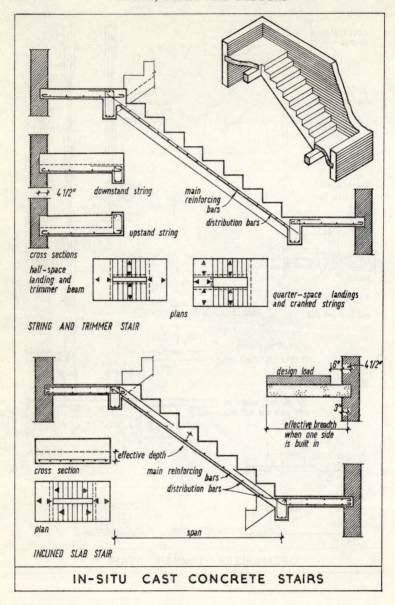

4 1/2"　downstand string

main reinforcing bars

distribution bars

upstand string

cross sections

half-space landing and trimmer beam

plans

quarter-space landings and cranked strings

STRING AND TRIMMER STAIR

design load

6"　4 1/2"

3"

effective breadth when one side is built in

effective depth

cross section

main reinforcing bars

distribution bars

plan

span

INCLINED SLAB STAIR

IN-SITU CAST CONCRETE STAIRS

strings. The landings will span between the trimmers and the enclosing staircase wall or frame. The strings may be upstand or downstand and, in the case of the latter, the effective depth will be from the soffit of the string to the internal junction of the treads and risers. The waist thickness of the flight need only be about 3 in. An upstand string is useful both from a functional and an aesthetic point of view. It prevents dropped articles and cleaning water from falling over the sides of the stair and it gives weight and smoothness of flow to a stair designed to appear as a slab flowing between floors. When an intermediate flight is incorporated, producing quarter-space landings, it is necessary to use cranked strings, and as these must run across the flights, it is necessary to use downstand beams.

For freestanding stairs, a single substantial central string may be designed to carry the flight which cantilevers on each side. The flight may be cast *in situ* or be made up of precast elements bolted or tied into the *in situ* cast string, to give a smooth, inclined soffit or a stepped soffit. Precast concrete treads or laminated timber are often used to produce an open riser stair in this form.

Inclined Slab Stair (page 368). Unless the span of the flight is very long, or strings are required for visual reasons, the stair can be designed without strings, the flight being designed to act as a slab spanning between the trimmers. In this case the span of the flight is the horizontal distance between the centres of the trimmers. The effective depth is the waist thickness of the slab, which is designed on the same basis as a floor slab. In the case of slabs designed to span in the direction of the flight, one side of which is built into a wall not less than $4\frac{1}{2}$ in., B.S. Code of Practice 114 (1957) permits a 6 in. wide strip next to the wall to be deducted from the loaded area, and the effective breadth of the slab to be increased by 3 in.

Cranked Slab Stair (page 370). In this stair there are no trimmers and the top and bottom landings, together with the flight, are designed as a single structural slab spanning between enclosing walls or frame. The appearance is clean and the thickness of the slab is not unduly great if the flight is not too long. This form of stair is useful when there are no side supports available for trimmer beams, as in the case of completely glazed sides to a projecting staircase. Should supports be available at the ends of the landings so that they may be made to span at right-angles to the direction of the flight, the landing slab may be considered as a beam supporting the flights, in which case B.S. Code of Practice 114 (1957) requires that the effective span of the flight should be taken as the going of the flight plus, at each end, either half the width of the landing or 3 ft, whichever is the smaller.

Monolithic Cantilever Stair (page 370). In this stair the flights and landings

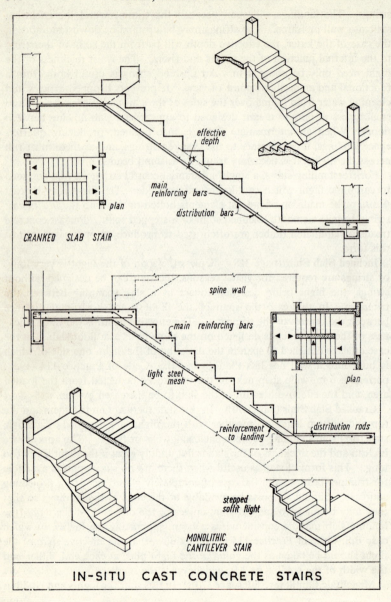

CRANKED SLAB STAIR

effective
depth

main
reinforcing bars

distribution bars

plan

spine wall

main reinforcing bars

light steel
mesh

reinforcement
to landing

distribution rods

plan

stepped
soffit flight

MONOLITHIC
CANTILEVER STAIR

IN-SITU CAST CONCRETE STAIRS

are cast *in situ* and cantilever out from a wall, either the enclosing wall to the staircase or a central spine wall. The soffit may be smooth or stepped, the latter resulting in a fairly thin slab, the compression zone of which is stiffened by the folded form. When the stair cantilevers from a central spine wall, it becomes completely self-supporting and, if projecting from the face of a building, may be fully glazed all round. This form of stair also provides a useful solution to problems of sound insulation when the stair, for this reason, is required to be separated from the surrounding structure, since it is possible to leave an insulating gap all the way round at all points. From a structural point of view, in the case of the stair with a central spine wall, the landings would be partially supported by the end of the wall and partly by the ends of the adjacent flights, and reinforcement would be designed accordingly.

Continuous Slab Stair (page 372). This is a double-flight stair with a half-space landing which receives support only at the floors above and below. It consists structurally of a continuous slab, monolithic with the floors, which runs from one floor to the landing level, turns on itself and continues without any support to the next floor. This is not a cheap stair to construct since not only the normal stresses of bending and shear, but also those of torsion have to be resisted. The slab may be reduced in width to form a wide shallow beam carrying open riser cantilever treads. It may be placed centrally under the treads or eccentrically, so that they cantilever entirely over one side. With materials strong in tension, such as reinforced or pre-stressed concrete or laminated timber, the latter arrangement is practicable even with broad flights, although torsion stresses in the slab are increased.

In these types of stairs without trimmer beams the relationship of the end risers of the flights at a half-space landing affects the positions of the intersections of the sloping soffits and the landing soffit, as well as the form of the handrail turn. If the top riser of the lower flight is set back to line approximately with the second riser of the upper flight, it is possible to make the intersections of the sloping soffits and the landing coincide on the same line which can be the face edge of the landing, without the latter being made excessively thick. This gives a clean appearance on the underside, simplifies detailing of applied finishes and permits a satisfactory handrail turn. This point is illustrated and discussed in *Advanced Building Construction (Components, Services and Finishes)*.

Spiral Stair. In its simplest form, this is one of the oldest types of stair. It can take up a smaller area than any other type but, as all the steps are winders, to be comfortable in use it usually requires more space than a rectangular stair.

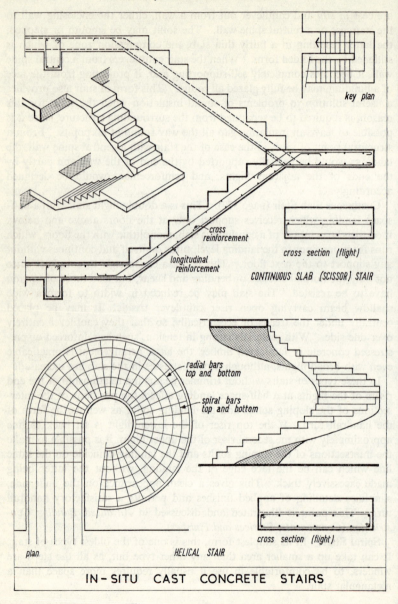

key plan

cross reinforcement

longitudinal reinforcement

cross section (flight)

CONTINUOUS SLAB (SCISSOR) STAIR

radial bars top and bottom

spiral bars top and bottom

plan

cross section (flight)

HELICAL STAIR

IN-SITU CAST CONCRETE STAIRS

The newel type of spiral stair in its smaller form is usually constructed of precast concrete and is discussed later; the larger stairs are constructed on a large core as a monolithic cantilever stair.   The core may be solid or hollow, in the form of a duct.

The open well, or helical stair, page 372, although visually very fine if well designed, is complicated in structural design and construction.   A large proportion of steel is required to resist the bending, shear and torsion stresses, and the shuttering is complicated.   The slab usually varies in thickness from top to bottom, increasing towards the bottom, and may vary in thickness across the width.   There are two or three sets of reinforcement with top and bottom layers in each: continuous bars running the length of the spiral, cross or radial bars and sometimes diagonal bars laid tangential in two directions to the inner curve.   The large amount of steel reinforcement and complicated shuttering makes this an expensive stair to construct.

The helical stair may also be designed with closed strings with the flight slab spanning between.   The effect of a helical stair depends upon the free flow of the curve from one floor to another.   In many cases the limitations on the number of steps in a flight makes it impossible to design such a stair without intermediate landings, which interrupt the flow of the stair.

Precast Concrete Stairs.   The concrete stairs discussed above are primarily *in situ* cast stairs.   Although precast concrete has long been used for simple solid or open riser steps projecting from a wall, either as a cantilever or with the outer ends hung on tension rods, or for small utilitarian spiral stairs, some examples of which are shown on page 374, the precasting of large stairs has not been common.   However, with the general use of cranes on building sites, many large stairs which once would have been constructed only *in situ* are now precast.   These may be precast in the separate parts of strings, open treads, or steps; or they may be cast in complete flights and landings, depending upon the nature of the particular job and the size of the crane to be used.

Page 375 shows a 4 ft 6 in. stair in which the steps are in the form of an "L" with only the building-in end as a solid rectangle.   This considerably reduces the weight of the stair.   Masonry walls should be built in cement mortar for at least 12 in. above and below the line of a cantilever stair.

On page 376 is shown a cut string and open riser stair in which the strings are stepped to take the treads, in this case of timber, which are screwed on. Precast concrete treads could be used and bolted to the strings in a similar way, or they could be secured by projecting rods and a small amount of *in situ* concrete cast in mortices or grooves left for the purpose.

A closed string type is shown on page 377, in which the strings are precast and post-tensioned and on the inside of which are cast stepped bearings to

· 13

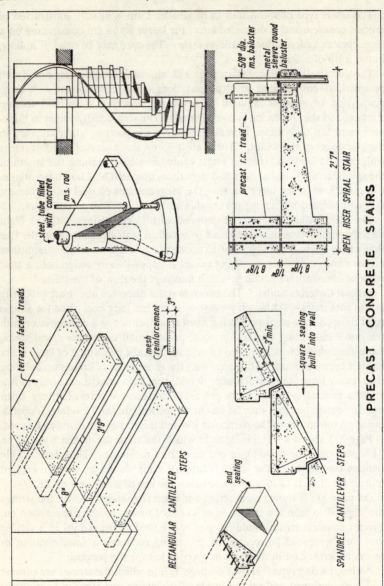

OPEN RISER SPIRAL STAIR

5/8" dia. m.s. baluster

metal sleeve round baluster

precast r.c. tread

2' 7"

8 1/8"   1/8"   8 1/8"

steel tube filled with concrete

m.s. rod

terrazzo faced treads

mesh reinforcement

3"

3' 9"

8"

RECTANGULAR CANTILEVER STEPS

3" min.

square seating built into wall

end seating

SPANDREL CANTILEVER STEPS

PRECAST CONCRETE STAIRS

take the ends of the precast treads. To position the treads and to avoid subsequent movement a stub is cast on each end which drops into an accommodating mortice in the stepped bearings on the string.

An alternative to the casting of the strings as separate elements is to cast them as a pair braced apart the required distance to form an open frame so that the whole can be hoisted by crane and set in rebates formed on the

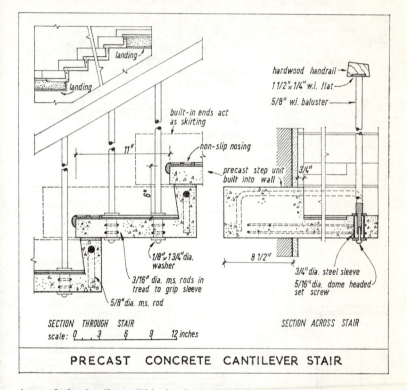

hardwood handrail
1 1/2" x 1/4" w.i. flat
5/8" w.i. baluster

landing
landing

built-in ends act as skirting
non-slip nosing
precast step unit built into wall
3/4"

11"
6"

1/8" x 1 3/4" dia. washer
3/16" dia. m.s. rods in tread to grip sleeve
5/8" dia. m.s. rod

8 1/2"

3/4" dia. steel sleeve
5/16" dia. dome headed set screw

SECTION THROUGH STAIR
scale: 0 3 6 9 12 inches

SECTION ACROSS STAIR

PRECAST CONCRETE CANTILEVER STAIR

edges of the landing. This is shown on page 378. The steps, precast individually, are positioned and grouted in recesses formed to take them in the top faces of the strings.

When a slab stair without strings or trimmers is required this can be cast in elements consisting of a flight and parts of the top and bottom landings, the ends of the landings bearing on rebates in the staircase wall or frame. The half-space landings are completed by *in situ* concrete filling placed

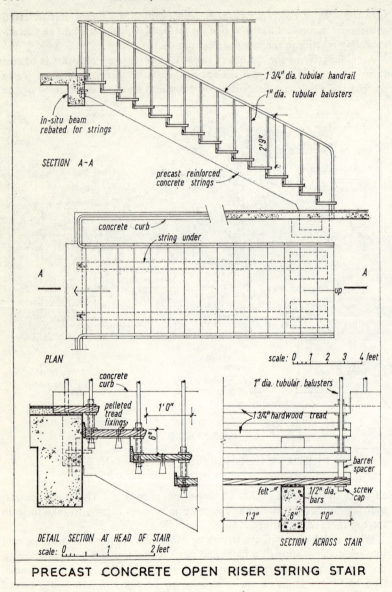

SECTION A-A

1 3/4" dia. tubular handrail

1" dia. tubular balusters

2'9"

in-situ beam rebated for strings

precast reinforced concrete strings

concrete curb

string under

A

A

up

PLAN

scale: 0 1 2 3 4 feet

concrete curb

pelleted tread fixings

1'0"

6"

1" dia. tubular balusters

1 3/4" hardwood tread

barrel spacer

felt

1/2" dia. bars

screw cap

1'3"

6"

1'0"

DETAIL SECTION AT HEAD OF STAIR
scale: 0 1 2 feet

SECTION ACROSS STAIR

PRECAST CONCRETE OPEN RISER STRING STAIR

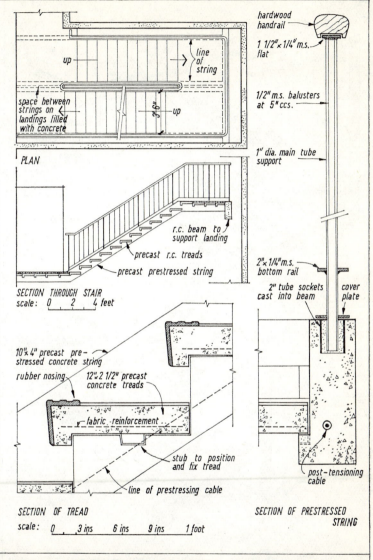

PLAN

space between
strings on
landings filled
with concrete

up

line
of
string

up

3'-6"

hardwood
handrail

1 1/2" x 1/4" m.s.
flat

1/2" m.s. balusters
at 5" ccs.

1" dia. main tube
support

2" x 1/4" m.s.
bottom rail

2" tube sockets
cast into beam

cover
plate

SECTION THROUGH STAIR
scale: 0   2   4 feet

r.c. beam to
support landing

precast r.c. treads

precast prestressed string

10" x 4" precast pre-
stressed concrete string

rubber nosing

12" x 2 1/2" precast
concrete treads

fabric reinforcement

stub to position
and fix tread

line of prestressing cable

SECTION OF TREAD
scale: 0   3 ins   6 ins   9 ins   1 foot

post-tensioning
cable

SECTION OF PRESTRESSED
STRING

PRECAST CONCRETE OPEN RISER CLOSED STRING STAIR

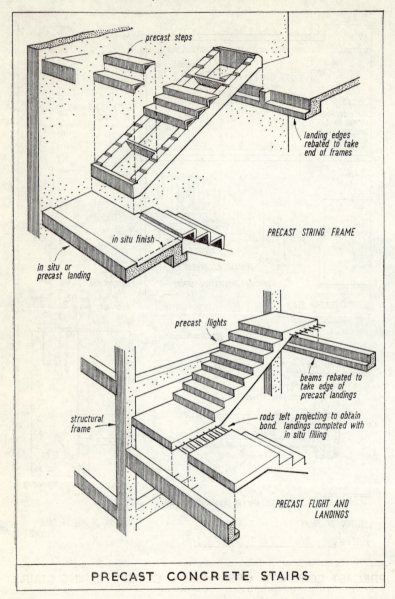

precast steps

landing edges
rebated to take
end of frames

PRECAST STRING FRAME

in situ finish

in situ or
precast landing

precast flights

beams rebated to
take edge of
precast landings

rods left projecting to obtain
bond. landings completed with
in situ filling

structural
frame

PRECAST FLIGHT AND
LANDINGS

PRECAST CONCRETE STAIRS

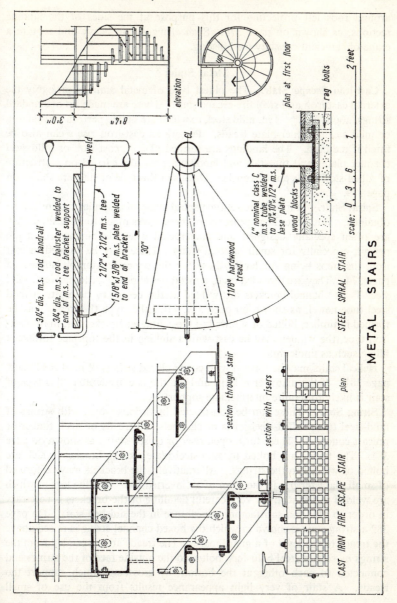

elevation

plan at first floor

rag bolts

weld

3/4" dia. m.s. rod handrail

3/4" dia. m.s. rod baluster welded to end of m.s. tee bracket support

2 1/2" × 2 1/2" m.s. tee

1 5/8" × 1 3/8" m.s. plate welded to end of bracket

30"

3'0"

8'4"

11/8" hardwood tread

4" nominal class C m.s. tube welded to 10" × 10" × 1/2" m.s. base plate

wood blocks

scale: 0 3 6 1 2 feet

STEEL SPIRAL STAIR

section through stair

section with risers

plan

CAST IRON FIRE ESCAPE STAIR

METAL STAIRS

around rods left projecting for this purpose at the sides of the landing sections, as shown on page 378. Such elements are heavy and require a crane of sufficient capacity for hoisting.

Metal Stairs

Cast-iron Escape Stair. The oldest type of metal stair is probably the external cast iron and steel fire-escape stair. These are made up of standard strings, about 7 in. × $\frac{3}{8}$ in. mild steel, to which are bolted perforated cast iron or mild steel chequer-plate treads. Perforated cast-iron risers can also be fitted if required. The landings are formed of $\frac{1}{2}$ in. cast iron or mild steel chequer plates and the stair and landing are usually carried on a structure of rolled-steel joists and channels. Details of this type of stair are shown on page 379.

Spiral Stair. Standard newel-type spiral stairs of a similar nature can be obtained. But since the appearance of these leaves much to be desired, they are often specially designed and constructed when the finances of a job permit, especially for small internal stairs. These may be formed in cast iron, the steps being similar to those for the concrete example shown on page 374. They are threaded on to a metal newel-post. Alternatively, mild steel T- or channel-brackets are welded at the necessary points to a mild steel tube newel, as shown on page 379. In either type the treads may be formed in timber, bolted or screwed to the cantilever brackets or, in the cast-iron type, the winder may be cast with a sinking in the top face to take a filling such as linoleum.

Helical stairs may be formed with cut or closed strings of mild steel plate, page 381. If the diameter is large and the rise is considerable, this type of stair is likely to require intermediate support.

String Stair. These can be constructed in various ways; with strings of mild-steel tube, rolled-steel joists or channels and treads of steel, timber or precast concrete. These form open riser or closed stairs, as shown on page 381. The treads are bolted to mild-steel plate seating brackets which are bolted or welded to the strings. Alternatively, the brackets may be formed of small diameter bar in the form of an inverted flat "U", the legs of which are welded to the string. Very careful detailing of the brackets is necessary in order to obtain a satisfactory appearance in the finished stair. On page 382 a string stair is shown in which the boxed channel string is raised above the treads to the level of a guardboard. The treads are suspended from the strings by square steel balusters, bolted to the outside face of the strings and connected to each other at the bottom by crossbars which support the treads. A stair of very light appearance results from the use of small

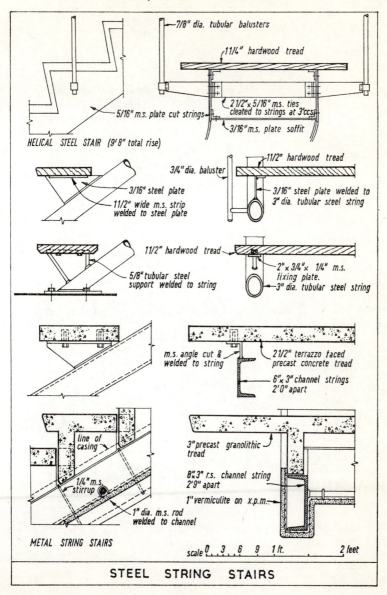

7/8" dia. tubular balusters

1 1/4" hardwood tread

5/16" m.s. plate cut strings

2 1/2" x 5/16" m.s. ties
cleated to strings at 3' c.c.s.

3/16" m.s. plate soffit

HELICAL STEEL STAIR (9' 8" total rise)

3/4" dia. baluster

1 1/2" hardwood tread

3/16" steel plate

1 1/2" wide m.s. strip
welded to steel plate

3/16" steel plate welded to
3" dia. tubular steel string

1 1/2" hardwood tread

5/8" tubular steel
support welded to string

2" x 3/4" x 1/4" m.s.
fixing plate.

3" dia. tubular steel string

m.s. angle cut &
welded to string

2 1/2" terrazzo faced
precast concrete tread

6" x 3" channel strings
2' 0" apart

line of
casing

3" precast granolithic
tread

1/4" m.s.
stirrup

8" x 3" r.s. channel string
2' 9" apart

1" dia. m.s. rod
welded to channel

1" vermiculite on x.p.m.

METAL STRING STAIRS

scale 0 3 6 9 1 ft. 2 feet

STEEL STRING STAIRS

13*

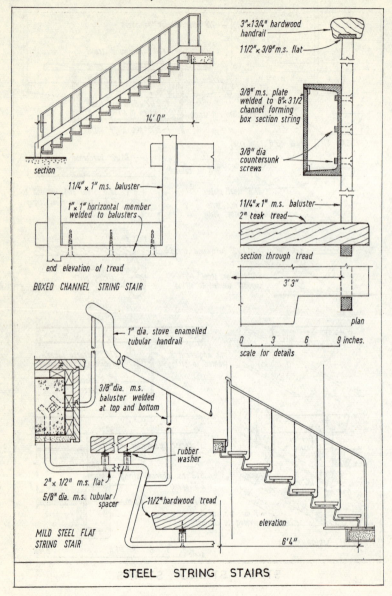

section

14' 0"

3"×13/4" hardwood handrail

11/2"× 3/8" m.s. flat

3/8" m.s. plate welded to 8"×3 1/2 channel forming box section string

3/8" dia countersunk screws

11/4" × 1" m.s. baluster

1" × 1" horizontal member welded to balusters

11/4" × 1" m.s. baluster

2" teak tread

end elevation of tread

section through tread

BOXED CHANNEL STRING STAIR

3' 3"

plan

0   3   6   9 inches.

scale for details

1" dia. stove enamelled tubular handrail

3/8" dia. m.s. baluster welded at top and bottom

rubber washer

2" × 1/2" m.s. flat

5/8" dia. m.s. tubular spacer

11/2" hardwood tread

MILD STEEL FLAT STRING STAIR

elevation

6'4"

STEEL   STRING   STAIRS

section steel strip as a string, used structurally in conjunction with a tubular metal handrail, to which it is connected by metal balusters. This is illustrated on the same page. It should be appreciated that the sizes of members indicated are of course suitable for short flights only, such as that shown.

Where some degree of fire resistance is required in the case of stairs likely to be used internally for escape purposes, the above types of stair would not be suitable, since in many cases the risers are open and steel is exposed. Where, in such cases, it is considered desirable to use steel strings, these must be provided with some protective coating. The illustration at the bottom of page 381 shows a staircase with mild steel channel strings enclosed with 1 in. vermiculite plaster on expanded metal and carrying precast concrete steps. The risers return at the ends in line with the outside face of the strings and the treads cantilever a considerable distance at each side.

Pressed Steel Stairs (page 384). These are constructed in light pressed metal. Each step is a pressing, consisting of the tread and the riser, secured at each end to a pressed-steel closed string or a deep boxed channel member, according to the span of the flights. The treads are designed to take a filling of granolithic, terrazzo, or similar material, to form the finished surface. Alternatively, the tread (and riser as well if desired) can be covered with timber or marble so that the stair becomes simply the structural element. The landings are constructed from dovetailed steel sheets which give a rigid structure and provide a good key for any filling. The soffits of flight and landing are usually fitted with steel clips to which expanded metal can be fixed for plastering or the lining methods shown may be adopted.

Stone Stairs

These are not very much used today, mainly because of the cost, and will only be mentioned briefly here. Stone stairs may be in the form of steps simply supported on end walls, or as cantilever flights and landings, or in the form of a circular newel or turret stair. Simply supported or cantilevered steps can be either rectangular blocks giving a stepped soffit, or spandrel steps, splayed on the underside to give a smooth soffit, as shown for precast concrete stairs, page 374. Cantilever stone steps should not usually exceed 5 to 6 ft in projection, the safe maximum depending upon the type of stone used. If landings are large, these are made up of a number of slabs with joggled joints. The turret stair is similar to the spiral newel stair in precast concrete. However, because of the transverse weakness of stone, the steps are not designed to cantilever out from the central newel where the stone is thinnest, but the outer ends are built into the enclosing wall so that each is a step simply supported on the wall and the newel.

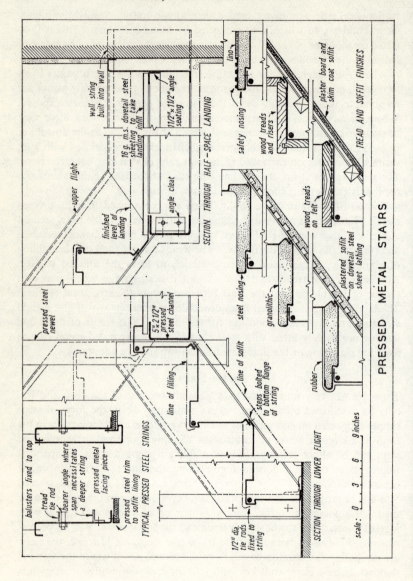

PRESSED METAL STAIRS

SECTION THROUGH HALF-SPACE LANDING

wall string built into wall

16 g. m.s. dovetail steel sheeting to take infill

1 1/2" × 1 1/2" angle seating

upper flight

finished level of landing

angle cleat

TREAD AND SOFFIT FINISHES

lino

plaster board and skim coat soffit

safety nosing

wood treads and risers

wood treads on felt

steel nosing

granolithic

plastered soffit on dovetail steel sheet lathing

rubber

pressed steel newel

5" × 2 1/2" pressed steel channel

line of filling

line of soffit

steps bolted to bottom flange of string

balusters fixed to top

tread tie rod

bearer angle where span necessitates a deeper string

pressed metal facing piece

pressed steel trim to soffit lining

TYPICAL PRESSED STEEL STRINGS

1/2" dia. tie rods fixed to string

SECTION THROUGH LOWER FLIGHT

scale: 0 3 6   9 inches

Universal Stairs

Staircases of any material are normally designed and constructed for each individual job because of the variation in floor to floor height in different buildings. In recent years standard or universal steps have been developed by means of which the rise and going of a flight may be varied within wide limits, and by the use of which staircases of any height and pitch can be constructed. This is accomplished by providing a sloping joint between tread and riser as shown below, so that, as the steps slide backwards or forwards for adjustment, every change in the going is accompanied by a proportional change in the rise. The proportion of rise to going is governed

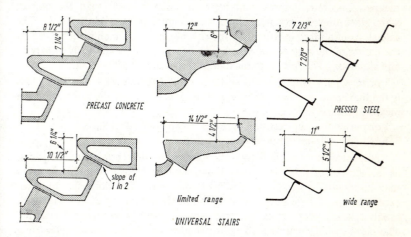

UNIVERSAL STAIRS

by the angle of the slope and is commonly governed by the rule that twice the rise plus the going should equal 23 or 24 in. The steps can be made of any suitable material and the same principle can be applied to a universally adjustable mould for casting *in situ* concrete stairs.[1]

RAMPS

These are mainly used for the passage of vehicles rather than for pedestrians, since they take up a large amount of space compared with a normal stair. They can, however, be used with good effect both functionally and architecturally where the space is available.

[1] A step of this type was used a number of years ago by Alva Aalto (centre of illustration). In Great Britain the design of universal stairs is protected by patent.

Car Ramps. Ramps for cars generally should have a slope of about 1 in 10 although they may be as steep as 1 in 7, especially if the ramp is short. The radius to the centre line of curved ramps should be not less than 23 ft, based on the turning circle of the average size car. Curved ramps should be slightly banked and the whole surface should be treated in some way to give a good hold for tyres. The width of the ramp will depend upon whether it is for one- or two-way traffic. With a minimum radius of 23 ft, a minimum width of 12 ft should be allowed for the former and not less than 24 ft for the latter, which allows for a central separating curb 1 ft wide with a width of 11 ft on the outside of the ramp where the radius is greater.

Pedestrian Ramps. Ramps, if properly designed, probably provide a safer means of pedestrian movement between different levels than the normal stair, since they do not necessitate the accurate placing of the foot. The safe slope of a ramp is limited by the risk of slipping, which is influenced by the nature of the surface and whether or not the ramp is internally or externally situated. The following maximum slopes are considered safe:

For reasonably slip-resistant surfaces subject to wetting—1 in 10. (This is the maximum gradient permitted in the L.C.C. area if the ramp affords a means of escape.)

For reasonably slip-resistant surfaces usually dry—1 in 8.

For highly slip-resistant surfaces—1 in 6.

Ramps steeper than 1 in 6 are sometimes required in certain circumstances, as in factories or other industrial situations where, for example, a footway may be required to follow an inclined conveyor. The slope should never exceed 1 in 3. These steeply sloping ramps should always be provided with evenly spaced cleats across the ramp, spaced apart to suit natural walking. The cleat spacing will depend upon whether or not the pedestrians using them are likely to carry loads. Table 26[1] indicates suitable spacings for slopes up to 1 in 3. As cleats require accurate foot placement, ramps on which they are used lose their main safety features and should be avoided if possible.

The minimum width of a ramp to be used by one person should be the same as those for stairs. Greater widths will be required when two or more persons will pass. This will depend upon the nature of the building in which the ramp is situated and the amount of pedestrian traffic likely to use the ramp. A landing at least equal in width and length to the width of the ramp

---

[1] This table is extracted from Industrial Data Sheet S.3, "Safe Access above Ground Level", issued by the Industrial Services Division, Department of Labour and National Service, Australia, from which much of the information on ramps and ladders has been obtained.

Table 26. Spacing of cleats on ramps steeper than 1 : 6

Slope of ramp	Recommended spacing	
	If load is carried	No loads carried
1:6	14 in.	18 in.
1:5	13 in.	17 in.
1:4	12 in.	16 in.
1:3	11 in.	15 in.

should always be placed at a change of direction in the ramp. The requirements for balustrades and handrails are the same as those for stairs.

A ramp should always be constructed with a good slip-resistant surface. Cement or granolithic surfaces may be finished with a wood float or swept with a stiff broom while still green. This exposes the particles of sand and provides a rough surface which does, however, wear smooth after a time, although the granolithic surface will give a more lasting result because a greater degree of roughness may be obtained initially. Abrasive grit materials may be added to the surface mix to increase the friction and reduce the wear. Slip-resistance is further increased by the provision of transverse grooves formed in the surface. If a suitable aggregate is included in the top, asphalt can provide a good slip-resistant surface. Wood, in a dry, unpolished state, is reasonably slip-resistant, but can become slippery when wet. Metal surfaces are not altogether satisfactory as even when formed with figured surfaces these soon lose their pattern and become slippery.

FIXED LADDERS

These are usually of metal and are used as a means of access to roofs and other high places and sometimes as a means of escape.

Ladders should be steep enough to make the user face them when descending, but vertical ladders should be avoided if possible because they are less safe and harder to climb. Whenever possible the minimum advisable pitch of 60° should be used. Ladders with a pitch of 75° or steeper should have rungs. Those with a lesser pitch should have flat treads. Landings should

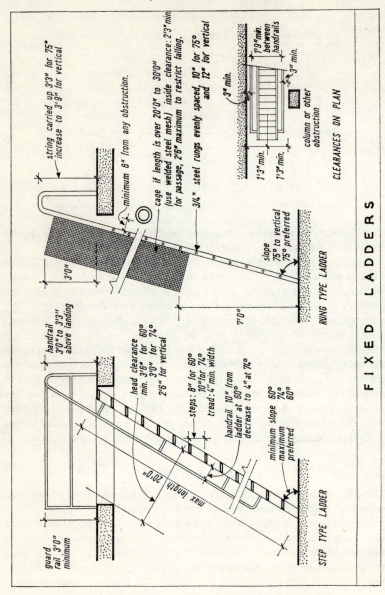

FIXED LADDERS

STEP TYPE LADDER

guard rail 3'0" minimum

handrail 3'0" to 3'3" above landing

head clearance min. 3'6" for 60° 3'0" for 74° 2'6" for vertical

steps: 8" for 60° 10" for 74° tread: 4" min. width

handrail 10" from ladder at 60° decrease to 4" at 74°

minimum slope 60° maximum 74° preferred 60°

max length 20'0"

RING TYPE LADDER

string carried up 3'3" for 75° increase to 3'9" for vertical

minimum 8" from any obstruction.

cage if length is over 20'0" to 30'0" (use welded steel mesh) inside clearance: 2'3" min. for passage, 2'6" maximum to restrict falling.

3/4" steel rungs evenly spaced, 10" for 75° and 12" for vertical

slope 75° to vertical 75° preferred

3'0"

7'0"

CLEARANCES ON PLAN

1'9" min. between handrails

3" min.

3" min.

column or other obstruction

1'3" min.

1'3" min.

always be provided at the top of ladders, and it should be remembered that when descending it is safer to step sideways rather than backwards on to a steep ladder. Single flights should generally not exceed 20 ft in length. When longer, intermediate landings should be introduced. Ladders exceeding 20 to 30 ft in height should be enclosed by a safety cage. Handrails should be provided on both sides of step-type ladders but the strings serve as hand rails for rung-type ladders. Details of recommended clearances, heights and sizes are given on page 388. Reference should be made to Chapter 10 for the requirements of the London County Council in respect of ladders used for escape purposes.

9
Roof Structures

A roof is an essential part of every building. Its most important function is to provide protection from the weather. In multi-storey buildings the span is usually not great and the roof is generally constructed in the same way as the floors. Domestic and small buildings of a similar nature are usually most economically covered by a pitched or flat roof of timber or light steel construction. The methods of constructing these are described in Chapter 10 of *Elementary Building Construction*. In this chapter single-storey buildings requiring roofs of medium and long span will be considered. In the design of these the structure of the roof is significant and is usually a critical factor.

Functional Requirements

The main function of a roof is to enclose space and to protect from the elements the space it covers. To fulfil this function efficiently it generally must satisfy the same requirements as the walls. These are the provision of adequate

> Strength and stability;
> Weather resistance;
> Thermal insulation;
> Fire resistance;
> Sound insulation.

In most buildings, because of its position, the provision of thermal insulation in the roof is essential, particularly in the case of single-storey buildings where the roof area may exceed that of the walls, with a consequent greater heat loss. Thermal insulation, however, is rarely a factor affecting the choice of the roof type since the normal methods of providing it are generally applicable to all forms of roof.

Most forms of roof construction provide for the majority of buildings an adequate degree of insulation against sound from external sources. Only in the case of buildings such as concert halls in noisy localities might special precautions be necessary and only in such cases is it likely to be a factor affecting the choice and design of the roof structure. The fact that weight and discontinuity of structure are important factors in sound insulating construction makes this problem peculiarly difficult in the case of roofs. Problems of thermal and sound insulation are discussed in *Advanced Building Construction* (*Components, Services and Finishes*).

The degree of fire resistance which a roof should provide depends upon the proximity of other buildings, the nature of the building which the roof covers and the structure of the roof. Adequate fire resistance is necessary in order to give protection against the spread of fire from any adjacent buildings and to prevent early collapse of the roof. The form of construction should also be such that the spread of fire from its source to other parts of the building by way of the roof cannot occur. These matters are discussed fully in Chapter 10.

Strength and stability are provided by the roof structure and adequate weather resistance by the roof coverings.

A major consideration in the design and choice of a roof structure is that of span. The wide variety of roof types in different materials which have been developed is, in the main, the result of the search for the most economic means of carrying the roof structure and its load over spans of varying degrees. In all types of structure it is necessary to keep the dead weight to a minimum so that the imposed loads can be carried with the greatest economy of material. Where spans are large this factor is of greatest importance. In the case of small buildings and in those divided into small areas, or in which columns in relatively large areas are not objectionable, the problem is simple because the roof may then be supported at reasonably close intervals and a simple, economic roof structure used. As already mentioned, in the majority of multi-storey buildings a flat roof similar in construction to the floors is normal and in multi-cell single-storey buildings and small houses a flat or pitched roof of simple construction. In these buildings the problem is easily and economically solved; it is in wide span single-storey buildings that the problem becomes difficult. Structures of this type involve problems peculiar to themselves due to the absence of intermediate support for the roof. The problem of wind resistance is often aggravated by large areas of wall and roof exposed to the wind with only a comparatively small amount of framing by which the wind effects can be resisted. The structural problem is primarily that of carrying relatively light loads over relatively large spans. Usually, for maximum economy, this must be accomplished by the use of the minimum weight of material in the structure. That is to say, it is the problem of obtaining the lowest dead/live load ratio consistent with other requirements.

MATERIALS FOR ROOF STRUCTURES

Steel, aluminium, reinforced concrete and timber are all commonly used for the construction of roofs. With the advent of plastics, constructional forms are being developed which take advantage in roof structures of the particular characteristics of these materials. At this point a brief comparison will be made of those properties of these five materials which are particularly relevant to their use in roof structures.

Steel

Strength. Steel has high strength in both compression and tension and a small amount of material is able, therefore, to carry large loads. The ultimate stress of structural mild steel is 28/33 tons per sq. in., and a working stress of 10·5 tons per sq. in. is permitted for all normal structural members by British Standard Specification 449.

Elasticity. A structural material under stress should not stretch or contract to an excessive degree. This is particularly important in horizontal members where large deflections due to loading must generally be avoided. The ratio of stress to resultant strain, known as Young's Modulus or the Modulus of Elasticity, indicates the manner in which the material can resist elastic deformation. If its resistance is high the material is stiff, the deformation under stress will be low and the deflection of a beam under load will therefore be small. Since the minimum depth of a beam is often dictated by deflection rather than by the strength of the materials used, a high modulus of elasticity permits either a shallower beam section for a given deflection or a greater span for a given depth of beam. This can be seen clearly in the expression for deflection of a beam,

$$d = \frac{\text{constant } (c) \times w \times l^4}{EI}$$

Steel has a modulus of elasticity of 30×10^6 lb per sq. in. indicating that it is a stiff material.

Ductility. Structural materials should be able to withstand large deformations without suddenly failing and cracking. In structural frames high stresses are often induced over restricted areas at some points and deformation will occur. Provided that the material is sufficiently ductile it will not crack, but what is known as plastic flow will take place and the load will be transferred to the surrounding material, so that at no point is the failing stress reached. Steel is a ductile material and, with a yield point of about 15 tons per sq. in., undergoes considerable strain after the elastic limit and before ultimate failure. This can be seen in the diagram of stress/strain curves below.

Generally. The properties of steel are such that the dead/live load ratio of steel members is small. That is to say they are able to carry heavy live loads at the expense of a comparatively small dead or self-weight.

Aluminium Alloys

Pure aluminium is quite soft and is alloyed with other elements to make it a suitable structural material. Aluminium alloys have the advantage of being

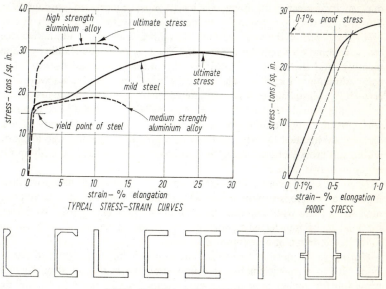

TYPICAL STRESS–STRAIN CURVES

PROOF STRESS

TYPICAL ALUMINIUM ALLOY STRUCTURAL SECTIONS

only about one-third of the weight of steel, but they suffer certain disadvantages.

Strength. The stress/strain curves of most aluminium alloys exhibit no sharply defined yield point, so that there is no clear indication of the elastic limit and no point which may be used as the basis of a working stress. A "proof" stress is, therefore, specified for this purpose. This is the tensile stress which produces a non-proportional extension of a defined amount of the original length. In Great Britain this is 0.1%. It will be seen from the diagram on this page that the proof stress on which the working stress is based lies close to the ultimate stress of the alloy. One of the commonly used structural alloys has an ultimate stress of 17 tons per sq. in., a proof stress of 14 tons per sq. in. and a working stress of 7 tons per sq. in. Stronger alloys with ultimate, proof and working stresses of 28, 24 and 11 tons per sq. in. respectively are available.

Elasticity. The modulus of elasticity of aluminium alloys is about one-third that of steel (10 to 11 $\times$ 10^6 lb per sq. in.). An aluminium alloy beam will, therefore, under the same conditions, deflect three times as much as a similar steel beam. The stiffness of a beam is measured by its flexural rigidity (EI), and in order to maintain a given deflection when the modulus of elasticity decreases, the moment of inertia must be increased (see page 392). This may be done by increasing the depth of the section to between $1\frac{5}{8}$ and $1\frac{3}{4}$ of the depth of the steel section. In addition, or as an alternative, the cross sectional area may be increased. The lack of elastic stability of thin members and the danger of local buckling must be guarded against when using aluminium sections. The web of a beam may buckle sideways if it is too thin or insufficiently stiffened, lateral buckling due to torsion may occur in an unrestrained slender beam, and local buckling may take place in a thin compression flange at the points of maximum bending moment. These dangers are avoided by using sections with greater flange and web areas or with a stiff cross-sectional shape such as box sections or sections with lipped edges as shown, page 393.

Ductility. The proof and ultimate stresses of aluminium alloys lie close together and there is very little elongation before failure occurs. In areas of high stress there will, therefore, be little plastic flow taking place to permit the load to be transferred to surrounding areas. This has to be borne in mind in the design of aluminium structures.

Generally. In normal conditions aluminium is highly resistant to corrosion. It has a coefficient of expansion about twice that of steel, so that provision for greater temperature movements must be made in aluminium structures.

Aluminium alloys may be applied to structures in a similar way to steel but result in a considerably lighter structure. They are most economically used in cases where the weight of the structure itself forms a substantial part of the load and the imposed loads are comparatively light. They are, therefore, obviously suitable materials for roof structures, particularly those of long span where the dead load rises rapidly and the dead/live load ratio is likely to be high. Because of their characteristics, aluminium alloys are best used in structures which are inherently stable and resistant to torsion and where the members can be kept short and directly loaded as in grid structures.

Reinforced and Prestressed Concrete

Strength. The average compressive strength of normal concrete is 2,000 to 6,000 lb per sq. in., but its tensile strength is only approximately one-tenth of this. Methods of making good this deficiency by reinforcement are described in Chapter 5, page 259, and the advantages of prestressing are described in the same chapter on page 281.

Elasticity. Concrete has a low modulus of elasticity ranging from 2 to 5 $\times 10^6$ lb per sq. in. For normal mixes this is taken as 2×10^6 lb per sq. in. for design purposes.

Generally. Over wide spans reinforced concrete used in beam and slab form has a high dead/live load ratio. It is most effectively used in structural forms which can take advantage of its monolithic character, particularly three-dimensional forms such as shells, doubly curved slabs and folded slabs. The prestressing of concrete brings about a considerable reduction in depth of spanning members and depth/span ratios from 1:30 to 1:120 are possible. The reduction in depth together with a reduction in the overall cross-sectional area, made possible by the increased resistance of prestressed concrete to shear, results in a considerable reduction in dead weight and results in satisfactory dead/live load ratios over wide spans.

Timber

Timber was one of the earliest materials to be used for structural purposes, but our knowledge of its behaviour and capabilities is comparatively new. Developments in methods of joining timber, particularly by means of metal connectors and glues, developments in the stress-grading of timber and research into improved methods of design have resulted in the more efficient use of the material. Timber is a comparatively light material and the species used for normal structural purposes have weights approximately one-sixteenth that of steel.

Strength. Timber is an organic material and the knots and faults brought about during growth or seasoning constitute zones of weakness. The technique of stress-grading is a means of establishing the loadbearing capacity of a piece of timber in terms of knots and other visible faults by which, on the basis of the strength of clear wood of the same species, a reduced allowable working stress is determined (see *Elementary Building Construction*). The strength of normal structural timbers in bending is approximately one twenty-eighth to one twenty-third that of steel. The basic stresses are as follows: 800 to 1,000 lb per sq. in. in flexure and compression parallel to the grain; 100 lb per sq. in. in shear parallel to the grain; 1,200 to 1,500 lb per sq. in. in tension.

The problem of joints is an important factor in timber design, and earlier forms of joints had an efficiency of no more than 15 to 20% relative to the timber entering the joint. Two methods of increasing their efficiency are by means of connectors and glues. Timber connectors consist of various forms of metal plates and rings through which a bolt passes (see page 448). Their effect is to increase the strength of the joint, particularly in tension and shear. Glues made from synthetic resins produce joints as strong and even stronger than the timber joined. A considerable number of these glues is available, all of which have different characteristics and some of which are immune to attack by dampness or decay. Glues can be used for lattice construction but are more advantageously used in building up laminated timber members, which can be much stronger than the same size section in solid wood. A further advantage of laminated construction is that different qualities of timber may be used in the same section, the better quality being placed in the more highly stressed zones. By means of gluing, continuity of structure is obtained and it is a simple matter to form curved members and portal frames with the greatest depth where the stresses are highest. The cost of manufacture makes "glulam" members about two-and-a-half times as dear as comparable solid members, and they should only be used when it is clear that a solid member is uneconomic.

Elasticity. The modulus of elasticity of normal structural softwoods is from $1 \cdot 2$ to $1 \cdot 3 \times 10^6$ lb per sq. in. Although some timbers such as Douglas Fir have a modulus of $1 \cdot 6 \times 10^6$ lb per sq. in., the modulus of elasticity of timber is low compared with that of other materials. In spite of this, however, having regard to the light weight of the material, comparative analysis with other materials shows that in terms of flexural rigidity timber is the most efficient from the point of view of weight and cost of material.[1]

Generally. The stiffness of timber per unit of weight and cost makes it particularly suitable for structures in which the load-carrying capacity is determined by its flexural rigidity (EI), such as structures which are large in relation to the load they carry. This includes roofs of all types, floors bearing moderate or light loadings and single-storey buildings, particularly those of large height and span. Philip O. Reece suggests as a rough guide that "structures which are liable to fail through elastic instability and for which timber is the most suitable material, are likely to be those with a load-intensity ratio, $\sqrt{P/l}$, less than about 3, where P is the compressive load in lb and l is the effective length of the member in inches".[2]

---

[1] See paper by Philip O. Reece, "A review of the Structural Use of Timber in the United Kingdom", Building Research Congress, 1951, papers in Div. 1, Pt 2.
[2] *Ibid.*

In addition to its use in framed and laminated structures timber may be used in the form of stressed skin plywood panels built up as folded or prismatic slabs or in the form of planks built up as doubly-curved shells. Very high strength to weight ratios are attained in this way, with weights per square foot of floor area covered as low as 5 lb. As a structural material timber has the advantage of ease of working and fabrication. Because of its comparatively light weight, built up members can be easily handled. When properly used it is a permanent material and has satisfactory thermal insulating properties, which is a further advantage when it is used in stressed skin forms of roof structure. Although it burns freely in thin sections, when used in the sizes normal in lattice construction it remains structurally stable during a fire for a greater length of time than steel (see Chapter 10).

Plastics

The development of synthetic resins has resulted in the production of completely new materials, known as plastics, with diverse characteristics and properties. At present the most important application of plastics in building is for non-structural purposes, but investigations have shown that there are great possibilities for the development of these materials for structural purposes in certain types of structure where advantage can be taken of their particular properties.

Plastics are light in weight and on an average weigh only about one-sixth of the weight of steel.

Strength. The tensile strength of plastics alone is only about 10,000 lb per sq. in., but when reinforced with suitable material, such as glass fibre, tensile strengths up to 200,000 lb per sq. in. (nearly 90 tons per sq. in.) are possible. Compressive strengths are about three-quarters of the tensile strength.

Elasticity. Thermo-setting plastics have a low modulus of elasticity, much the same as those for timber and concrete (1 to 4 $\times$ 10^6 lb per sq. in.), but when laminated and reinforced the modulus can rise to 6 $\times$ 10^6 lb per sq. in.

Ductility. Plastics are not ductile materials. Little plastic flow, therefore, takes place in areas of high stress and, as in the case of other materials of low ductility, this must be borne in mind in the design of structures incorporating plastics.

Generally. Plastics vary in weathering properties but some show great promise, although few actual tests have been carried out. Alone, they have a high coefficient of expansion, about 11 to 12 times that of steel, but when glass fibre reinforced they may have a smaller coefficient than steel. The light weight of plastics gives a favourable strength/weight ratio so that they

are particularly suitable for roof structures, provided these are of the type
in which the low stiffness of the material is overcome by the inherently stiff
form of the structure. The types of structure, therefore, to which plastics
can most advantageously be applied are space structures of the stressed skin
type, in which the strength is derived more from the geometry of the form
than from the quality of the material. Plastics have already been used in the
construction of many geodesic domes and in grid structures combining
plastic tetrahedra of different types, or doubly curved sheets, with grids of
metal rods.

ROOF LOADING

  (i) The dead load consists of the self-weight of the structure itself and of
      the roof claddings, coverings and internal linings.
 (ii) The superimposed load consists of the weight of snow, any incidental
      loads applied during the course of maintenance work and, in the case
      of flat roofs used as roof gardens, play areas or for other purposes,
      additional loads according to the purpose for which the roof is used.
(iii) Wind forces.

The dead load is usually based on the weights of materials specified in B.S.
648.

Superimposed Loads on Flat Roofs. Code of Practice 3, Chapter V (1952),
recommends for flat roofs (up to 10°), with no access provided other than that
necessary for normal maintenance purposes, an allowance for superimposed
loads of 15 lb per sq. ft measured on plan. When access in addition to that
necessary for maintenance purposes is provided, a superimposed load of
30 lb per sq. ft should be allowed for. This figure is the same as that for the
lowest class of floor loading and is subject to similar minimum imposed loads
on slabs and beams (see page 299). The figure of 30 lb includes a load in
respect of loose snow up to a depth of 2 ft. Loose freshly fallen snow weighs
approximately 5 lb per cu. ft, but compact snow may weigh 20 lb per cu. ft
and in districts subject to heavy snowfall an allowance should be made for
this.

Superimposed Loads on Pitched Roofs. The superimposed load allowance
on roofs with a pitch greater than 10°, to which no access is provided other
than for maintenance purposes, should be:

  (i) For a pitch of 30° or less—15 lb per sq. ft measured on plan.
 (ii) For a pitch of 75° or more—no allowance.

For pitches between 30 and 75° the load shall be obtained by interpolation.
To allow for loads incidental to maintenance works it is recommended

that all roof coverings, other than glass, at a pitch of less than 45° should be capable of carrying a load of 200 lb concentrated on any area 5 in. square.

Wind Forces. Some indication of the variations in wind pressure and suction over roof surfaces is given in the diagrams on pages 116, 346.[1] The allowances to be made for wind pressures normal to the surface of flat and pitched roofs are given in Table 27 from the Code of Practice, in terms of the basic wind pressure, p, given in Table 3 on page 115. The pressure on a curved roof may be calculated by dividing the curved portion into at least four equal segments, the pressures on each segment being determined by the values given in Table 27 appropriate to the slope of the chord of each segment. Reference should be made to the Code for multiple span roofs and the effect of wind drag.

Table 27. Design wind pressures on roofs
(wind normal to eaves)

Slope of roof on windward side	Wind pressure	
	Windward slope*	Leeward slope*
0°	$-1 \cdot 00\,p$	$-0 \cdot 75\,p$
10°	$-0 \cdot 70\,p$	$-0 \cdot 50\,p$
20°	$-0 \cdot 40\,p$	$-0 \cdot 45\,p$
30°	$-0 \cdot 10\,p$	$-0 \cdot 45\,p$
40°	$+0 \cdot 10\,p$	$-0 \cdot 45\,p$
50°	$+0 \cdot 30\,p$	$-0 \cdot 45\,p$
60°	$+0 \cdot 40\,p$	$-0 \cdot 45\,p$
70°	$+0 \cdot 50\,p$	$-0 \cdot 45\,p$
80°	$+0 \cdot 50\,p$	$-0 \cdot 45\,p$
90°	$+0 \cdot 50\,p$	$-0 \cdot 50\,p$

*Windward and leeward halves in the case of a flat roof.

The figures given above are average values, and in the design of individual roof panels or sheets the figures in Table 27 should be increased by $0 \cdot 3\,p$. As in the case of walls, greater suction occurs at gable ends and near the eaves, and the Code recommends that all fastenings for roof sheeting near the eaves and gables (within 15% of span or length of roof respectively) should be designed to resist a suction of twice the basic wind pressure, p.

The requirements for superimposed and wind loads laid down in the

[1] This is illustrated in greater detail in diagrams at the end of Code of Practice 3, Chapter V (1952).

L.C.C. By-laws and the Model Building Byelaws[1] are the same as those recommended in the Code.

When very light roof coverings are used, such as some forms of aluminium sheeting, the supporting sub-structure as a consequence tends to be light and the weight of the cladding and sub-structure as a whole may not be heavy enough to withstand the uplift of excessive suction occurring during short periods of very high wind. In such circumstances the roof structure as well as the fastenings to the claddings must be so designed and fixed to frame or walls as to prevent them being stripped off.[2] Reference is made elsewhere to the need for heavy foundations as a means of holding down the building structure as a whole when this is light in weight and extensive in area (page 414).

TYPES OF ROOF STRUCTURE

As indicated earlier in this chapter, roofs may be constructed of a number of different materials, all of which may prove suitable according to the requirements of a particular building or the particular type of roof structure selected. Some types may be constructed satisfactorily in more than one of these materials, but the basic principles of the structure are the same in each case. At this point, therefore, the various structural forms used for roofs of medium and large span will be reviewed, with particular reference to the principles on which they are based and which govern their structural behaviour, and the practical considerations which have led to their development. Later in this chapter these are discussed in terms of constructional methods and details in different materials (see page 446).

Roof structures may be considered broadly as two- or three-dimensional forms. Two-dimensional structures for practical purposes have length and depth only and all forces are resolved in two-dimensions in a single vertical plane. They can fulfil only a spanning function. Three-dimensional structures have length, depth and also breadth, and forces are resolved in three dimensions within the structure. These forms can fulfil a covering and enclosing function as well as that of spanning and are now commonly referred to under the general term of "space structures". Two-dimensional structures include beams or trusses on columns and rigid frames of all types, including arch ribs. Volume is created by the use of a number of such two-dimensional elements carrying secondary two-dimensional members in order to cover the required space. Three-dimensional, or space structures, include cylindrical and parabolic shells and shell domes; doubly-curved slabs, such as hyperbolic paraboloids and hyperboloids of revolution; folded slabs and

---

[1] L.C.C. By-law 2.02 and 2.03; M.B.B. Second Schedule (4) (5).
[2] See also *Building Research Station Digest* No. 122, "Wind Effects on Roofs".

prismatic shells; grid structures such as space frames, space grids and grid domes and barrel vaults; suspended or tension roof structures. All these forms cover space and in the case of domes are capable of completely enclosing.[1]

TRUSSES AND GIRDERS

Trussed Roofs. As in floor construction, roofs constructed of two-dimensional members are classified as single, double and triple roofs according to the number of stages necessary economically to transfer the loads to the supports. In a single roof, the roof covering is carried directly by the rafters. Where the span of the rafters would be excessive for economic construction a secondary member or purlin is introduced to provide intermediate support to the rafters, the purlin being strutted off suitable partitions or walls below. Where no such purlin support is available, a third structural member must be introduced to provide that support and this may be in the form of a roof truss or a roof frame. The former implies a double-pitched triangulated structure and the latter a structure with continuity between vertical and spanning members; frames are discussed later. Small span trussed roofs are described in *Elementary Building Construction*.

Trussed roofs are widely used for single-storey and shed-type buildings (page 402). Triangulation of the truss will vary according to the span and the various methods adopted are illustrated in most textbooks on structural design. Light types of factory building requiring a clear internal height of about 12 ft and a span from 30 to 40 ft can be economically constructed with steel trusses spaced from 10 to 12 ft apart bearing on the tops of stanchions as shown on page 402 (A, E). The normal fixing at the feet of the truss produces a reasonably unrestrained joint with the stanchion. The normal methods of fixing the column feet to the foundation blocks produces a comparatively rigid joint at this point. Side wind pressure will set up bending stresses in the columns as they react as vertical cantilevers, so that the stress distribution will be zero at the top of the columns increasing to a maximum at the foundation, which it will tend to rotate. Within the limits of sizes given above, the bending stress at the base will be comparatively small and the rotational tendency on the foundation will be slight. Thus columns of comparatively small cross-section can be used and, with foundation blocks sized to take the vertical loads, the stresses on the soil due to wind-pressure can usually be kept within safe limits.

When the span is greater than 40 to 50 ft and for functional reasons the

[1] For an excellent analysis of the principles of these and all other structural forms see *Principles of Structural Design*, by Niels Lisborg, M.Sc., M.Ing.F., A.M.I.C.E. (Batsford).

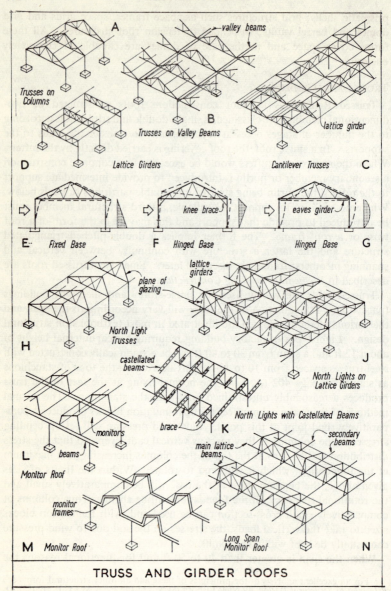

A

valley beams

Trusses on
Columns

B   Trusses on Valley Beams

D   Lattice Girders

lattice girder

C   Cantilever Trusses

E   Fixed Base

knee brace

F   Hinged Base

eaves girder

G   Hinged Base

plane of
glazing

lattice
girders

H   North Light Trusses

J   North Lights on Lattice Girders

castellated
beams

brace

K   North Lights with Castellated Beams

monitors

beams

L   Monitor Roof

main lattice
beams

secondary
beams

monitor
frames

M   Monitor Roof

N   Long Span Monitor Roof

TRUSS AND GIRDER ROOFS

columns must be high, the column section increases rapidly and large turning moments are applied to the foundation slabs. In these circumstances, to avoid uneconomic foundations a non-rigid or hinged joint between the column base and the foundation may be introduced to relieve the latter of any rotational tendency, since no bending stresses can be transferred through such a joint. In order to provide the necessary rigidity against lateral wind pressure a knee brace may be introduced to provide a stiff joint between the columns and the roof truss, page 402 (F). The stress in the columns will then be somewhat reduced and will be zero at the foundation and a maximum at the knee brace. Because of the rigid joint, some bending will be transferred to the feet of the truss which must be designed to withstand it, but the foundation slabs may be limited to the size required solely by the vertical loading. The introduction of rigid and hinged joints in this way results in the structure acting as a whole under side pressure of wind, with a tendency to "uplift" on the windward side, which may be marked in the case of light structures.

An alternative method, which reduces bending in the columns and avoids bending stresses in the truss, is to introduce horizontal eaves girders instead of knee braces, page 402 (G). This is an economic method for high buildings provided the building is not too long or is divided at intervals by walls or braced cross frames. The columns are designed with unrestrained top and bottom joints so that the bending stresses are a maximum at the centre and zero at top and bottom. Induced bending stresses in foundation and truss are therefore avoided. Lateral rigidity is provided by the horizontal eaves girders which pick up the wind pressure on roof and walls through the columns and transmit it to the ends of the building or to cross walls or frames. Intermediate foundations are thus relieved of any vertical component due to wind pressure.

Roof trusses may be constructed in steel, aluminium alloy or timber, in spans up to more than 200 ft when required. In the case of very large spans the pitch is kept low in order to avoid excessive internal volume and to reduce the area of roof to be covered and the weight of the structure.

Roof Girders. Trussed or lattice girders are widely used for medium and large spans when a flat or low pitch roof is required (page 402 (D)). Rolled-steel joists are not economic for spans much above 35 ft, although this can be extended by the use of castellated beams. Reinforced concrete beams have an economic limit of about 30 ft. Prestressed concrete, however, is very suitable for wide span roof beams since small depth/span ratios are possible.

Trussed girders may be designed with parallel chords or with the top chord double-pitched or curved where a low pitched roof is required. This is normal for large spans, but in the case of smaller spans a parallel chord beam is sometimes pitched in the middle to give a low double-pitched roof.

Girders may be used as valley beams in multi-span trussed roof structures to permit the wider spacing of internal columns, the girders supporting a number of trusses (page 402 (B)). Where very wide column spacing is required the depth of the girders will increase excessively the height of the building. In this case what is known as cantilever truss or "umbrella" truss construction is used. In this the girders are made the full depth of the truss and are placed in the line of the ridge so that the truss cantilevers out on each side of the beam, the feet of adjacent trusses meeting at the valleys as at (C). The economic depth of trussed girders is from one-sixth to one-tenth of the span and, owing to the large depth of beam at the junction with the supporting columns, the beam to column joint can be comparatively rigid. Suitable materials for the construction of trussed girders are steel, aluminium alloys and timber.

Vierendeel girders without diagonal members, but with rigid joints between the chords and the vertical members, are only occasionally used in special circumstances in single-storey structures. These are described in Chapter 5.

Beyond a span of about 40 ft, depending upon the standard of lighting required, reasonable natural lighting through the walls is not likely to be sufficient unless the structure is very high. In order to provide satisfactory lighting to the interiors of extensive single-storey buildings a number of roof forms have developed.

North Light Roofs. This type of roof may be in shell form, which is described later, or in trussed form. In lattice construction it is an asymmetrical truss, the steeper and shorter side of which is glazed and is sited to face north as shown on page 402 (H). As in the case of symmetrical trusses, the supporting columns may be placed at greater distances apart, say three bays, with the intermediate trusses picked up on valley beams. Where the greater column spacing is required and the valley beams become excessively deep, lattice girders in the line of the ridge are used to form cantilever north light construction. To obtain wide spacings of the main lattice beams the construction may be in the form of trussed rafters spanning between the beams, with the plane of glazing running from the ridge, that is the top of the lattice beam, on to the "back" of the adjacent trussed rafter (page 402 (J)).

An alternative to the north light truss is the use of castellated beams, which are suitable for long spans carrying light loads, spanning between the top chord of one lattice girder and the bottom chord of the adjacent girder. The plane of glazing is the depth of the main beam (K).

Monitor Roof. A monitor is a mono-pitch lantern light with glazing at the sides only.   The side facing north is usually large in area and that facing south is small.   This roof provides very even lighting at the working plane for a comparatively small volume of roof; good lighting may be achieved with quite low ceilings, the spacing of the monitors being arranged for any given height to provide an even distribution of light.   Where spans are not great and the columns may be spaced about 15 ft apart, the monitor frames may be built off steel joists or shallow lattice beams (page 402 (L)) or, alternatively, the monitor frames may be formed as integral parts of a cranked beam of welded steel or *in situ* or precast concrete (M).   Where wide column spacing is essential, deep lattice beams are used spaced 20 to 25 ft apart, according to spacing required for the monitors, which support shallow lateral beams on the bottom chords spaced about 15 ft apart.   These secondary beams carry the monitor frames which straddle the top of the main beams (N).   Instead of separate secondary beams and monitor frames, cranked welded steel beams may be used spanning from the top chord of one main beam to the bottom chord of the adjacent beam.

RIGID OR PORTAL FRAMES

Over large spans, deep lattice girders and pitched roof trusses, particularly the latter, may result in excessive volume within the roof space of the building which, because of the obstruction by beams and ties, may not always be useful space.   Further, with an increase in span the extra material necessary to provide adequate strength must be added to a simple beam or truss at the points where its own dead weight will increase the bending moments in the structure.   The use of rigid frame construction overcomes these disadvantages to a very large extent.   The characteristic of the rigid frame is continuity of structure due to the stiff, or restrained, joints between the parts, and because of the nature of the stress distribution within such frames, less material is required at the centre of the spanning elements than in a comparable simply supported beam.   With increase in span, the whole of the necessary extra material is not required to be placed in the beam element, so that the maximum economic span is much greater.   The smaller depth of the beam elements results in comparatively unobstructed, usable space for the full height of the building.   The difference between these two forms of construction in this respect can be seen in the diagram on page 406 (A) which shows a rigid frame and a trussed roof construction spanning very much the same distance; the overall height of the rigid frame structure, the space within which is wholly utilized, is approximately the same as the overall height of the truss which encloses a large volume of space lying above the

14

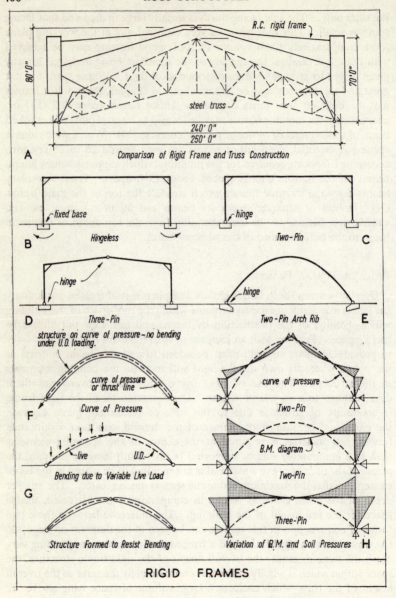

80'0"

70'0"

240' 0"
250' 0"

A   Comparison of Rigid Frame and Truss Construction

R.C. rigid frame

steel truss

fixed base

B   Hingeless

hinge

C   Two-Pin

hinge

D   Three-Pin

hinge

E   Two-Pin Arch Rib

structure on curve of pressure – no bending
under U.D. loading.

curve of pressure
or thrust line

F   Curve of Pressure

curve of pressure

Two-Pin

live   U.D.

Bending due to Variable Live Load

B.M. diagram

Two-Pin

G   Structure Formed to Resist Bending

Three-Pin

H   Variation of B.M. and Soil Pressures

RIGID FRAMES

volume of the building below. In some types of building, this space is, of course, valuable for housing services.

The result of the continuity arising from the introduction of stiff or rigid joints between the parts of the frame is illustrated below, where a portal frame rigidly fixed to its foundations is compared with a beam structure simply supported on two columns. It can be seen that the bending in the beam of the portal frame is transferred through the rigid joints to the columns. The resistance to this bending offered by the column results, however, in a reversed bending at the ends and a reduction of bending at the centre of the beam. The nature of the deflections in each structure can be seen. There is little or no bending in the columns of the simple structure

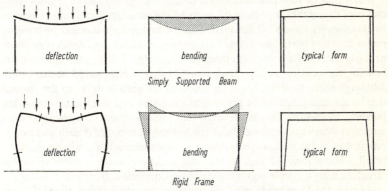

COMPARISON OF RIGID FRAME AND BEAM CONSTRUCTION

and only a single curve deflection in the beam, but there is considerable variation in curvature in the rigid frame. The points at which the direction of curvature changes, that is the points of contraflexure, are points at which there is no bending moment and at which the bending stresses in the members change "signs". This can be seen in the bending moment diagrams, which also show that the stiff junctions of beam and columns in the rigid frame are zones at which the bending moments are large. In contrast, the bending moments at the unrestrained junctions between columns and beam in the simple frame are small. These differences in stress distribution in the structure produce differences in form. In the simple structure the columns may economically be of a uniform section, but the beam, with its maximum bending moment at the centre, will in large spans be most economically constructed if greatest in depth at that point. In the rigid frame, the stresses at the top of the columns will often be greater than those at the base, requiring a greater amount of material at that point. In the beam there will be less disparity between the stresses at the ends and mid-span, so that a horizontal member of uniform depth will be economic. The relative proportion of end and mid-span moments depends on the relative stiffness of beams and columns. If the columns are slender compared with the beam they will provide little fixity at the ends and the mid-span moment will approach that of a simply supported beam; the end moments will be small. In some cases where the bending moments at the ends or haunches are considerably greater than those at mid-span, the depth of the beam at the centre may logically be less than that at the ends.

It can thus be seen that continuity, because of the transfer of stresses from one part to another, results in all parts of the structure providing resistance to the stresses set up by the load with a consequent reduction in bending moment at any particular point. As mentioned earlier, less depth is required at the centre of the horizontal member of the rigid frame, thus reducing the bending moment further by the amount of dead weight saved at this point. Although more material has been added at the ends to take up the stresses due to the stiff junctions, it lies over the columns and does not increase the bending moment. This is an important consideration in large span construction where the dead weight of the horizontal member is such an important factor in the design, particularly in cases where the available depth is small. Some form of rigid frame will usually provide a more economic structure than a simple combination of unrestrained columns and beams.

As with the knee-brace truss construction described above, the stiff joints between columns and beam in the rigid frame provide lateral rigidity and make it possible to introduce hinges when necessary. The *hinged joint* is also referred to as a non-rigid, unrestrained or pivoted joint. In structural frames a hinge implies a junction between two parts that can transmit a thrust and shearing force but not a bending moment, since it permits free rotation. This, for the designer, simplifies the analysis of the structure by making it statically determinate. Direct stresses only exist at such joints and, since these can be resisted with less material than bending stresses, the shape of the structure can be varied accordingly and produces what are now typical forms in rigid frames with hinged joints (page 409). For practical purposes hinged joints may facilitate the site erection of prefabricated frame components since they may be simply executed in comparison with the forming of continuous joints, particularly in concrete frames. In addition, pin jointed base hinges may be used as fulcrum points when lifting half-frames into position. They also serve, as explained already, as a means of relieving foundations of all tendency to rotate under the action of wind or other imposed loads on the frame. The actual form of hinge will depend upon its main purpose and upon the extent of freedom from restraint it is required to give. It need not necessarily be a true hinge or pivot provided the rigidity of the structure at the hinge point is low. "Split" hinges without metallic parts can be used in concrete since the movements and degree of rotation are comparatively small. Methods of forming hinged joints of various types are illustrated on pages 452, 453 and 455.

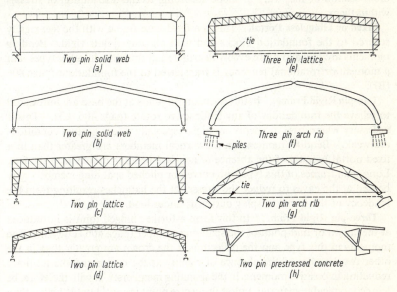

Two pin solid web
(a)

Three pin lattice
(e)
tie

Two pin solid web
(b)

Three pin arch rib
(f)
piles

Two pin lattice
(c)

Two pin arch rib
(g)
tie

Two pin lattice
(d)

Two pin prestressed concrete
(h)

TYPICAL RIGID FRAMES

It has already been pointed out that rigid structures of all types are sensitive to differential settlement of the foundations and to movements due to changes in temperature. The effects of these movements must be borne in mind at the design stage, the former by considering the superstructure and foundation design together, and the latter by the provision of expansion joints or hinges where necessary.

Rigid frames can be constructed in steel in lattice or solid web form; in aluminium alloy in lattice form; in timber in lattice or solid web form, and in concrete.

Types of Rigid Frames

The fundamental and constant characteristic of the single-storey rigid frame in all its forms is the stiff or restrained joint between the supporting and spanning members. Apart from this the form can vary in a number of ways. The spanning member may be horizontal, pitched or arched; the junctions of the vertical members with the foundations may be restrained or hinged; a hinge may be introduced in the middle of the spanning member, and the structure itself may be solid or latticed. The members may be regular in cross section or may vary in shape according to the distribution of stresses within them.

Fixed or Hingeless Portal. This is a fixed-base frame with the feet rigidly secured to the foundation blocks and with all other joints rigid. Bending moments are less and more evenly distributed in this than in other types, but a moment or rotational tendency is transferred to the foundations (page 406 (B)).

Two-pin Rigid Frame. In this form hinged joints at the base are introduced to relieve the foundations of any tendency to rotate (page 406 (C)). This is necessary where base moments are high, especially where ground conditions are weak. Bending moments in the vertical members are greater than in a fixed portal because of the absence of negative bending moments at the feet. Long span frames of this type with curved or pitched spanning members may be tied at the eaves to reduce the stresses at the haunches resulting from the tendency of the frame to splay outwards under load.

Three-pin Rigid Frame. In this form a further hinged joint is introduced at the crown or mid-point of the spanning member (page 406 (D) (H)). The moments in this type and the deflection at the crown are greater than in the other two because of the absence of rigidity at the centre and the resultant reduction in positive moments in the spanning members. It will, therefore, be less economical in material, unless the centre point is considerably higher than the eaves. The presence of the three hinges, however, makes this form of frame statically determinate and simpler to design. In precast concrete or lattice forms this type is usually easier to erect than the portal or two-pin frame.

Rigid frames impose horizontal thrusts of some magnitude on the foundations which must be met by adequate resistance in the soil or, where necessary, by the use of inclined foundation slabs, piled foundations or ties between the foundations (see *e, f, g*, page 409). This is of particular importance in fixed and two-pin frames in which even a small horizontal movement will cause considerable redistribution of moments in the frame, with possible adverse effects on the structure as a result.

The horizontal thrust will vary with the stiffness of the frame and with the relative proportion of spanning member to vertical members. It will, therefore, be large with three-pin frames. In all types the greater the span is relative to the height, the greater will be the horizontal thrust (page 406 (H)).

Arch Rib. This is a rigid frame but has no vertical members as such (page 406 (E)). It may be fixed, two-pin or three-pin in form. A fixed arch rib exerts bending moments on the foundations as well as vertical and horizontal thrusts and is used only where the soil can offer adequate resistance. Changes in temperature and, in the case of concrete, shrinkage, affect the stresses in the structure. The function of the base hinges in a two-pin arch rib is the same as those in normal rigid frame. The introduction of a crown hinge with hinges at the feet produces a statically determinate structure. Small differential settlements of the foundations will not affect the thrusts on the foundations and, therefore, stresses in the structure will not be altered. Some form of tying in of the foundations is often necessary with arch ribs since the horizontal thrust is often greater than in other types of rigid frames. The intensity of these horizontal thrusts will vary not only with the loading on the arch but also with its slope: as the curve becomes less steep so will the horizontal thrust increase.

Forces acting on a structure will set up a "natural line of forces" through which the loads would, in theory, be transferred most economically to the bearings. For example, a rope or chain, uniformly loaded, will take up a catenary or near-parabolic curve through which all the forces act directly in tension, with no rotation or bending in the rope. The depth of the curve will depend upon the resistance at the ends of the rope. A similar "thrust line" or "curve of pressure" is set up in an arch under uniform load through which the load is transmitted to the abutments. It is, in fact, the bending moment diagram for the loading. If the arch form follows closely this parabolic curve it will be in direct compression at all points with no bending stresses in it (F). Loading, however, is not always uniform and the arch may be subject to appreciable wind loads or other variable loads, so that in practice it may not be possible to eliminate bending entirely. But, by designing the arch to follow as closely as possible the bending moment diagram due to the particular loading, bending can be kept to a minimum (page 406 (G)). In many circumstances, however, it may not be economical to shape an arch in this way, nor indeed may the arch form be so suitable as the normal rigid frame.[1]

The magnitude of the bending moments induced in an arch or rigid

[1] For further consideration of this subject see *Principles of Structural Design* by Niels Lisborg (Batsford).

frame which does not follow the "thrust line" will vary as the modified shape diverges from the curve of pressure (page 406 (H)). Any point of an arch rib or frame lying on the curve of pressure will be free of bending moment, as at the points of contraflexure or at all hinged joints which, as they are incapable of transferring bending, must always lie on the curve of pressure. Those parts lying furthest from the curve will be under greatest stress. Whilst the use of a crown hinged joint will automatically produce a zero bending moment at the joint and simplify analysis of the structure, the frame will be far stiffer and a more even stress distribution will occur if continuity is maintained and hinges are restricted to the base connections. This will be clear from the illustrations if it is borne in mind that the moments at various points in the frame are in direct proportion to the distance from the "curve of pressure".

It will be seen that the arch or near-arch form is usually subject to smaller bending moments than the normal rigid frame because its shape is likely to be nearer that of the bending moment diagram due to the loads it carries. It is, therefore, particularly useful for very wide spans in which economy in dead weight is a critical factor in the design. When a curved shape running right down to the ground level is not suited to the function of the building, the arch form is often used as the spanning member of a normal rigid frame so that the curve springs from a point at a reasonable distance above the floor level, see page 409.

Spacing of Main Bearing Members

The spacing of main bearing members, unless determined by other requirements, is fixed by the most economical combination of frames and purlins. For the common types of lattice truss and beam construction in all materials, the spacing lies between 12 and 25 ft, although for very wide spans it may be economical to increase the spacing to as much as 50 ft. For rigid frames of various types the spacing lies between 15 and 40 ft. With *beam and frame* construction, primarily subject to bending stresses as distinct from direct stresses, the wide spacing of wide span frames usually has economic advantages because the cost of the smaller number of more heavily loaded frames and the deeper purlins is not so great as that of the greater number of more lightly loaded frames which would result from a closer spacing. The reasons for this are connected with the different rates at which bending moments and deflection vary with variations in the span and in the unit loading. Increase in the height of the columns carrying the roof structure increases the overall cost of the structure and, when columns are tall, economies can similarly be effected by increasing the spacing, since, within limits which will vary for each case, the cost of fewer more heavily loaded columns, as in the case of the spanning members, will be less than that of a greater number of more lightly loaded columns. The reason for this is that in tall columns buckling is usually the critical factor in design and not the load bearing capacity. These aspects are discussed more fully in Chapter 5 on page 214.

In simple *steel truss and purlin* structures the closer the trusses are spaced the lower will be the overall steel content of the structure. This is because variations in the spacing of the trusses has a much greater effect on the weight of the purlins than on the weight of the trusses. An increase in spacing necessitating the use of the next largest angle section for the purlin results in the increased cost of the purlins more than offsetting the saving arising from the smaller number of trusses and columns required. There is, however, a practical limit on the spacing of the trusses. This is reached when the trusses are so lightly loaded that the smallest standard steel sections are too large to permit the members to be reduced to the areas required for design purposes. This limit occurs at spacings just under 10 ft. Within limits the weight of the purlins per sq. ft of floor area is largely independent of the truss span and is nearly constant for any particular spacing of trusses. For spans ranging from 40 to 70 ft a spacing of 12 ft 6 in. is often satisfactory in practice, the optimum span being about 50 ft. For maximum overall efficiency of the structure, however, particularly in the wider spans, the spacing of the main members will not be the same for all spans. When spans are large, fabrication costs of the main members increase, and for spans greater than about 70 ft it is economically desirable to space the trusses at wider centres, in some cases to distances at which lattice purlins can economically be used. In some circumstances where a wide column spacing is required, rather than space the trusses further apart with larger purlins, it may prove cheaper to carry a number of trusses on valley beams supported on widely spaced columns, even though the direct transfer of load from truss to column is normally the most economical method.

In some cases the use of steel decking permits purlins to be omitted if the frames are sufficiently closely spaced for this purpose. The omission of one stage in the supporting structure in this way may reduce the overall cost of the structure. This can sometimes be done by using bearing members which are particularly suited to light loads over long span. These include castellated beams and cold formed lattice beams.

RIGIDITY AND STABILITY OF FRAMED STRUCTURES

Rigidity against wind pressure must be provided in all forms of framed structure. In roof structures lateral rigidity may be provided by stiff joints

14*

in the frames either between the vertical members and the spanning member or between the frame and the foundations.   The significance of these alternatives and the use of eaves beams have already been discussed.   Wind pressure in a longitudinal direction would cause "racking" or tilting over of the frames. This, in structures with only light purlins spanning between the trusses or frames, is resisted by bracing which may be placed either in the plane of the roof or, in the case of roof trusses, in the plane of the ties (see below, (A)).   This wind bracing should be placed at each end of the building and, in long structures, at intervals of 100 to 200 ft.   With large span trusses it is advisable to brace continuously at tie level along the length of the structure.

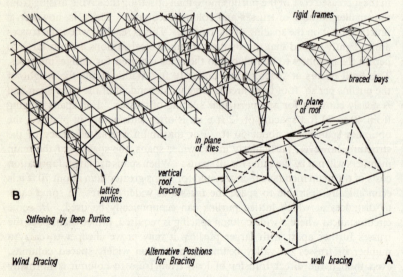

rigid frames

braced bays

in plane of roof

in plane of ties

vertical roof bracing

B

lattice purlins

Stiffening by Deep Purlins

Wind Bracing

Alternative Positions for Bracing

wall bracing   A

Vertical bracing in the plane of the "king rod" between the gable end and one or two end trusses gives increased rigidity; alternatively, vertical bracing can be provided in the wall panels.   In large structures with greater spacing of trusses or frames, the purlins will be deep and may provide adequate longitudinal rigidity without separate wind bracing (B).

The rigid joints at the haunches of portal frames or between roof trusses and columns makes the structure act as a whole in a lateral direction, and hinged joints at the feet result in a tendency for the whole structure to rotate about the leeward hinge and to lift up at the windward hinge (see page 402 (F)).   In large, comparatively light structures, this uplift may be so great that the dead weight of the structure is insufficient to anchor it down, and very large concrete foundation blocks may be required for this purpose, or tension piles may be used. The base must then be designed with long holding down bolts at the joint and heavy reinforcement in the foundation blocks.

The structures discussed so far are all two-dimensional structures. There are numerous forms of three-dimensional, or space structures, and these may be constructed of slabs or plates of solid material or of lattice framework, either form of which can be plane or curved in shape.

SHELL ROOFS

The term "shell" is usually applied to three-dimensional structures constructed with a curved solid slab or membrane acting as a stressed skin, the stiffness of which is used to transfer loading to the points of support. They may be considered as single curvature shells, based on the cylindrical or parabolic form, and double curvature shells, based on the spherical and other more complicated forms. The term "doubly curved shell" is commonly applied only to forms other than the spherical shell.

The main characteristic of a shell construction is a very thin curved membrane. This thin membrane is made structurally possible by providing restraint at the edges such that bending stresses in it are so small as to be negligible or are completely eliminated. The membrane is then subject only to direct stresses within its thickness (page 417 (A)). Many examples of the membrane shell form are to be seen in nature. For example, the bamboo rod, the crab shell, the bird's egg, all of which are exceedingly light but exceedingly strong. A blown egg has been known to support more than 100 lb distributed load. The efficiency of many modern shell constructions can be judged from the fact that they are relatively thinner than the shell of an egg. Long span concrete barrel vaults may be as thin as $2\frac{1}{4}$ to $2\frac{1}{2}$ in. thick for spans up to over 100 ft. Short span barrels will be somewhat thicker than this and domes of 150–160 ft span may be as thin as $3\frac{1}{2}$ in. Thicknesses as much as $1\frac{1}{2}$ in. are possible over spans of 100 ft with some double curvature forms such as hyperbolic paraboloids.

In practice, for application to building work at least, the basic form of sphere or cylinder, for example, must be cut. The cut or free edges represent zones of structural weakness because direct stress can then only be transmitted in a direction parallel to the cut edge. In order therefore to make full use of the structural properties of the remaining parts of the curved membrane, it is necessary to strengthen the edges by means of ribs or edge members which are called edge beams, or in the case of a dome, a ring beam. The latter will be subject to direct tensile stresses and, if the dome is supported on columns, to bending stresses as well. The edge beams of a cylindrical shell vault will be subject to bending stresses. In addition to edge beams, stiffening members are required at the open ends of cylindrical shells (page 417 (A)). These end frames, as they are called, stiffen the cut end of the shell against buckling, the maintenance of the shape of the shell being essential in order to develop the membrane stresses within it.

Single Curvature Shells

These are barrel vaults of which there are two forms: long- and short-span barrels, typical examples of which are shown on page 417 (B, H).

Long-span Barrel Vaults act primarily as a "beam", the span of which is the length of the vault. The shell constitutes the compression member and the edge beams the tension members or flanges. Although the direct stresses in a shell are mostly compressive, shear forces are set up near the supports which give rise to diagonal tension (page 417 (A)). In the case of reinforced concrete shells, this must be resisted by reinforcement placed at 45° across the corners of the shell as shown on page 457. The width of the barrel should be one-half to one-fifth of the span and the rise from the underside of the edge beams to the crown of the vault about one-tenth of the span for single span, and one-fifteenth for continuous span vaults. The depth of the edge beams is usually about half of the total rise, but in the smaller spans this may sometimes be reduced. In multi-bay buildings, the edge beam may be eliminated altogether, provided the necessary rise is obtained by increased curvature of the shell membrane (page 417 (F)). In these circumstances the fold in the shell constitutes a beam. In the case of a concrete shell it is a disadvantage to have an excessive rise to the shell as this prevents easy placing of the concrete. Various ways of forming edge beams and end frames are shown at E–G.

The width of a long-span barrel is usually not more than 40 ft with a maximum practicable width of 50 ft. The maximum economic span is about 100 to 150 ft. When the end frames are as far apart as this, equilibrium without bending moment in the shell is generally not possible, but where such a span is necessary, a satisfactory solution can be obtained by a suitable choice of rise to span and depth of edge beams. In order to avoid excessive rise of the structure, the radius of curvature of the shell reduces as the span and, therefore, the width increases. For small spans a radius of about 20 to 25 ft is used, for spans from 50 to 100 ft a radius of 30 ft, and for spans over 100 ft a radius of 40 ft. Lighting openings may be formed in the crown of a shell vault provided it is kept clear of the ends and is not more in width than about one-fifth the width of the barrel in reinforced concrete shells and about one-third in timber shells. Circular lighting openings in reinforced

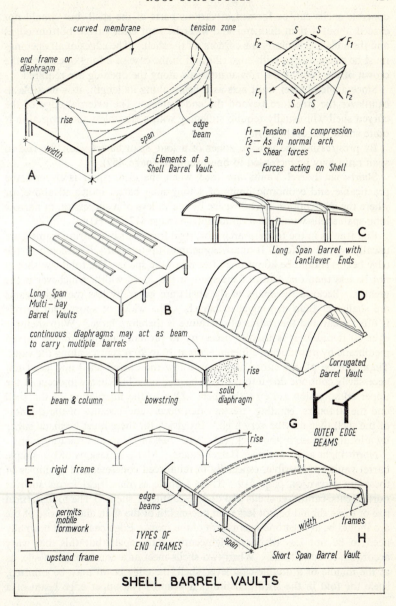

A — Elements of a Shell Barrel Vault

curved membrane · tension zone · end frame or diaphragm · rise · width · span · edge beam

Forces acting on Shell

F_1 — Tension and compression
F_2 — As in normal arch
S — Shear forces

B — Long Span Multi-bay Barrel Vaults

C — Long Span Barrel with Cantilever Ends

D — Corrugated Barrel Vault

continuous diaphragms may act as beam to carry multiple barrels

E — beam & column · bowstring · solid diaphragm · rise

F — rigid frame · permits mobile formwork · upstand frame · rise

TYPES OF END FRAMES

G — OUTER EDGE BEAMS

H — Short Span Barrel Vault · edge beams · width · frames · span

SHELL BARREL VAULTS

concrete shells can be formed in various parts of the shell, but should not exceed about 4 ft in diameter and must be kept clear of the bottom edges and the ends, particularly the corners, of the shell. The edges of all openings must be strengthened with edge ribs and in the case of a long opening in the crown of the vault, cross ribs at intervals along the opening are required.

Since a shell-barrel vault acts as a beam along its length, it is possible to cantilever the structure beyond the end frames. The external edge of the curved shell will usually require stiffening with a rib unless the projection is quite small (page 417 (C)).

By prestressing the tension zones of a long span barrel vault the rise to span ratio may be increased to one-twentieth (page 457).

Short-span Barrel Vaults are used when the clear span is beyond the practicable and economic limits of a long-span barrel indicated above, or where the interruption of roof space by the valleys of a succession of narrow long-span shells would be a disadvantage (page 417 (B, H)).

End frames in the form of arch ribs, rigid frames or bow-string frames, are usually spaced 30 to 40 ft apart, sometimes up to 60 ft. The depth of the edge beams should be about one-fifteenth of the span. The total rise should not be less than one-tenth of the span or the chord width, whichever is the greater. Because the spans of the shells are generally less the edge beams are shallower than in long-span barrels. The width of short-span barrels is often great and the radius of curvature is therefore large. With shells of over 40 ft radius it is usually necessary to prevent buckling of the curved membrane by introducing stiffening ribs at 10 to 20 ft centres along the vault. These can be placed either above or below the curved shell and need not necessarily continue down to the edge beams, since buckling will occur in the upper compression zone of the shell. Due to the interaction of the shell and the stiffeners, bending stresses often occur, and because of the thinness of the shell they may be very high. Provision for these must be made either by a local increase in the thickness of the shell or by special reinforcement.

North Light and Cantilever Barrel Vaults. Many variations of the simple barrel vault are possible, especially in reinforced concrete, and examples of these are shown on page 419. These include asymmetrical forms such as north lights, cantilever shells and double-cantilever shells. The total vertical rise of these should be not less than one-eighth of the span and the rise of the arc should be at least one-twentyfifth of the span. Edge beams will normally need to be not less than one-eighteenth of the span, but this may vary according to conditions. When two shells meet at a considerable angle, as at the middle of a double-cantilever shell, the edge beam may be omitted, since the fold in the shell constitutes a beam. The upper edge beam of a north light shell is usually very small as it is supported generally by struts at 6 to 9 ft centres in the plane of the north light glazing.   These struts bear on the side of the valley gutter which is therefore designed as a deep "L" edge beam to the bottom of the adjacent shell.   In cantilevered shells the end frames carry the whole of the roof load and their depth must therefore be

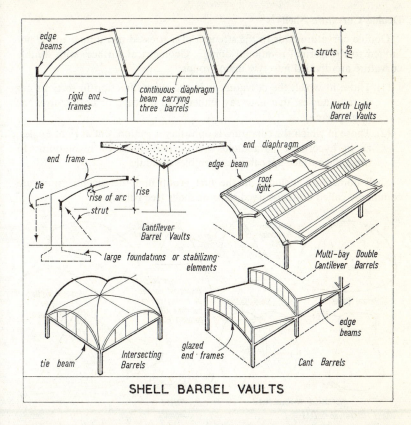

SHELL BARREL VAULTS

substantial.   In the case of a single-cantilever shell the foundations to the end frames must be designed to prevent overturning, or struts or ties must be provided to ensure stability.   End frames in all forms of shell may be placed either above or below the curved slab.   Cylindrical vaults may intersect to form cross vaults or be "canted" as shown above.   This permits glazed lights to be formed between the stiffening frames of adjacent barrels.

Barrel vaults may also be constructed as parabolic or elliptical shaped shells springing direct from the foundations and stiffened with ribs at intervals. Alternatively, in concrete a corrugated shell can be used in which the stiffening effect of the ribs is provided by corrugations in the surface of the shell which, when repeated, forms a continuous corrugated surface as shown on page 417 (D).

Double Curvature Shells

Double curvature adds to the strength of a stressed membrane and is not limited to the normal rotational dome.   Geometrical surfaces with double curvature are divided into two main groups:

(1) Those in which the curvature is in the same direction in sections cut at right-angles, that is to say, either both concave or both convex, as in a sphere.

(2) Those in which the curvature is opposite in sections cut at right-angles, as in hyperbolic paraboloids and hyperboloids of revolution.   In these the surface appearance resembles a saddle.

Shell domes are included in the first group and the second group are commonly called doubly-curved slabs or shells (see below).

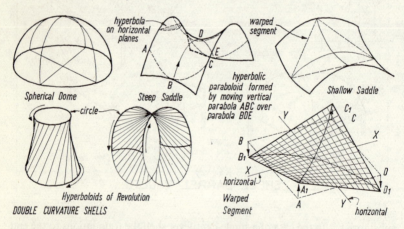

Spherical Dome   *Steep Saddle*   *Shallow Saddle*

hyperbola on horizontal planes

warped segment

hyperbolic paraboloid formed by moving vertical parabola ABC over parabola BDE

—circle—

Hyperboloids of Revolution

DOUBLE CURVATURE SHELLS

Warped Segment

horizontal

Shell Domes.   The simplest form is the spherical dome which has been constructed in concrete over spans of 150 ft or more.   The shape may vary according to the plan shape to which the edges are cut.   All cut edges must be stiffened with edge beams.   To avoid horizontal thrust in circular shell domes it is necessary to construct the shell of approximately elliptical cross

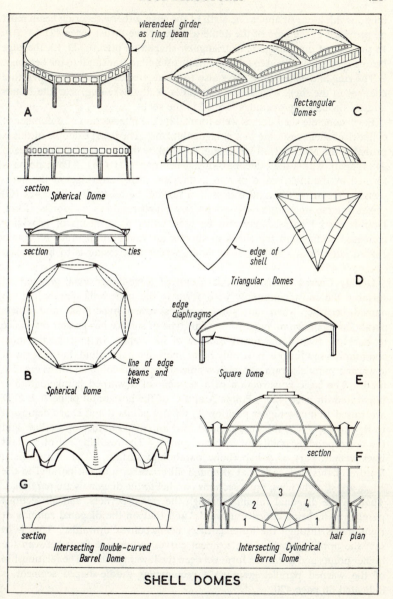

vierendeel girder
as ring beam

A

Rectangular
Domes C

section Spherical Dome

section ties

B Spherical Dome

line of edge
beams and
ties

Rectangular
Domes C

Triangular Domes D

edge of
shell

edge
diaphragms

Square Dome E

section F

G

half plan

section Intersecting Double-curved
Barrel Dome

1 2 3 4 1

Intersecting Cylindrical
Barrel Dome

SHELL DOMES

section with a rise of about one-sixth of the span, otherwise a ring beam must be provided at the base of the dome to take up the thrust (page 421 (A, B)). In the case of domes square or triangular shaped on plan (C, D, E), the edge beams must be designed to take up this thrust and to transfer it to the bearings.

The ring and edge beams serve also to resist stresses set up by temperature changes in the shell, which may sometimes need thickening near the beams and also round any openings formed in the shell.

Early concrete shell domes were formed by the intersection of a number of cylindrical shells resulting in a polygonal form. The finest example of this is probably the Market Hall at Leipzig, covered by three octagonal domes each 248 ft span, with a shell thickness of $3\frac{9}{16}$ in. (page 421 (F)). Each dome is formed by the intersection of four cylindrical shells, the ridges at the intersections replacing the rigid frames in a normal barrel vault. Page 421 (G) shows intersecting double-curved barrels which result in a "dome" form. Double-curved barrels may also be used either as a means of providing increased stiffness to the shells in short-span vaults or in order to obtain curved edge beams in long-span vaults when prestressing is to be applied (see page 457).

Doubly Curved Shells. Of this group of three-dimensional geometrical surfaces the most commonly used form is the hyperbolic paraboloid, so named because, when cut, some sections reveal hyperbolas and others parabolas as shown on page 240. This type of surface has greater resistance to buckling than dome forms because of its shape. In practice the most commonly used form is part only of a hyperbolic paraboloid, in the form of a warped parallelogram although saddle-shaped and conoidal forms are also used. The basic construction of a segment of a warped parallelogram is illustrated on page 420. Points A and C of the horizontal plane A B C D are raised to a new higher position $A_1 C_1$ and points B and D are depressed to B_1 and D_1. The sides are divided into an equal number of sections and the corresponding points on each are joined. The resulting net of straight lines defines part of a hyperbolic paraboloid surface. The characteristic feature of this surface is that although all cross sections cut parallel to the edges are straight lines, cross sections parallel to the diagonals are parabolas. That on the diagonal running through the raised corners, and all sections parallel to it, being concave upwards, and that on the diagonal running at right-angles through the lower corners being convex upwards. That is to say, the upper surface of the segment curves in concave form between the higher points and in convex form between the lower points. The relationship of the warped parallelogram to a rectangular saddle-shaped segment is indicated on page 420.

In spite of its complicated shape the stresses in a hyperbolic paraboloid shell can be more easily analysed than in most other surfaces. The shell may be considered as a series of arches and suspension cables intersecting each other at right-angles; the shell is in direct compression in directions parallel to the convex or "arched" section and in direct tension in directions parallel to the concave or "cabled" section. Because of the great stiffness given by the double curvature, and as all the stresses are direct, the shell may be exceedingly thin. For spans in the region of 100 to 130 ft a reinforced concrete shell will be from $1\frac{1}{2}$–2 in. thick. The forces exerted on the edges by the "arches" and "cables" are the same, and since they act also at equal angles to the edge but in opposite directions, they resolve into shear forces along the edge with no component perpendicular to the edge to cause bending stresses. Since the principal stresses are equal, the shell itself is in a state of uniform shear and, as the stress is the same over the whole surface, the practical design in terms of reinforcement in a concrete shell or the boarding in a timber shell is simplified. Edge beams are required to carry the edge shear forces. The depth of these should be disposed equally above and below the shell membrane. They may be placed wholly above or below the shell but the cross section of the beam will need to be larger. The overall rise of the shell, that is the difference in height between the low and high corners, is important. If this is small the shell will be shallow and if too shallow it will tend to buckle. The ratio of this "rise" to the diagonal span is, therefore, a significant factor and this should be as large as possible and never less than one-fifteenth.

Doubly-curved panels may be used singly or in combination and the number of supports required will depend upon the way in which the panels are related to each other. In the case of a single rectangular panel only two supports are required. If the roof is supported at the two lower corners the edge beams will be in compression and a horizontal outward thrust will be exerted on the supports. This thrust can be resisted either by a heavy buttressed support or by a tie rod between the lower corners of the shell. If the panel is supported at the two high points the edge beams will be in tension and an inward pull will be exerted on the supports. This must be resisted by a strut running between the high points. The tie is the cheapest of these three methods but the reduction in clear headroom it causes and the possibility that it may spoil the interior appearance are disadvantages (see page 424). The buttressed supports may be costly if the columns are high because of the high bending stresses which will be set up by the outward thrust of the shell. Some provision must be made for tying down the unsupported corners against wind forces, particularly if the sides of the building

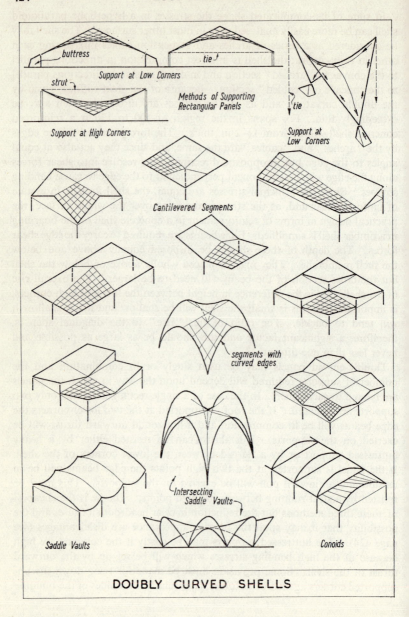

buttress

Support at Low Corners

tie

strut

Methods of Supporting Rectangular Panels

Support at High Corners

Support at Low Corners

tie

Cantilevered Segments

segments with curved edges

Intersecting Saddle Vaults

Saddle Vaults

Conoids

DOUBLY CURVED SHELLS

are not enclosed.   When the building is enclosed at the sides the edge beams are fastened to the heads of the enclosing walls.

Some combinations of doubly-curved panels are illustrated on page 424. It will be seen in some cases that the edges of some panels lie alongside those of adjacent panels, so that the forces in each balance each other.   In certain combinations of panels the inclined edge beams of adjacent panels can be integrated with the corner supports to form a rigid frame in order to obviate the use of a tie.   The bounding edges of doubly-curved shells need not necessarily be straight, but may be curved in parabolic form.   An example of this is shown, together with the conoidal form.   The development of the hyperboloid of revolution is shown on page 420.   Shells can be constructed in reinforced concrete, timber and occasionally in steel plate.

FOLDED SLAB ROOFS

This form of construction is also called folded plate and, when there are a large number of facets, prismatic structure.   It is another form of stressed skin or membrane structure in which the stiffness of the skin is used to distribute the loading to the points of support.

If a flat slab is folded or bent it can behave as a beam spanning in the direction of the fold and with a depth equal to the rise of the folded slab. When loaded, compression and tension stresses will be set up at the top and bottom of the section respectively and shear stresses in the slabs on each side of the fold.   Each slab spans between the folds and must be thick enough to span this distance and to have sufficient stiffness to distribute the loads longitudinally.   End frames or diaphragms must be provided at the supports to collect the forces in the slabs and transfer them to the supports (see page 426 (A)).   The shape of the roof may vary from a simple pitched roof of two slabs to a multi-fold form involving several plates, some examples of which are given on the same page (B–F).

The span and width of each bay governs the overall depth.   As an approximate guide this should not be less than between one-tenth and one-fifteenth of the span, or one-tenth of the width, whichever is greater.   The width of each slab is limited only by the requirements of adequate lateral stiffness which dictate the thickness.   In practice, it is often cheaper to use a large number of narrow slabs rather than a few wider slabs.   This is because, although a greater number of folds must be formed, thinner slabs can be used and the amount of material and the dead weight of the structure is less. When "barrels" are formed of a large number of "facets" or slabs, say 10–12, the influence of the rigidity of the folds will be proportionately greater than when fewer and, therefore, wider slabs are employed.   One-twentieth

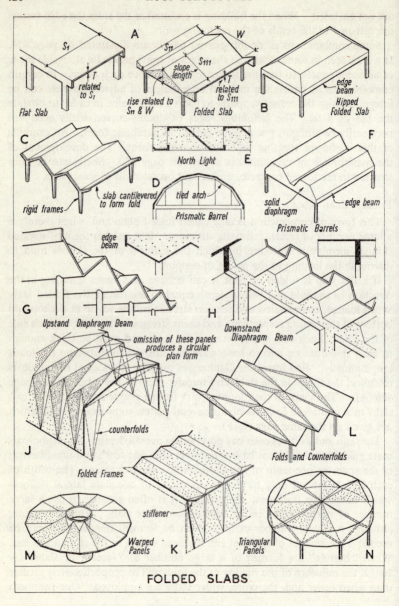

Flat Slab — S_1, T related to S_1

Folded Slab — S_{11}, slope length, S_{111}, rise related to S_{11} & W, W, T related to S_{111}

B — **Hipped Folded Slab**, edge beam

C — slab cantilevered to form fold, rigid frames

E — North Light

D — tied arch, Prismatic Barrel

F — Prismatic Barrels, solid diaphragm, edge beam

G — Upstand Diaphragm Beam, edge beam

H — Downstand Diaphragm Beam

J — omission of these panels produces a circular plan form, counterfolds

L — Folds and Counterfolds

M — Warped Panels

K — Folded Frames, stiffener

N — Triangular Panels

FOLDED SLABS

to one-twentyfifth has been given as a reasonable value for the thickness/slope length ratio for the slab element. The slab thickness will generally be thicker than that in comparable cylindrical shells for spans in excess of about 15 ft. Folded slab construction is competitive with these shells, however, because the flat shuttering is comparatively inexpensive. It is possible to use composite construction using repetitive precast concrete slab elements as permanent shuttering to an *in situ* structural topping (see page 459). The free edges of folded slabs should be stiffened. They must either be supported along their length, be provided with edge beams or be cantilevered a short distance to form a fold (page 426 (C, F, G)).

There are various methods of retaining the folds in position at the points of support where the loads are taken down to the foundations. A solid diaphragm beam, a lattice truss or a rigid frame may be used, to which the ends of the slabs are rigidly secured. When vertical supports down to the ground can be permitted, columns may be placed under each fold carrying a beam which follows the shape of the folded slabs. Diaphragms may be placed above or below the slabs as required. The diaphragm need not necessarily be vertical in order to fulfil its function: it may be sloped to form a hipped end, the angle folds then serving to transfer the loads to the supports (page 426 (B)). Wide span diaphragms may carry a number of folded elements (F, H).

The slabs may be perforated where light is required through the roof and, provided sufficient slab is left on each side of the perforations and adjacent to the folds, the slab can be reduced to a series of struts. It becomes then, in effect, a Vierendeel girder, the top and bottom flanges of which are the folds in the slabs. Folded slabs can be used over continuous spans and as cantilevers. Depth/span ratios as low as one-fortieth have been used over continuous spans.

This form of construction can be used to extend down to the ground in arch or rigid frame form as well as for simple span roofs supported on columns or walls. A great variety of complicated and interesting forms can be obtained by the introduction of reverse or counterfolds at various points. These, also, can be used to provide end stiffening (J, K, L). Dome and vault forms can also be constructed. Circular shapes can be covered with folded slabs developed to form a horizontal roof structure as distinct from the dome form. This necessitates variation in the slab widths, the introduction of counter-folds, the use of triangular shaped slabs or the warping or twisting of the slabs, which then become hyperbolic paraboloids. Either the centre or perimeter supports may be omitted and the structure then becomes cantilever in form with tension and compression rings replacing the stiffening diaphragms. Two examples are shown at M and N.

Folded slab structures derive most of their strength from their shape. The folded form gives great rigidity and makes possible the efficient use of material of high elasticity such as plastics and aluminium alloys, the use of which in other forms of construction often results in excessive deflections. Concrete and timber are most commonly used at the present time.

GRID STRUCTURES

These are also called space frameworks or three-dimensional frameworks. Grid structures, apart from single layer flat grids, are three-dimensional or "space structures". Unlike shells or folded slabs, however, they are constructed not with solid membranes but with lattice or grid frameworks. In some systems, however, the grid is formed by the edge junctions of bent or folded sheet panels of suitable material in which the skin strength of the sheet element forms a very large proportion of the total strength of the structure.

Grid frameworks are ideally suited to structures which are to carry heavy concentrated loads. Because of the interconnection of the parts, a concentrated load is distributed between all the members of the grid, decreasing the high stresses in the directly loaded area. The stress distribution in grid frameworks under heavy concentrated loads is therefore comparatively even. These structures usually provide a simple and economic method of covering very large areas without internal intermediate support. As they permit the prefabrication and standardization of the component parts, and as the dead weight is small compared with many other forms of structure, there are considerable savings in construction costs, the savings increasing with the increase in span. The economy of these structures as far as prefabrication and standardization is concerned is related to the simplicity, or otherwise, of the jointing technique and the multiplicity, or otherwise, of members of similar length and section.

Single layer grids are very stiff, particularly diagonal grids, so that in addition to their value in dispersing heavy concentrated loads, which is likely to be useful in wide span floor construction, they are very useful for situations where deflection and not load is the criterion. That is, where the span is great and the load is small, as is often the case in roof construction. The structural depth can be quite small because of the stiffness of the structure. In the case of space grids, that is double-layer flat grids, folded grids and curved grids, stiffness is greater and the stresses in all the members are direct, except for some slight transverse bending moments in diagonal members. Weights as low as 10–30 lb per sq. ft of floor area covered have been achieved generally and, in some cases, far less.

Grid structures may be constructed in metal, reinforced concrete, timber or plastic. The majority at the present time are constructed in metal or timber, both of which lend themselves to the prefabrication and standardization of the component parts of a structure, and for which comparatively simple methods of joining the parts can be developed. *In situ* cast reinforced concrete is suitable for heavily loaded single layer grids, but is less suitable for double layer grids where the stiffness is provided primarily by triangulation and in which prefabrication and standardization of the parts is logical. Although this can be done with concrete in the form of precast elements post-tensioned together, it is not an ideal medium for this purpose. Plastics, although not widely used at the moment for structural purposes, are admirable for this form of structure which is extremely stiff, particularly when they are used in sheet form as three-dimensional folded or curved elements.

Grids can be applied in many arrangements to flat, curved or folded roofs. Their application to floors in the form of rectangular grid and diagonal beam construction has already been mentioned in Chapter 6. The application to roofs can be broadly classified as follows:

(1) Space frames;
(2) Flat grids;
(3) Folded grids;
(4) Folded lattice plates;
(5) Braced barrel vaults;
(6) Braced domes;
(7) Tension roof structures.

Space Frames. Although all the structures under consideration, apart from single-layer flat grids, are in fact space frameworks, the term "space frame" is usually applied to a hollow section or three-dimensional lattice beam (page 431 (A)). The hollow shape confers greater lateral rigidity on the beam whilst retaining the economic advantages resulting from optimum depth/span ratios. A convenient and common cross-sectional shape for such a beam is a triangle, since this is an inherently stable shape not requiring additional bracing. The longitudinal members at the apices of the triangle will be either in tension or compression and the shear stresses will be taken by the diagonal members in the sides of the triangle.

Flat Grids. These may be single-layer or double-layer grids, each of which will be considered in turn.

A single-layer flat grid is, in fact, a two-dimensional structure, but is considered here rather than earlier because of its grid nature and certain characteristics which it has in common with double-layer grids, particularly the ability to disperse heavy concentrated loads throughout all the members of the grid. It has two or more sets of parallel beams intersecting at right- or oblique-angles and the beams are rigidly connected at all intersections, which produces bending and torsion of all the members (pages 309, 319).

The interconnected beams may be arranged in various layouts and the boundaries of the grid may be rectangular or circular. The rectangular grid, although widely used, is not the most efficient in terms of stress distribution since there are no members in the corners and these are in fact the most highly stressed zones in a rectangular slab. In theory, the beams could be arranged in such a way as to follow the trajectories of the principal stresses in the slab. Thus they would be where they are most needed. As the beams would have to be curved, such a layout is not likely to be economic, particularly as far as reinforced concrete is concerned, although Nervi has done this in Italy using "ferro-cement" pans[1] as shuttering. A close approximation to this arrangement can, however, be obtained by a diagonal grid layout. Because the beams tend to follow the lines of principal stresses, the stress distribution in this type of layout is much more even than in rectangular grids. The square and diagonal grid are described in Chapter 6 under "Rectangular Grid" and "*In situ* Diagonal Beam" floors.

Triangular or three-way grids are extremely strong and lead to very uniform stress distribution in the structure, and a very uniform distribution is also obtained in hexagonal grids. These layouts are used for the larger spans within the economic range of 50–80 ft. Depth/span ratios as low as one-thirtieth for rectangular grids and only one-fortieth for diagonal grids are often possible.

Double-layer flat grids may be lattice grids, that is, they are formed by intersecting lattice beams, or they may be space grids. In lattice grids, each set of bottom horizontal members lies immediately under the top set in the same vertical plane, as in normal lattice beams, but in double-layer flat space grids they do not lie in the same vertical plane. Thus, in its simplest rectangular grid form the structure consists essentially of two sets of interconnected triangular space frames. Lattice grids may be two- or three-way grids (page 431 (B, C)), and the space grids, of which there are a great number of variations, in addition can be hexagonal (D–G).

These structures are usually fabricated from circular or rectangular section metal tubes which may be welded together or joined by connectors at the junctions, or reinforced concrete precast compressive members can be used together with tensile members in steel. Precast concrete members post-

---

[1] These are thin slabs $\frac{3}{4}$–$1\frac{1}{2}$ in. thick, of cement mortar, reinforced with superimposed layers of wire mesh and small bars. They are strong and light in weight and can also be used as permanent shuttering. See *The Structural Engineer*, May 1956, paper by Pier Luigi Nervi, "Concrete and Structural Form". See also page 462.

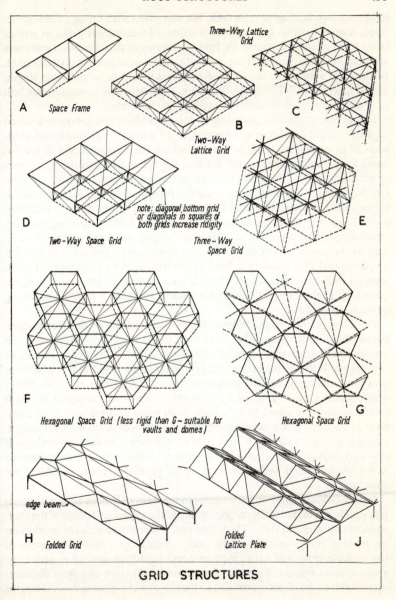

A — Space Frame

B — Two-Way Lattice Grid

C — Three-Way Lattice Grid

D — Two-Way Space Grid

note: diagonal bottom grid or diagonals in squares of both grids increase ridigity

E — Three-Way Space Grid

F — Hexagonal Space Grid (less rigid than G — suitable for vaults and domes)

G — Hexagonal Space Grid

H — Folded Grid

edge beam →

J — Folded Lattice Plate

GRID STRUCTURES

tensioned together can also be used, but compared with tubular metal structures, concrete results in large dead weights. Double-layer grids, as well as other types of space frameworks, lend themselves to prefabrication and there are a considerable number of commercial prefabricated systems on the market. In the ideal system, all the framing members would be of the same length, joined together with identical connectors, so designed as to require one bolt only at the end of each member entering the connector.

In addition to systems consisting of individual bars and connectors joined together on the site, some systems consist of individual prefabricated units, such as pyramids, made up of bars, of which the edge members of the flat bases are joined together on the site and the apices tied together by tie bars in each direction. These are fixed to bosses on the apex of each pyramid (see page 464). Instead of open pyramids formed of bars or tubes, pyramids formed of thin sheets of aluminium, plastics or plywood can be used, fixed in the same way along the top edges by means of bolting, riveting, welding, or glueing. The apices of all units are connected together in the same way by tie members, forming a two-way or three-way bottom grid, and flat or corrugated roof sheeting is fixed to the top edges or flanges to act as an integral load-carrying element of the whole structure. Stressed skin space grids such as this are very light and economic and have a high load-carrying capacity (page 464).

Double-layer flat grids are generally not competitive with other systems below about 70 ft span. They have been used for spans of over 300 ft but greater spans than this are economically possible. The depth should be one-twentieth to one-thirtieth of the span so that the depth of a double-layer grid for spans around 100 ft would be about 3 ft 6 in. to 5 ft. This allows ample working space and space for services. Spans in the region of 300 ft require a depth of about 10 ft. These wide spans and the very large cantilever projections which can be used, are possible because of the light weight, strength and great rigidity of this type of structure. It does not collapse if one part fails. Large areas can be removed when required or be omitted in the original design without destroying the stability of the remainder of the structure.

Folded Grids. These are space grids in the form of bent or folded diagonal plane grids, the folds usually corresponding to the valleys and ridges of the roof, as shown on page 431 (H). The folded grid is therefore a series of continuous intersecting beams cranked at the folds. Folded grid roofs are usually of the multiple ridge and valley type or north light type and cover very large areas without internal support. Structures of this type can span distances up to 300 ft in the direction parallel to the ridges and almost unlimited lengths in the other direction. Folded grids can also be applied to the hipped roof form. Longitudinal members are required at the folds to give rigidity to the structure, particularly on wide spans. Although over small spans they might be omitted, rigidity would not be great and, in any case, some members would be required to support the roof covering and its sub-structure. Edge beams are required at all boundaries. Folded grids are usually constructed in steel using ordinary rolled steel sections for the diagonal members and channels for the edge beams.

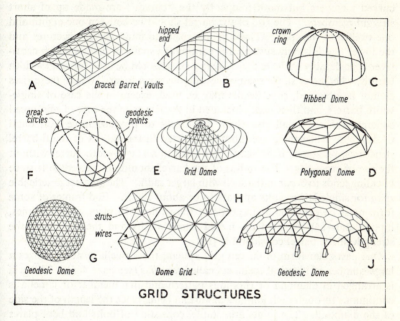

A   *Braced Barrel Vaults*   B

hipped end

crown ring   C

Ribbed Dome

great circles   geodesic points

F   E   *Grid Dome*

Polygonal Dome   D

H

struts   wires

G   *Geodesic Dome*   *Dome Grid*   *Geodesic Dome*   J

GRID STRUCTURES

Folded Lattice Plates. In principle, this is the same as folded slab construction in reinforced concrete or timber, but the planes or plates are constructed as lattice beams, usually of steel, although occasionally of timber. The adjacent edges are interconnected at the folds, usually at intervals at the node points (page 431 (J)). The roof profiles to which it can be applied and all other considerations are the same as for folded slabs. Folded lattice plate structures in steel can span greater distances than folded slabs in reinforced concrete on account of their lighter weight.

Braced Barrel Vaults. Although similar in form to reinforced concrete shells, braced barrel vaults, being an assembly of bars, are non-homogeneous (page 433 (A, B)). The members can be arranged to follow directly the lines of maximum stresses. In practice, several types of bracing are used each of which results in a different type of structural behaviour. The shape of the barrel is of great importance in relation to the stress distribution and although the cylindrical form is not the best shape, it is very useful from a practical point of view since prefabrication is facilitated by the fact that the slope of all the members is the same, the length of the bars can be the same and identical connectors can be used at all joints. In some cases the barrel is formed of curved members but more frequently the "curves" are made up of short straight members. The rise of the barrel should be between one-eighth and one-twelfth of the span. These figures relate to multi-barrel structures and the lower figure is only suitable for continuous spans or barrels which canti-lever considerably at the ends. Greater rises should be used for single-width barrels, whether of single span or continuous span form. Where these rises cannot be obtained, edge beams may be used, except in the case of single-width barrels, and their depth included in the rise as in the case of reinforced concrete shells. Small rise shells are likely to produce large horizontal thrusts and, while these are mutually resisted in the valleys of multi-barrel structures, resistance is not easily provided in a single-width barrel without the use of cross-ties. The radius of the barrel should not exceed 36 ft since buckling tends to occur in the shell with larger radii. The greatest practicable span for single layer vaults appears to be about 120 ft. End frames of some form must be provided at the ends of the vaults. In place of end frames, hipped ends can be used on traced barrel vaults and these increase the strength of the barrel considerably (B).

One particular form of curved grid system, the Lamella system, utilizes a large number of identical members called *lamellas* (see page 466). The grid is arranged in diamond or rhombus pattern and one member or lamella is continuous through each joint, each lamella being twice the length of the side of the diamond. The joints are simple, consisting of bolts and bent plates which are assembled on the site. With the simplest form of single bolted connection, the ends of the two opposite lamellas butting on to the con-tinuous lamella at the joint are slightly staggered; by means of somewhat more complicated connections the lamellas may be made to line through. Decking or purlins are used to triangulate the diamond to make the structure stable in the plane of the surface. The lamellas are made of timber or steel, thin cold-rolled sections sometimes being used for this purpose.

By means of double-layer grids, vaults may be constructed with spans up to 300 ft or widths up to 100 ft.

Braced Domes. These are constructed either with curved members lying on a surface of revolution, or of straight members with their connecting points lying on such a surface. By this means obstruction of the internal space is avoided (page 433). Some forms of braced domes consist of ribs or inclined bars running from the base to the crown, usually connected by a number of horizontal polygonal rings. The quadrilaterals so formed are sub-divided by diagonals into triangles, which provides the necessary stiffness to prevent movement under unsymmetrical loading. Other types are constructed as space grids similar to those used for barrel vaults.

The first group includes ribbed domes, consisting of meridional ribs connected only at the crown or at a crown compression ring, when there is a top opening (C). The other types in this group all have horizontal polygonal rings and diagonal stiffening members and differ in the number of diagonals, the relationship of the polygonal rings to each other in terms of rotational position and in the number of sides making up the dome (D). In addition to these there is the stiffly jointed "framed" dome which consists of continuous meridional ribs and polygonal horizontal rings rigidly connected at all intersections. This type is constructed in welded steel but is not often used in practice because it is not easily amenable to modern prefabrication techniques. Three-pin ribbed domes are frequently used because the ribs, being identical, can be easily prefabricated. Erection is simple, only a small central tower being required to provide temporary support for the crown ends of the ribs until they are all interconnected.

Space grid domes may be constructed as lamella or as two- or three-way or hexagonal grids. Lamella domes are constructed of lamella ribs, producing the typical diamond or lozenge shaped pattern as described under braced barrel vaults, and domes of over 300 ft span have been built in this way. The other types of grid dome systems vary in the grid pattern, the material used, the connecting system, which may be by welding, bolting or specially designed node connectors or clamps, and in the degree of prefabrication adopted (E). As with lamella domes, they are extremely economical and spans of well over 300 ft have been covered. For these very large spans, double-layer three-way or hexagonal grids are used to give greater stiffness against buckling.

Another widely used grid form is the geodesic dome. Points on a sphere lying on a "great circle" are called geodesic points, a great circle being any circle running round the surface of the sphere having the same radius as that of the sphere itself. Lines joining such points are called geodesic lines (see page 433 (F)). Since a sphere encloses the maximum volume with minimum surface area, a true geodesic dome would enclose the maximum volume with the minimum amount of structural material. This necessitates the use of curved members lying on great circles (G), and surface coverage is usually achieved by repetitive straight-edged patterns, using triangles and hexagons, in which the nodes only are geodesic, these being connected by straight members which are not geodesic (H, J). As with any other form of braced structure geodesic domes may be single-layer or double-layer, the latter being extremely rigid and suitable for very large spans. They may also be of stressed skin construction in which the covering acts as an integral part of the structural system, or of what may be termed formed surface construction, in which flat sheets of suitable material are bent and interconnected along their edges to form the main structural grid of the dome (page 468).

A pin-jointed triangular frame is rigid and this shape is therefore used, or hexagonal grids are broken down into triangles. It is impossible to cover a complete sphere entirely with hexagons, a certain number of pentagons being essential. Apart from exceptionally simple layouts, the members will be of different lengths and, further, a level alignment of the members at the base of such domes is not possible. This needs careful architectural consideration.

Double layer geodesic domes have been built over spans of more than 380 ft.

TENSION ROOF STRUCTURES

Tension, suspended or "hanging" roof construction commonly uses a network of cables or pin-connected links to support the cladding or covering material. This type of roof may also be formed by a continuous suspended membrane, but this method presents certain difficulties. Not many structures have been constructed in this manner.

Structures which have to resist bending are basically inefficient since the stresses involved are complex. Even when the structure is designed so that the individual components are directly stressed, as in lattice girders or space grids, there are certain members in compression which need to be stiffened against buckling. Shell or arch structures represent attempts to use materials in direct stress but it is impossible to eliminate all bending in any but the smallest forms of these structures.

The principal advantage of using a suspension system to support a roof is that the only direct stresses which occur are tensile. This avoids the buckling effect associated with other structures. Furthermore, the supporting compression structure may be concentrated at certain points where the bulkiness necessary to provide adequate resistance to buckling does not interfere with the planning of the usable space. Typical arrangements of the supporting cable structure for roof suspension systems are illustrated on page 437. One of the problems associated with the application of this technique is that of "flutter". This occurs because the roof is comparatively light in weight and frequently assumes shapes which induce greater suction or "lift" at certain wind speeds (A). To reduce this effect it is desirable to prestress the

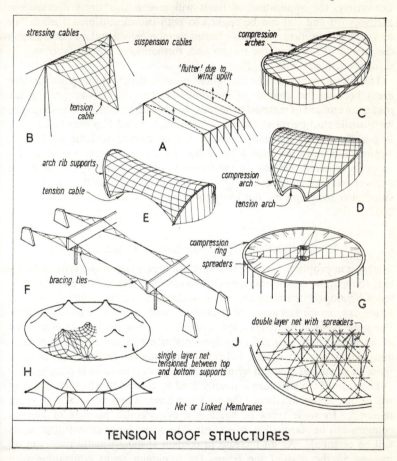

TENSION ROOF STRUCTURES

principal suspended cable system by another system of cables curved in the opposite direction. Applications of this are seen in the illustrations. In principle there are three methods: (i) a doubly-curved system of cables in which the main cables are prestressed by another set at right-angles (B–E), (ii) bracing ties which tension the two cables in concave form (F), (iii) spreaders which

15

tension the two cables in convex form (G). The effect of suction will be to reduce the tension in the principal cables following the catenary paths and to increase the tension in the restraining cables following "arched" paths. Conversely, the application of loads will reverse this stress distribution. Methods (ii) and (iii) can be applied to both two-dimensional "beams" or to a grid arrangement. A net or linked membrane will assist in distributing the stresses throughout the system and, furthermore, can be fabricated of similar length elements (H, J).

This type of roof provides the lightest possible structure for spanning large areas because the absence of buckling due to compression permits the minimum amount of material to be used, and because the use of high-strength, high-tensile steel permits wires or linked rods of small diameter to be used. It has the further advantage that it can be erected without scaffolding. Against this must be placed the following disadvantages: the expensive supports required, whether in the form of compression ring or props and anchors and, secondly, the complications in cladding. At the present time suspension structures are not likely to be economic over spans much below 200 ft.

CHOICE OF ROOF STRUCTURE

The most appropriate form of structure will depend upon the type of building, foundation conditions, spans to be covered, nature and magnitude of loads, lighting requirements and accommodation for services, the possibility of future alternation and speed of erection, as well as aesthetic considerations. For some types of buildings a few solutions only are possible, as in the case of an auditorium with rigid requirements of space, acoustics and volume and ventilation. In others, industrial buildings for example, particularly those of small and medium span, a wide range of structures is possible.

The span of the structure is usually fixed by the use to which the building will be put, as this will dictate the minimum areas of unobstructed floor space required. In some types of building a considerable number of internal columns will be permissible, whereas in others very large unobstructed areas will be essential. As an increase in column spacing usually results in an increase in the cost of the frame, the minimum spans compatible with requirements of clear floor area should always be adopted in design.

The clear internal height of the building is another factor governed largely by the use of the building. In industrial buildings sufficient clearance must be provided for the installation and maintenance of plant, and the widespread use of fork trucks requires minimum headrooms for efficient working. Much ancillary equipment is now hung from the roof structure and the provision of sufficient headroom below this will govern the minimum internal height.

Lighting requirements may have a profound effect upon the form of structure used, particularly in the case of very wide buildings, in which the central areas cannot adequately be lit from the side walls. Roof lighting must then be provided and this will affect the shape of the roof. Generally speaking, with a height of 18 ft reasonable natural light cannot be obtained from wall windows if the distance between them exceeds about 40 ft. Various types of roof structure designed to provide adequate lighting for the interior have already been described, and the suitability of a particular form will depend not only upon lighting requirements but on other functional requirements.

Apart from considerations of lighting, and the other considerations mentioned above, the roof structure must be thought of in relation to the heating requirements of the building. From this point of view the structure which, while fulfilling other functional requirements, restricts the internal volume of the building to a minimum and at the same time offers the minimum exposed roof surface area, will be the most efficient (see page 406). The reduction in volume reduces the amount of space to be heated and the reduction in roof surface area keeps heat losses through the roof to a minimum. From this point of view alone, therefore, the flat roof is the most acceptable form.

Although it may not always be acceptable for other reasons, it may be generally accepted that as far as lighting and heating requirements are concerned the larger the span the lower should be the pitch of the roof. To achieve this, where functional requirements demand large span roofs and wide column spacing, the use of forms of construction which are more expensive than others may be economically justified. When rigid frames are used to decrease the volume of enclosed space it is often economically advantageous to pitch the spanning members sufficient to permit the use of forms of sheet roof covering which require a fall of a few degrees.

The need to suspend equipment from the roof must be considered, particularly if the loads to be carried are heavy and are point loads. Shell roofs, which are essentially designed to carry comparatively light uniformly distributed loads, may not for this reason be suitable. Point loads of any magnitude should, wherever possible, as in other structures, be restricted to the main stiffening beams and end frames of shell structures. If, however, it is essential to suspend from the shell, all loads greater than about 1 cwt should be spread by plates or cross reinforcement. In addition to suspended equipment, provision may have to be made for ventilating or extract ducts and, particularly if these are large, they will have to be related to the roof structure at an early stage.

The choice of structure will sometimes be weighted by considerations of adaptability and maintenance. Steel construction is generally more adaptable than reinforced concrete if alterations are necessary, and it is comparatively easy to strengthen the structure where required by means of additional material welded on. It is usually easier in steel and in timber to fix further equipment to the structure, although fixing to matured concrete can be made by metal fixing studs applied by cartridge hammer.

Concrete generally requires less maintenance than steel, which must be painted periodically. Steel lattice construction of all forms offers a large surface area for corrosion and is difficult to paint. Rigid frames built up of welded steel plates, on the other hand, expose less surface to the air and are easier and cheaper to paint. In highly corrosive atmospheres it may be more economical to use aluminium alloy instead of steel in order to reduce maintenance costs, even though the cost of the structure itself may be higher than in steel. Timber structures do not require protective coatings, particularly internally, and maintenance costs are therefore considerably less than for metal structures.

Very often speed and cost of erection will have a bearing upon the nature of the structure to be used. This is discussed in more detail later.

Span and Type of Structure. Short-span construction will usually be the cheapest as far as structure is concerned, but functional requirements often dictate medium or large spans. For this the most economic form must then be selected.

Of the wide variety of roof structures available, some only are economic over very large spans. As far as the materials of the structure are concerned, some, such as aluminium alloys, are only really economic when used in large-span construction, others only when there is considerable repetition of the structure and its parts on one particular job. Care must be taken in design, therefore, not to use materials which can be exploited most favourably only over wide spans when, in fact, large spans are not justified by other requirements, nor to select forms of structure the economic use of which depends on repetition, when the job is too small to provide adequate repetition.

As with all types of structure the characteristics of the soil on which the building rests must be considered. In circumstances of weak soil requiring expensive foundations, it may be cheaper to use widely spaced, wide-span construction in order to limit the number of foundation points.

Research on the comparative costs of different forms of roof structure in different materials has shown that the variation in cost of structural frames alone of the same span and loading, and fulfilling the same requirements, is generally small. Bearing in mind that the cost of the structural frame may be as low as one-sixth of the total cost of the building,[1] it will be appreciated that quite large variations in this element will have only a relatively small effect on the total cost. Nevertheless, in large buildings in particular, one-sixth of the total cost may be a substantial sum and consideration must be given to the problem of keeping this figure to a minimum.

For simple shed-type buildings where lighting is not important, the truss and column frame is probably the cheapest structure for spans up to about 100 ft. The space above eaves level, however, is obstructed by the trusses and over the wider spans this type of structure encloses a considerable volume of space. For spans above 100 ft "umbrella" construction or north light roofs with lattice girders in the plane of the ridge can be used up to about 150 ft span, at spacings not exceeding 60 to 70 ft. The unit weight and cost of a steel folded lattice plate and an "umbrella" roof of the same span and spacing of supports are about the same, but the folded plate construction has the advantage of unrestricted space under the roof.

In trusses or girders and in structural systems relying upon "beam effect" such as space frames, economy in the use of any material will result when increased moments of inertia are produced by increased depth of structure. Structures which are more closely related to the space which they enclose, such as rigid frames or arch forms, will frequently be more expensive span for span than those incorporating deep beams, girders or trusses, but may compensate for this by reducing the volume of the building and the area of cladding and finishes.

Rigid frames in welded steel and reinforced concrete either "square" or "arched", although not always economic over smaller spans, are frequently used because of the advantages which have been mentioned above. Reinforced concrete rigid frames can be economic over 60 to 100 ft spans. For spans of over 100 ft, and certainly over 150 ft, rigid steel frames with lattice structure are likely to be cheaper than those with solid web designed on the elastic theory, but not necessarily those designed on the plastic theory. For spans of 200 ft or more, arch rib construction is likely to be the most economic.

Prestressed concrete is usually competitive in cost with uncased steel for solid web frames, so that where lattice frames are not suitable there is likely to be an economic advantage in using prestressed concrete.

Over spans of more than 80 ft the saving in weight over steel in an

---

[1] *Factory Building Studies*, No. 7, "Structural Frameworks for Single-Storey Factory Buildings". H.M.S.O. 1960.

aluminium structure may be as much as four-fifths. In spite of this, the cost of an aluminium structure may not be lower than that of steel, and aluminium only begins to be competitive with steel over very large spans of 200 feet or more.

In suitable types of building advantage can be taken of the great strength and light weight of timber construction. Bowstring trusses with laminated timber top chords can span up to 230 ft or more, and lattice rigid frames have been constructed over spans of 100 ft or more. Laminated timber "bents" forming rigid frames and laminated timber arches are used over spans of more than 200 ft.

Medium span structures in reinforced concrete can be competitive with steel, if constructed of standardized precast members, and sometimes when constructed of non-standard members cast on the site. Shell concrete construction can be economic in medium and wide span roofs, using long-span barrels up to spans of 100–150 ft, above which short-span barrels would be used. There will not be much difference in the relative cost of steel and shell structures provided that the shell is repeated more than four to five times. Although shell construction may not always be competitive in cost with steel, nor usually in speed of erection, it is in other respects equal to steel and superior to it as far as maintenance is concerned.

Shell vaults can be prestressed, with a consequent reduction in the rise to span ratio, but the structural advantage of prestressing must be weighed against the increased cost and complication of placing of ducts, anchorages and cables and it is unlikely that this will be justified for spans much below 110 ft. Above this span the advantage of prestressing increases.

Shell construction in laminated timber produces a very light structure. A timber hyperbolic paraboloid shell 60 ft square will be about 2 in. thick and weigh approximately 5 lb per sq. ft; a comparable concrete shell would be about $2\frac{1}{2}$ in. thick weighing about 30 lb per sq. ft. Laminated timber domes and vaults show similar weight advantages. Elliptical shell domes have been constructed over 150 ft long and barrel vaults over spans of up to 100 ft.

Grid structures in flat or curved form are particularly useful over very wide spans where the advantage of rigidity and light weight are important. Single-layer flat grids are economical up to 50–80 ft span. Braced barrel vaults have the advantage over reinforced concrete shell vaults of considerable reduction in weight and of rapid erection on the site. They require no shuttering and may be partially or completely prefabricated. For spans above about 60 ft, they are about 10% cheaper than reinforced concrete shells or even 20% in some cases. By the use of folded grids and double-layer flat grids, spans of over 300 ft can be covered economically. Where the circular or polygonal plan form is acceptable, braced domes of various types can be used over spans of up to 300 to 400 ft. As explained on page 394 aluminium alloys are advantageously employed in grid structures.

The relative advantages of steel, aluminium alloys, concrete and timber are discussed on pages 392–397. The metals are produced not only as "I", channel and other common sections, in hot-rolled steel or extruded aluminium alloy, but also as tubes, hollow sections and, in the case of steel, as cold-formed sections produced from thin strip steel.

The manufacture of cold-formed steel sections and the design considerations involved in their use are described on page 252. Although they are used for two- to three-storey structural frames as described in Chapter 5, they are used to greatest advantage in roof structures where a low dead/live load ratio is important. For spans up to about 50 ft the weight of cold-formed steel construction per sq. ft of floor area is about 40 to 60% less than that of similar riveted steel construction, the greater savings being over the shorter spans. This is largely due to the fact that when hot-rolled sections are used for short-span structures, sections for the various members cannot be obtained down to the minimum area required for stress resistance, as this is limited by the smallest sections rolled. In addition, the wide variety of shapes which can be cold-formed makes it possible to avoid eccentric loading of the members and the use of gusset plates, and this further decreases the weight of the structure. As far as cost is concerned, beyond very small spans the increased cost of fabrication, and sometimes of the material, is likely to make the price equal to or more than that of ordinary hot-rolled construction, but against this must be placed the advantages of the comparative ease with which sections of different shapes can be produced, the simple fixing of roof claddings and ease and speed of erection. A light lifting pole only is required for erection purposes because the fabricated units are much lighter than those in hot-rolled construction. Savings in erection costs are given as around 15–25% for trusses and 10% for purlins and bracings. Provided that detailing is simple, construction in cold-formed sections can be very economical when used on standard units or with a high degree of repetition. Over medium spans with light loading, cold-formed lattice beams show savings over hot-rolled lattice beams although these savings are not so great as in the case of trusses. Because of the efficient distribution of metal in cold-formed sections and the advantages shown in their repetitive use, considerable economies result when they are used as purlins, particularly as zed sections, in conjunction with main roof members of riveted steel.

Roof structures constructed from welded steel tubes will be considerably lighter than similar structures constructed in ordinary steel sections. The weight of a tubular framework per sq. ft of floor area may be from 25 to 40% less than that of a riveted hot-rolled structure for spans up to about 50 ft. As in the case of cold-formed sections the greater savings are made in the shorter spans. Actual savings will depend upon the simplicity of detailing. Although there will be a saving in weight by the use of tubular construction, a reduction in cost compared with that of normal steel construction is unlikely unless simple detailing is used and gussets are reduced or eliminated. However, if these points are watched and there is considerable repetition, tube frameworks will generally be cheaper, or at least competitive, in overall cost with riveted or bolted hot-rolled sections. Efficient large-span construction can be obtained by using both tubes and hot-rolled sections together: the latter as tension members and the former as compression members. This is because tubes are a more efficient section in compression, and are designed to a lower basic tension stress than, for example, hot-rolled angles. Erection takes rather longer than with ordinary steel frames in spite of the fact that tubular frames are lighter and stiffer in lifting. This is largely because erectors cannot walk as easily along tubular members, so that in carrying out fixing operations they cannot so readily work on the structure itself.

If welding instead of bolting of normal steel sections is employed there will be an overall saving in the weight of the structure, but not necessarily a saving in cost unless there is considerable repetition of the work and simple detailing. This is because the saving in weight is offset by the increased cost of fabrication. In order to reduce the fabricating cost to a minimum, welding should be restricted to the shop or to the floor on the site. Where possible, any connections required to be made when the structure is erected in position should be bolted. Solid web welded portal frames show a saving in material when they are designed on the basis of the "plastic theory", but this saving is generally not so great in the case of larger frames where the cross section at different points can be more effectively varied to suit the variations in stresses. The overall cost of a welded "plastic" frame of this type involving site welded joints and an alternative comparable frame designed on the "elastic theory" with site bolted connections, will generally be about the same, as the saving in material tends to be offset by the comparatively expensive welding costs.

Speed and Economy in Erection. As already indicated, the cost of erection in terms of the speed and facility with which it may be carried out is an important factor in the overall cost of a roof construction. Metal and timber structures are generally quicker to erect than those in *in situ* concrete. Reference has already been made to the ease with which structures fabricated from cold formed sections are erected. The use of precast concrete, which can be assembled fairly quickly, reduces the time disadvantage of concrete. The erection time of wide-span concrete structures can be reduced by the use of prestressing with precast concrete elements.

The precasting of concrete roof frames from 20 to 130 ft or so in span, the large ones being cast in three to four units, bolted together on the site, is common practice. By this means they can be easily and quickly erected by the use of simple derricks or mobile cranes. The erection of large rigid frames cast in three or four sections is carried out with the use of a timber trestle, either on a track or moved by crane into each frame position, which supports the separate units until the joints between them are bolted up. Three-pin frames in lattice construction, particularly in aluminium, may be erected in two halves and hoisted into position using the base hinge connections as fulcrum points. In the case of large span concrete structures, erection can be speeded up and a great amount of expensive shuttering avoided by the application of post-tensioning to small precast units. These can be stressed into a single element and then hoisted into position by cranes or hydraulic jacks.

Although rigid concrete frames of various types are those most commonly carried out in precast construction, beyond certain heights it may sometimes be cheaper to precast small shell vaults and domes on the ground and then hoist them into position. Twenty-four feet square shell concrete domes weighing 13½ tons each have been precast on site and lifted into position by a pair of cranes. Lightweight concrete shell barrel vaults over 60 ft long and weighing 20 tons each have similarly been cast and hoisted into position. In each case a number of such units was cast for the job. In the case of the domes twelve, and in the case of the barrel vaults, six units were required.

In each of these examples the weight of the units was within the lifting capacity of a crane or pair of cranes, but in certain circumstances it may be cheaper than other forms of construction to cast very much larger units and lift by hydraulic jacks. Groups of prestressed concrete barrel vaults linked together by end frames into units measuring 186 ft × 110 ft overall and weighing almost 1500 tons have been cast on the floor of a building, with all internal roof finishings and external roof coverings applied at ground level, and then raised nearly 50 ft by means of hydraulic jacks. Two pairs of jacks were positioned at each of the four supporting column positions, the columns being built up on the jacks with specially designed interlocking concrete blocks placed in position at the completion of each lift by the jack.

Grid structures of all types are fabricated on the site as a whole, or in large

15*

sections from prefabricated units, and are then lifted into position usually by crane, or by hydraulic jack in the case of very large structures raised as a whole. Steel lattice grids more than 300 ft sq. and 10 ft deep, weighing over 1,000 tons have been lifted in a similar manner to lift slab construction in reinforced concrete.[1]

CONSTRUCTIONAL METHODS

The basic principles and economic applications of roof structures have been described in the preceding pages. It now remains to describe the constructional methods adopted in the application of different materials to the various types of structure.

BEAMS

These are constructed in timber, steel and concrete.

Timber. Glued and laminated beams: These are commonly called "glulam" beams and may be constructed of laminations arranged vertically or horizontally. Horizontal lamination allows a more economical use of timber, particularly for larger section beams, since the depth of the beam may be formed of multiple laminates and is not limited by the width of any given plank. Furthermore, horizontal lamination facilitates shaping (see also page 451). The thickness of each laminate is usually about 2 in. for straight members, reducing to $\frac{5}{8}$ in. according to the radius of curve for shaped members. The shapes of beams may be varied to give sloping upper surfaces, slight cambers and sections of varying depth, page 447. Beams much over 60 ft in length are not usually formed in glulam construction. Beams may be secured to brickwork or supported on solid or laminated timber columns and secured by metal angles, plates and bolts as shown on page 447.

Web beams: For spans of up to 40 or 50 ft a more economical distribution of material is obtained by the combined use of solid timber flanges and webs of plywood. Such beams may be stiffened by using a number of webs to form a hollow box section and additional cross sectional area may be added to the flanges between the webs to accommodate larger bending moments, page 447. For spans over 60 ft and up to 100 ft the use of laminated glued and nailed beams of I-section will produce a more economical structure than solid rectilinear laminated beams. The webs and flanges are formed of boards approximately 1 in. thick fixed together with glue and carefully calculated

[1] For a full discussion of the economic aspect of single-storey construction, see "Economics of Framed Structures", by Leonard R. Creasy, B.Sc. (Eng.), M.I.C.E., *Proceedings of the Institution of Civil Engineers*, Vol. 12, March 1959. See also *Factory Building Studies* No. 7, "Structural Frameworks for Single-Storey Factory Buildings". H.M.S.O. 1960.

nailing (see below). This system enables short pieces of timber to be used economically, each flange being composed of a number of overlapping lengths and the web formed from diagonal boarding braced where necessary by the addition of vertical stiffeners glued and nailed to it.

Investigations are being carried out at present on the post-tensioning of prefabricated unit box beams, stressed on the site, and on the glueing of pre-tensioned wires between the laminations of glulam beams.

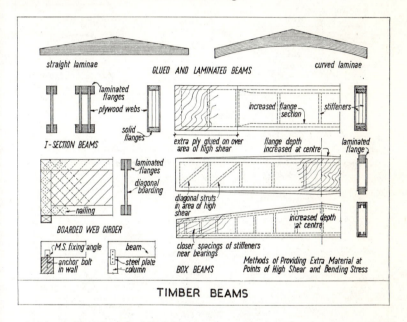

TIMBER BEAMS

Steel. British Standard R.S.J.'s may be used where head room is critical and minimum beam depth is desirable. Reference should be made to Chapter 5 where the merits of mild and high-tensile steel sections and castellated beams are discussed. (See page 227 and also page 403.)

Concrete. For spans much over 20–30 ft reinforced concrete is not likely to be economical for beams, but wide spans can be covered economically if the beams are prestressed (see page 395).

TRUSSES AND LATTICE GIRDERS

Timber. Girders and trusses may be fabricated with connectors, nails or glues. *Elementary Building Construction* shows simple trusses with con-

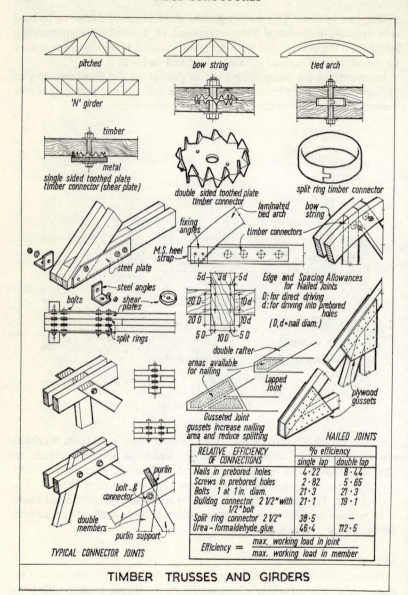

pitched

bow string

tied arch

'N' girder

timber

metal

single sided toothed plate
timber connector (shear plate)

double sided toothed plate
timber connector

split ring timber connector

laminated
tied arch

bow
string

fixing
angles

timber connectors

M.S. heel
strap

steel plate

steel angles

bolts

shear
plates

split rings

5d   3d 5d

20 D   10d

20 D   10d

5 D   10 D 5 D

Edge and Spacing Allowances
for Nailed Joints
D: for direct driving
d: for driving into prebored
holes
(D, d = nail diam.)

double rafter

areas available
for nailing

Lapped
Joint

plywood
gussets

Gusseted Joint
gussets increase nailing
area and reduce splitting

NAILED JOINTS

purlin

bolt &
connector

double
members

purlin support

TYPICAL CONNECTOR JOINTS

RELATIVE EFFICIENCY OF CONNECTIONS	% efficiency	
	single lap	double lap
Nails in prebored holes	4·22	8·44
Screws in prebored holes	2·82	5·65
Bolts 1 at 1 in. diam.	21·3	21·3
Bulldog connector 2 1/2" with 1/2" bolt	21·1	19·1
Split ring connector 2 1/2"	38·5	—
Urea – formaldehyde glue	46·4	112·5
Efficiency = $\dfrac{\text{max. working load in joint}}{\text{max. working load in member}}$		

TIMBER TRUSSES AND GIRDERS

nectored joints.   Toothed connectors are useful for joining sawn timber.
Split-ring connectors carry greater loads than toothed connectors but require
accurately machined grooves cut in the timber and the timbers are usually
faced on four sides and prepared in the shop (see page 448).   Although design
is ideally based on the triangulated centre line principle, in many cases some
eccentricity at the joints cannot be avoided.   The upper chords of girders
may be curved, parallel or inclined, and are usually laminated in the larger
spans. Typical methods of jointing are shown on page 448 and below. Gussets
give greater fixing areas in both nailed and glued joints.   Girders up to about
150 ft and trusses to about 200–250 ft may be constructed on these lines.

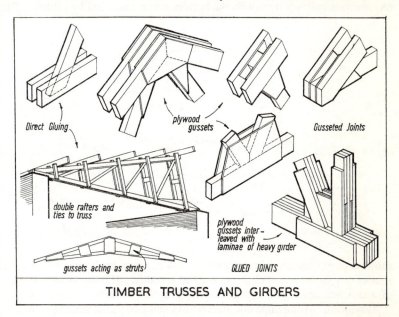

Direct Gluing

plywood
gussets

Gusseted Joints

double rafters and
ties to truss

plywood
gussets inter-
leaved with
laminae of heavy girder

gussets acting as struts

GLUED JOINTS

TIMBER TRUSSES AND GIRDERS

Steel.   Conventionally fabricated steel girders of riveted and bolted construction, with members connected by the use of gusset plates, are described
and illustrated on pages 233–234.   Conventional steel trusses are illustrated
in *Elementary Building Construction*.   More recently, steel trusses and
girders have been fabricated from welded tubes which possess the advantage
of lightness and stiffness.   This form of construction is discussed on page
444, where the need for simplicity of detailing and, as far as possible, the
avoidance of gussets is emphasized.   Typical joints are shown on page 450.

Light lattice beams formed from angles and flats are used extensively for lightly loaded roof structures up to spans of 40 ft. Such beams frequently incorporate high-tensile steel bottom chords. Increasing use has also been made of cold-rolled steel sections welded or riveted together in lattice beams. This is discussed on page 443. Examples of these beams are illustrated on page 336 and below.

Concrete. Modern light concrete trusses have resulted from the introduction of prestressing which enables small members to be drawn together by the stressing cables, so that the tension members of the trusses are pre-compressed (see page 292). Some typical examples are shown on page 451. (A) shows a built-up truss with the bottom boom tensioned by cables. (B)

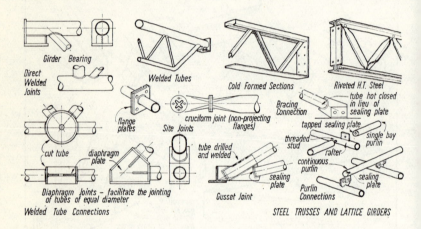

Girder Bearing

Direct Welded Joints

Welded Tubes

Cold Formed Sections

Riveted H.T. Steel

tube hot closed in lieu of sealing plate

Bracing Connection

flange plates

Site Joints

cruciform joint (non-projecting flanges)

tapped sealing plate

threaded stud

single bay purlin

cut tube

diaphragm plate

tube drilled and welded

rafter

continuous purlin

Diaphragm Joints – facilitate the jointing of tubes of equal diameter

sealing plate

Gusset Joint

sealing plate

Purlin Connections

sealing plate

Welded Tube Connections

STEEL TRUSSES AND LATTICE GIRDERS

shows a large concrete bowstring girder and (C) a lattice beam formed in a similar way from precast elements stressed together. (D) shows an example of a concrete beam with exposed stressing cables, forming a trussed beam.

Aluminium. Aluminium and steel trusses and girders are generally similar in form. As explained on page 394 care must be taken to prevent local buckling of members in compression, and while typical aluminium sections will be used some members may need to be doubled up to produce adequate stiffness.

RIGID FRAMES

Timber. The techniques used in fabrication of timber beams, trusses and girders are also applicable to the construction of rigid frames. Lattice frames are built up with bolted or glued joints on the same lines as the trusses and girders which are illustrated. On page 452 are shown examples of rigid frames constructed in hollow box, solid laminated, and built-up "I" form. Where glued laminations are employed in frames with curved angles or in arch ribs the laminates must be thin enough to bend easily. The ratio of the radius of curvature to the thickness of the laminates must not be less than 100, and 150 is normal practice. The cost of fabrication rises as the laminates get thinner, therefore sharp curves should be avoided where possible. Metal

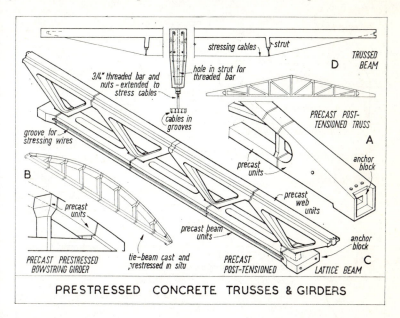

PRESTRESSED CONCRETE TRUSSES & GIRDERS

fittings are employed to connect the members and details of connections will vary according to the degree of rigidity required at the joints. Base connections are formed by cleats or by locating the feet of frames in metal shoes bolted to concrete foundations. In larger frames hinged metal bearings are bolted to the feet of the frames. Crown joints are either bolted through the apex or secured by splice plates to provide a rigid connection, or are provided with a hinged bearing. Boxed plywood frames are used for spans up to about 60 ft, glulam frames up to about 80 ft and lattice and built-up "I" section frames up to about 150 ft. Arch ribs are constructed in glulam up to spans of more than 200 ft.

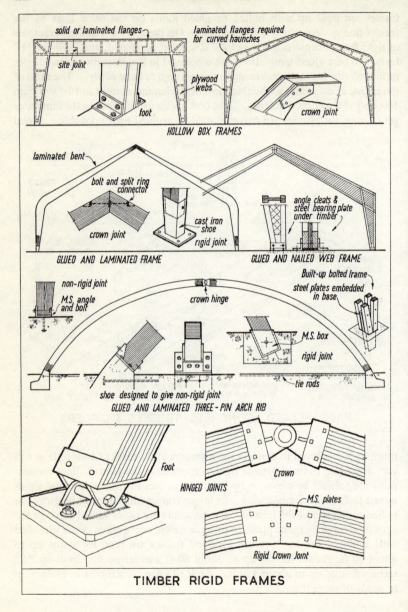

solid or laminated flanges

laminated flanges required for curved haunches

site joint

plywood webs

foot

crown joint

HOLLOW BOX FRAMES

laminated bent

bolt and split ring connector

crown joint

cast iron shoe

rigid joint

angle cleats & steel bearing plate under timber

GLUED AND LAMINATED FRAME   **GLUED AND NAILED WEB FRAME**

non-rigid joint

M.S. angle and bolt

crown hinge

Built-up bolted frame steel plates embedded in base

M.S. box

rigid joint

tie rods

shoe designed to give non-rigid joint

GLUED AND LAMINATED THREE-PIN ARCH RIB

Foot

Crown

HINGED JOINTS

M.S. plates

Rigid Crown Joint

TIMBER RIGID FRAMES

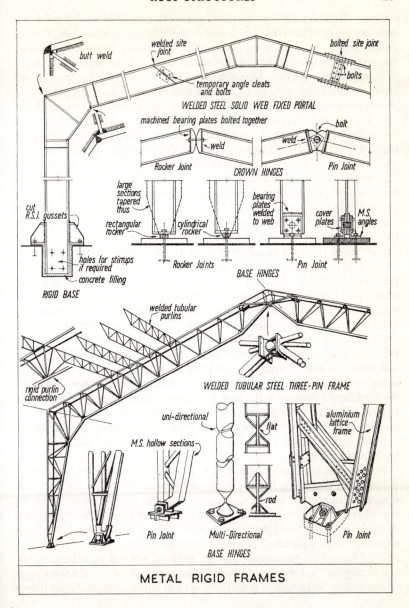

butt weld

welded site joint

bolted site joint

bolts

temporary angle cleats and bolts

WELDED STEEL SOLID WEB FIXED PORTAL

machined bearing plates bolted together

bolt

weld

weld

Rocker Joint

CROWN HINGES

Pin Joint

cut R.S.J. gussets

large sections tapered thus

rectangular rocker

cylindrical rocker

bearing plates welded to web

cover plates

M.S. angles

holes for stirrups if required

concrete filling

RIGID BASE

Rocker Joints

Pin Joint

BASE HINGES

welded tubular purlins

WELDED TUBULAR STEEL THREE-PIN FRAME

rigid purlin connection

uni-directional

flat

aluminium lattice frame

M.S. hollow sections

rod

Pin Joint

Multi-Directional

Pin Joint

BASE HINGES

METAL RIGID FRAMES

Steel. Rigid frames constructed in steelwork may be of welded solid web construction or of conventional riveted or welded lattice construction. Some typical forms are shown on page 409. The lattice form is commonly employed in the construction of large-span frames. A number of lightweight prefabricated frames have been developed for short to medium spans which are of welded angle, tube or cold-rolled steel construction. On page 453 is shown an example of a welded steel solid web fixed portal. Where, as in this case, the foundations contribute to the stability of the structure, the feet of the frames must be rigidly fixed to the concrete bases. The illustration shows one method involving embedding the foot in the concrete. Another method which uses a wide rigid base bolted to the concrete slab is shown on page 242. The welded tubular steel three-pin frame shown on the same page is a space frame in form, the triangular cross-section giving great rigidity to a structure constructed of quite small tubes. The nature of the junction between frame and closely spaced purlins gives a rigid joint and provides lateral rigidity to the whole building. It also results in considerable membrane action so that the whole of the roof structure will act to some extent as a lattice grid. Methods of forming crown and base joints are illustrated. These vary in complexity and rigidity. In all of them it will be seen that the frame is free to rotate (one permits rotation in all directions) but is held in position. It should be noted that unless rocker and bearing-plate hinges incorporate long bolts they can resist no vertical tension and little horizontal force.

Concrete. Concrete rigid frames are generally cast *in situ* when the span is large. Medium-span and small-span frames are most frequently precast and joined on site. "Split" hinged joints in *in situ* concrete are formed by reducing the member to a very small section through which passes "bundled" reinforcement which holds the base in position and resists any shear stresses. Crown joints in three-hinged frames are formed in a similar manner. Some typical examples are shown on page 455, on which is also shown a metal pin joint and a rocker joint formed by welding steel flange plates to the reinforcement.

Precast concrete frames fabricated in large sections are joined on site by bolting or by concreting-in connecting reinforcement left projecting from each section. Frames are usually connected at points of low stress or at the haunches where the required increase in section can be provided by addition of one element to another (see page 455). Simple bolted hinge joints are sometimes used with small precast frames, as shown. Precast frames may also be formed of prestressed concrete sections, stressed by cables or rods connecting the "column" and "beam" members as shown on the same page.

Aluminium. Aluminium is normally used in lattice form, and rigid frames in this material are basically similar to steel lattice frames, although they will differ in detail because of the structural characteristics of the metal (page 453).

SHELLS

Timber. Some details typical of timber shell construction are shown on page 456. Site constructed barrels usually use layers of boarding nailed and

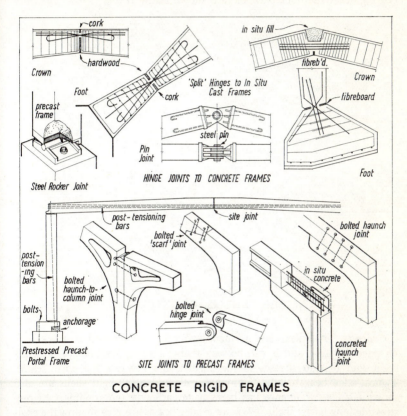

CONCRETE RIGID FRAMES

glued together. (A) shows a detail of a 100 ft span barrel vault the board membrane of which is stiffened by ribs at 5 ft centres. Detail (B) shows a shell, prefabricated in 4 ft units, constructed as a sandwich panel of ply and paper honeycomb core. Edge beams may be of built-up box form or laminated form as shown.

Timber shell domes are normally built up with boards glued and nailed or screwed together, with laminated edge beams (C).   In hyperbolic paraboloids, constructed in the same way, the majority of layers of boarding have, in the past, been laid parallel to the edge beams and at right-angles to each other with some laid diagonally but it has been found that greater rigidity results from laying the majority diagonally.   A detail of the edge beam and shoe bearing of a hyperbolic paraboloid is shown below at (D).

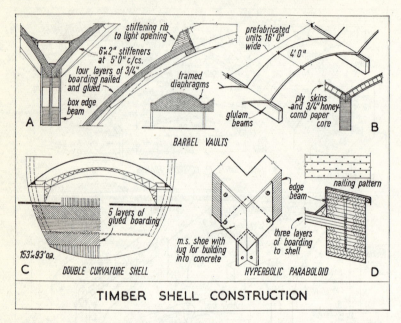

TIMBER SHELL CONSTRUCTION

Concrete.   A typical reinforcement layout for a long barrel vault is shown on page 457 (A), and it will be seen that it follows the lines of principle shear and tension stresses in the corners and towards the edge beams. Typical edge beam details for long barrels and north-light shells are also shown (B, C).   Reference has been made earlier to the possibility of pre-stressing long barrel shells.   When the edge beams are very shallow the post-tensioning cables are placed in the lower parts of the shell.   They are, however, placed more easily within edge beams.   A double curved barrel gives the advantage of straight cables.   These alternatives are shown at (D).

Corrugated barrels, such as that shown on page 417, are constructed on a framework of ribs of tubes, angles or timber shaped to the curve of the shell,

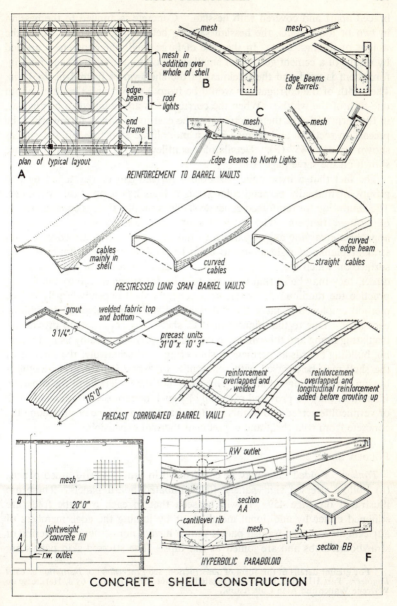

A plan of typical layout

mesh in addition over whole of shell

edge beam

roof lights

end frame

B mesh — mesh — Edge Beams to Barrels

C mesh — mesh — Edge Beams to North Lights

REINFORCEMENT TO BARREL VAULTS

cables mainly in shell

curved cables

curved edge beam

straight cables

PRESTRESSED LONG SPAN BARREL VAULTS **D**

grout — welded fabric top and bottom

3 1/4"

precast units 31'0"x 10'3"

115'0"

reinforcement overlapped and welded

reinforcement overlapped and longitudinal reinforcement added before grouting up

PRECAST CORRUGATED BARREL VAULT **E**

mesh

20'0"

lightweight concrete fill

r.w. outlet

RW outlet

section AA

cantilever rib

mesh

3"

section BB

HYPERBOLIC PARABOLOID **F**

CONCRETE SHELL CONSTRUCTION

braced apart and covered with hessian. Concrete is applied to the hessian in two or more coats, the hessian sagging between the supports under the weight of the first coat. In the case of large shells the concrete is applied by means of a cement gun. For small shells up to about 40 ft span no reinforcement is used and the thickness of the shell varies from $\frac{3}{4}$ in. to $1\frac{1}{2}$ in. The width of the corrugations would be from 3 to 6 ft and the depth about one-fifth of the width.[1] When the corrugations are required to be angular, in the form of folds, the structure may be cast in *in situ* on formwork or be precast in sections and formed into a monolithic structure on the site as shown on page 457 (E). Details of a cantilever hyperbolic paraboloid are shown on the same page (F).

The fact that a hyperbolic paraboloid surface can be developed by two groups of mutually perpendicular straight lines has a practical advantage. The shuttering for reinforced concrete shells is simple, since it consists wholly of straight timbers. The straight supporting bearers are placed at the appropriate varying angles parallel to the edge beams and are covered with straight planks at right-angles to them to produce the final doubly-curved surface on which the concrete is cast. As all the stresses in these shells are direct, they may be as thin as $1\frac{1}{2}$ in. to 2 in. for spans of 100 to 130 ft. In practice the minimum thickness of a concrete shell depends largely on the method employed to place the concrete and such thin slabs makes guniting necessary. Due to the thinness of R.C. shells it is important to provide an insulating lining and this can often be conveniently achieved by using insulating building boards as permanent shuttering. Alternatively, the interior of the shell may be sprayed with vermiculite or asbestos fibre, these methods having the advantage of allowing inspection of the underside of the concrete. Insulation may be provided externally by such materials as woodwool, cork or vermiculite screed and in this position has the advantage of protecting the concrete from solar heat and consequent thermal expansion.

FOLDED SLABS

Timber. Folded slabs may be constructed in timber as (i) framed panels, (ii) hollow stressed skin panels, (iii) laminated board panels. These are illustrated on page 459. It will be seen that in each case the folds are stiffened either by additional members or by joining the edge members of adjacent slabs. The framed panels shown have a non-structural covering of strawboard slabs and are joined at the hips. The stressed skin panels are

---

[1] For greater details of this form of construction, see *Proceedings of Institution of Civil Engineers*, Part III, Aug. 1953: "Corrugated Concrete Shell Roofs", by J. Hardresse de Warrene Waller and Alan Clift Aston.

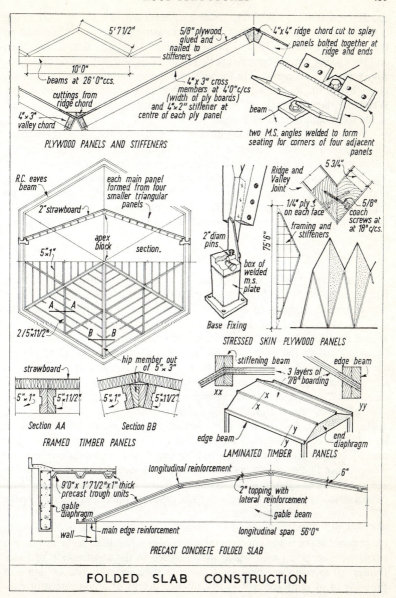

PLYWOOD PANELS AND STIFFENERS

5'7 1/2"

5/8" plywood glued and nailed to stiffeners

4"x 4" ridge chord cut to splay panels bolted together at ridge and ends

10'0"
beams at 26'0"ccs.

4"x 3" cross members at 4'0"c/cs (width of ply boards) and 4"x 2" stiffener at centre of each ply panel

cuttings from ridge chord

beam

4"x 3" valley chord

two M.S. angles welded to form seating for corners of four adjacent panels

R.C. eaves beam

each main panel formed from four smaller triangular panels

2" strawboard

apex block   section.

Ridge and Valley Joint   5 3/4"

1/4" ply on each face

5/8" coach screws at at 18" c/cs.

framing and stiffeners

5"x 1"

y

2" diam pins

box of welded m.s. plate

75'6"

A A

Base Fixing

B B

2/5"x11 1/2"

STRESSED SKIN PLYWOOD PANELS

strawboard

hip member out of 5"x 3"

stiffening beam

edge beam

3 layers of 7/8" boarding

5"x 1"   5"x11 1/2"

5"x 1"   5"x11 1/2"

xx

Section AA   Section BB

FRAMED TIMBER PANELS

edge beam

x
x

y
y

yy

end diaphragm

LAMINATED TIMBER PANELS

longitudinal reinforcement   6"

9'0"x 1'7 1/2"x1" thick precast trough units

2" topping with lateral reinforcement

gable diaphragm

gable beam

wall   main edge reinforcement   longitudinal span 56'0"

PRECAST CONCRETE FOLDED SLAB

FOLDED SLAB CONSTRUCTION

coach screwed at the folds, thus uniting adjacent edge members.   At the top is shown an example of a timber folded slab using $\frac{3}{8}$ in. plywood stiffened on the underside by ribs.   The top members are splay cut and are bolted together, and the ends of adjacent panels are bolted together over the supporting beams which are at 26 ft centres.   In the valleys, support and fixing to the beams is given by 18 in. long brackets formed from angle irons welded toe to toe. When the slabs are built up with layers of boarding they must be stiffened at the folds with laminated beams.

Concrete.   Concrete folded slabs may be cast *in situ* or composite construction can be adopted.   This can be carried out in two ways: (i) by casting full size panels and uniting a pair with an *in situ* valley joint before hoisting. The ridge joint will then be formed with *in situ* concrete uniting projecting reinforcing bars; (ii) by using smaller precast trough units spanning from fold to fold as shown on page 459.   Steel is placed at the longitudinal folds and mesh and shear reinforcement on the top before the structural topping is cast.

SPACE FRAMES

Timber.   The application of timber to space frame construction has not been fully developed and timber in folded slab or shell form appears to have received more attention to date.   The main problem in applying timber to space frame constructions is one of connection between timber members in several planes.   One solution is to use three lattice girders and connect them by metal lugs at the nodes, as shown on page 461.   On the same page is shown a suggested approach using steel lugs bolted to the ends of each member by means of which they are fixed to pressed or cast metal "multi-directional" connectors similar to that shown on page 464.

Steel.   Steel space frames may be constructed of cold-rolled sections, angles or tubes riveted, bolted or welded together or to suitably shaped gusset plates or connectors.   Tubes are very suitable since they may be more easily joined at any angle, and due to their better performance in compression will produce lighter structures, particularly over large spans.   On page 461 are shown three examples of steel space frame construction together with details of joints in angles and tubes.   The types of connectors shown on page 464 are also used for space frames.

Concrete.   The development of precasting and prestressing techniques has made possible the use of concrete members of comparatively light weight and small cross sectional area which may be used in the construction of space frames.   The members may be connected together with site bolting and grouting in of reinforcement *in situ*.   Some details of a concrete roof con-

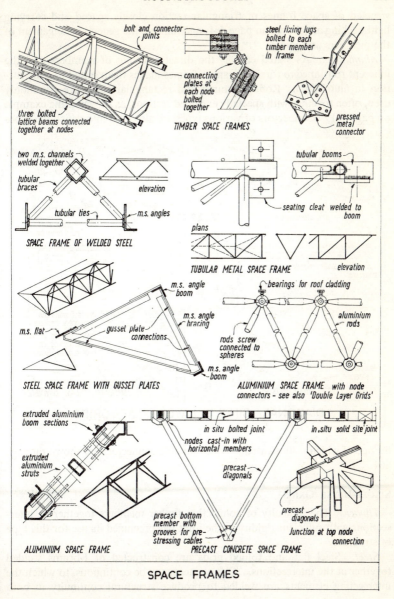

bolt and connector joints

connecting plates at each node bolted together

three bolted lattice beams connected together at nodes

TIMBER SPACE FRAMES

steel fixing lugs bolted to each timber member in frame

pressed metal connector

two m.s. channels welded together

tubular braces

tubular ties

elevation

m.s. angles

SPACE FRAME OF WELDED STEEL

seating cleat welded to boom

tubular booms

plans

TUBULAR METAL SPACE FRAME

elevation

m.s. angle boom

m.s. angle bracing

m.s. flat

gusset plate connections

m.s. angle boom

STEEL SPACE FRAME WITH GUSSET PLATES

bearings for roof cladding

aluminium rods

rods screw connected to spheres

ALUMINIUM SPACE FRAME with node connectors – see also 'Double Layer Grids'

extruded aluminium boom sections

extruded aluminium struts

ALUMINIUM SPACE FRAME

in situ bolted joint

nodes cast-in with horizontal members

precast diagonals

precast bottom member with grooves for pre-stressing cables

in situ solid site joint

precast diagonals

Junction at top node connection

PRECAST CONCRETE SPACE FRAME

SPACE FRAMES

structed of space frames of triangular section closely spaced and carrying light decking are shown on page 461, and indicate the general arrangement of the members and joints.

Aluminium. As stated earlier, the direct stressing of members and the inherent resistance to torsion in space frames makes them suited to construction in aluminium. Rods or round and rectangular tubes are commonly used, often together with specially extruded sections, as shown in the example on page 461. Connectors of various types are also used into which the tubes

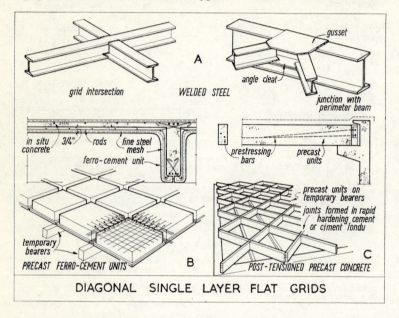

DIAGONAL SINGLE LAYER FLAT GRIDS

fit, one of which is illustrated. Other suitable connectors are shown on page 464.

SINGLE-LAYER GRIDS

Timber. The difficulty of connecting timber members together at intersections with sufficient rigidity at the joint has precluded its use for this type of structure.

Steel. Steel flat and folded grids are constructed of I-beams welded together at the intersections. One element may be continuous, to which the intersecting elements are welded to produce structural continuity in both directions. Alternatively, the beams are "halved" to each other before welding to facilitate positioning of the beams. (See page 462 (A).)

Concrete. Concrete grids have commonly been cast *in situ* and this remains the likely method for heavily loaded grids. Precast "ferro-cement" permanent shuttering has been used to facilitate the accurate casting of the ribs, as shown on page 462 (B). (See also page 430.)

For lightly loaded roofs of long span a lighter structure can be obtained with post-tensioned precast concrete units (page 462 (C)).

Aluminium. The structural limitations of aluminium mentioned earlier preclude its economic use in single layer flat grids.

DOUBLE-LAYER FLAT GRIDS

Timber. The problem of jointing is identical with that in space frame construction and the methods used are the same. Two-way space grids may be constructed with lattice beams in a similar way to the space frame illustrated on page 461, but with the horizontal lattice replaced by top and bottom lateral members connected at the node points to form an interconnected system of triangular space frames (see page 464).

Steel and Aluminium. Double-layer grids are constructed in steel and aluminium in basically the same way as described under space frames. On page 464 are illustrated typical arrangements of members in grids based on prefabricated inverted pyramids built of tubes and angles which are joined together on site as shown. Instead of "open" pyramids, sheet aluminium or plastic can be used to form them as shown on page 464, and they are connected in a similar way but with node connectors to join them to tubes. On the same page are shown methods of connecting together separate members of steel and aluminium tube and cold-rolled channels.

FOLDED LATTICE PLATES

Timber. Two examples are shown on page 465. In one, each of the lattice beams is constructed from prefabricated rectangular frames, each braced with diagonal steel bars or stressed wires. They are bolted together and the whole roof is prestressed by post-tensioned bars at the eaves. The other example shows a roof with wide plates formed of rafters, trussed to give stiffness to the plates, carrying purlins covered with diagonal boarding. Lattice girders are formed in the plane of the slab at the eaves, from which tension cables run to the ends of the ridge which acts as a strut.

Steel and Aluminium. Lattice plates can be constructed of angle sections joined by gussets or in tubular welded construction. Each lattice is prefabricated and the adjacent chord members joined by site welding or bolting

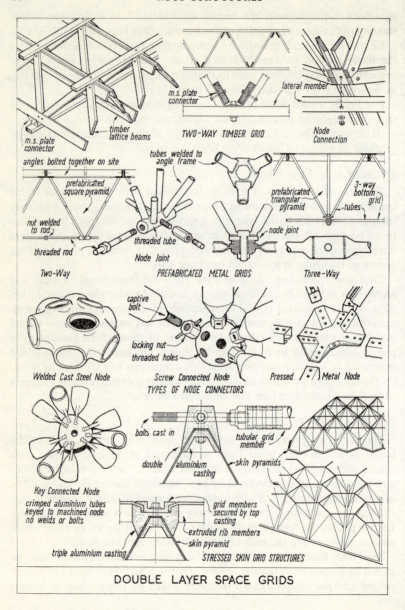

m.s. plate connector
timber lattice beams
TWO-WAY TIMBER GRID
m.s. plate connector
lateral member
Node Connection

angles bolted together on site
prefabricated square pyramid
tubes welded to angle frame
prefabricated triangular pyramid
3-way bottom grid
tubes
nut welded to rod
threaded rod
threaded tube
Node Joint
node joint
Two-Way
PREFABRICATED METAL GRIDS
Three-Way

captive bolt
locking nut
threaded holes
Welded Cast Steel Node
Screw Connected Node
TYPES OF NODE CONNECTORS
Pressed Metal Node

Key Connected Node
crimped aluminium tubes keyed to machined node no welds or bolts
bolts cast in
double aluminium casting
tubular grid member
skin pyramids
triple aluminium casting
grid members secured by top casting
extruded rib members
skin pyramid
STRESSED SKIN GRID STRUCTURES

DOUBLE LAYER SPACE GRIDS

together suitable flanges welded to them (see below). Metal glazing bars may be screwed or welded to the framework where roof lighting is required, and solid areas may be covered with prefabricated panels clipped to the members. Alternatively, the frame may be covered with concrete on expanded metal with the internal surfaces sprayed with vermiculite plaster.

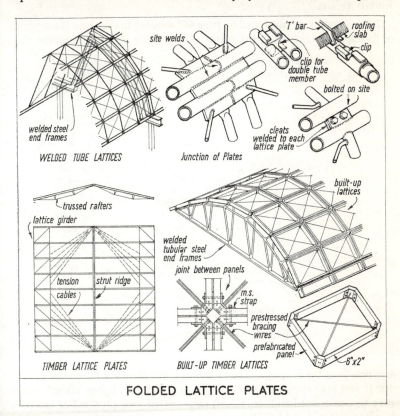

WELDED TUBE LATTICES

Junction of Plates

'T' bar

roofing slab

clip

clip for double tube member

bolted on site

cleats welded to each lattice plate

welded steel end frames

built-up lattices

trussed rafters

lattice girder

welded tubular steel end frames

joint between panels

tension cables

strut ridge

m.s. strap

prestressed bracing wires

prefabricated panel

6"x2"

TIMBER LATTICE PLATES

BUILT-UP TIMBER LATTICES

FOLDED LATTICE PLATES

BRACED BARREL VAULTS

Timber. "Lamella" construction, described on page 434, can be used for braced barrel vaults. This is illustrated on page 466, where the lamellas are shown joined with simple bolted connections. A modified form has a more complicated joint involving steel plates, but which preserves the visual continuity of the ribs.

Steel and Aluminium. Braced barrel vaults are constructed in these metals on the lines described for other grid systems. The methods of covering have been described above under lattice plates. Steel and aluminium lamella construction can also be used.

RIBBED DOMES

Two examples are illustrated on page 467 showing in each case the methods of forming the junction at the crown, by connector or by compression ring,

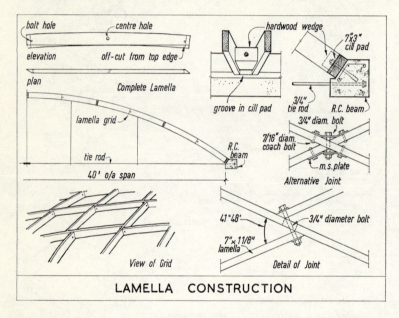

LAMELLA CONSTRUCTION

and details of the bracing. The timber example shown is for a span of over 300 ft and is covered with woodwool slabs. Smaller, lighter ribbed domes may be constructed with laminated ribs covered with plywood or layers of tongued and grooved boarding.

GRID DOMES

Timber. "Lamella" construction or triangular stiffened ply or framed panels similar to those on page 459 may be used for grid domes.

Steel. Tubular steel grid domes may be constructed with node connectors into which the tubes are inserted and welded, similar to those used for double layer grids, but using six-way instead of eight-way connectors to form a three-way grid, as shown on page 468.

Concrete. Grid domes may be formed in concrete either *in situ* or by the two methods shown on page 462 for plane grids.

Aluminium. Aluminium grid domes may be constructed with members

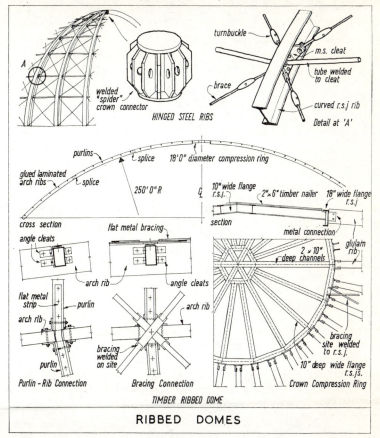

RIBBED DOMES

joined by types of connectors already described. Another form is shown on page 468 in which channel section members are bolted to a cast hexagonal connector. An alternative for two-way grids using rectangular aluminium tubes cross-halved to each other is also shown. The tubes are extruded or built up from extruded sections according to the size of the domes.

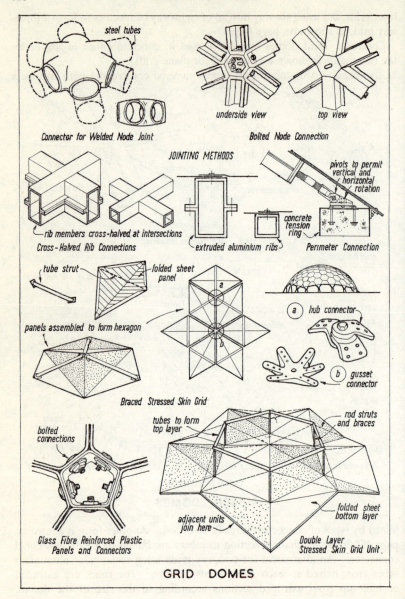

steel tubes

Connector for Welded Node Joint

underside view

top view

Bolted Node Connection

JOINTING METHODS

rib members cross-halved at intersections

Cross-Halved Rib Connections

extruded aluminium ribs

pivots to permit vertical and horizontal rotation

concrete tension ring

Perimeter Connection

tube strut

folded sheet panel

a

b

panels assembled to form hexagon

a hub connector

b gusset connector

Braced Stressed Skin Grid

bolted connections

tubes to form top layer

rod struts and braces

folded sheet bottom layer

adjacent units join here

Glass Fibre Reinforced Plastic Panels and Connectors

Double Layer Stressed Skin Grid Unit

GRID DOMES

The use of sheet material by means of which the grid members are formed, and are strengthened against buckling by the membrane action of the sheets, has been described. One system (page 468), uses prefabricated diamond-shaped sheet aluminium panels, three of which form a basic hexagon when joined together. When fabricated the struts form an external hexagonal grid. A similar but double-layer system is also shown.

Plastics. Aluminium is not the only material which can be used for stressed skin structures of this type. Sheet steel would be satisfactory. But as explained earlier in this chapter, materials which lack great stiffness, such as aluminium, or are brittle in addition, such as plastics, can most effectively be used in this way. One application of plastics is shown on page 468 in which flanged triangular panels of glass fibre reinforced polyester resin, are bolted together to form a geodesic dome. Two sizes of panel are used with hexagonal and pentagonal connectors at the apices.

TENSION STRUCTURES

Details of this form of construction vary widely. Cable structures can be clad with light metal sheets such as corrugated aluminium, tongued and grooved timber boards or lightweight slabs or panels covered with waterproof membrane, "gunite" concrete sprayed on to expanding metal lathing or with sprayed-on plastic of a suitable type.

Some details are shown on page 470. Temperature changes affect the length of the cables and some provision for movement must be made in the cladding, similar to that shown at the joint between the plywood panels.

MOVEMENT CONTROL

Settlement Movement. Where settlement joints are provided in the structure, as described in Chapter 5, the joint in the roof slab must be designed to permit relative movement as in the case of floors and will be designed in a similar way. Methods of weatherproofing the joint will in principle be similar to those adopted for expansion joints (see page 224 (R, S)).

Thermal Movement. Thermal insulation placed on top of the roof slab may be sufficient to keep movement to a negligible amount in small buildings, but in large buildings, although movement will be reduced, expansion joints will usually be required. Long parapets should always be provided with expansion joints. Typical details of expansion joints in roofs are shown on page 224. Extensive roofs will require joints in both directions and a method of forming a four-way junction at an intersection is shown at (U). Provision for movement in long beams to framed roof structures is made by means of hinged, roller and rocker bearings. Reference is made in Chapter 5,

16

page 221, to the magnitude of thermal movements and to constructional details of expansion joints generally.

When a long roof slab is supported on loadbearing masonry walls, damage to the walls may be caused by the outward thrust at the ends of the roof unless

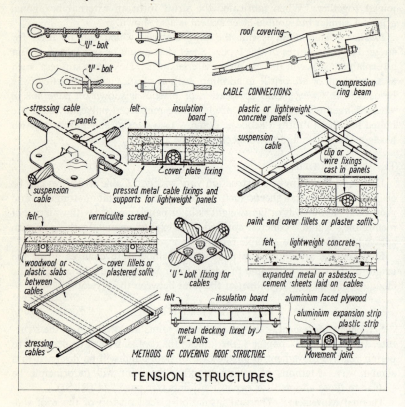

CABLE CONNECTIONS

METHODS OF COVERING ROOF STRUCTURE

TENSION STRUCTURES

(i) continuous expansion joints are formed in the roof and walls, or (ii) expansion joints are formed in the roof and a sliding bearing on the walls is incorporated. Cracking in top floor partitions caused by roof movement can be avoided by isolating the top of the partition from the roof slab. Plaster should not be carried over the junction of walls or partition with the roof slab[1] (see page 221).

[1] See *Principles of Modern Building*, Volume 1, 3rd Edition, Chapter 2, and *Building Research Station Digest* No. 12.

10
Fire Protection

Fire protection is the protection of the occupants, contents and structure of a building from the risks associated with fire. The subject is so important and is so linked with the construction of buildings that it is essential to have an understanding of the factors which influence the nature and form of fire protection and of the principles which are the basis of the various regulations. It is for this reason that it is discussed in this chapter in relatively broad terms, involving as it does considerations of planning as well as of construction, rather than in terms merely of the constructional aspects of protection which, in fact, are conditioned by, and cannot be separated from, planning aspects.

Fires are almost always the result of negligence. The rate of growth, ultimate severity and nature of risks involved in the event of fire depend largely on the use to which the building is being put. For example, a theatre or concert hall, because of the large number of people accommodated, involves a high life risk even though the combustible contents may be low. But a large warehouse storing much combustible material involves a considerable risk of extensive damage to structure and contents but a low risk to occupants because their number is likely to be small. The degree of damage finally sustained will be influenced by the structure, its effectiveness in confining the fire and its ability to remain stable at the seat of the fire and remote from it.

It is the purpose of fire protection, therefore, to protect life, goods and activities within a building. This it does by inhibiting the combustion of the materials from which it is constructed and by preventing the spread of fire internally throughout the building and to other buildings. In addition, by ensuring that the elements of construction fulfil their functions during a fire for a sufficient length of time to enable the occupants to escape and the fire brigade to deal effectively with the outbreak and thus limit the total damage. The protective measures to accomplish this involve suitable forms of construction, suitable planning of the building internally and in relation to adjacent buildings, and satisfactory planning and construction of the means of escape.

GROWTH OF FIRE IN BUILDINGS

The origin of a fire is usually the result of negligence, ranging from direct acts such as lighted cigarettes left burning to more indirect causes such as poor installation and maintenance of electrical wiring and the ineffective control of vermin.

The growth of a fire depends on the amount and disposition of combustible material within the building, either in the form of unfixed materials or parts of the fabric such as wall and ceiling linings, which will contribute to the fire.[1] At the beginning of a fire materials near the source of ignition receive heat and their temperature rises until, at a certain point, inflammable gases are given off. Ignition of the material then occurs and it begins to produce heat instead of merely receiving it. This "primary" fire then preheats the remaining combustible material and raises its temperature to ignition point. After this a spark or, for example, a flame burning along a floor board, will in a moment start an intense fire involving the whole of the contents. The time taken for this flash spread of the fire, or "flash-over" as it is termed, to occur depends on the proximity of combustible materials to the source of the fire and on the presence or otherwise of an adequate supply of oxygen. In full-scale tests on domestic living rooms this "flash-over" occurred after about fifteen minutes.[2] At an early stage the structure at the seat of the fire becomes involved and the strength of some non-combustible materials such as steel, for example, is affected.[2]

The further spread of fire occurs by the usual methods of heat propagation, that is, by conduction, convection and radiation, together with the process of flame spread across the surfaces of combustible materials.

Depending on the construction and design of the building, heat can be conducted through walls causing temperatures high enough to ignite spontaneously any combustible materials stacked on the side remote from the fire.

Any unprotected flue-like apertures such as stair-wells, lift shafts, or light-wells may permit the spread of fire by the passage of convection currents and flying brands.

Heat can be radiated to ignite combustible materials at some distance from the source. In this way fire is spread to other areas as well as to nearby buildings.

The spread of fire is more rapid where combustible linings are used, and

---

[1] See "Combustible Materials", page 479.
[2] "Studies of the Growth of Fire", *Fire Protection Association Journal*, Reprint No. 1.

particularly where air spaces exist behind them as this provides two surfaces over which flame can spread.

The later stages in the progress of a fire are mostly affected by the behaviour of the particular structure involved. The deformation of supporting columns and beams in a framed building structure may cause apertures in enclosing walls and floors through which direct flame spread can occur. Ultimately, the complete collapse of a building may happen as a result of the weakening of the structure and the gutting of all but the incombustible parts such as brick walls. It should be noted that structures with a high degree of continuity can be particularly hazardous in this respect, since the collapse of one component can produce far-reaching effects throughout the rest of the building.

The hazards associated with fire may be considered in order of importance as:

Personal: the hazard to the occupants of the building.

Damage: the hazard to the structure and contents.

Exposure: the hazard due to the spread of fire to other buildings.[1]

The hazards to occupants are due to the following factors:

Reduction of Oxygen. This is due to the consumption of oxygen by the fire and is accompanied by toxic or asphyxiating gases evolved by the fire, particularly carbon monoxide. An associated additional hazard is smoke which results from incomplete combustion. Staircases usable as means of escape and corridors giving access to them, where exposed to any particular risk, should be protected by fire-resisting partitions and self-closing fire-resisting doors. Wherever possible staircases should be ventilated to the open air in all storeys.

The degree of hazard to occupants is influenced by the distance between points of escape, size and number of exits and stairs, and the existence or otherwise of a sprinkler system.

Increase in Temperature. Breathing is difficult above a temperature of 300°F, and since this temperature will be reached well in advance of the path of the fire, it is essential that automatic alarms be provided, designed to operate at given temperatures (120°–158°F).

Spread of Flame. The risk here is of burning by physical contact with flame and should be minimized by enclosing escape routes with non-combustible materials, or materials of low flame spread.

The practical requirements in dealing with these hazards are discussed in more detail in later sections of this chapter.

---

[1] See *Post-War Building Study* No. 20, "Fire Grading of Buildings, Part I", H.M.S.O.

FIRE-GRADING

The term "fire-grading" has a two-fold application. (*a*) It is applied to the classification or grading of the elements of structure of buildings in terms of their degree of resistance to fire. (*b*) With a broader meaning, it is applied to the classification of buildings according to the purpose for which they are used, that is, according to occupancy, and according to the fire resistance of the elements of which they are constructed.

This grading of buildings is considered from two points of view, firstly in terms of damage and exposure hazard, for which the protection is mainly provided by structural precautions, and secondly in terms of personal hazard, for which protection is provided primarily by easy means of escape. The first is considered here and the second later under the sections on fire escape.

The severity of a fire depends largely upon the amount, nature and distribution of combustible material in a building. Thus in determining the requisite degree of fire protection it is necessary to take into account the use and size of a given building, and by this means to assess the probable amount and type of combustible material which would contribute to a fire.

Fire Load

The assessment of the severity of a fire due to the combustible materials in a building is made by reference to what is known as the "fire load", which is the amount of heat, expressed in British Thermal Units, which would be generated per square foot of floor area of a compartment of the building by the complete combustion of its contents and any combustible parts of the building. The fire load is determined by multiplying the weight of all the combustible materials by their calorific values and dividing by the area of the floor; it is based on the assumption that the materials are uniformly distributed over the whole area of the floor.

The calorific value is the property of a material which indicates the amount of heat which will be generated by a particular quantity of that material and it governs the ultimate severity of a fire. Thus the maximum heat is evolved from materials having highest calorific values, e.g.

bitumen	15,200	B.Th.U.'s/lb
cork	7,200	,,
paper	7,000	,,
petrol	20,000	,,
rubber	17,000	,,
wood	8,000	,,[1]

[1] See *Post-War Building Study* No. 20, Appendix III, for list of calorific values.

An office, therefore, with 5 lb/sq. ft of combustible furniture and papers would have a fire load of 35,000–40,000 B.Th.U.'s/sq. ft.

The fire load is used as a means of grading occupancies, and the grading set out by the Joint Committee on Fire Grading of Buildings[1] is shown in Table 28.

Table 28

Grade of occupancy	Low fire load	Moderate fire load	High fire load
Fire load B.Th.U.'s/ sq. ft	Not exceeding 100,000 (200,000 on limited isolated areas)	100,000 to 200,000 (not exceeding 400,000 on limited isolated areas)	200,000 to 400,000 (not exceeding 800,000 on limited isolated areas)
Building types	Flats, offices, restaurants, hotels, hospitals, schools, museums, public libraries	Retail shops, e.g. footwear, clothing, furniture, groceries. Factories and workshops generally	Warehouses, etc., used for bulk storage of materials of non-hazardous nature
Equivalent severity of fire in hours of standard test	1	2	4

Materials of the same calorific value can give rise to differences in fire risk according to ease of ignition, rate of burning and whether or not, for example, they are explosive or emit dangerous fumes. These would constitute exceptional risks. In addition, certain processes such as paint spraying with inflammable materials, or the application of heat to combustible materials, also constitute exceptional risks.[2] Any building in which these risks are likely to arise or in which the fire load is greater than the maximum for High Fire Load grading must be considered separately.

[1] See *Post-War Building Study* No. 20.
[2] *Ibid.* Appendices I and II for lists of abnormal materials and occupancies.

FIRE RESISTANCE

It has been stated earlier in this chapter that protective measures against fire include means for limiting the spread of fire together with the provision of structural elements capable of fulfilling their functions during a fire without the risk of collapse. The first, to some extent,[1] and the second entirely, depend upon the use of elements of structure[2] of an appropriate degree of fire resistance.

The term "fire resistance" used in connection with fire protection has the precise meaning defined in B.S. 476.[3] It is limited to elements of structure and is not applied to a material. Fire resistance depends on the way in which materials are used in an element and not solely on whether they are combustible or not. This standard lays down tests for establishing the fire resistance of various elements of structure by means of which different forms of construction may be graded according to the length of time during which they will function satisfactorily under the action of the standard test fire (see page 480).

Measurements have been taken of the severity of fires caused by different fire loads. This information has enabled the degrees of severity of fires due to known fire loads to be expressed in terms of periods of exposure to the standard test fire.

For design purposes the equivalent severities shown in Table 28 were adopted by the Joint Committee on Fire Grading of Buildings.

This means that if a building is to contain a fire load of 150,000 B.Th.U.'s/sq. ft, walls, floors and other elements of construction having a fire resistance of 2 hrs would resist the effects of fire without collapse or penetration of the fire even if all the material within it burned.

The determination of the necessary fire resistance of every structure on the assumption that it must withstand the complete burn-out of the contents would pay no regard to the effect of other means of protection, such as fire-fighting and automatic sprinklers, for example, and would render impractic-

---

[1] Other factors in limiting the spread of fire are the use of non-combustible linings and planning considerations.

[2] These are defined in L.C.C. By-law 1.03, under "element of construction", as

(a) Any floor, beam or column.
(b) Any partition or wall which separates parts or divisions of a building used for different purposes or tenanted by different persons.

M.B. Byelaw 45 gives a similar list of elements.

In both cases separate reference is made to external, party and fire division walls—L.C.C. By-laws 9.02, 9.03; M.B. Byelaws 38–42.

[3] B.S. 476:1953, Part I: "Fire Tests on Building Materials and Structures"—"a relative term used to designate that property by virtue of which an element of structure as a whole functions satisfactorily for a specified period whilst subjected to prescribed heat influence and load."

able many sound forms of construction and make the cost of the structure high. Lesser degrees of resistance relative to fire load become practicable, however, by assuming a rational combination of all methods of fire protection and by having regard to the fact that in smaller buildings escape and fire fighting is easier, and fires can more easily be brought under control with less chance of the structure collapsing.

In practice, therefore, the necessary fire resistance in any particular case is determined with reference to fire load, the areas of floors and the height and cubic capacity of the building.

For convenience the required fire resistance for the elements of structure determined in this way with reference to the size and use of different building types is given in building regulations which tabulate this information to assist designers.[1]

MATERIALS IN RELATION TO FIRE

Effect of Fire on Materials and Structures

1. Non-combustible Materials. These are materials which if decomposed by heat will do so endo-thermically, that is, with the absorption of heat or, if they oxidize, do so with negligible evolution of heat. Also included are those materials which require a temperature beyond the range of most fires before they react in any way.

Non-combustible materials do not contribute to the growth of a fire but are damaged when the temperature is reached where decomposition, fusion or significant loss of strength occurs. When incorporated in the structure the loss of strength may be such that they no longer maintain the integrity of the structure. Examples of such materials are metal, stone, glass, concrete, clay products, gypsum products and asbestos products.

Apart from marble and gypsum, which liberate free lime under severe heat, the majority of these materials do not decompose chemically under the action of fire. However, certain natural stones, concrete, gypsum and asbestos products decompose by losing their water of crystallization, and in so doing acquire pronounced fire endurance. Although metal and glass suffer negligible decomposition, these materials lose considerable strength at high temperatures and glass and some metals such as aluminium and lead, fuse or soften under heat. Asbestos cement is liable to shatter in intense heat and will disintegrate when struck by water during a fire.

---

[1] (1) Table as Part III, Byelaw 45, p. 32, Model Building Byelaws, Series IV, 1953, (2) Table as Part IX, By-law 9.02, L.C.C. London Building (Constructional) By-laws. 1952. (3) L.C.C. principles for guidance entitled "Buildings of Excess Height and/or Additional Cubical Extent".

16*

Steel. It should be noted that steel loses strength and rigidity above a temperature of 570°F and at 800–900°F, a temperature well within the normal range of building fires, there is a loss of strength of up to 80%. This potential weakness, together with the expansion which takes place under heat, means that in the early stages of a fire unprotected steelwork will bend, buckle and expand. This causes walls and floors to fall away and leaves the fire free to spread into other areas which might not have been affected had the structure been maintained. This is an example which underlines the fact that non-combustible materials are not necessarily fire-resisting and this may be further emphasized by considering timber, which although combustible will, if of adequate section, fulfil its structural function longer than mild steel.

Aluminium. The poor performance of aluminium structures in this respect should also be noted. Aluminium has a much lower critical temperature than steel and for elements under load this has been given as 400°F as against 932°F for steel.[1] No reference is made in the by-laws to methods of protecting structural work in aluminium alloy from fire. It would appear that this material is only suitable for buildings of low fire risk or where the solution to the structural problem transcends the fire risk as, for example, in the case of hangars.

Concrete. The behaviour of concrete under action of fire depends largely upon the type of aggregate used. Flint gravel expands greatly and causes spalling of the concrete. Other stones, apart from limestone, behave similarly to a lesser degree, but crushed clay brick and slag do not cause spalling. Provided spalling does not occur, disintegration is slow. Thus additional protection can be given to reinforcement or steel members by increasing the concrete cover so long as non-spalling concrete is used. If a spalling type is used the cover tends to break and fall away.

In terms of fire resistance, aggregates are classified as follows, those in Class 1 being the non-spalling types:

Class 1   Foamed slag, pumice, blast furnace slag, crushed brick and burnt clay products, including expanded clay, well-burned clinker, crushed limestone.

Class 2   Flint, gravel, granite and all crushed natural stones other than limestone.

At temperatures higher than those required to produce spalling the free lime in the cement is converted into quicklime after which, if the concrete is exposed to water, or even moist air, the lime slakes and in expanding causes complete disintegration of the concrete.

[1] International Convention for the Safety of Life at Sea, 1948. M.O.T. recommendation.

2. Combustible Materials. These are materials which, within the temperature range associated with fires, will combine exothermically with oxygen. That is to say, in their reaction with oxygen considerable heat is evolved and they flame or glow.

Such materials, whether forming part of the structure or the contents of the building, are responsible for the growth of a fire and its ultimate severity. Examples of such materials are wood or wood products, vegetable products, animal products and manufactured products such as fibre-board and straw-board. Within this classification are flammable materials which ignite readily and react vigorously, producing rapid flame spread. Examples of these materials are volatile liquids (petroleum distillates), certain plastics (nitro-cellulose products) and certain paints based on the latter material.

Timber. Although timber is a combustible material it will, as pointed out earlier, function as a structural member for a longer period than one of metal provided it is of adequate section. If of sufficient size timber is extremely difficult to burn. Some species such as teak, iroko, jarrah and others are highly resistant to fire.

Wood boarding up to ⅜ in. thick ignites relatively easily and continues to burn. But timbers about 6 in. thick will char in depth and this inhibits rapid combustion of the wood beneath. Tests have indicated that for any given cross-sectional area and load, a beam having a square cross section will have the longest fire endurance, that is, the time elapsing before collapse occurs.

The degree of combustibility of timber can be reduced by treatment with a suitable fire-retardant. Pressure impregnation gives better results than brush applications. Treated timber is difficult to work and should be worked to finished sizes before impregnation.

The following characteristics of combustible materials will influence the precautions necessary in providing adequate protection.

Ignitability. A measure of the ease of ignition expressed as the minimum temperature at which the material ignites under given atmospheric conditions, e.g. wood, wood products and cellulose materials 430–570°F, plastics 500–900°F, synthetics of nitro-cellulose origin upwards of 280°F, bitumen upwards of 150°F, petrol distillates 400–900°F.

Flammability. The property of a combustible material which determines the severity of flame and flame spread. It is related to volatility and the vigour with which volatile gases react with oxygen. In addition to actual volatile liquids which may be stored within a building, many organic natural and synthetic materials exhibit this property, particularly when well dispersed as in fabrics.

Calorific Content. The rate at which heat is generated in the reaction between all combustible materials and oxygen is related directly to the flammability of a material, and the ease with which the reaction occurs is related to the ignitability of the material. This has been discussed briefly, page 475.

It will be obvious from what has been said regarding the effect of fire upon materials and structures that in the design of buildings it is essential to have some means of assessing the likely behaviour in fire of various materials and forms of construction, particularly at a time when new materials and combinations of new materials to form structural elements are constantly being introduced. B.S. 476: 1953, Part 1, provides means for grading or classifying both materials and structures for this purpose. This has been referred to briefly already with regard to elements of structure and will now be considered generally.

Fire-Resistance Grading

The fire-resistance grading of elements of structure is determined by tests carried out in accordance with British Standard 476 by the Department of Scientific and Industrial Research and Fire Offices' Committee Joint Fire Research Organization. The tests are applied to elements of structure whether composed of one or more materials. The elements are graded according to the length of time during which, while exposed to the heat of special furnaces,[1] they satisfy certain conditions laid down in the Standard.

It must be understood that the grading is applied to the structural element as a whole and to a precise specification of that element. What may appear to be minor changes in the details of construction of an element may result in a great change in its fire resistance.[2]

The notional periods of fire resistance ascribed to elements of structure comprising various materials are shown in the illustrated Tables on pages 512–523. The information in these Tables is extracted from Tables A–G, Schedule VI, L.C.C. (Constructional) By-laws, 1952, and Tables A–D, Schedule IV, and Appendix, Model Building Byelaws, 1953. It should be borne in mind, however, that other parts of the by-laws, in controlling the details of construction, may make provisions in excess of the requirements of these Tables. For example, L.C.C. By-law 6.02 (Revised) lays down minimum solid covers to steel beams and columns in external walls and for steelwork likely to be adversely affected by moisture from adjoining earth,

---

[1] These are fully illustrated in *National Building Studies Research Paper* No. 12, "Investigations on Building Fires".

[2] B.R.S. Digest 106, "Fire: Materials and Structure", gives as an example the fire resistance of a 4½ in. brick wall which may be increased from just less than 2 hr to 6 hr by the application of ½ in. gypsum perlite plaster on each side.

which are greater than those required for the shorter periods of fire resistance. The Model Byelaws refer to the relevant B.S. Codes of Practice for the design of steelwork and reinforced concrete and these should be consulted in conjunction with Tables C and D, Schedule IV, in arriving at the required cover to steel members and reinforcement.

It should be noted that the Model Byelaws do not classify the requirements for staircases in the same manner as the L.C.C. By-laws.

CLASSIFICATION OF COMBUSTIBLE MATERIALS

Whilst building regulations published by local authorities require specific periods of fire resistance to be attained by various parts of a structure, they do not include comprehensive instructions for the use of combustible materials, although they are specific about the use of non-combustible materials. At present the only comprehensive instructions for the use of certain combustible materials are those for school buildings given in *Ministry of Education Building Bulletin* No. 7, "Fire and the Design of Schools". However, since the Model Building Byelaws lay down a requirement for thermal insulation of houses, and since an adequate degree of thermal insulation is acknowledged as normal desirable building practice, it is clear that combustible materials are likely to be employed in building.

Some materials are obviously combustible. Others are not obviously so because they burn so slowly. Yet in a fire they could contribute to its severity. Further, wall and ceiling linings, which present large surfaces, provide an easy means for the spread of fire when constructed of combustible materials. Particularly is this so where air spaces or cavities exist behind such linings, so permitting the rapid and undetected spread of fire. For practical design purposes some method is required to determine whether or not a material is combustible, and also the ease with which flame is likely to spread over its surface. British Standard 476 specifies two tests in this connection: (*a*) combustibility; (*b*) surface spread of flame. The first decides whether or not a material will burn or contribute to a fire, although no degree of combustibility is defined; the second compares the rate and extent of flame spread along the surfaces of different materials, and classifies the results as follows:

Class 1—Surfaces of very low flame spread
Class 2—Surfaces of low flame spread
Class 3—Surfaces of medium flame spread
Class 4—Surfaces of rapid flame spread.

The results of these tests and the results of fire-resistance tests under the same standard, should not be confused. A material which satisfies the combustibility test might fail under the conditions for fire-resistance test; a building-board having Class 1 flame spread classification may or may not make a significant contribution to the fire resistance of a composite structure in which it is used. Apart from one type of ceiling to timber floors building regulations do not at present give any fire-resistance periods for structures

---

Table 29   Spread of flame classification of wall and ceiling linings

---

Class 1

    Plaster board
    Wood wool slabs
    Metal-faced plywood
    Fibre insulating board with surface treatment of certain flame-retardant
        paints
    Fibre insulating board with asbestos paper face
    Fibre insulating board with $\frac{3}{16}$ in. skim plaster coat
    Hardboard with surface treatment of certain flame-retardant paints
    Hardboard with impregnation by certain flame-retardant agents
    Compressed straw slabs with asbestos paper face
    Compressed straw slabs with surface treatment of certain flame-retardant
        paints
    Compressed straw slabs with $\frac{3}{16}$ in. skim plaster coat
    Asbestos and other non-combustible boards

Class 2

    Synthetic-resin-bonded paper and fabric sheets
    Compressed straw slabs (uncovered)

Class 3

    Timber weighing more than 25 lb/cu. ft
    Plywood weighing more than 25 lb/cu. ft
    Wood-particle board
    Hardboard
    Compressed straw slabs (paper covered)
    Glass-reinforced polyester-resin sheets (with fire-retardant additives)
    Fibre insulating board with two coats of distemper

Class 4

    Timber weighing less than 25 lb/cu. ft
    Plywood weighing less than 25 lb/cu. ft
    Fibre insulating board
    Acrylic sheets (polymethyl methacrylate)
    Glass-reinforced polyester-resin sheets (without fire-retardant additives)

---

incorporating combustible materials such as building boards (although provision is made for the addition of this information at a later date) but the results of fire-resistance tests of some elements of structure incorporating building boards have been published[1] and these are shown on pages 512–523. Table 29 shows the surface spread of flame classification for various types of building board and slab.

It will be noticed that the classification of a material may be altered by the application of a paint or fire-retardant solution, but too great a dependence should not be placed on these treatments. Some materials achieving a particular surface classification in this way may, in fact, under certain conditions aid the development of a fire to a greater extent than those achieving the same classification without treatment. This has been shown by the results of fire tests in rooms fully lined with various materials.[2]

These tests also indicate that in terms of aiding the development of fire there is not a great difference between this type of Class 1 lining and Class 3 linings. In view of this, therefore, when Class 1 linings must be used it is probably advisable to limit the choice to those achieving this class without surface treatment, as is required by the *Ministry of Education Building Bulletin* No. 7, "Fire and the Design of Schools". Further, the behaviour of these paints and solutions during the use of a building is not fully known, and it is possible that their effectiveness may be reduced by heat and condensation, for example. For this reason insurance companies prefer inherently low surface flame spread materials if incombustible alternatives are out of the question for reasons of economy, and this is reflected in the premiums charged.

The fact that Class 1 covers materials each of which, under the same conditions, can assist the growth of fire to a different extent has resulted in the development of a test which provides a better basis of comparison of the behaviour of these materials and at the same time is simpler than the spread of flame test. It is likely to replace the latter in future editions of B.S. 476.

THE USE OF COMBUSTIBLE MATERIALS

As has previously been mentioned, combustible linings are potentially more dangerous when there are air spaces behind them. This condition arises when these materials are used as a wall lining on battens, as a cladding to timber or metal studs in partitions or as false ceilings to mask beams and

---

[1] See Fire Protection Association leaflet "Fire-Resistance Grading in Buildings" and Fire Notes Nos. 1 and 2—"Fire Resistance of Floors and Ceilings" and "Protection of Structural Steel against Fire" (H.M.S.O.).
[2] See *Building Research Station Digest* No. 106.

services. It often occurs in light factory-type buildings where the inner insulating lining is separated from the outer cladding by the structural framing supporting both (see below, A). The hazard is particularly great in the case of roofs, since the lateral spread of flame causes the main fire to spread by radiation and by the fall of burning pieces of the lining itself. Linings should

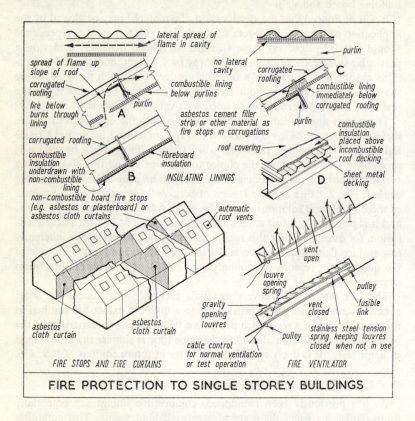

FIRE PROTECTION TO SINGLE STOREY BUILDINGS

therefore be of Class 1 spread of flame and non-combustible or underdrawn with a non-combustible sheeting if combustible, as at B. To avoid continuous air spaces, the lining should be placed directly below the roof covering, and fire breaks or non-combustible infillings provided where corrugated or other profiled sheeting is used, as at C. Further fire breaks can be formed in roof spaces by enclosing roof trusses with fire-resisting building boards.

Where a decking is used, combustible insulating linings should be placed above the deck and below the roof covering to avoid the creation of air spaces, page 484 D. However, advantage should be taken of non-combustible linings by placing them below the deck in order to protect it from fire below. To avoid continuous air spaces above false ceilings formed with combustible linings, the lining should be placed directly below any downstand beams tight against the soffits.

An example of good all-round performance is that of wood wool slab decking, which is self-spanning, of good insulation value and Class 1 spread of flame classification.

In addition to the fire hazard of insulating lining materials, roof coverings may contribute to a fire. Although regulations require non-combustible coverings generally, they permit the use of combustible coverings on a non-combustible base or in circumstances where the building in question is well away from any adjacent property.[1] Combustible coverings used are mastic asphalt, bitumen felts of both mineral and vegetable base and bitumen protected metal. Mastic asphalt can be considered as of low fire risk due to the large proportion of inert material in it, but bitumen burns easily and should only be used directly on a non-combustible and fire-resistant decking or layer, since collapse of the deck would spread fire into the building from outside and fire to the roof from the inside. In the form of protected corrugated metal sheeting, bitumen coverings are particularly hazardous when combined with combustible linings, as was shown in the Jaguar Car Factory fire in 1957. One of the chief factors contributing to the spread of that fire was the fall of flaming bitumen and lining material on to the factory floor well in advance of the main fire.

The introduction of asbestos into the make-up of bituminous roof coverings considerably reduces their fire hazard. Both asbestos based felts and asbestos shrouded protected metal sheeting afford good protection since, although the bitumen burns, the blanket of asbestos resists the penetration of fire.

In addition to wood wool already mentioned, the following insulating materials may be used without fire hazard: asbestos insulating board, plasterboard, vermiculite, glass fibre and mineral wool (the last two without a bitumen binder or paper covering).

B.S. 476:1958, Part 3, specifies a test to assess the capacity of a roof construction to prevent the penetration of fire from outside and the degree to which the covering will spread fire. The test is less severe than those used

[1] L.C.C. By-law 11.01.   M.B. Byelaw 49.

to establish fire resistance and the resulting roof gradings are not called fire resisting.

Translucent and transparent corrugated plastic sheets are combustible, but the behaviour of different types varies. Specific requirements for this type of material are to be found only in the Model Byelaws issued by the Department of Health for Scotland. These, at the moment, restrict its use in roof lights to certain types of building, and limit the amount and the situation of the material in a roof. But developments in the realm of plastics may permit some relaxation to be made on their future use.

The usual requirements of the L.C.C. when approving the use of resin bonded fibreglass roof lights are that (i) The area of any panel shall not exceed in any one part 30 sq. ft; (ii) Every part of the roof not covered with the material shall be covered with a non-combustible material; (iii) The distance between any two adjacent panels (*a*) measured along the roof parallel to the eaves shall not be less than the width of the panels, (*b*) measured up the slope of the roof shall be not less than the length of the panels (*width* is measured parallel to the eaves, *length* up the roof slope); (iv) No part of any panel shall be nearer the ridge or the eaves than the length of that panel.

The material must contain a fire retardant and must have been tested by the Joint Fire Research Organization and the weight of the glass fibre mat in it must weigh not less than 2 oz per sq. ft. The Council also lays down requirements regarding the joints between the sheets and between the sheets and roof covering.

FACTORS AFFECTING DESIGN

GENERAL DESIGN AND PLANNING

The broad approach to planning for fire protection is to design the elements of construction to withstand the action of fire for a given period dependent on the size and use of the building, to compartmentalize the building so as to isolate the fire within a given section or area, to separate specific risks within the building and generally to prevent the uncontrolled spread of fire from its source to other parts of the building. Further, a building must be planned to allow the occupants to escape by their own unaided efforts. Suitable separation must be provided to prevent fire, hot gases and smoke from spreading rapidly by means of common spaces such as corridors, staircases and lift shafts, thus trapping the occupants and causing panic.

Separation. The structural elements used to prevent horizontal and vertical spread of fire are the walls and floors, together with any structure necessary to support them, all of which must be of adequate fire resistance.

Any openings within these elements of separation must be protected in a manner which does not nullify the effect of that element during a fire, whilst affording access during normal use. Such protection may be given by self-closing, fire-resisting doors or steel doors or roller shutters held open by fusible links and arranged to close automatically in the event of fire. Glazing must be fire resistant where light is required to penetrate the separating elements.

It has been found in practice that where fires occur in large undivided spaces within a building, the greater intensity of heat and volume of smoke generated prevents fire-fighters from attacking the fire at its source. They are driven out of the building, where their hoses become less effective. It is generally considered that 250,000 cu. ft is the maximum volume of any one compartment which could reasonably be tolerated from a fire-fighting stand-point. This figure will vary in practice according to the use to which a building is put and according to such circumstances as the availability of fire-fighting services and the provision of automatic sprinklers.

Further precautions must be taken to prevent the spread of fire between compartments by way of external enclosing surfaces common to them, that is, roofs and external walls. For this reason separating walls are often required to extend above adjacent roofs to prevent lateral spread of flame, although in certain types of building lateral spread of fire is considered to be adequately countered by interposing a non-combustible firebreak between adjacent roof spaces extending up to the underside of a non-combustible roof covering. It has been considered essential that the horizontal separation afforded by the floors should not be curtailed at the outer perimeter of a building in a manner which would allow fire to spread vertically between compartments or storeys. Thus regulations require horizontal separating elements to be projected a suitable amount in front of openings in compartments vertically adjacent, or be "bent up" as an upstand wall to separate sufficiently the lower extremity of an opening in one storey from the head of an opening in the storey below.[1]

The risk of fire spreading across the ends of walls separating horizontally adjacent compartments must also be minimized. The London County Council requires precautions to be taken where such walls separate adjacent properties by requiring a minimum distance of 3 ft between any window and

[1] L.C.C. By-law 5.26 (2.b.) M.B. Byelaw 47. Interim results of an investigation being carried out by the Fire Research Station on various types of framing elements and panels indicate that "a reduction in the fire resistance of the under window panels from ½ hr to nil did not significantly increase the hazard of flames from the ground floor room igniting the contents of the room above it, even with the maximum fire load of 80,000 B.Th.U's/sq. ft". It is also shown that a projecting element is of little use as a firestop. (*Fire Research Annual Report*, 1958 (H.M.S.O.).)

the centre of a party wall or boundary of the site.[1]　Similar conditions apply to division walls, that is internal fire break walls used to sub-divide trade buildings into smaller compartments.[2]　The M.B.B. do not limit the proximity of openings to party walls or site boundaries nor the proportion of openings to wall area.

Rooms of high fire risk such as Boiler Rooms, Oil Fuel Storage Rooms and Electrical Intake, Transformer and Switch Rooms, must be separated from the remainder of the building and be ventilated direct to the open air.　Large solid and oil fuel boiler rooms should be provided with smoke extracts.　Oil fuel boiler rooms should be situated against an external wall and oil fuel storage rooms should be as near as possible to an external wall, with access from the open air if possible, or from the boiler room.[3]

The danger of spread of fire within a building is always accompanied by that of the spread from adjacent buildings.　The fundamental protection between buildings is *space* in sufficient dimensions to prevent spread of fire by radiation or actual flame contact.　However, certain structural precautions, in addition, are still necessary.　External, enclosing walls should be constructed of non-combustible materials and have a good fire resistance (L.C.C. 4 hr, M.B.B. 2 hr),[4] although relaxations to this are made in respect of small houses and certain single-storey buildings according to the distance of the building from the nearest boundary.　These are indicated on the annotated diagrams on pages 490–493.　Roofs should not be penetrated unduly by openings.　Where openings occur the amount of glazing should be limited, or fire resisting glass should be used.[5]　Similarly the total openings in the external walls of a building should be limited to resist the outward spread of flame and the potential number of points of entry of flame into a building from an adjacent building[6].

Shafts and Ducts.　Flue-like apertures such as shafts, ducts and deep lightwells, should be avoided in the general design of buildings, but where they are necessary as in the case of lift shafts and staircase enclosures, they should be vented at the top to allow smoke and hot gases to disperse to the atmosphere (page 502).

Fire Venting.　The large single-storey shed-type building housing continuous factory processes, which cannot easily be sub-divided, presents a particular problem.　In such buildings the unconfined spread of smoke and

---

[1] L.C.C. By-law 5.26, but see page 503 regarding waivers now granted.
[2] L.C.C. Principles for guidance entitled "Buildings of Excess Height and/or Additional Cubical Extent".
[3] See footnote 2.　See also C.P. 3002 "Oil Firing", Part 1, 1961.
[4] L.C.C. 9.03 with 9.02 (3); M.B B. 38.
[5] L.C.C. By-law 11.01 (7).
[6] L.C.C. By-law 5.26, but see page 503 regarding waivers now granted.

carbon-monoxide fumes resulting from incomplete combustion after the initial supply of oxygen has been consumed, constitutes a hazard to fire-fighters and prevents them from reaching the seat of the fire. Also, when trapped in a building, the heat generated by the fire causes high temperatures and renders materials more inflammable by preheating them well in advance of an approaching conflagration. It is, therefore, desirable to make provision for the removal of heat, smoke and fumes as quickly as possible (often done by breaking holes in the structure with a fireman's axe) by a simple self-operating means of ventilation. Although this supplies more air and possibly intensifies the fire it will, nevertheless, confine it and assist fire-fighters to see and approach nearer the seat of the fire. It has been shown by experience that to be effective, such automatic ventilation must be above the fire because cross-ventilation may only serve to drive heat and smoke in a particular direction, possibly towards the fire-fighters. By providing automatic fire vents in the roof, therefore, smoke, heat and fumes are enabled to rise quickly out of the building and draughts are created which draw air towards the fire, thus helping to contain it. Where separation walls are impossible, the building should be sub-divided into limited areas by fire-resisting curtains or non-combustible board fire stops fixed within the roof space. They should extend down to at least the level of the tie members and automatic fire vents should be placed within the bays thus created, page 484.

At present no standard of fire venting is laid down, but research into the question of the desirable area of vents and their arrangement, together with fire curtains for buildings of different types, is in progress. It has been suggested, however, that exhaust ventilation should be provided with an effective free area of from $0 \cdot 5\%$ up to 5% of the total floor area, depending on the fire risk, height and area of the building in question.

A method of providing automatic fire ventilation in such a manner that normal ventilation requirements are also fulfilled is shown on page 484.[1]

Building Regulations contain specific sections devoted to fire-resisting construction[2] but many other sections contain requirements which affect the fire protection design of a building. These are sections concerned with the stability of walls, design of steel and reinforced concrete frames, chimneys and fireplaces, roofs and space about buildings. The principal requirements of the L.C.C. By-laws and Model Building Byelaws in respect of "normal" buildings, are shown on pages 490–493.

---

[1] It should be stated that considerable difference of opinion still exists as to whether such roof ventilation should be automatic or operable and controlled by the fire-brigade.
[2] Model Building Byelaws 31-49; L.C.C. By-laws, Part IX.

Fire Resisting Construction: Main Requirements of the L.C.C. By-laws

Note: The following is based on the London Building (Constructional) By-Laws, 1952, but is no a direct extract. Reference should be made to the By-Laws for further details.

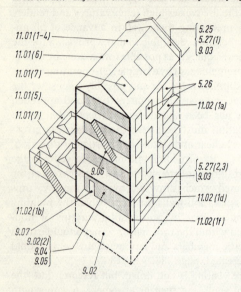

11.01(1–4)
11.01(6)
11.01(7)
11.01(5)
11.01(7)
9.06
11.02(1b)
9.07
9.02(2)
9.04
9.05
9.02

5.25
5.27(1)
9.03
5.26
11.02(1a)
5.27(2,3)
9.03
11.02(1d)
11.02(1f)

By-Law 5.25: (1) Party wall to be carried up above roof covering (3 ft for warehouse class building over 30 ft high, 15 in. for domestic building, measured at right angles to the roof slope).
Exceptions to foregoing:

(2) (*a*) Where levels of adjacent roofs differ by 3 ft or more.

(*b*) Where an oversailing slab is provided of non-combustible material of 4 in. min. thickness projecting 4½ in. each side of party wall and the roof covering is bedded solidly on top thereof.

(*c*) Where abutting roofs are not less than 5 in. thick, non-combustible and solid for 9 in each side of party wall.

(*d*) In terraces not exceeding 150 ft long and of not more than 8 houses of 2 storeys, or a pair of semi-detached houses not exceeding 3 storeys, the roof covering may be bedded on top of the party wall in mortar.

(3) Party wall to be carried up to same height as any roof within 4 ft of it.

(4) The party wall shall also be carried up to the same height as any dormer, lantern or other penetrated roof feature and is to exceed the width of such feature by 12 in. at each end.

(5) In a terrace of 3 or more houses the party wall is to be corbelled out to project at least 1 in. beyond eaves or other projections, formed of combustible materials which are within 1 ft of the centre line of the party wall. Roof covering to be solidly bedded on to top of the corbel.

By-Law 5.26: (1) Openings above the level of the soffit of the first floor to be limited to reduce spread of fire between storeys.

(2) (*a*) Aggregate elevational area of openings not to exceed 50 per cent of the area from the first floor soffit to the eaves level or roof level.

(*b*) Openings other than to balconies or flat roofs are not to be nearer the floor than 2 ft 6 in. and not higher than the soffit of the floor above.

(*c*) No opening to be nearer the centre line of a party wall than 3 ft.

(*d*) No opening to be nearer a boundary than 3 ft.

(3) Exceptions to (2) (*b–d*) above are domestic buildings not more than 30 ft high and to (2) (b) staircase windows with fire resistance as required by Part IX of the By-laws.

By-law 5.27: (1) No timber to be built into required thickness of party wall.

(2) Except for structural timber no timber to be built into thickness of any other wall.

(3) Woodwork in an external wall to be set back 4 in. from the face of the wall except timber carrying wall, cills and frames of windows of houses not exceeding 3 storeys where the cill may project 3 in., and woodwork to shop fronts (11.02).

Part 9 of the By-laws requires each element of construction of a building to resist fire for the period shown under the classification in the Table shown in 9.02 under use and size. Schedule VI sets the standard of compliance. Other materials must be to satisfaction of the L.C.C. and give similar results under test (B.S. 476) to those described in the By-laws. (Note variations to dimensions given in classi-fication tables—9.02 (4), (6) and (7) and proviso 9.02 (8)).

By-law 9.02: (2) Fire division walls between parts of a building used for similar purposes to be of 2 hr fire resistance.

(3) When a fire resistance of 1 hr is required, the materials are to be non-combustible.

(5) Where floor is over 42 ft above footway or ground level the building is to be of 1 hr fire resisting construction.

(9) Where a single storey building is less than 25,000 cu. ft or 25 ft in height a steel frame need not be protected against fire (see, however, 6.02 re protection against corrosion).

(10) In a basement storey the fire resistance period is to be twice that for the rest of the building but need not exceed 2 hr.

(11) Joints between and within elements to be resistant to the passage of smoke or flame to the satisfaction of the District Surveyor.

By-law 9.03: Separation of buildings by party and external walls to be of 4 hr fire resistance period (note external walls are not defined as "elements of construction" under 1.03 but adequate fire resistance is generally ensured by the requirements of stability for walls under Part V).

By-law 9.04: (1) Enclosures shall be formed to all lobbies corridors and passages used communally and separations provided between tenancies for different purposes.

(2) (*a*) i. Enclosures and separations between tenancies of similar use are to have fire resistance as rest of building, and such enclosures are to be in bricks, blocks or reinforced concrete (2 (*a*) ii).

(*b*) i. Enclosures and separations between parts of building used for different purposes are required to have fire resistance as described in 9.02 for the longest period applicable, and in any event not less than the fire resistance of the building as a whole. Such enclosures to be of bricks, blocks or reinforced concrete ((2) (*b*) ii).

By-law 9.05: Any separations required under 9.04 which are in the topmost storey must be taken up to the underside of the roof covering except where a ceiling is provided, when they need only be taken up as fire breaks within the roof space at 80 ft centres.

By-law 9.06: Staircases, including landings, are to have the same fire resistance as the building containing them, but if enclosed by walls equal in fire resistance to the rest of the building they need only be of 1 hr fire resisting construction. Where staircase in a single staircase building is required to have ½ hr fire resistance it shall be constructed of non-combustible materials.

By-law 9.07: Notwithstanding 9.02 (2), 9.04 and 9.05 and subject to 5.11, openings can be formed in separating walls (except between tenancies) and in the required enclosures and fire checks. Such openings must be fitted with self-closing fire resisting doors in frames having a fire resistance of half the period for the wall in which they are situated or a minimum of ½ hr fire resistance.

By-law 11.01: (1) Maximum of two storeys in roof.

(2) Maximum roof pitch 75 degrees (47 degrees for warehouse class buildings unless built of non-combustible materials).

(3) (*a*) Non-combustible coverings; slates tiles metal or other non-combustible material. Excludes barge boards up to 12 in. deep, doors and window frames to roof erections.

(*b*) Where roof is constructed of non-combustible materials:

(i) External coverings may be rock asphalt (not to contain more than 17 per cent bitumen by weight) or bituminous felt ⅜ in. thick bedded on the roof with viscous material or on ¼ in. insulating material, itself bedded on roof with viscous material. Where the slope exceeds 20 degrees the external layer of bituminous felt shall be surfaced with mineral chippings or similar dressing.

(4) On the surface of the covering mentioned in (3) (*b*) may be laid ⅛ in. impervious material containing not more than 40 per cent of bitumen or similar non-combustible material.

(5) Flat roofs up to 20 degree pitch may have an external covering of rock asphalt, or ½ to 1 in. bitumen macadam (min. 93 per cent stone chippings and not more than 7 per cent bitumen), provided that layers of compressed impervious material may be placed under these external coverings and, if this is combustible, it shall not exceed three layers bedded solidly with viscous material, the whole not to exceed ⅜ in. thickness.

(6) No gutter formed with combustible material shall adjoin an external wall unless such wall is carried up at least 1 ft above any part of the gutter.

(7) The total area of lights or other roof openings is not to exceed 50 per cent of the roof area (measured in the plane of the roof) but wired glass in non-combustible metal frames not having a melting point of less than 1,800° F. may be of unrestricted area.

By-law 11.02: (1) (*a*) Projections from buildings to be non-combustible (except frames to bay windows, shop fronts and up to 3 storey dwellings, where cills may project 3 in.).

(*b*) Copings, porticos, balconies, balustrades, etc., are to be non-combustible, but an external staircase to a house (not being the sole means of access) may be of 1¾ in. hardwood.

(*d*) No combustible part of a shop front is to exceed 25 ft height above ground level.

(*e*) No combustible part of a shop front may be nearer than 4 in. to the centre line of a party wall or to the external wall of an adjoining building.

(*f*) Where a shop front projects more than 4 in. from the face of a building it shall be set an equal distance away from the centre line of a party wall unless a pier 4 in. wide, projecting 1 in. beyond the shop front, is interposed between adjacent premises.

Fire Resisting Construction: Main Requirements of the Model Byelaws

Note: The following is based on the Model Building Byelaws, 1953, but is not a direct extract Reference should be made to the Byelaws for further details.

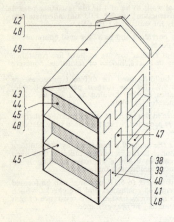

Bye-laws 31, 32: Where required to be fire resisting, walls should either conform to the 3rd schedule (Traditional construction—rules for thickness and stability) or to the 4th schedule (Notional periods of fire resistance for various forms of construction). Constructions not complying with the foregoing should conform to the requirements of the fire resistance test, B.S. 476:1953. Other elements of structure must conform to the 4th schedule or to the requirements of the B.S. fire resistance test as above. Definitions:

Non-combustible throughout: applied to a wall means made of non-combustible materials, except for internal linings.

Externally non-combustible: applied to a wall means made of non-combustible materials as above *or* having external non-combustible panels or coverings.

Bye-law 38: External walls generally to be of 2 hr fire resistance and non-combustible throughout.

Bye-law 39: (i) Special case of 1 storey buildings: reduction of fire resistance requirements depending on cubic capacity and distance from boundaries (Table A) for domestic and public buildings, other than small houses.

(ii) Special requirements for 1 storey storage warehouses depend on distance from boundary (Table B).

(iii) When a building is sub-divided by division walls (43) the requirements of (i) and (ii) are satisfied if external walls of each part have fire resistance and non-combustibility of a building of equal cube to such part.

Bye-law 40: External panel wall and frame may have 1 hr fire resistance if: building is domestic (other than shop or small house) of 2 storeys or more, has non-combustible panels in reinforced concrete or steel frame and is not less than 10 ft or half height of building from nearest boundary.

Bye-law 41: Special case of storage warehouse buildings exceeding 250,000 cu. ft or 75 ft high. Walls to be non-combustible and of 4 hr fire resistance. If sub-divided by division wall (43) each part may be assessed as a separate building of equivalent size.

Bye-law 42: Separating walls of houses and other buildings, except small houses (35) or flats (44), to be:

   i. Non-combustible throughout.

   ii. 6 hr fire resistance (except domestic buildings other than shops, which shall be 4 hr).

   iii. All openings in separating walls to be protected with doors or shutters of half fire resistance period of wall penetrated.

   v. No combustible material to be buried in or on wall except structural timber protected with 4 in. brick or iron beam box. Roofing battens may cross wall if embedded in mortar.

   v. Wall to extend above underside of roof covering if roofs not of non-combustible materials:
      (a) 18 in. if warehouse or public building
      (b) 12 in. if domestic over 5 storeys.

   vi. Other cases than v; Wall need not be extended if battens are bedded in mortar on wall.

By-law 43: Fire division walls to be as (42) i, iii, iv, v and vi. Fire resistance as follows:
   Storage warehouse: 4 hr.
   Other buildings: 2 hr.

By-law 44: Walls separating flats *within* a building (other than load bearing wall as (45)) to be non-combustible and 1 hr fire resistance if domestic and exceeding 50 ft height or 2,500 sq. ft on any one storey. ½ hr in all other cases.

By-law 45: Other than in small houses: Buildings of more than 1 storey and of class specified in Table in by-law to have fire resistance specified therein in respect of: Floors above lowest storey; load bearing walls other than external wall, separation or fire division wall; columns, beams other than as described in (48) and walls enclosing "common" stairways or lift shafts. Provided that where more than one fire resisting period is shown the longer shall be taken and where a building is separated as (43) or comprises 2 premises (houses or shops included) each part shall be assessed as a separate building. Openings in staircase and lift enclosing walls to be protected with doors or shutters of half the fire resistance of wall and not less than ½ hr.

By-law 47: Openings in external walls. (In buildings other than 2 storey houses): Cills not less than 3 ft above heads below and not less than 2 ft above floor level, *or* a projection of solid non-combustible material to project 2 ft from wall and extend laterally past the limits of overlap: 1 ft if lower or neither opening continues beyond limit, 2 ft if upper does.

By-law 48: Any part of a frame carrying an external wall, separating wall or division wall to have same fire resistance as that required for the wall that it carries.

By-law 49: Roofs: Warehouse, public buildings or houses over 36,000 cu. ft or where forming part of block of houses to be covered so as to avoid spread of fire to other buildings or into the building. In other buildings the above will apply unless they are twice their height from the nearest boundary

No restriction on area of glazing in a roof is given.

Fire Resistance—Small Houses.   By-laws 33 to 37.

Definition:

A 1-storeyed private dwelling less than 18,000 cu. ft or private dwelling of two stories neither of which storey has a floor area of more than 1000 sq. ft but does not include a flat or maisonette.

External walls to comply with the 3rd schedule or must have the following degrees of fire resistance: An internal fire resistance of ½ hr and where:

  D not less than 10 ft: no other requirement

  D from 5 ft to 10 ft: externally non-combustible

  D from 3 ft to 5 ft: non-combustible throughout

  D is less than 3 ft: non-combustible throughout, and to have external fire resistance of ½ hr.

where D is the distance from wall to nearest boundary.

Separating walls to comply with 3rd schedule or must have 1 hr fire resistance. But walls separating groups of houses in blocks of small houses must have a fire resistance of 2 hr, where the construction of the external walls is as follows:

  i. Blocks of more than 2 small houses with external walls having combustible external covering or panels (2 hr fire resisting walls to separate each pair in block and to extend 9 in. beyond face of external walls and 15 in. above roof where latter is not a slab of non-combustible material).

  ii. Blocks of more than 4 small houses with external walls having combustible frames but with non-combustible external panels or covering (2 hr fire resisting walls to separate each group of four houses and no part of combustible construction of walls shall pass over ends of any separating wall).

  iii. Blocks of more than 8 small houses with external walls of non-combustible materials (2 hr fire resisting walls to separate each group of eight houses).

(Note: separating walls to small houses to comply also with 42 (iv and vi) with regard to building in of joists, etc.)

Floors and interior walls

  i. Where small houses have 2 storeys the upper floor shall be capable of satisfying B.S. 476:1953 Test for Fire resistance as to freedom from collapse for ½ hr and as to rise of temperature and freedom from cracks for 15 min. Floors in accordance with the 4th schedule will satisfy this condition.

  ii. Load-bearing walls other than separating or external walls shall have ½ hr fire resistance.

Exempted buildings

Note: Certain buildings are exempt from the by-laws although some are required to have a proportionate degree of isolation according to their external fire resistance. These buildings are described n By-laws 7 to 12.

Access for Firefighting. When buildings are of excessive height or cubical extent special precautions must be taken in the provision of division walls to reduce the size of the compartments, page 487. Such buildings must be carefully sited to allow the heaviest fire-fighting units to approach close to all elevations. To provide adequate accessibility for these appliances the L.C.C. requires a portion of every building to abut upon a thoroughfare or open space not less than 40 ft wide.[1]

When vehicle access is required to a building or part of a building not abutting on a street it should be not less than 8 ft 6 in. wide and 11 ft 6 in. high to permit the entry of fire-fighting appliances.

In the case of tall buildings external access by ladders can only serve a limited purpose, since floors above 100 ft are beyond the reach of most fire brigade ladders. Further, when a tall building is designed on a "podium" of much larger area two or three storeys high, no external access for fire appliances is possible for any floor, so that internal access must be designed as an integral part of the building. This is provided in the form of at least one lobby approach staircase, regarded for fire-fighting purposes as an extension of the street. The staircase must be separated from the accommodation on each floor by an enclosed lobby in which all the necessary fire-fighting equipment is installed. Both staircase and lobby must be sited next to an external wall and be provided with adequate ventilation to ensure freedom from smoke logging (see page 497). The enclosing walls to staircase and lobby must be constructed to have twice the standard fire resistance for the building. In trade buildings and certain office buildings this may result in a 4 hour standard of construction being required. No openings are permitted in the enclosure other than those for ventilation on to the street and those giving access to the building. The latter must be provided with self-closing fire-resisting doors; in addition, at basement levels and in certain other circumstances, further protection by steel roller shutters is required. As well as such a staircase a firemen's lift must be provided situated where possible within the staircase lobby or if not, within the staircase or a separate enclosure adjacent having the same degree of fire resistance.[2] (See footnote 1, page 498.) This lift need not travel to the top floor. (For details of firemen's lift see *Advanced Building Construction (Components, Services and Finishes)*.)

[1] Buildings exceeding   250,000 cu. ft : At least $\frac{1}{6}$ perimeter.
      ,,   ,,   1,000,000 ,, ,, : ,,   ,, $\frac{1}{4}$,,
      ,,   ,,   2,000,000 ,, ,,: ,,   ,, $\frac{1}{2}$,,
      ,,   ,,   3,000,000 ,, ,,: ,,   ,, $\frac{3}{4}$,,
      ,,   ,,   4,000,000 ,, ,,: On an island site.
[2] L.C.C. Principles for guidance entitled "Buildings of Excess Height and/or Additional Cubical Extent" give guidance on the requirements of the Council in respect of these classes of buildings.

MEANS OF ESCAPE

The object in providing means of escape is to permit unobstructed egress from within a building by way of definite escape routes (exit ways, corridors and stairs) to a street or an open space or to an adjoining building or roof from which access to the street may be obtained.

The primary danger to occupants is that staircases and corridors leading to them from rooms or compartments may be filled with hot gases and smoke, trapping the occupants and causing panic.[1] It is, therefore, important that such escape routes should be enclosed with adequate fire-resisting enclosures. In addition they should be separated by fire-resisting doors planned in strategic positions to prevent the spread of smoke and fire from storey to storey via lift shafts and staircases, and to keep the latter free from smoke when used as an escape route.

The requirements of building regulations in this respect vary with the size, construction, use and height of the building in question, the critical heights of floors being 20 ft. and 42 ft. In the former case it is dangerous to jump from a building; in the latter case the standard 50 ft wheeled escape ladder, available in most areas, is at its maximum extension. For smaller buildings with few occupants, approach lobbies with two sets of self-closing fire-resisting doors giving access on to one staircase, may provide adequate protection to means of escape. In larger buildings alternative means of escape are required, either (i) to an adjoining building via a roof access which must be properly separated from the downward going flights of the staircase, or (ii) directly to the open air at ground level by means of secondary stair-cases properly protected and enclosed with fire-resisting walls. In buildings over 100 ft high the L.C.C. require an enclosed stair at each end: in an office building, not more than 25 ft, and in a residential building, not more than 35 ft from the end wall. One of these may be the lobby-approach "fireman's stair". The general escape requirements of the L.C.C. are given in Table 30 and are illustrated on page 497.

In residential buildings alternative means of escape may often be provided by open balconies. This permits greater distances between escape stairs, since there is less danger from smoke concentration.[2] Escape from tall residential blocks has been provided by means of close planning round a single fire-resisting staircase, direct access to it from each flat being through an

[1] See *Ministry of Education Building Bulletin* No. 7—"Fire and the Design of Schools", Part I, for an excellent discussion on the behaviour of fire in this respect.

[2] CP 3, Ch. IV Part 1, 1962 "Fire Protection in Flats and Maisonettes", while maintaining the need for alternative means of escape to maisonettes, suggests that this is not necessary for flats provided the bedrooms open directly on to the entrance lobby of the flat with their doors nearer the flat entrance door than those to the kitchen and living room.

Table 30   Means of Escape in case of Fire

New buildings (other than dwellings with no floors above 20 ft) require means of escape as follows:

Class	Maximum floor height	Type of escape	Max. travel distance	Notes on escape
Class 1. Office or Trade buildings up to 1000 sq. ft (max. 1st floor area) with timber floors and plastered ceilings or other suitably protected ceilings. Class 2. ditto, ditto, up to 2000 sq. ft (max. 1st floor area) with non-combustible floors. Class 3. ditto, ditto, up to 3500 sq. ft (ditto), ditto.				
1a 2a, 3a	Up to 42′ „	A, D or E „	60′ 100′*	Buildings in more than one occupation on top floor require lobbies at that level with D. * 60′ of this distance to be within protected corridor.
1b 2b, 3b	1 above 42′ „	B or C „	60′ 100′*	
1c 2c	2 above 42′ „	B or C „	60′ 100′*	Upward escape to be screened at lower of 2 top floors with B.
1d 2d, 3c	2 or more over 42′ „	C „	60′ 100′*	Direct access to roof (*or other independent alternative*) to serve all floors above 42′
Class 4. Small Office or Trade building in single occupation with no floor above 42′.				
4	Up to 42′	F	60′	Building of limited height and size not requiring staircase enclosure or lobby approach.
Class 5. Office or Trade building with 2 staircases. (Of larger area than 1–4 or with different floor construction.)				
5	Below 80′	No. 2 as D, or No. 2 as E, or D with E or G	100′† (max. 200′ apart)	† 60′ and 120′ where timber floor construction. Shops, Stores, etc.: Floors above 80′ to have P.S/C to street. Escalators in enclosed compartments with lobbies giving on to street may be acceptable.
Class 6. One storey Office or Trade buildings of unlimited floor area.				
6	—	Exits to open air	60′	Where inflammable materials or liquids are used or stored, at least 2 exits to be provided.
Class 7. Dwellings occupied by one family (part use for business permissible), single staircase.				
7a	Up to 42′	—	—	Minor protective works where special hazards exist.
7b	1 or more above 42′	Alternative escape to floors above 42′	—	Escape by balcony to next building or to open S/C acceptable.
Class 8. Blocks of Flats and/or Maisonettes with one staircase.				
8a	Up to 42′	H, I or J	100′	Max. 6 dwellings per floor (4 if timber floors). Dwellings to have Entrance halls. Fire Brigade access to bedrooms not off hall, and to upper level of maisonettes unless hall is protected and lower rooms have SCFRD's.
8a	1 or more above 42′	H, I or J	100′	Alternative escape for dwellings over 42′ to roof or balcony giving access to adjacent building. Note: Balcony access flats with 1 floor above 42′ may have auxiliary S/C to balcony below as alternative means of escape.
8b	Below 80′	K	—	All habitable rooms to be off entrance hall of dwelling. Lobby ventilation: min. area 25% cross sectional area of lobby or 30 sq. ft.
8b	Above 80′	K	—	Ditto, ditto. Fire Brigade access strip required at ground level. Also consult Sect. 20, 1939 Act.
8c	Below 80′	L	—	Where it is necessary to pass another dwelling to reach S/C. as 8b, and Fire Brigade access strip to enable any part of balcony to be reached
8c	Above 80′	L	—	Open balconies on both sides to floors above 80 ft. giving access to common staircase.
Class 9. Blocks of Flats and/or Maisonettes with two staircases.				
9	—	No. 2 as I	90′§ (Max. 180′ apart)	§ Distance measured from dwelling entrance to S/C. Means of escape from all bedroom floors as class 8 generally. N.B. Max. travel limit is not applicable when open balcony access used.

S/C = staircase; SCFRD = self-closing fire-resisting door; P.S/C = protected staircase.

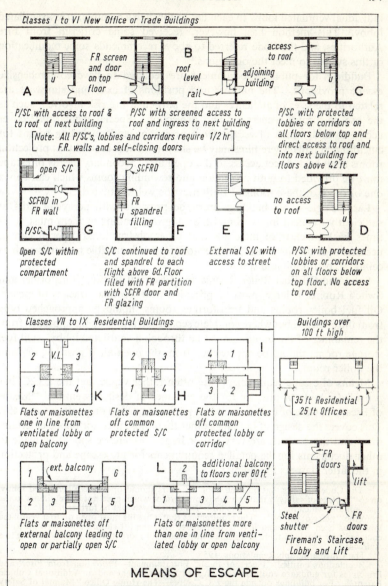

Classes I to VI New Office or Trade Buildings

A P/SC with access to roof & to roof of next building

FR screen and door on top floor

B P/SC with screened access to roof and ingress to next building

roof level — rail — adjoining building

[Note: All P/SC's, lobbies and corridors require 1/2 hr F.R. walls and self-closing doors]

C P/SC with protected lobbies or corridors on all floors below top and direct access to roof and into next building for floors above 42 ft

access to roof

G Open S/C within protected compartment

open S/C — SCFRD in FR wall — P/SC

F S/C continued to roof and spandrel to each flight above Gd. Floor filled with FR partition with SCFR door and FR glazing

SCFRD — FR spandrel filling

E External S/C with access to street

no access to roof

D P/SC with protected lobbies or corridors on all floors below top floor. No access to roof

Classes VII to IX Residential Buildings

K Flats or maisonettes one in line from ventilated lobby or open balcony

2 V.L. 3 / 1 4

H Flats or maisonettes off common protected S/C

2 3 / 1 4

I Flats or maisonettes off common protected lobby or corridor

4 1 / 3 2

J Flats or maisonettes off external balcony leading to open or partially open S/C

ext. balcony / 1 6 / 2 3 4 5

L Flats or maisonettes more than one in line from ventilated lobby or open balcony

additional balcony to floors over 80 ft / 2 / 1 3 4 5

Buildings over 100 ft high

[35 ft Residential
25 ft Offices]

Fireman's Staircase, Lobby and Lift

FR doors — lift — Steel shutter — FR doors

MEANS OF ESCAPE

The illustrations above are to be read in conjunction with Table 30 opposite.

individual ventilated lobby to each flat or through a common cross-ventilated lobby. This method has, however, received some criticism from Fire Authorities, and the Code referred to above recommends some modification of this system to meet the objections.[1]

Buildings for public entertainment are required to have comprehensive escape provisions. The number and positions of exits and stairways are related to the sizes of audiences and the particular fire risk involved, such as the use of theatre scenery or film projection. Special regulations[2] cover access to and means of escape from projection and rewinding rooms for cinemas and halls where films may be shown. These require that projection rooms shall have direct access to the open air. Secondary means of escape must be provided to both projection and rewinding rooms which can be via one or other of these rooms. Both must be well ventilated.

Large single-storey buildings must be provided with perimeter exits at sufficiently frequent intervals and the gangways leading to them must at all times be kept clear of materials and other obstructions. Special care is necessary for buildings used for the storage of inflammable materials such as celluloid, petrol, oil and spirit.

Solid and Oil Fuel Boiler Rooms and Electrical Intake, Transformer and Switch Rooms, if large, must be provided with secondary means of escape. Oil fuel boiler rooms and transformer rooms should be approached only from the open air, but where complete separation is impossible approach from the remainder of the building must be through a ventilated lobby. Oil fuel storage rooms should be approached from the open air if possible, or from the boiler room.

Means of escape requirements are often rather vague, but the L.C.C. has provided a code of practice for the guidance of designers entitled "Means of Escape in Case of Fire" which is in part summarized on pages 496 and 497. This covers the design of buildings other than those used for public entertainment and those which are very tall or large. Reference should be made to other documents for the detailed requirements for fire escape and protection in the latter classes of building.[3]

---

[1] The Code suggests that on each floor the stairs should open, via a ventilated lobby, on to "a place of safety", that is a lobby or corridor which need not be ventilated to the open air and which may contain the lift. No doorway should be further than 15 ft away from the "place of safety". The requirement that a fire lift must open on to a ventilated lobby has been waived and it is recommended that the lift should now open on to an enclosed hall provided there is a smoke-stop door not more than 15 ft away leading to a staircase.

[2] The Cinematograph Regulations, 1955.

[3] Regulations entitled "Places of Public Entertainment—Protection from Fire" and Principles for guidance entitled "Buildings of Excess Height and/or Additional Cubical Extent". For buildings outside the L.C.C. area—The Home Office "Manual of Safety Requirements in Theatres and Other Places of Public Entertainment".

FIRE-RESISTING CONSTRUCTION

DESIGN AND CONSTRUCTION ASSOCIATED WITH MEANS OF ESCAPE

The following information extracted from the L.C.C. Code of Practice, "Means of Escape in Case of Fire", gives a desirable standard for fire-resisting constructional detail for all elements related to a means of escape.

Staircases. Staircases should be placed next to an outer wall and should be entered from any floor level in the direction of the flow towards the exit from the building. Landings should be arranged at the top and at the bottom of each flight equal in width to the stair. Flights should be straight without winders, consisting of not more than 16 risers, each not more than $7\frac{1}{2}$ in. high with treads not less than 10 in. wide, measured clear of nosings. (6 in. and 11 in. for places of assembly and not less than 3 risers in a flight.)

Protection not less than 3 ft high should be provided on both sides of all staircases and landings (not less than 3 ft 6 in. when next to open wells or in places of assembly), measured perpendicularly from the centre of the treads or landing level. Handrails should be provided on both sides of a stair more than 3 ft 4 in. wide, and on one side if less. An outer handrail should continue round all landings. The width of stairs and landings, measured between finished surfaces of walls or the inner side of balustrades, should not be decreased by any projection other than the handrail which should not project more than 3 in. The clear width of exit doorways from staircases, measured when the door or doors are fully open, should not be less than the required width of the staircases concerned. Where an exit from a ground floor or basement accommodating a large number of people also delivers into a staircase landing or exit lobby, the doorway to the street or open space should be increased in width in proportion to the total number of people on all floors. Unless specifically required to be otherwise by the By-laws, or by considerations applicable to public buildings, internal staircases including landings and floors within the staircase enclosure, are permitted to be of wood construction, having not less than a half-hour fire resistance (see "notional periods of fire resistance", pages 512–523).

External staircases,[1] including balconies and gangways, should be of non-combustible materials with the stairs arranged as described above for internal stairs, and of similar dimensions. Protection on both sides is required not less than 3 ft 6 in. high with handrails on both sides. Where iron steps and landings are used, they may be solid or perforated, provided openings are

---

[1] External staircases are open to attack by fire from adjacent doors and windows and may become unsafe under certain weather conditions. It is preferable not to use them for other than two-storey buildings.

not more than $\frac{1}{2}$ in. wide, with $1\frac{1}{2}$ in. deep solid nosings.   Where open risers
are provided nosings should overlap the back of treads below by 1 in.

Spiral staircases may form secondary means of escape for small numbers
of people if they are of non-combustible material not less than 5 ft in
diameter and not exceeding 30 ft in height.

Step ladders not exceeding two storeys of limited height and not steeper
than 60° may be accepted as upward secondary means of escape for not more
than 30 persons.   Treads must be 5 in. wide not more than 8 in. apart.

Vertical ladders may form means of escape for small numbers of people.
They should be not less than 18 in. wide fixed 4 in. clear of the wall face with
strings carried up 3 ft 6 in. to form hand grips.   Intermediate landings should
be provided if the ladder is more than 20 ft high and if the height exceeds
30 ft suitable guards must be provided to form an enclosure about the ladder,
as shown on page 388.

Ramps which afford a means of escape should be protected at the sides and
have a gradient of not more than 1 in 10.   Steps should not be introduced.

Escape routes over roofs should be protected with railings, balustrades or
parapets not less than 3 ft 6 in. high.

Enclosures.   The enclosures to protected stairs, landings, corridors, passages, lobbies and doorway recesses within the staircase enclosures and exits
from staircases should have a standard of fire resistance of not less than one
half-hour.   Wood or linings of rapid flame spread are not permitted, nor
cavities behind linings, within the protected enclosures of a staircase forming
the only means of escape.   Borrowed lights, fanlights and other glazing,
where permitted in enclosures, should be of fire-resisting construction.

Doors.   Doors to protected staircases and corridors should be hung to
open in the direction of exit and to swing clear of steps, landings, passage-
ways and the public way; they should open the full width with sufficient
clearance between two sets of doors.

Doors to enclosed staircases and to external staircases should be of solid
timber not less than $1\frac{3}{4}$ in. finished thickness or have a fire resistance of not
less than one half-hour.   They should be properly framed together and the
door frames bedded solid.[1]   Panelled doors in existing buildings may be
retained (i) where the thickness of the stiles is not less than $1\frac{3}{4}$ in., if the panels
on the face of the door away from the staircase are entirely covered with
asbestos millboard or asbestos wallboard not less than $\frac{3}{16}$ in. thick or with

---

[1] *Ministry of Education Building Bulletin* No. 7, "Fire and the Design of Schools", Part I,
makes a distinction between a "smoke-stop" door to be used to prevent the passage of
smoke to escape stairs and corridors and "fire check" doors to be used to provide a
barrier to fire.   The requirements of fire resistance and frame detail applying to the latter
in accordance with B.S. 459, Part 3, do not apply to the former.   (Appendix 5.)

other approved material, (ii) where the thickness of the stiles is less than $1\frac{3}{4}$ in., if the panels on the face of the door away from the staircase are made up solid flush with stiles and rails and that face of the door is protected all over with plasterboard or asbestos wall board not less than $\frac{3}{16}$ in. thick. In existing buildings converted to residential accommodation, panelled doors with stiles not less than $1\frac{1}{2}$ in. thick may be retained if protected in the panels by asbestos wallboard not less than $\frac{3}{16}$ in. thick.

Doors to protected or to external staircases should be rendered self-closing and the use of steel bushed rising-butt hinges may be permitted for this purpose in certain cases. Sliding doors where permitted should be self-closing.

Except in factories, exit doors to the street may open inwards provided they are fixed open whilst the building is occupied.

Glazing over, in or at the sides of doors which are required to be fire resisting, should be also fire-resisting and fixed shut, and may, where appropriate, be of glass bricks.

Doors at the head of staircases giving access to roofs should be glazed in the upper panels.

Doors in factories, warehouses and buildings or portions of buildings involving special hazards must conform to the standards of fire resistance required under the relevant Acts and By-laws.

Revolving doors will not be accepted in escape doorways. Where it is desired to instal such a door, an emergency exit with ordinary hinged doors should also be provided adjacent to the revolving door. This exit should be adequately indicated.

Doors affording access to external escape staircases, balconies and gangways, should be fastened with simple fastenings, easily operated from inside without a key. Exit doors to and from staircases and to places of assembly should be fitted with automatic bolts.

Windows. For purposes of rescue a reasonable number of windows on floors above the ground floor, facing a street or open space to which fire appliances have access, should be made to open at sill level or within 12 in. of the sill level (where a sill ledge is provided). The opening portions should be not less than 2 ft 9 in. high by 1 ft 3 in. wide in the clear.

Windows giving access to external escape stairs should be fitted with simple fastenings easily operated from inside without a key, as required for doors serving the same purpose.

All glazing vertically under or within 6 ft of an external staircase should be fire resisting and fixed shut except for that portion statutorily required for the purposes of ventilation or when required for means of escape to the staircase.

17

Lifts. The motor chamber should be fully enclosed with non-combustible materials and separated from the lift shaft except for openings necessary for the passage of wires and cables.

In enclosed lift shafts, a smoke outlet to the open-air should be formed, at or near the head of the shaft, or other smoke outlets provided (see *Advanced Building Construction* (*Components, Services and Finishes*). The smoke outlet should be not less than 1 sq. ft in area, fitted with an openwork metal grille or widely-spaced louvres.

Gates, doors and shutters to lifts should be provided with automatic control to ensure that they cannot be opened, except the door opposite the lift cage when it is at rest at floor level.[1]

Buildings with One Staircase. In blocks of flats or maisonettes the lift shaft will not be permitted within the staircase enclosure. The shaft should be wholly enclosed in fire-resisting materials not less than 3 in. thick and with solid wood doors or steel-shielded gates.

In buildings of other classes under 42 ft in height, where the motor chamber is at the bottom of the shaft, the lift shaft may be within the staircase enclosure if protected by solid fire-resisting enclosures and solid wood doors or steel-shielded gates. When the motor chamber is at the head of the shaft the enclosure to the lift may be of metal grilles with collapsible lattice gates at openings.

Buildings with Two or More Staircases. Lifts may be within the stair enclosure provided that each stair is available for escape for all occupants. Such lifts may be enclosed with metal grilles and collapsible lattice gates irrespective of the position of the motor chamber.

Residential Buildings with Lift Shaft Independent of the Staircase. The lift shaft should be wholly enclosed in fire-resisting material and with solid wood doors or steel-shielded gates.

It should be noted that although in some cases solid enclosures to a lift shaft are not essential, these may become necessary in order to complete the separation between basement and street exit and to preserve the screened access above the 42 ft level.

DESIGN AND CONSTRUCTION ASSOCIATED WITH THE LIMITATION OF THE SPREAD OF FIRE

Walls. The function of walls in providing fire protection and the regulations relating to them have been discussed already. The latter are given in outline on pages 490 to 493. These normally, of course, refer to forms of

---

[1] See C.P. 407.101:1951, and Factories Act 1937 to 1959 for requirements in respect of lifts outside the L.C.C. area.

solid wall constructed of non-combustible materials, although when distances from boundaries are sufficiently great and when, as in the case of the *Ministry of Education Bulletin* No. 7, the requirements for escape are stringent, the use of combustible materials and light claddings is permitted. In other cases, however, the use of light external claddings and, in particular, curtain walling, which are functionally appropriate to framed buildings, presents a number of practical difficulties.

Curtain Walling. The constructional aspects of curtain walling have been considered in Chapter 4. In considering the system from the point of view of fire protection it is necessary to have regard to the requirements of building regulations as far as external walls are concerned. These have been discussed on page 487 and it will be clear that any system of frame and panel walling such as the curtain wall must act as a whole in fulfilling these requirements, but at the same time be light and economical of space if it is to be successful. Clearly no system which employs unprotected steel or aluminium framing can meet the by-law requirements for external walls, however fire resistant the panel infillings may be, since these metals have no acknowledged fire resistance. Further, the provision in L.C.C. By-law 5.26 that glazing or glass in the thickness of a wall shall be considered an opening has presented difficulties in the development of the curtain wall. The L.C.C. does, however, now grant waivers to this by-law subject to the use and siting of the building, which in effect permit windows and curtain walling to extend the full width of the wall and permit the introduction of glass fronted panels in curtain walling.[1] In addition, waivers have been granted to permit the fire separation between storeys to be provided by a fire-resisting "back-up wall" with the panel infillings of the curtain wall performing the function of a facing only (see page 504 (A)).

The requirements of the *Ministry of Education Building Bulletin* No. 7 enable curtain walling to be used since (i) for buildings of two or more storeys external walls are required only to be constructed of non-combustible materials, and (ii) external panel walls, if not protecting the structural frame, require no fire resistance in buildings up to three storeys, and for four storeys and over a fire resistance of only $\frac{1}{2}$ hr.[2] As an additional precaution it is suggested that for five storeys and over the heads and sills of windows be separated by a 3 ft high continuous panel with a fire resistance of about 1 hr, or by a non-combustible horizontal projection. Proportion of window area to wall area is governed by the distances from site boundaries.[3]

---

[1] L.C.C. publication 4063, "Construction of Buildings in London", Supplement No. 1.
[2] *Ministry of Education Building Bulletin* No. 7, Tables VI and VIII.
[3] *Ibid*, Table IX.

Under Scottish By-laws an all-glass curtain wall would be permitted when a fire resistance of only $\frac{1}{2}$ hr was required, with not more than 50% window and the remainder wired glass panels. This is possible because a wall with only $\frac{1}{2}$ hr fire resistance is not required to satisfy the "insulation" requirement of the B.S. 476 fire test.

In view of the difficulty of providing a sufficiently light fire-resisting framing it has been suggested that the panel infilling be anchored to the main structure, thus relieving the frame of its weight and, if of fire resisting

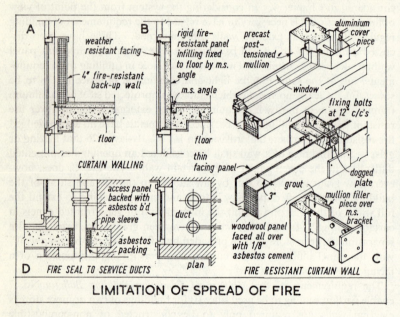

LIMITATION OF SPREAD OF FIRE

material, it could then be construed as part of the structure—providing the necessary vertical separation between storeys (see (B) above). Alternatively, the framing must be of adequate fire resistance and must be tied back with fixings suitably protected from fire. Detail (C) shows a system using pre-stressed concrete mullions in conjunction with fire-resistant panels forming the fire-resistant wall and having an independent facing of glass or other suitable cladding material held in a metal frame. This system has a fire resistance of 2 hr.

The following points should be borne in mind when selecting or designing a curtain wall system of this type:

(i) the panel and the frame must act together as one fire-resisting element and be tested as a whole under B.S. 476; (ii) fixings must be protected from fire and should not conduct heat to a vulnerable material. They should be designed to allow for exceptional expansion in a fire.

Openings in Walls. Doors and windows require to be fire resisting to retain the integrity of a fire-resisting wall or partition. Windows of wired glass in steel frames and electro-copper reinforced glass attain a ½ hr and glass blocks a 1 hr standard only and are therefore restricted in use. Fire-resisting glazing must, in most cases, be fixed shut. A door and its frame form one unit or element and fire tests are made on this unit. As shown in the illustrated Tables of fire-resisting construction, timber doors require deep rebates to prevent flame penetration between the door and frame. A steel frame is necessary if a steel or composite door is to develop its full fire resistance (see page 506). Although not complying strictly with B.S. 476 for ½ hr fire resistance the 1¾ in. finished thickness solid timber door is accepted as the standard "fire check" door of the ½ hr type. B.S. 459: Part 3, 1951, "Fire check flush doors and frames", specifies the construction for flush doors with ½ hr and 1 hr resistance. These are described in detail and illustrated in *Advanced Building Construction* (*Components, Services and Finishes*). Alternatives are shown on page 506.

Where a fire resistance of 1 hr or more is required doors are usually of steel or steel and asbestos or, on occasion, steel-encased timber. Uninsulated iron and steel doors and shutters are effective in preventing fire spread for up to 2 hrs although they transmit a lot of radiant heat. Doors and shutters fitted on each side of an opening are accredited with double the fire resistance of one door only. Any doors provided in addition to steel shutters must be arranged so that they do not interfere with the normal operation of the shutters whether open or closed. Doors should not be placed between double shutters.

Typical details of steel doors and shutters are shown on page 506, embodying the requirements of the L.C.C. and Fire Offices Committee regarding the construction, together with the main requirements regarding the openings in which they are set.[1] Unless special consent is obtained openings in division and party walls in the L.C.C. area must not exceed 7 ft in width nor 8 ft in height, except when the doors or shutters are not less than 24 in. apart when the height may be up to 9 ft 6 in. A number of openings should not aggregate more than half the length of the wall in any storey in which they are formed.

[1] See London Building Acts (Amendment) Act 1939, Section 21; L.C.C. Steel Roller Shutter Regulations, 1939; Rules of the Fire Offices Committee.

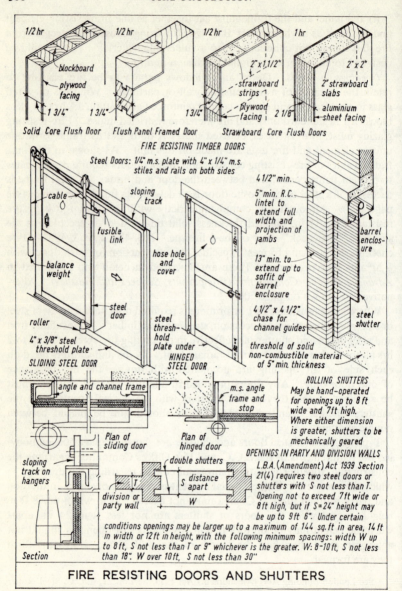

1/2 hr — blockboard, plywood facing, 1 3/4"

Solid Core Flush Door

1/2 hr — 1 3/4"

Flush Panel Framed Door

1/2 hr — 2" x 1.1/2", strawboard strips, plywood facing, 1 3/4"

1 hr — 2" x 2", 2" strawboard slabs, aluminium sheet facing, 2 1/8"

Strawboard Core Flush Doors

FIRE RESISTING TIMBER DOORS

Steel Doors: 1/4" m.s. plate with 4" x 1/4" m.s. stiles and rails on both sides

cable — sloping track — fusible link — balance weight — roller — steel door — 4" x 3/8" steel threshold plate

SLIDING STEEL DOOR

hose hole and cover — steel threshold plate under

HINGED STEEL DOOR

4 1/2" min.

5" min. R.C. lintel to extend full width and projection of jambs

13" min. to extend up to soffit of barrel enclosure

4 1/2" x 4 1/2" chase for channel guides

threshold of solid non-combustible material of 5" min. thickness

barrel enclosure — steel shutter

angle and channel frame

Plan of sliding door

m.s. angle frame and stop

Plan of hinged door

sloping track on hangers

division or party wall — double shutters — distance apart — T — S — W

Section

ROLLING SHUTTERS
May be hand-operated for openings up to 8 ft wide and 7 ft high. Where either dimension is greater, shutters to be mechanically geared

OPENINGS IN PARTY AND DIVISION WALLS
L.B.A. (Amendment) Act 1939 Section 21(4) requires two steel doors or shutters with S not less than T. Opening not to exceed 7 ft wide or 8 ft high, but if S = 24" height may be up to 9 ft 6". Under certain conditions openings may be larger up to a maximum of 144 sq. ft in area, 14 ft in width or 12 ft in height, with the following minimum spacings: width W up to 8 ft, S not less than T or 9" whichever is the greater. W: 8-10 ft, S not less than 18". W over 10 ft, S not less than 30"

FIRE RESISTING DOORS AND SHUTTERS

Special automatic fire doors are required in factories where division walls are penetrated by conveyors. These are generally of the "garrotting" type comprising a fire door which is released by the action of fire on a fusible link to fall across the track of the conveyor. These doors, or dampers, may have to be double in some cases. Alternatively, protection may be provided by a tunnel incorporating a water drencher system automatically operated in the event of fire.

Floors. None of the timber floor constructions given in the L.C.C. and M.B. Byelaws has more than a ½ hr fire resistance but higher gradings are now possible.[1] In the L.C.C. area timber floors cannot be used when a fire resistance of not less than 1 hr is required, since the by-laws provide for the use of non-combustible materials in such circumstances.[2] This restriction is not, however, imposed by the Model Building Byelaws, so that by using appropriate forms of ceiling linings to give periods of more than ½ hr resistance, the wider use of timber floors is possible. To obtain this greater degree of resistance special measures are usually necessary, e.g. the use of side hangers, fixed to the sides of the joists, to support the lining or its background (such as metal lathing), in order to avoid the fixings coming away. It should be borne in mind that the increased protection in such floors is to the underside only, and with boarded joists spread of fire to lower floors may occur through the ignition of the boards by fire on the upper surface.

Ministry of Education Building Bulletin No. 7 provides for combustible floors in schools up to four storeys in height (except floors or landings within stair enclosures).[3] Floors must have a fire resistance of a ½ hr up to four storeys. For five storeys and over the floors must have a resistance of 1 hr and be non-combustible.[4] When floors are combustible the building should be sub-divided by division walls into compartments not exceeding 125,000 cu. ft, in order to restrict structural damage. As mentioned earlier the stringent escape requirements of this Bulletin makes the use of combustible materials permissible.

In certain types of industrial buildings with vertical forms of processing, requiring considerable perforation of the floors to permit the passage of hopper, conveyors and chutes, it becomes impracticable to limit the spread of fire by fire-resisting floor divisions. Thus, provided the area of each floor is

---

[1] See Fire Note No. 1, "Fire Resistance of Floors and Ceilings" (H.M.S.O.).
[2] The use of intermediate timber floors in multi-storey maisonette blocks is referred to on page 302. The L.C.C. now grant a waiver to permit ½ hr timber floors *within* maisonettes up to a height of 100 ft.
[3] *Ministry of Education Building Bulletin* No. 7, Table VI.
[4] *Ibid*, Table VIII.

sufficiently small and means of escape is good, timber floors can be used, with non-combustible fire-resisting floors limited to the enclosed areas round the vertical circulation of lifts and staircases.

Openings in Floors. Apart from lifts and staircases which are enclosed throughout their height, openings in floors may occur where vertical services communicate with successive storeys. Where these are contained in ducts the latter should be sealed off at each floor level with a non-combustible filling to give a fire resistance equal to that of the floor. This prevents them acting as flues to spread fire vertically and may be accomplished by arranging for the floors to close the vertical shaft, openings of the correct dimension to accommodate services being left when the floor is formed. Pipes passing through slabs can be encircled by a ferrule set in the floor and sealed with asbestos to allow for expansion movement (page 504 (D)). The duct enclosures are built off the floor slabs. As an alternative to this method the opening in the floor slab may be the full area of the duct. Subsequent to the installation of the service pipes, this may be filled in tigthtly round the pipes with a suitable non-combustible material. These can be fairly easily removed and replaced when repairs to the services are necessary. Such fillings are asbestos fibre or slag wool with retarded hemi-hydrate plaster, foamed slag concrete or vermiculite concrete, all of which can be laid on asbestos board or expanded metal. Open ducts, or chutes, passing through fire division floors, should be provided with double steel dampers with fusible links and counterweights.

Roofs. The problems of roof construction have already been discussed in the earlier sections of this chapter, see pages 484, 486, 489.

Cavities. The need to avoid continuous cavities in wall and roof construction when formed by the application of combustible linings has been referred to on page 483. Cavities may also be formed in framed structures behind claddings and in curtain walling. In all cases the possibility of the cavity acting as a flue for the passage of flames and smoke in the same way as a duct must always be considered. The two-storey balloon-framed timber wall in which the vertical studs run through the two floors is an example of a cavity arising from the structure used. It requires fire-stops at first floor and roof levels. The Model Building Byelaws require fire-stops to be provided in cavity walls built wholly or partly of combustible materials at the junctions with other walls, floors, ceilings and roof and at intervals in the length of the wall not exceeding 15 ft.[1]

Fireplaces and Flues. The construction of fireplaces and flues must obviously be designed to contain the fire and prevent the spread of heat by

[1] M.B. Byelaw 46.

conduction or radiation to combustible parts of the structure, and to ensure that where there is any possibility of the accidental fall of hot embers a non-combustible surface is provided to receive them. Building regulations lay down certain thicknesses and dispositions of non-combustible materials, limit the presence of combustible materials near a fireplace or flue and require that all joints in flues shall be properly tight against the passage of smoke or flame. The main requirements in these respects are summarized on pages 510 and 511. (See also page 345 and *Elementary Building Construction*.)

MECHANICAL EQUIPMENT

Fire Alarms. In order to give adequate warning to the occupants of a building of the approach of fire various alarm systems are used, operated by the heated air which precedes the conflagration. These are: (i) Sprinkler operated, in which a gong is operated by the loss of water pressure in the system of pipes feeding the sprinkler system when the sprinkler heads are set in operation, and (ii) Electrically operated.[1]

Methods of Extinguishing Fires

Fire Mains. Fire mains, feeding hose points in the building, may be of the wet riser type constantly filled with water from the local supply or they may be of the dry riser type into which the fire brigade can pump water through a connection outside the building. Up to 200 gallons per minute can be provided in buildings up to 150 ft high by means of a 4 in. dry rising main and from 150 to 200 ft by a 6 in. riser. Above 200 ft fire brigade pumps are inadequate and a 6 in. wet rising main with automatic booster pumps and water storage tanks is necessary. The positions of all mains, hose points and extinguishers should be planned to be readily accessible from a staircase or the exterior of the building.

Automatic Sprinklers. These are for the internal protection of premises against fire and may be required by local authorities in the case of buildings, or compartments of buildings, exceeding 250,000 cu. ft. (For full details of Sprinkler Installations see *Advanced Building Construction* (*Components, Services and Finishes*).)

Drenchers. Drenchers, which form a water curtain, are generally used for the external protection of a building and are normally required only where the risk of fire entering from an adjoining building is particularly great. They are also provided together with safety curtains in theatres and to ducts.

[1] See B.S. Code of Practice 327.404/402.501:1951, "Installation of Electrical Fire Alarms", and "Rules of the Fire Offices Committee for Automatic Fire Alarm Installations".

Portable Fire Extinguishers.   These are intended for immediate use on an outbreak of fire and the apparatus must be approved by the Fire Offices Committee.   A number of British Standards now cover the various types.

The foam, powder and CO_2 types are suitable for small oil and spirit fires. Foam machines and large foam generators are available.   For large oil and spirit fire risks, permanent foam installations similar to automatic sprinkler systems are used.   For small electrical fires powder and CO_2 are suitable. For highly inflammable liquids, motor vehicle fires and electrical fires the single liquid type is used.   It is quite safe for electrical fires because the liquid is non-conductive, even at high voltages.

Fireplaces and Flues (Fire Protection): Main Requirements of the L.C.C. By-laws

Note: The following is based on the London Building (Constructional) By-laws, 1952, but is not a direct extract.   Reference should be made to the By-Laws for further details.

By-law 10.01. Flues to be enclosed by flue pipes, chimneys or chimney shafts.

By-law 10.02. A flue shall not serve more than one fire or heating appliance, although two fires in the same room may be served so long as oil burning and solid fuel burning appliances are not so united.

By-law 10.04. A fire shall be so installed that the temperature of adjacent combustible material is not raised above 150°F when in use.   To achieve this no timber (other than wood fixing plugs, not nearer than 6 in. to inside of flue or fireplace) is to be built in within 9 in. of a fireplace opening or the inside of a flue or within 12 in. of a ventilating valve, 15 in. of a soot door or 9 in. of a flue pipe serving a gas-fired food-cooking appliance (unless the pipe is sleeved and 1 in. asbestos or similar annular packing interposed between pipe and sleeve), or 1 in. of a flue pipe serving any other gas-fired appliance (unless sleeved to leave 1 in. air-space between pipe and sleeve) or 9in. of any other flue pipe (other than that serving a gas appliance).

By-law 10.05. Flue pipes are to be of cast iron (to B.S. 41, 1946) or M.S. plates at least 3/16 in. thick or, except for the first 6 ft of pipe above fire outlet, of asbestos cement (to B.S. 835, 1948).   Alternatively, for gas-fired fish-frying ranges 16 S.W.G. sheet metal may be used and 20 S.W.G. for other gas-fired appliances in premises where food is prepared.   For gas appliances generally, asbestos cement (to B.S. 567, 1948) or sheet metal (to B.S. 715, 1951) may be used.

A flue pipe may only act within the room it serves, except for certain gas-fired appliances protected to the satisfaction of the District Surveyor.

By-law 10.06. Chimneys must be constructed of solid bricks or blocks or R.C. and must be stable and supported to the satisfaction of the District Surveyor.   Flues to be a minimum of 7½ in. in each direction internally, and must be parged, rendered or lined with fireclay or other non-combustible lining. The walls and withes of chimneys shall be at least 4 in. thick (although soot doors, ventilating valves and branch flues may penetrate the walls).   The walls of a flue serving an oven, furnace or boiler used for trade purposes shall be 8½ in. thick from floor level to the level of the floor or roof surface immediately above the ceiling of the room over the room containing the appliance.   (Except that a closed fire used for trade purposes, having an outlet of 80 sq. in. max. area, may discharge into an existing flue with 4 in. walls if lined to the same level with non-combustible pipes to the satisfaction of the District Surveyor.)

Walls of chimneys enclosing flues exceeding 150 sq. in. in area are to be at least 8½ in. thick (exclusive of any insulating lining) unless such walls are supported at the floors by R. C. or structural steel, when any insulating bricks may contribute to the thickness or the full thickness may be composed of insulating bricks of diatomaceous earth of min. crushing strength, 750 lb/sq. in. (see page 357).

Except when on the outer face of an external wall, a chimney having walls less than 8½ in. thickness shall be rendered throughout its full height to the outer surface of the roof.   The upper surface of a flue inclined at less than 45° is to be enclosed by at least 8½ in. of non-combustible material.

By-law 10.07. Chimneys shall extend 3 ft min. above highest point of intersection with roof (18 in. for chimneys to gas-fired appliances).

By-law 10.08. Walls at back of fireplace may be 4 in. thick except party walls, which must be 8½ in. carried up (i) 12 in. above fireplace opening in the case of back-to-back fireplaces, or (ii) to the ceiling of the room when the flue is not back-to-back.

By-law 10.09. Hearths are to be 6 in. thick of non-combustible material.   R. C. is to be cast *in situ* in one operation (a hollow block R.C. floor may be used instead of solid concrete).   The surface of a hearth shall lie in the same plane as the floor and shall be 10 in. min. above any timber or other combustible material beneath the slab (except that a fillet 2 in. × 1½ in. may be fixed to the trimming joists of a timber floor to give support to the edges of an R.C. slab).   The slab shall project at least 16 in. in front and 6 in. at each side of the fireplace opening.   (*Note:* Tiling to hearths does *not* count as part of the constructional hearth even though non-combustible.)   Where new fires are installed in existing fireplace openings the hearth is to comply with the foregoing but may project only 12 in. in front of the fire which itself must not project more than 2 in. in front of the constructional jambs unless the District Surveyor is satisfied that the hearth is 6 in. min. thickness of solid non-combustible material or a super-imposed hearth of non-combustible material, 3 in. min. thickness, is bedded down over the whole area of hearth and fireplace when the fire may project 6 in. in front of the constructional jambs, so long as the front of the hearth projects 12 in. in front of it. Hearths serving free-standing slow combustion stoves must project at least 12 in. in front of them. (In the case of new hearths the full 6 in. thickness is required, in the case of additions to existing hearths, 2 in. thickness is adequate provided this is not directly under the stove.)

By-law 10.10. Where the required hearth is less than 16 in. in front of the fire a raised curb is to be provided within the limits of the constructional hearth (to be 4 in. wide, 1 in. high if well fire and 2 in. high if basket fire, with its outer edge 12 in. min. from front of fire). Such curb may be incorporated in a superimposed or tiled hearth, the height being measured above the finished upper surface.

By-law 10.11. Domestic gas fires to have flues at least 20 sq. in. in area (or area of spigot if greater), surrounded by 1 in. min. non-combustible material (4 in. behind single flues in party walls—carried up from hearth level to top of wall). Such flues to discharge into the open air and be fitted with an anti-downdraught terminal or into a ventilated roof space and fitted with a guard (as 10.05 (4) (b)). Gas fires shall have ⅛ in. thick non-combustible hearths with 6 in. projection at sides and 12 in. at front (alternatively a metal hearth may be incorporated in the fire at least ⅛ in. in height and of 10 in. projection). Panel fires need have no hearth if the flame or incandescent material is over 9 in. above floor level.

By-law 10.12. Floors or roofs not built of non-combustible materials and less than 5 ft above any heating appliance having a grate area not exceeding 2 sq. ft to be protected by an adequate ceiling of plaster or other non-combustible material (3/16 in. min. thickness) extending over 100 sq. ft. to satisfaction of the District Surveyor. Where appliances exceed 2 sq. ft. grate area or are less than 18 in. below the floor or roof above, protection shall be given to the ceiling over by a false ceiling of non-combustible material, 2 in. min. thickness, suspended by non-combustible material to give a 2 in. min. clear air-space above.

By-law 10.13. Hearths under appliances not heated by gas or electricity and not situated within a fireplace shall be 6 in. solid concrete (or 2 in. thickness of materials giving a similar heat resistivity), extending 18 in. on all sides of the appliance (12 in. if a slow conbustion appliance).

Bye-law 10.14. Where the floor under a gas or electric appliance is wholly or partly of combustible construction it shall be protected by a solid slab of such non-combustible material as will prevent the temperature of any part of the floor from exceeding 150°F, projecting 2 in. min. all round. No slab is required if appliance is designed effectively to prevent the temperature of floor exceeding 150°F.

By-law 10.16. (2) Chimney shafts may be constructed within buildings to the approval of the District Surveyor provided they are constructed of suitable solid bricks jointed with suitable mortar and that proper precautions are taken to prevent damage to the building by heat or by corrosion of structural steel within that building.

Fireplaces and Flues (Fire Protection):
Main Requirements of the Model Byelaws

Note: The following is based on the Model Building Byelaws, 1953, but is not a direct extract. Reference should be made to the Byelaws for further details.

Byelaw 52. Every chimney, the back and jambs of every fireplace opening and every hearth are to be of non-combustible materials so arranged as to prevent the ignition of any part of the building.

Byelaw 54. Fireplaces are required to have 6 in. thick non-combustible hearths projecting 16 in. in front of the fireplace opening and 6 in. at each side. The upper surface of the hearth shall not be lower than the level of any combustible floor with which it is in contact and no combustible materials other than timber fillets supporting the hearth are to be within 10 in. of the upper surface. Where sunken ashpits are used these are to be of brick or concrete not less than 2 in. thick resting on solid ground and set back 10 in. min. from any combustible material if the distance from the fire to any inner surface of the ashpit is less than 12 in. (3 in. if fire is not less than 12 in. from the inner surfaces of ashpit).

Byelaw 55. The jambs of fireplace openings are to be 8½ in. min. thickness.

Byelaw 57. Fireplaces set back to back may have 4 in. min. thickness common back (except when in a separating (party) wall when the common back wall shall be 8½ in. min. thickness). The backs of single fireplaces shall be 4 in. min. thickness when situated in an external wall otherwise 8½ in. extending 2 ft 6 in above hearth where serving an open fire and 1 ft 0 in. above the fireplace opening in all other cases.

Byelaw 59. The walls and withes of any chimney shall be 4 in. min. thickness of bricks or blocks or *in situ* concrete, 6 in. min. if in stone. Chimneys in walls separating buildings to have 8½ in. min. thickness at back, up to roof level, when not situated back to back. Flues inclined at a lesser angle than 45° must have 8½ in. min. thickness to the upper inclined surfaces. Where a flue passes through a roof covered in thatch or other combustible material the walls shall be 8½ in. min. thickness for a distance of 4 in. below the lowest point of intersection of the flue with such roof covering to 4 in. above the highest point of intersection. A flue serving a fireplace in a habitable room is not to communicate with another room except that a back-to-back grate may be discharged into one flue.

Byelaw 60. Every chimney is to be properly lined, parged or otherwise protected.

Byelaw 61. Other than chimneys constructed of blocks having no vertical joints, all chimneys constructed of bricks, stone or blocks less than 8½ in. thick are to be rendered or otherwise protected within a building.

Byelaw 62. No timber or combustible material is to be built within 9 in. of the interior of a flue or fireplace opening except fixing plugs or fillets set no nearer than 6 in. thereto. Combustible structural materials are to be kept at least 1½ in. away from the face of the rendering required on the surfaces of chimneys (61).

Byelaw 63. Metal fastenings for combustible materials are not to be within 2 in. of the interior of a flue or fireplace opening.

Byelaw 65. Chimneys to extend 2 ft min. above ridge when passing through ridge of a pitched roof (10° or more). In all other cases 3 ft above highest point of intersection with roof.

Byelaw 104. A free-standing heating or cooking apparatus heated other than by gas, electricity or oil is to be set upon a non-combustible slab or plate of sufficient thickness extending 6 in. at the sides and back and 16 in. at the front (9 in. in case of domestic heating or cooking apparatus).

Byelaw 105. Gas fires are to have an "adequate" flue discharging into a chimney, communicating only with the outside air, or directly to the open air through a suitable terminal. (Not applicable to a "flueless" heater rated below 6000 B.Th.U's per hr.)

TYPES OF CONSTRUCTION GIVING FIRE RESISTANCE PERIODS AS SHOWN IN COLUMN A–D

	A — 4 hours (not LCC)	B — 2 hours	C — 1 hour	D — ½ hour — WALLS	notes
Brickwork	BRICKWORK (not LCC) 8½" unplastered, ½" plaster, 4"	BRICKWORK 8½" unplastered, ½" plaster, 4"	BRICKWORK as col. D	BRICKWORK clay concrete / sand / lime unplastered, 4"	MODEL BYELAWS ALSO GIVE 6 HR PERIOD TO 8½ in. BRICK WALL WITHOUT PLASTER. 4 in. walls in cols. A & B not to exceed 10 ft in length or h't. M.B.B. specify ½ in. gypsum vermiculite plaster for col. A. LCC By-laws do not permit 4 in. wall in col. A.
Reinforced concrete	REINFORCED CONCRETE 7", 6"	REINFORCED CONCRETE min. cover 1 inch, 4", 6"	REINFORCED CONCRETE as col. D	REINFORCED CONCRETE min. cover 1 inch, 3", 9"	MODEL BYELAWS ALSO GIVE 6 HR PERIOD TO 9 in. R.C. WALL WITH TWO LAYERS OF REINFORCEMENT AT 6 in. c/c. LCC specify aggregate as By-law 3.02. M.B.B. specify that reinforcement shall be (i) not less than 0·2 % vol. of concrete, (ii) in two layers in walls over 5 in. thick.
Solid concrete blocks		SOLID CONCRETE BLOCKS class 1 agg. / class 2 agg. ½" plaster, 4", 4"	SOLID CONCRETE BLOCKS class 1 agg. ½" plaster both sides, 3" / 2½" class 2 agg. 4" / 3"	SOLID CONCRETE BLOCKS class 1 agg. ½" plaster both sides, 2½" / 2" class 2 agg. 3"	Class 1 Aggregate: foamed slag, pumice, blast furnace slag, crushed brick and burnt clay products, crushed limestone. Class 2 Aggregate: flint, gravel, granite, and other crushed stones other than limestone.
Gypsum blocks		GYPSUM BLOCKS ½" plaster, 3", 4"	GYPSUM BLOCKS ½" plaster, 3", 2"	GYPSUM BLOCKS with or without plaster, 2"	HOLLOW GYPSUM BLOCKS of equal thickness to solid blocks and 70 % solid material may be used in lieu of solid blocks in cols. B, C, D.

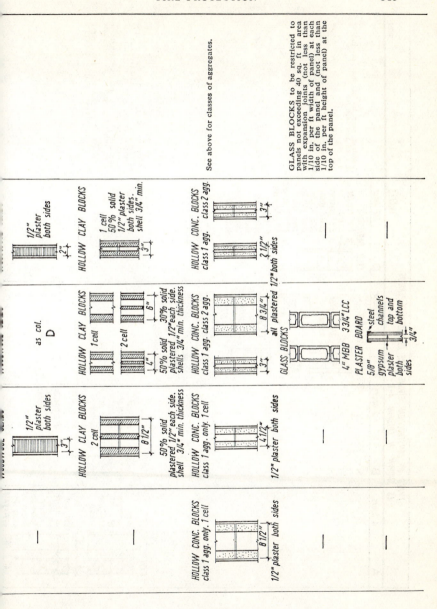

HOLLOW CONC. BLOCKS
class 1 agg. only. 1 cell
8 1/2"
1/2" plaster both sides

HOLLOW CONC. BLOCKS
class 1 agg. only. 1 cell
4 1/2"
1/2" plaster both sides

HOLLOW CLAY BLOCKS
2 cell
8 1/2"
50% solid
plastered 1/2" each side.
shell 3/4" min. thickness
1/2" plaster both sides

as col.
D

HOLLOW CLAY BLOCKS
1 cell   2 cell
4"   6"
50% solid 30% solid
plastered 1/2" each side.
shells 3/4" min. thickness

HOLLOW CONC. BLOCKS
class 1 agg. class 2 agg.
3"   8 3/4"
all plastered 1/2" both sides

GLASS BLOCKS
4" MBB   3 3/4" LCC

PLASTER BOARD
5/8" gypsum plaster both sides
steel channels top and bottom
3/4"

HOLLOW CLAY BLOCKS
2"
1/2" plaster both sides

HOLLOW CLAY BLOCKS
3"
1 cell 50% solid
1/2" plaster both sides.
shell 3/4" min.

HOLLOW CONC. BLOCKS
class 1 agg. class 2 agg.
3"   2 1/2"
1/2" both sides

See above for classes of aggregates.

GLASS BLOCKS to be restricted to panels not exceeding 40 sq. ft in area with expansion joints (not less than 1/10 in. per ft width of panel) at each side of the panel and (not less than 1/10 in. per ft height of panel) at the top of the panel.

TYPES OF CONSTRUCTION GIVING FIRE RESISTANCE PERIODS AS SHOWN IN COLUMN A-D

A — 4 hours	B — 2 hours	C — 1 hour	D — 1/2 hour	notes
		STUD PARTITIONS	STUD PARTITIONS	
		3/4" plaster board	a 1/2" plaster board · b 3/8" plaster board with 3/16" single coat plaster both sides · c 1/2" P.C. plaster, P.C. lime plaster or gypsum plaster on metal or timber lathing both sides.	Studding may be of steel or timber (L.C.C. and M.B.B.).
		2" x 3/8" plaster boards		
		1/2" plaster brd. 3/8" plaster or 3/8" perforated plaster board with 1/2" plaster		
		3/4" P.C. PLASTER, P.C. lime plaster or gypsum plaster on timber or metal lathing		
CAVITY WALLS	CAVITY WALLS			CAVITY WALLS TO BE CONSTRUCTED IN ACCORDANCE WITH BY-LAW 5.16 (L.C.C.)—Load-bearing external or party wall not exceeding 25 ft h't and 30 ft length in bldgs. other than public or warehouse class, etc. MODEL BYELAWS DO NOT GIVE VALUES FOR CAVITY WALLS.
clay, concrete or sandlime bricks	ext. leaf as col. A int. leaf solid or hollow concrete blocks class 1 or 2 aggregates or hollow clay blocks			
ext. leaf as above int. leaf of solid or hollow conc. blocks of class 1 aggregate				

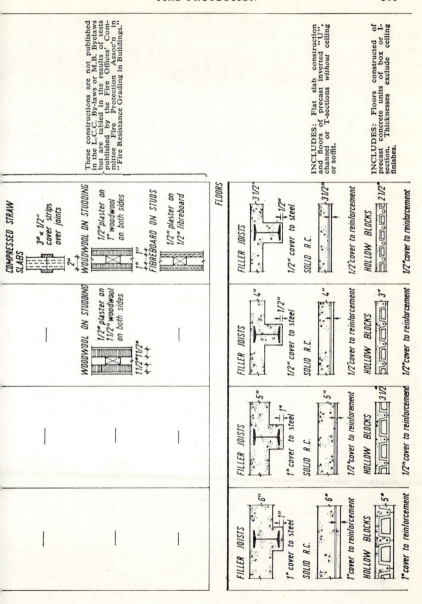

These constructions are not published in the L.C.C. By-laws or M.B. Byelaws but are tabled in the results of tests published by the Fire Protection Assoc'n in "Fire Resistance Grading in Buildings."

INCLUDES: Flat slab construction and floors of precast inverted "U", channel or T-sections *without* ceiling or soffit.

INCLUDES: Floors constructed of precast concrete units of box or I-section. Thicknesses exclude ceiling finishes.

COMPRESSED STRAW SLABS
3" × 1/2" cover strips over joints
2"

WOODWOOL ON STUDDING
1/2" plaster on 1" woodwool on both sides

FIBREBOARD ON STUDS
1" 1"
1/2" plaster on 1/2" fibreboard

WOODWOOL ON STUDDING
1/2" plaster on 1 1/2" woodwool on both sides
1 1/2" 1 1/2"

FLOORS

FILLER JOISTS
1 1/2"
3 1/2"
1/2" cover to steel
SOLID R.C.
3 1/2"
1/2" cover to reinforcement
HOLLOW BLOCKS
2 1/2"
1/2" cover to reinforcement

FILLER JOISTS
1 1/2"
4"
1/2" cover to steel
SOLID R.C.
4"
1/2" cover to reinforcement
HOLLOW BLOCKS
3"
1/2" cover to reinforcement

FILLER JOISTS
1"
5"
1" cover to steel
SOLID R.C.
5"
1/2" cover to reinforcement
HOLLOW BLOCKS
3 1/2"
1/2" cover to reinforcement

FILLER JOISTS
1"
6"
1" cover to steel
SOLID R.C.
6"
1" cover to reinforcement
HOLLOW BLOCKS
5"
1" cover to reinforcement

TYPES OF CONSTRUCTION GIVING FIRE RESISTANCE PERIODS AS SHOWN IN COLUMNS A–D

A 4 hours	B 2 hour	C 1 hour	D 1/2 hour				notes
			FLOORS — **TIMBER FLOORS** — Joists 1½" minimum width			**MODEL BYELAWS** *(Figures in columns below indicate required thickness of plaster (or lining board as the case may be))*	
			Plain Edge Boarding	3/4" T&G Boarding	periods for small houses MBB 37(1)	linings to ceilings	
—	—	—	—	—	5/8" (p.e. or t&g bdg)	timber lath & plaster	
			5/8"	—	—	timber lath and plaster covered with 1/2" plasterboard	
			—	5/8"	—	ditto covered with 3/8" plasterboard	
			5/8"	5/8"	—	metal lath and plaster	
			—	—	1/2" (p.e. bdg) 3/8" (t&g bdg)	one layer of plasterboard	
			—	—	1/2" (p.e. bdg)	1 layer 3/8" plasterboard finished with gypsum plaster	
			1/2"	3/16"	—	1 layer 1/2" plasterboard finished with gypsum plaster	
			1"	7/8"	3/4" (p.e. bdg)	2 layers of plasterboard of total thickness	
			—	—	1/2" (p.e. bdg) 3/16" (t&g bdg)	1 layer 1/2" insulating board finished with gypsum plaster	
			3/16"	3/16"	—	woodwool slab 1" thick finished with gypsum plaster	

| linings to ceilings | periods for small houses M.B.B. 37(1) | 2 — T & G boarding on 7×2″ joists | | L.C.C. BY-LAWS ONLY | 3 — 7/8″ plain edge boarding on 7×2″ joists |
		M.B.B. 1″(nom.) bdg.	L.C.C. 7/8″bdg.		
timber lath and plaster	—	5/8″	5/8″		
metal lath and plaster	—	5/8″	5/8″		
1 layer of plasterboard	3/8″	5/8″	3/4″		
2 layers of plasterboard each of minimum thickness	—	3/8″ or to total 3/4″	3/8″		
1 layer of 3/8″ plasterboard finished with gypsum plaster	—	1/2″	5/8″		
1 layer of 1/2″ plasterboard finished with gypsum plaster	—	3/16″	—		
1 layer of 1/2″ insulating board finished with gypsum plaster	—	1/2″	—		
1 layer of insulating board	1/2″	—	—		
woodwool slab 1″ thick finished with gypsum plaster	—	3/16″	—		
metal lath and plaster					5/8″
timber lath & plaster covered with 3/8″ plaster bd.					5/8″

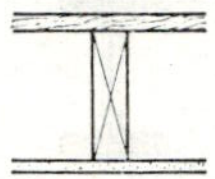

this construction is not published in the L.C.C. or M.B.B. but has been tested by the Joint Fire Research Organisation

1″ t & g boarding
7″×2″
1″ mineral wool mat
1/2″ asbestos fibreboard fixed by screws
1/2″ asbestos fibreboard secured to underside of joist by angle fillet fixed to side of joist.

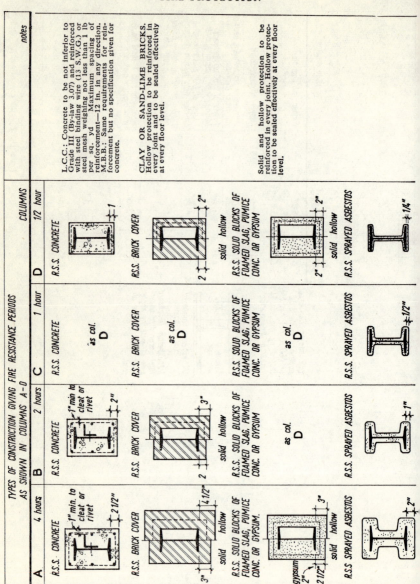

TYPES OF CONSTRUCTION GIVING FIRE RESISTANCE PERIODS AS SHOWN IN COLUMNS A–D

	A 4 hours	B 2 hours	C 1 hour	COLUMNS D 1/2 hour	notes
	R.S.S. CONCRETE	R.S.S. CONCRETE	R.S.S. CONCRETE	R.S.S. CONCRETE	L.C.C.: Concrete to be not inferior to Grade III (By-law 3.07) and reinforced with steel binding wire (13 S.W.G.) or steel mesh weighing not less than 1 lb per sq. yd. Maximum spacing of reinforcement—12 in. in any direction. M.B.B.: Same requirements for reinforcement but no specification given for concrete.
	R.S.S. BRICK COVER solid hollow	R.S.S. BRICK COVER solid hollow	R.S.S. BRICK COVER as col. D	R.S.S. BRICK COVER solid hollow	CLAY OR SAND-LIME BRICKS. Hollow protection to be reinforced in every joint and to be sealed effectively at every floor level.
	R.S.S. SOLID BLOCKS OF FOAMED SLAG, PUMICE CONC. OR GYPSUM. solid hollow	R.S.S. SOLID BLOCKS OF FOAMED SLAG, PUMICE CONC. OR GYPSUM as col. D	R.S.S. SOLID BLOCKS OF FOAMED SLAG, PUMICE CONC. OR GYPSUM as col. D	R.S.S. SOLID BLOCKS OF FOAMED SLAG, PUMICE CONC. OR GYPSUM solid hollow	Solid and hollow protection to be reinforced in every joint. Hollow protection to be sealed effectively at every floor level.
	R.S.S SPRAYED ASBESTOS	R.S.S. SPRAYED ASBESTOS	R.S.S. SPRAYED ASBESTOS	R.S.S. SPRAYED ASBESTOS	

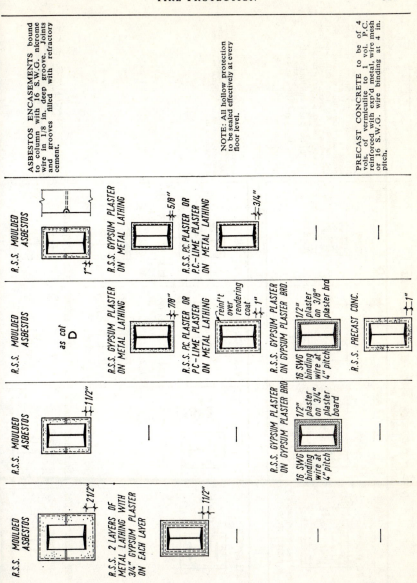

ASBESTOS ENCASEMENTS bound to column with 16 S.W.G. nichrome wire in 1/8 in. deep groove. Joints and grooves filled with refractory cement.

NOTE: All hollow protection to be sealed effectively at every floor level.

PRECAST CONCRETE to be of 4 vols. of vermiculite to 1 vol. P.C. reinforced with exp'd metal, wire mesh or 16 S.W.G. wire binding at 4 in. pitch.

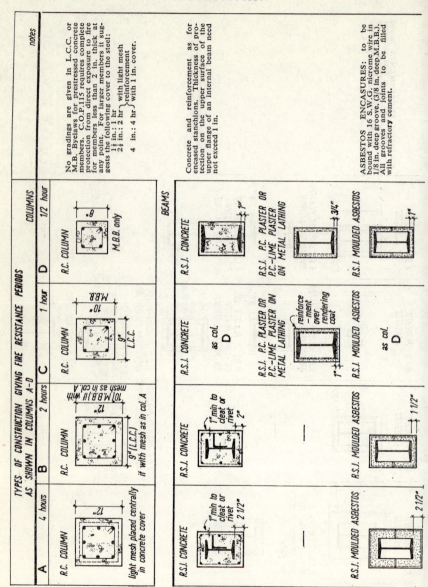

TYPES OF CONSTRUCTION GIVING FIRE RESISTANCE PERIODS AS SHOWN IN COLUMNS A–D

COLUMNS

A — 4 hours

R.C. COLUMN

12"

light mesh placed centrally in concrete cover

B — 2 hours

R.C. COLUMN

12"

9" (L.C.C.)
10" M.B.B.II with mesh as in col. A

if with mesh as in col. A

C — 1 hour

R.C. COLUMN

10" M.B.B.
9" L.C.C.

D — 1/2 hour

R.C. COLUMN

8"

M.B.B. only

Notes (columns):
No gradings are given in L.C.C. or M.B. Byelaws for prestressed concrete members. C.O.P. 115 requires complete protection from direct exposure to fire for members less than 2 in. thick at any point. For larger members it suggests the following cover to the steel:

1½ in.: 1 hr ⎫ with light mesh
2½ in.: 2 hr ⎬ reinforcement
4 in.: 4 hr ⎭ with 1 in. cover.

BEAMS

A

R.S.J. CONCRETE

1" min to cleat or rivet
2 1/2"

R.S.J. MOULDED ASBESTOS

2 1/2"

B

R.S.J. CONCRETE

1" min to cleat or rivet
2"

R.S.J. MOULDED ASBESTOS

1 1/2"

C

R.S.J. CONCRETE

as col. D

R.S.J. P.C. PLASTER OR P.C.–LIME PLASTER ON METAL LATHING

1"
reinforce–ment over rendering coat

R.S.J. MOULDED ASBESTOS

as col. D

D

R.S.J. CONCRETE

1"

R.S.J. P.C. PLASTER OR P.C.–LIME PLASTER ON METAL LATHING

3/4"

R.S.J. MOULDED ASBESTOS

1"

Notes (beams):
Concrete and reinforcement as for encased stanchions. Thickness of protection on the upper surface of the upper flange of an internal beam need not exceed 1 in.

ASBESTOS ENCASURES: to be bound with 16 S.W.G. nichrome wire in 1/8 in. deep groove. (3/8 in. deep M.B.B.) All grooves and joints to be filled with refractory cement.

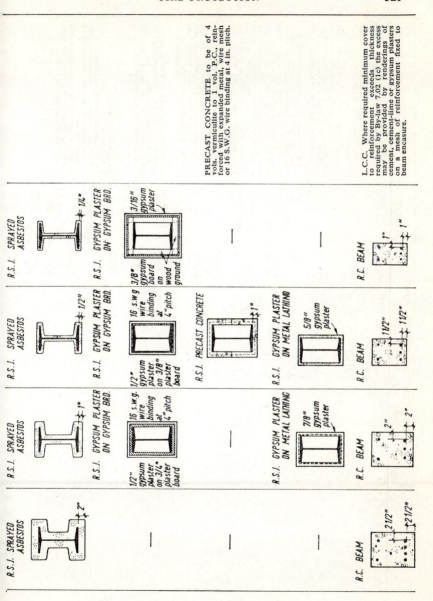

PRECAST CONCRETE to be of 4 vols. vermiculite to 1 vol. P.C., reinforced with expanded metal, wire mesh or 16 S.W.G. wire binding at 4 in. pitch.

L.C.C. Where required minimum cover to reinforcement exceeds thickness required by By-law 7.02 (1) the excess may be provided by renderings of cement, cement-lime or gypsum plasters on a mesh of reinforcement fixed to beam encasure.

R.S.J. SPRAYED ASBESTOS — ¼"

R.S.J. GYPSUM PLASTER ON GYPSUM BRD.

3/16" gypsum plaster

3/8" gypsum board on wood ground

R.S.J. SPRAYED ASBESTOS — ½"

R.S.J. GYPSUM PLASTER ON GYPSUM BRD.

16 s.w.g wire binding at 4" pitch

½" gypsum plaster on 3/8" plaster board

R.S.J. PRECAST CONCRETE — 1"

R.S.J. GYPSUM PLASTER ON METAL LATHING

5/8" gypsum plaster

R.C. BEAM — 1½" 1½"

R.S.J. SPRAYED ASBESTOS — 1"

R.S.J. GYPSUM PLASTER ON GYPSUM BRD.

16 s.w.g. wire binding at 4" pitch

½" gypsum plaster on 3/4" plaster board

R.S.J. GYPSUM PLASTER ON METAL LATHING

7/8" gypsum plaster

R.C. BEAM — 2" 2"

R.S.J. SPRAYED ASBESTOS — 2"

R.C. BEAM — 2½" 2½"

notes	TYPES OF CONSTRUCTION GIVING FIRE RESISTANCE PERIODS AS SHOWN IN COLUMNS A–D			STAIRCASES	
	A 4 hours	B 2 hours	C 1 hour	D 1/2 hour	

TABLE INDICATES L.C.C. REQUIREMENTS ONLY. M.B.B. Appendix Clause X requires the following for common stairs to flats and maisonettes:

Buildings over 50 ft in ht or over 2,500 sq. ft area on any one floor: staircase to be constructed of non-combustible material. Buildings not exceeding the above limits: staircase to be constructed of:

(a) Of non-combustible material, or

(b) Of timber 1¼ in. min. finished thickness; all joints in treads and risers and in flooring on landings cross tongued or tongued and grooved, or

(c) As (b) above but of no specified timber thickness, with soffit made up as follows: (i) 5/8 in. plaster on wood lath, or (ii) 3/8 in. plaster on plasterboard, or (iii) 3/16 in. plaster on ⅜ in. plasterboard, or (iv) one or two layers of plasterboard of a total thickness of ⅜ in., or

(d) Of timber of no specified thickness with soffit made up as follows: (i) 5/8 in. plaster on metal lath, or (ii) 5/8 in. plaster on wood lath, with a covering of 3/8 in. plasterboard, or (iii) ⅜ in. plaster on ⅜ in. plasterboard.

(a) All joints in treads and risers and in flooring to be cross-tongued or tongued and grooved.

(b) Thickness means solid finished thickness of timber structure.

As (a) and (b) above.
Soffit linings:
1. 5/8 in. plaster on metal lathing, or
2. 3/16 in. sheets of non-combustible material on ⅜ in. close-jointed boarding, or
3. 3/16 in. sheets of non-combustible material bedded on plaster and fixed securely to carriages and joists.

Column C (1 hour):

R.C. PRECAST CONCRETE — 2"

R.C. IN-SITU — 2 1/2"

Column D (1/2 hour):

R.C. IN-SITU — 1 1/2"

TIMBER — unprotected soffit — minimum thickness in any part: 1 3/4."

TIMBER — protected soffit — min thickness in any part 1 1/8" — alternative soffit linings as (1) (2) (3)

Doors and glazing types are given only in L.C.C. By-laws. Steel doors and shutters are not described in Schedule VI (see page 506 for details).

Timber Doors

1. Stops to be continuous round sides and head of frame.

2, 3. Fire Check Doors (flush) complying with B.S. 459, Part 3, 1951. For 2, frame must be solid.

(a) Glass in direct combination with metal having a melting point not lower than 1800°F in squares not exceeding 24 sq. in. in area.

(b) Glass reinforced with wire not less than 26 S.W.G. laid to ⅜ in. square mesh electrically welded at intersections, or to a hexagonal mesh 1 in. across the flat sides.

Glass fixed as in 1, 2 or 3 may be used in windows, doors, borrowed lights, lanterns and skylights.

Note: On application for a waiver the L.C.C. now permits glazing areas up to 12 sq. ft for construction 1 when wired glass is used and the metal frame is not aluminium.

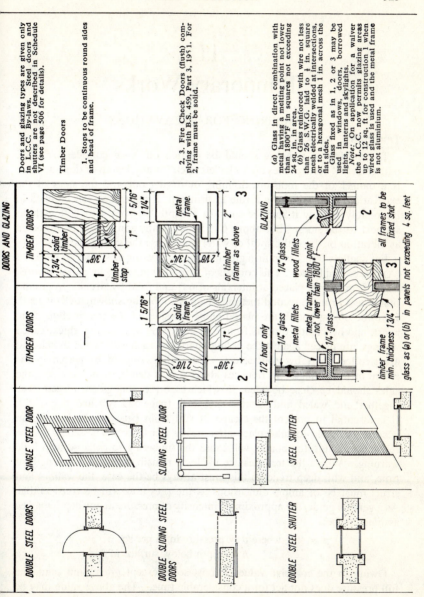

DOORS AND GLAZING

TIMBER DOORS

1 — timber stop, 1¾" solid timber, 1⅜", 1", 1 5/16"

3 — metal frame, 1⅜", 2⅛" or timber frame as above, 1¼", 2"

TIMBER DOORS

2 — solid frame, 1⅜", 2⅛", 1", 1 5/16"

GLAZING

1/2 hour only

1 — ¼" glass metal fillets, metal frame, melting point not lower than 1800°F, ¼" glass, timber frame min. thickness 1¾"

glass as *(a)* or *(b)* in panels not exceeding 4 sq. feet

2 — ¼" glass, wood fillets, all frames to be fixed shut

3 — ¼" glass

SINGLE STEEL DOOR

SLIDING STEEL DOOR

STEEL SHUTTER

DOUBLE STEEL DOORS

DOUBLE SLIDING STEEL DOORS

DOUBLE STEEL SHUTTER

11

Temporary Works

TIMBERING FOR EXCAVATIONS

TRENCHES

The cutting of trenches should be carried out with considerable care, particularly if the trenches are to be left open for any length of time, as there is a danger of the moisture draining or drying out and the sides of the excavation falling in. As a rule in firm soil, if the trench can be filled in reasonably quickly it may be sunk to a depth of from 4 to 6 ft without support to the sides. But above 6 ft in depth any soil should be timbered as vibration or the withdrawal of water may cause the sides to collapse.

For shallow trenches in firm ground, open timbering as shown on page 525 (A) can be employed. This consists of pairs of 9 in. × 1½ in. poling boards, 3 to 4 ft in length, placed at intervals of 6 ft and fixed by struts. In ground that is less firm the second method of open timbering shown at (B) is used. Here the poling boards are placed along the sides of the trench about 9 in. apart, and horizontal timbers from 6 to 9 in. wide by 2 to 4 in. thick, called walings, are placed against the poling boards on each side of the trench and are strutted apart by stout struts. The walings should be placed in the centre of the polings. In trenches above 6 ft in depth, or in loose soil, the sides should be close boarded, in which case the polings are placed close together and waled and strutted as before (page 525 (C) and page 527). It is essential to prevent the escape of soil from between the boards, an occurrence liable to take place after heavy rains, as any lessening of the resistance behind the boards will cause the timbering to collapse with little warning. Where the trenches are liable to remain open for any length of time, and with deep trenches this must always be the case, the walings and struts must be of ample dimensions as the pressures will be considerable. As a general guide, the approximate intensity of pressure at any depth may be assumed to be:

$$p = 40h, \text{ where } p = \text{pressure in lb per sq. ft}$$
$$h = \text{depth below surface in feet}$$

Owing to the cohesive value of most soils, except gravel and sand, the full pressure does not act for a considerable time. The above value may be safely reduced in most cases to $p = 20h$ but the condition of the soil may in some cases require the full value of $40h$ to be taken.

Struts are usually square in section and should not be less than 4 in. × 4 in. A rule-of-thumb method of estimating the size of square struts which are not intermediately supported over spans from 4 ft to about 13 ft, is to make the

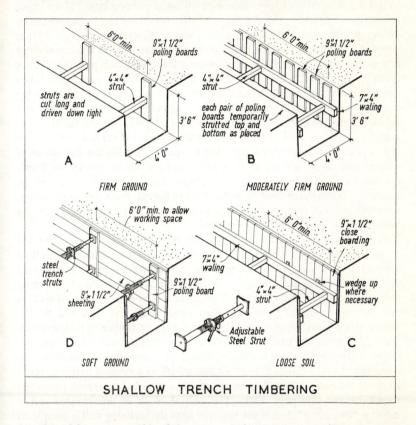

SHALLOW TRENCH TIMBERING

breadth of face one twelfth of the span. It is common practice now to use adjustable tubular steel struts in place of timber struts and wedges.

Shallow trenches in very soft ground are sometimes sheeted, that is, the sides are lined with 9 in. × 1½ in. boards laid horizontally, as shown at (D) above. The ground is excavated 9 in. at a time and the sides lined with a pair of boards, these being temporarily strutted. When the full depth is reached poling boards are placed in pairs, one on each side of the trench against the sheeting, and strutted. The temporary struts are then removed.

When trenches over 4 ft in depth are required in very soft soils, runners should be employed. Runners are sawn timbers 2 to 3 in. thick, usually about 9 in. wide and up to 20 ft long. The lower ends are bevelled and shaped to give a cutting edge and are often shod with steel or hoop iron. If the upper soil is reasonably firm, the first stage of the excavation can be supported by poling boards and the following procedure, illustrated on page 527, is adopted. Two 3 in. × 2 in. continuous guides are fixed to the top walings and struts, between which the runners are driven as far as is possible without damage to the head. The soil between is then excavated, care being taken not to remove soil within 12 in. of the toe of the runners, after which driving proceeds again. At approximately 4 ft intervals, frames of walings and struts are inserted, the lower walings acting as guides to the runners and keeping them in a vertical plane as they are driven. If the soil at the top is not firm enough to permit excavation for poling boards, the top frame of walings and struts is fixed at the surface and continuous guides are firmly framed up about 2 to 3 ft above the ground level to permit driving of the runners. When the excavation is deeper than the maximum length of runner, a further stage of runners must be driven inside the first, continuous guides being fixed to one of the frames above.

Page 528 shows a method of timbering employed where the ground has to be excavated for a basement and a trench sunk for a retaining wall to support the soil outside the building. In this case the basement is excavated first. For the first stage about 3 ft of soil is removed; the dotted lines show the soil left in at this stage. The top row of poling boards and walings and the top system of shores are then fixed. The soil indicated by the dotted line is then removed and the next system of timbering and shores is fixed, after which the trench for the retaining wall is excavated and timbered. When a deep excavation is near buildings or streets the basement area is often not at first excavated, the wall being built in a strutted trench in order to avoid the risk of movement when, as on many jobs, the trench runs right round the site (see page 527). The central block of unexcavated soil is called a "dumpling", and is not removed until the retaining wall is completed and is functioning.

Large continuous trenches, if made in bad ground, are generally timbered as shown on page 529. At intervals guide piles are driven in, to which walings are bolted to act as lower guides to an upper stage of runners about 10 ft long, inserted between the piles; continuous guides are fixed to the piles 2 to 3 ft above the ground. The runners are driven a short distance into the

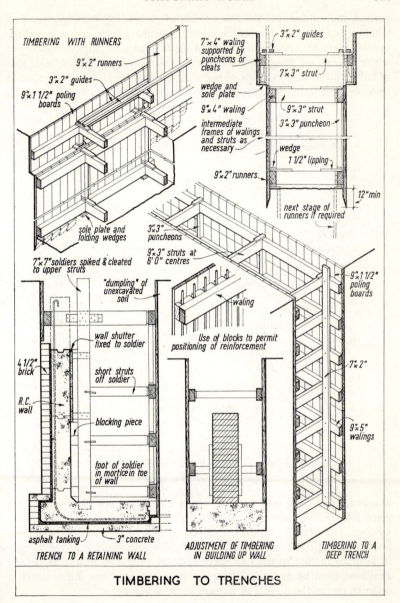

TIMBERING WITH RUNNERS

9"× 2" runners

3"× 2" guides

9"× 1 1/2" poling boards

sole plate and folding wedges

7"× 7" soldiers spiked & cleated to upper struts

7"× 4" waling supported by puncheons or cleats

wedge and sole plate

9"× 4" waling

intermediate frames of walings and struts as necessary

9"× 2" runners

3"× 2" guides

7"× 3" strut

9"× 3" strut

3"× 3" puncheon

wedge

1 1/2" lipping

12" min

next stage of runners if required

3"× 3" puncheons

9"× 3" struts at 6' 0" centres

"dumpling" of unexcavated soil

wall shutter fixed to soldier

short struts off soldier

blocking piece

foot of soldier in mortice in toe of wall

4 1/2" brick

R.C. wall

asphalt tanking

3" concrete

TRENCH TO A RETAINING WALL

waling

Use of blocks to permit positioning of reinforcement

ADJUSTMENT OF TIMBERING IN BUILDING UP WALL

9"× 1 1/2" poling boards

7"× 2"

9"× 5" walings

TIMBERING TO A DEEP TRENCH

TIMBERING TO TRENCHES

ground, the soil between the two systems of piles being then taken out to within a foot of the bottom of the runners, which are again driven in and the process repeated. After excavation of the first stage, walings, consisting of whole timbers, are placed in position and strutted apart, the struts being also of balk timber. Short strips of board called lippings, or lips, are nailed to the ends of the heavy struts to facilitate handling and fixing, or, alternatively,

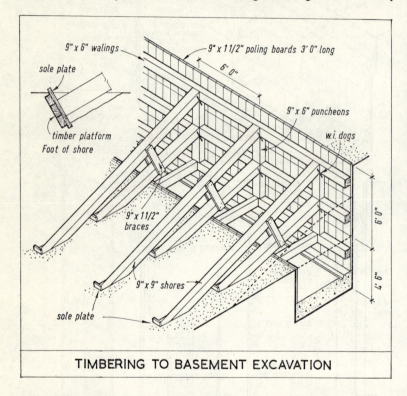

TIMBERING TO BASEMENT EXCAVATION

temporary props are used until the struts are wedged up. Long struts are given intermediate support by short uprights or puncheons, secured to them by dogs. Puncheons are also placed between the waling pieces as each fresh one is inserted. A fresh system of piles and runners is next driven slightly in advance of that to the first stage and the ground excavated as before. Provision must be made for changing the positions of the upper struts in order to permit the driving of runners in the lower stages.

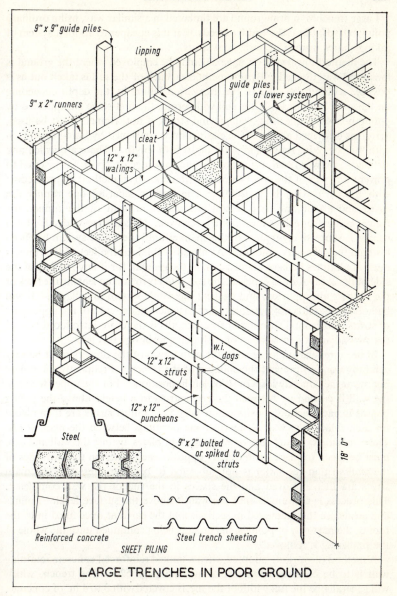

9" x 9" guide piles

lipping

guide piles of lower system

9" x 2" runners

cleat

12" x 12" walings

12" x 12" struts

w.i. dogs

12" x 12" puncheons

9" x 2" bolted or spiked to struts

18' 0"

Steel

Reinforced concrete

Steel trench sheeting

SHEET PILING

LARGE TRENCHES IN POOR GROUND

Large trenches in firm ground are timbered in a similar way, using ordinary poling boards, but if the width exceeds 30 ft it is cheaper to adopt a system of raking shores instead of horizontal struts.

The method illustrated on page 531 may be employed where the ground is loose and waterlogged. By this method as much of the soil is taken out as is possible without the sides of the excavation falling in, the depth depending on the soil conditions. If the soil will permit, the first stage is supported by poling boards or sheeting, walings and struts, if not, runners must be used, driven as described above. The excavation is continued by lining the trench with 9 in. × 2 in. runners about 9 or 10 ft in length. These are waled and strutted. Between each runner and waling a wedge or "page" is inserted to prevent any slip of the soil behind the runners. The method of proceeding with the excavation is as follows: The wedges securing one runner are eased and about one foot of soil is removed in front of the runner, the runner being dropped as the ground is removed. It is then re-wedged. Each runner is successively treated in this manner until the whole system has been lowered the necessary amount. As already explained the feet of the runners must at all times be kept about 12 in. in the ground, for if any portion of the side of the excavation is exposed, the soil is likely to fall out leaving the back of the runners unsupported, and causing the whole system to collapse. It will be noticed that it is not possible to drive runners under each of the upper pair of struts. Horizontal sheeting in short lengths is therefore introduced behind the two adjacent end runners of each panel to bridge this gap.

In deep trenches in loose soils, the withdrawal of the timbers must be very carefully done to prevent the collapse of the trench. Frequently the poling boards at the concrete level must be left in position. For the upper sections, the wall is carried up between the cross struts to a height above the poling boards in each section, as shown on page 527. Short struts are then placed on each side of the wall at intermediate positions between the main struts. These subsidiary struts bear on short upright plates against the wall and care must be taken to place them exactly opposite each other on the two sides of the wall so that the latter is not subjected to bending stresses. The main struts are then removed and the spaces in the run of the wall completed. This process is continued until the wall is above the surface level. Polings and struts are then removed in sections and the earth at once filled in to the foot of the next row of polings, the process being continued until the whole of the timbering is removed.

A method of working adopted when a tanked reinforced concrete retaining wall is to be constructed is also shown on page 527. The trench, which will generally be the full width of the toe, is covered with 3 to 4 in. of concrete,

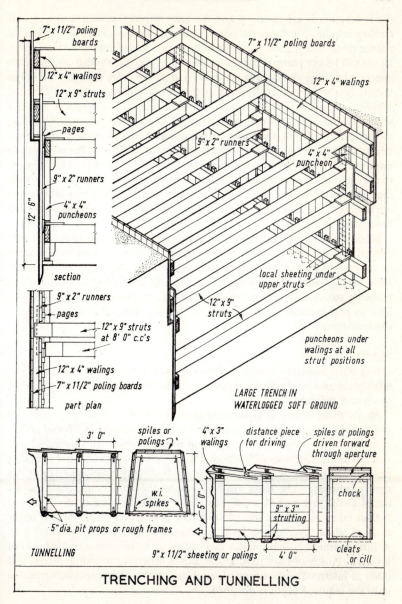

7" x 11/2" poling boards

12" x 4" walings

12" x 9" struts

pages

9" x 2" runners

4" x 4" puncheons

12' 6"

section

9" x 2" runners

pages

12" x 9" struts at 8' 0" c.c's

12" x 4" walings

7" x 11/2" poling boards

part plan

7" x 11/2" poling boards

12" x 4" walings

9" x 2" runners

4" x 4" puncheon

local sheeting under upper struts

12" x 9" struts

puncheons under walings at all strut positions

LARGE TRENCH IN WATERLOGGED SOFT GROUND

3' 0"

spiles or polings

4" x 3" walings

distance piece for driving

spiles or polings driven forward through aperture

chock

w.i. spikes

5" dia. pit props or rough frames

9" x 3" strutting

TUNNELLING

9" x 11/2" sheeting or polings

5' 0"

4' 0"

cleats or cill

TRENCHING AND TUNNELLING

the lower boards are removed and the brick protective skin to the asphalt tanking is built up as far as the soil will permit.   (In very loose soils it may be necessary to use precast concrete walings or precast concrete sheet piling which will be left permanently in position.).   After the asphalt is laid on the concrete blinding and against the lower part of the brick skin, the toe to the wall is cast with mortices formed in the top face to take vertical posts or soldiers.   These are later erected with their feet in the mortices and are spiked and cleated to the upper horizontal struts.   To permit the pouring of the first lift of wall, the lower struts are removed and replaced by shorter struts bearing on the soldiers.   The shuttering to the face of the wall is built up in panels and these are fixed to the soldiers.   This process of building up the brick skin, asphalting and pouring subsequent lifts of concrete, is then repeated to the top of the wall.   As the wall rises and the upper cross-struts are removed, the lower part of the soldiers can be blocked off the completed lower parts of the wall.

When no external tanking is to be applied and the wall is cast directly against the soil, the position of the vertical reinforcing bars will be close to the poling boards or sheeting and the walings will obstruct them.   In these circumstances the walings are blocked off the poling boards by short blocking pieces with spaces between them at the bar centres to permit the bars to pass through them between the walings and the poling boards, as shown on page 527.

Shafts

It is often necessary to sink shafts for foundations.   These are made from 4 ft square and upwards, the former being the smallest size a man can work in without difficulty.

Shafts from 4 to 9 ft square are timbered as shown on page 533.   In ordinary soils the earth is first excavated to a depth of at least 3 ft and in firm soils 6 ft.   The sides of the excavation are then lined with poling boards strutted apart by frames of horizontal walings, a pair of which are placed in position against two opposite sides, and strutted apart by another pair driven tightly between.   The latter are held against the remaining sides by cleats nailed to the first pair of walings as shown at (A).   Another depth of soil is then taken out, and a second system of poling boards placed, the upper ends of which overlap the lower ends of the first system by about 1 ft. A further frame is then placed in position as before, securing both sets of boards.   Puncheons are fixed in the angles between the waling pieces, and often at intermediate positions along their length.   This process is repeated until the required depth is obtained.

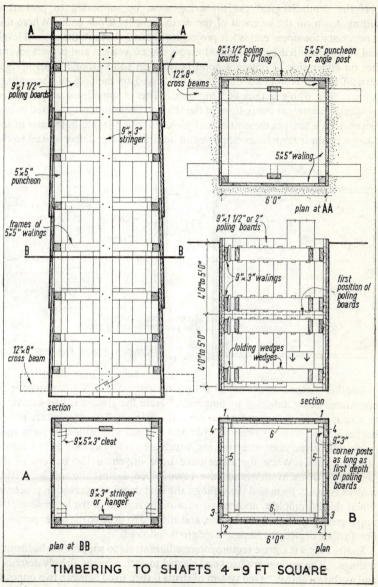

A A

9"×1½" poling boards

12"×8" cross beams

9"×1½" poling boards 6'0" long

5"×5" puncheon or angle post

9"×3" stringer

5"×5" puncheon

5"×5" waling

frames of 5"×5" walings

B B

12"×8" cross beam

section

9"×5"×3" cleat

9"×3" stringer or hanger

A

plan at BB

plan at AA

6'0"

9"×1½" or 2" poling boards

9"×3" walings

first position of poling boards

4'0" to 5'0"

4'0" to 5'0"

folding wedges wedges

section

1   1
4   4
6
5   5
6
3   3
2   2
6'0"

9"×3" corner posts as long as first depth of poling boards

B

plan

TIMBERING TO SHAFTS 4–9 FT SQUARE

18

If the depth is great the timbering must be supported to prevent it sliding down on the removal of the earth from its lower end. Where this is necessary the upper end is left projecting about 3 ft above the ground level, and two substantial beams are laid across the excavation and project several feet on either side to obtain a good bearing on solid ground. An upright vertical timber is notched over this and spiked to the face of the walings below. The whole is thus tied together. This is sometimes supplemented by similar timbers at the bottom of the shaft. These timbers are fixed in two pieces, with a scarf in the centre, and project about 3 ft into both sides of the pit. A chain is sometimes employed in addition to the timber spiked to the walings.

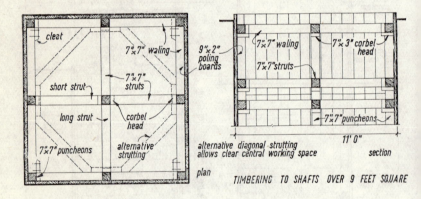

TIMBERING TO SHAFTS OVER 9 FEET SQUARE

Another method employed is shown on page 533 (B), the sequence of operations being indicated by numerals. Here the ground is first excavated to a suitable depth, depending on the soil. 9 in. × 3 in. walings are placed between 3 in. vertical corner boards and wedged in position to form rigid guides for driving the poling boards, which are usually as long as two depths of excavation. When the latter have been driven to the bottom of the first depth of excavation and have been forced against the soil by driving wedges between them and the walings, the next depth of excavation proceeds. When this is complete, another set of walings is fixed at the lower level, the upper polings are eased one by one, and allowed to drop to the lower position. For further depths the same procedure is followed.

Shafts over 9 ft square require intermediate struts to support the horizontal walings. The walings are fixed and cleated to each other as already described and as shown above. One system of struts is then fixed between two opposite sides. The struts that support the remaining sides butt against the first system as shown. The struts in the first system are supported by puncheons, on the upper ends of which short timbers are placed, projecting beyond the sides of the strut. These act as corbels upon which the shorter struts bear.

Diagonally placed struts are often used to provide a clear central hoistway as shown by broken lines. Soil is raised from the bottom of the shaft, if of great depth, by means of hoisting tackle. If the shaft is shallow, timber stages are often erected in 6 ft heights, the soil being shovelled from one to the other until the top is reached.

TUNNELS

In building operations it is sometimes necessary to form a tunnel in order to construct drains, for example. The process is carried out as follows. The tunnel is made just large enough for a man to work in, that is, from 4 to 7 ft square. The soil is taken out in sections of about 3 ft at a time. Poling boards of the same length are then placed against the upper surface, and kept in position by a system of strutting, consisting of a head, sill, and two uprights, out of either round or square timbers, as shown on page 531. The sill is placed in position first, being partly bedded in ground to prevent lateral movement, and being bedded at the correct level by boning through from the sills previously laid. The head is positioned next and then the struts, which are cut and driven tightly between the two. The next section is then excavated, commencing at the top with just enough soil taken out to allow the next system of poling boards to be inserted. These are arranged to overlap the first system at their back end, the two being finally strutted up together. This process is repeated till the tunnel is finished. Two methods are illustrated on page 531. If the soil is bad and the sides are liable to fall in, they must also be lined with poling boards which are kept in place by the uprights.

Large spikes, similar in shape to floor brads, are driven into the head and sill to secure the struts. The heads are left projecting to permit easy withdrawal. Wood cleats are often used in place of these.

SHEET PILING

A form of steel sheet piling, called trench sheeting, is often used instead of timber runners, and the strutting can then be more widely spaced. Light trench sheeting consists of corrugated sheets of steel about 14 to 16 in. wide which are driven by compressed air or petrol hammers so that the edges overlap (see page 529). Withdrawal is by crane, usually with a shackle fixed through a hole in the pile or with pulling tongs or grips which grip the faces of the sheets. Other types of heavier steel sheet piling with interlocking edges, and precast reinforced concrete sheet piles, are used for heavy or permanent works, such as for retaining walls and coffer dams, as well as for excavation work (see page 529). These are driven by drop hammer, diesel hammer or double-acting steam or compressed air hammer. Alternatively, a system which vibrates the pile into the ground can be used which drives at a very high rate with much less noise. These piles are withdrawn by large extracting grips used in conjunction with a crane, a double acting hammer or hydraulic jacks. Normally only steel sheet piling and timber piling when used in temporary works, is extracted, and then generally only when the piles are less than about 40 ft in length. Piles over this length require a very large extracting force and it is sometimes cheaper to leave the pile in position rather than withdraw it.

SHORING

Shoring is the means of providing temporary support to structures that are in an unsafe condition till such time as they have been made stable, or to structures which might become unstable by reason of work being carried out on or near them, such as the underpinning of foundations.

Timber has always been used in the past and is still the most commonly used material for shoring, although effective flying and raking shores can be constructed with tubular scaffolding. But so many struts, ties and couplers are necessary to maintain rigidity that timber is usually found to be quicker and more economical of labour. Steel stanchions and, particularly, steel needles are often used for dead shoring. Tubular scaffolding is less frequently used for this purpose.

Classification. There are three general systems of shoring, (i) raking shores, (ii) horizontal or flying shores, (iii) dead or vertical shores.

RAKING SHORES

These consist of inclined timbers called rakers placed with one end resting against the face of a defective wall, the other upon the ground (see page 543). The most convenient and best angle for practical purposes is 60°, but this may vary up to 75°. The angle is often determined in urban areas by the width of the footway. On tall buildings these shores are fixed in systems of one or more timbers placed in the same vertical plane, inclined at different angles to support the building at varying levels, as shown on page 537.

The purpose of a raking shore is to prevent the over-turning of a wall—not, in the case of a tilting or bulging wall, to force it back.

A wall-piece, consisting of a 2 or 3 in. deal, is fixed to the wall by wall-

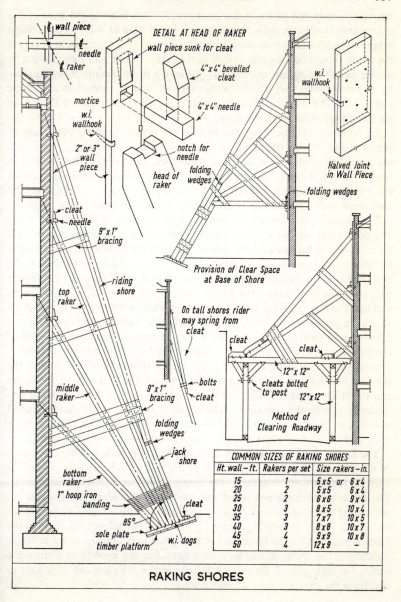

DETAIL AT HEAD OF RAKER

wall piece sunk for cleat

4"x4" bevelled cleat

4"x4" needle

mortice

w.i. wallhook

notch for needle

head of raker

folding wedges

¢ wall piece

needle

¢ raker

2" or 3" wall piece

w.i. wallhook

cleat

needle

9"x1" bracing

top raker

riding shore

middle raker

9"x1" bracing

folding wedges

jack shore

bottom raker

1" hoop iron banding

85°

sole plate

timber platform

w.i. dogs

cleat

Halved Joint in Wall Piece

w.i. wallhook

folding wedges

Provision of Clear Space at Base of Shore

On tall shores rider may spring from cleat

bolts

cleat

cleat

cleat

12"x12"

cleats bolted to post

12"x12"

Method of Clearing Roadway

COMMON SIZES OF RAKING SHORES		
Ht. wall – ft.	Rakers per set	Size rakers – in.
15	1	5x5 or 6x4
20	2	5x5 6x4
25	2	6x6 9x4
30	3	8x5 10x4
35	3	7x7 10x5
40	3	8x8 10x7
45	4	9x9 10x8
50	4	12x9 –

RAKING SHORES

hooks driven in the joints of the brickwork. This receives the ends of the rakers and distributes their thrusts over a larger area of wall. For a single raker the width of the wall-piece is usually about 9 in. In a system of rakers the width should be the same as that of the rakers. The wall-piece should be in one piece throughout the system. If, owing to the length, it is necessary to join two pieces they should be halved and securely spiked as shown on page 537. The length of the longitudinal bevelled halved joint should be six times the thickness of the plate.

To form an abutment for the end of the rakers, needles, consisting of pieces of 4 in. × 4 in. timber about 13 in. long, and cut as shown on page 537, are passed through a mortice in the wall-piece, and project into the wall at least 4½ in., half-bricks being taken out to receive them. The function of the needle is to resist the thrust of the raker and prevent it slipping on the wall-piece and to transmit the thrust through the wall-piece to the wall.

The following considerations determine the position of the needles. The end of a raker should only be placed where there is something such as a floor or roof at the back of the wall to resist the thrust, otherwise the wall is liable to bulge inwards at that point. Near the top of a building there is the possibility of the head of the wall being pushed off if there is insufficient weight above the raker. The centre line of rakers should, therefore, pass through the centre of the bed of any wall-plates in the wall. If the joists should be parallel to the wall, the produced centre lines of the floor, wall and raker should meet at a point, since it may be assumed that the resultant of the dead weight of the wall and any thrust from the floor passes approximately through this point (see page 540). The needle should be placed so that the pressure exerted by it takes place along the centre line of the raker, the upper end of which should be notched to receive the needle, thus obviating any tendency to lateral movement. The shoulder bearing on the needle should not be less than 3 in. wide. The needle is supported at its top side by a 9 in. × 4 in. × 4 in. cleat housed into the wall-piece to which it is nailed.

The feet of the rakers rest upon an inclined sole plate usually embedded in the ground. It is the same width as the rakers and 3 to 4 in. thick. It must be long enough to take all the rakers as well as a cleat on the outside. The angle between the sole plate and the rakers should be less than 90° to permit the latter to be tightened up gradually by means of a crowbar. A maximum of 85° is usually adopted. Wedging should not be used as the vibration caused would be detrimental to what may already be an unstable building. The shore should be forced tight, but not enough to disturb the wall. On soft ground the sole plate is bedded on a platform of timber to distribute the pressure over a greater area.

When the shore has been tightened it is secured to the sole plate by iron dogs and a cleat is nailed to the sole plate tight against the outside of the raker. Where more than one raker is used, the bottom ends are bound together by hoop iron or pieces of boarding nailed across all of them on each side to connect them all at this part, and prevent disturbance or damage. At intervals in the height, boards called bracings are nailed to the sides of the rakers and the wall-piece. These have the effect of binding the system together, and of stiffening the long outer rakers by shortening the unsupported length. On a tall building the outer rakers become very long and to obviate this the top raker may spring from the back of the raker below, its foot bearing on a shorter length of shore lying on the lower raker and picking up on the sole plate. The upper length is called a *riding shore* and the shorter length a *jack shore*. This and other variations are shown on page 537.

The horizontal distance between the systems on unperforated walls is usually not more than 8 ft; but on walls pierced with windows they are placed on the intervening piers.

HORIZONTAL OR FLYING SHORES

These are used to provide temporary support to two parallel walls, where one or both show signs of failure, or where previous support, in the form of floors, has been removed. 30 ft between the walls is usually considered to be the maximum length for single flying shores. For larger spans, from 30 ft to 40 ft, a compound or double flying shore is necessary. Details of these are given on page 540. They are used mostly in urban areas, usually where one of a number of terrace buildings is to be removed, to provide temporary support to the buildings on either side. They are erected as the old structure is being removed, and are taken down when the new building is of a sufficient height to provide support.

A single flying shore consists of a horizontal timber set between the walls to be supported, the ends resting against wall-pieces fixed on the walls. It is stiffened by inclined struts above and below it at each end. These struts also provide two more points of support to each wall. The method of fixing is as follows. Two wall-pieces are fixed, one on each wall, in a similar manner to those described for raking shores, with needles fixed as bearings to the horizontal timber. Care is taken to keep these, as far as possible, in the line of the floors of the buildings on either side. The horizontal shore is placed in position, having a straining sill out of about 6 × in 3 in. nailed on the upper and lower sides. The shore rests upon the needles, and a pair of folding wedges is inserted at one end between the wall-piece and the end of the shore and driven up tightly. The upper struts are then fixed, and lastly, the lower

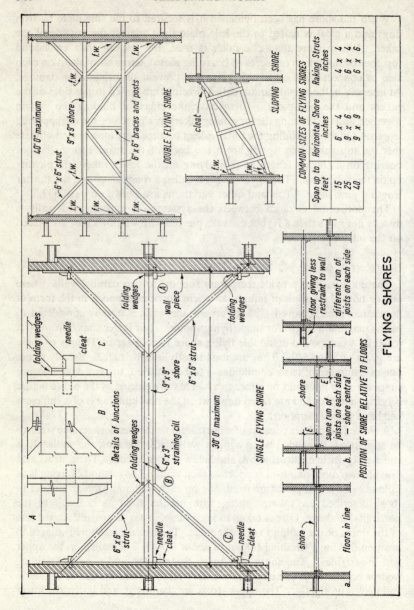

COMMON SIZES OF FLYING SHORES		
Span up to feet	Horizontal Shore inches	Raking Struts inches
15	6 × 6	4 × 4
25	9 × 6	6 × 4
40	9 × 9	6 × 6

DOUBLE FLYING SHORE

40' 0" maximum

9" × 9" shore

6" × 6" braces and posts

6" × 6" strut

f.w.

SLOPING SHORE

cleat

f.w.

folding wedges

wall piece (A)

folding wedges

needle cleat

C

Details of Junctions

A

B

6" × 6" strut

folding wedges

9" × 9" shore

6" × 6" strut

6" × 3" straining cill (B)

30' 0" maximum

needle cleat

needle cleat (C)

SINGLE FLYING SHORE

floors in line

a.

POSITION OF SHORE RELATIVE TO FLOORS

same run of joists on each side — shore central

E

E

shore

b.

floor giving less restraint to wall

different run of joists on each side

shore

c.

FLYING SHORES

struts.   The details at the junction of struts with wall-piece are the same as in a normal raking shore.   Folding wedges placed in the positions shown are used to tighten up the whole shore.   In the case of the demolition of a terrace building, the wall-pieces are fixed before demolition, then the horizontal shore and the struts are fixed in the order given when the demolition process has come down to that level.   By proceeding in this manner, the party walls are supported by the shores before the old work has been removed.

Position of Horizontal Shore with Reference to Floor Levels.   The three conditions of floor positions that are likely to be met in practice are shown on page 540:

(a) Floors on each side at the same level.   The centre line of shore should coincide with centre line of joists, whether these are parallel with or normal to the walls being supported.

(b) Floors at different levels with the same run of joists on each side.   The horizontal shore is placed halfway between the two floor levels.

(c) Floors at different levels with different runs of joists on each side.   In this case, the wall which is not supported laterally by a floor bearing on it is the weaker of the two.   The horizontal shore should therefore be placed in line with the floor joists which run parallel with this wall.

Where, in (b) and (c), the shore is positioned between floors, the wall-piece should be stiff enough to transmit any thrust to the floors.

Where walls are of different thicknesses or in different states of repair and with differing floor levels, this must also be taken into consideration in deciding the best position for the shore.

Double flying shores are framed up as shown on page 540.   They are erected in basically the same manner as single shores.

Where one building is higher than another it may be necessary to erect a raking shore upon a flying shore or sloping shores may be suitable.

Horizontal flying shores are usually erected at 10 to 15 ft intervals on plan. Where considered necessary, horizontal struts are introduced between the shores to act as lateral bracing.

VERTICAL OR DEAD SHORES

Shores placed vertically are termed dead shores.   They are used for temporarily supporting the upper parts of walls, the lower parts of which are required to be removed, either in the process of underpinning or reinstatement during repair, or for the purpose of making large openings in the lower parts.   Where a dead shore immediately under the wall is not convenient a system of dead shores is used, comprising a pair of shores supporting a horizontal beam. The wall is then carried by the beam. If, for example, the lower part of a building is to be removed in order to form a large opening, the procedure would be on the lines illustrated on page 543.

The whole of the floors, the roof, and any other load bearing on the wall are supported by a system of strutting to relieve the wall of all weight normally taken by it. This system of strutting should be firmly supported by a sole piece on the solid ground below the lowest floor. The sole piece should be bedded continuously in mortar and be sufficiently stiff to distribute the weight over its whole length.

Perforations are next made in the wall a short distance above the line of the top of the beam that will ultimately support the wall. Through the holes horizontal beams called needles are inserted, consisting of balk timbers or steel beams. These should not be placed a greater distance apart than 6 ft in unperforated walls, but when there are windows the needles must be placed under the piers.

The needles are supported by dead shores of timber or steel stanchions, one under each end of the needle. The dead shores rest at their lower ends on sleepers which are horizontal balks of timber properly bedded in mortar for their whole length. It is essential that the sleepers should be bedded on the solid ground, not on the crown of vaults or any other voids. Should there be voids of any kind the work must be solidly strutted below. Pairs of hardwood wedges are placed between the dead shores and the sleepers. Before these are driven up tightly, a bed of cement mortar should be placed on the top of the needle at the point where it passes through the wall to ensure a proper and solid bearing of the wall on the needles. When the wedges are driven home the whole is allowed a few days to set. Lateral bracing is often provided by nailing thick boards diagonally to the faces of the shores.

Where it is not possible to place the inner shores in position in one piece, these must be in two sections. The lower halves are placed first with a transom laid across them. The upper halves are then placed on the transom directly over the lower sections and under the needle at its upper end.

It is essential that the needles and dead shores should have an ample margin of strength, to avoid settlement of the wall through deflection of the needle or compression of the shore or sole piece. The needles, shores and sleepers and any transoms must all be well dogged together before any brickwork is removed. All window openings must be strutted to prevent deformation taking place. In ordinary small windows this consists of an upright against each reveal, with two or three struts between, cut long and driven up tightly. In large openings a stronger framing is necessary and any arches will require

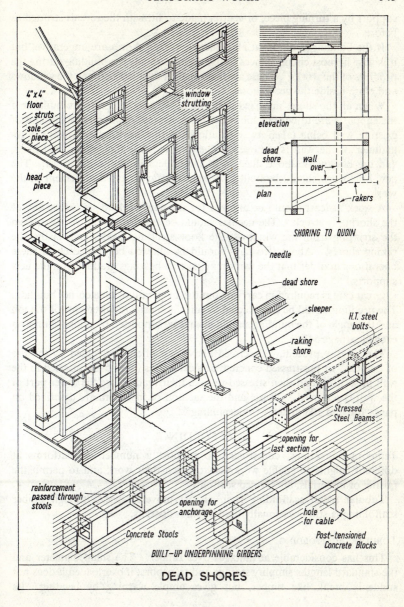

4"x4" floor struts

sole piece

head piece

window strutting

elevation

dead shore

plan

wall over

rakers

SHORING TO QUOIN

needle

dead shore

sleeper

raking shore

H.T. steel bolts

Stressed Steel Beams

opening for last section

reinforcement passed through stools

opening for anchorage

hole for cable

Concrete Stools

Post-tensioned Concrete Blocks

BUILT-UP UNDERPINNING GIRDERS

DEAD SHORES

support by a turning piece, or centre, made to fit, with the reveals strutted as before.

If the building is old or at all defective, raking shores are imperative, but it is wise in most circumstances to use them to steady the building during the progress of the works. These are fixed against the piers between the windows and close beside the dead shores.

When all the shores are fixed in position, the two end piers are built, or if the supports are to be stanchions these are erected, the minimum amount of existing wall being taken away to allow for this work, after which the remainder of the wall is removed. The new beam is then raised and fixed, and the brickwork above filled in to the underside of the old work. The new brickwork should be built in cement mortar to avoid settlement in the work.

A week at least should be allowed for the new work to set before any of the shoring is struck. The needles should be eased and removed first, then the strutting from the windows, the floor strutting inside, and, lastly, the raking shores. About two days should be allowed between each of these operations in order that the work may take its bearings gradually on the new supports.

Great care is required in carrying out these operations on a corner building. The needling would be constructed to suit the special requirements of the job and the angle of the building should always be supported by raking shores on each face (page 543).

The lengthy procedure described above can often be avoided by the use of "stools" or prestressed concrete or steel beams (page 543), inserted in the wall in sections and then stressed to take their load before the lower part of the wall is removed. These, and the method of insertion, are described on pages 106 and 108 under "Underpinning".

SCAFFOLDING

Temporary erections, constructed to support a number of platforms at different heights to enable workmen to reach their work and to permit the raising of materials, are termed scaffolds.

Tubular metal scaffolding is in almost universal use, although timber scaffolding is still occasionally used in rural districts.

TUBULAR SCAFFOLDING

This has considerable advantages over timber. The small diameter and the standard lengths simplify storage and transport; if overloaded it does not suddenly break like timber, but gives ample warning by bending. Its adaptability to any purpose required on a building job, such as storage racks for timber or any other material, or the framing for temporary buildings and sheds, constitutes a valuable asset.

The tubing employed is $1\frac{1}{2}$ in. internal diameter weld-less steel steam tubes, No. 6 gauge, $3\frac{1}{2}$ lb per ft run, or light alloy tubing weighing only 1 lb per ft run. The standard length of the unit is 18 ft, but shorter and longer lengths can be obtained. The shorter lengths in most common use are 6 ft, 12 ft and 14 ft. The weight of a standard length of steel tube is 63 lb and the external diameter is nominally 2 in.; it can thus be easily handled by the average man.

Standard couplings are used to frame up the tubes. Various types of these and other fittings are shown on page 546.

Square or circular base plates are provided with a central pin that fits into the base of the standards. These are sufficient to take the weight of the scaffold on ordinary firm ground. For soft ground or over cellars or pavement lights stout planking is used to distribute the pressure. The base plates can be spiked to the planking, holes usually being provided in them for this purpose. Adjustable bases are available with a range of height of a few inches. The tubing can be extended to any length, by means of end to end couplers.

For bricklayers' scaffolds, where the putlogs have a bearing on the wall, the putlog tube may be flattened out and the end driven into the joint. Alternatively, a putlog head may be used. This is a plate which can be coupled to the end of a putlog.

A reveal pin is used to secure a tube vertically or horizontally between the reveals of window or door openings, to form a rigid fixing to which putlogs or ties to independent scaffolds may be coupled. It consists of a bolt and ferrule which fits the bore of the tube. At one end is a bearing plate. It has a hexagonal end and when placed in the end of the tube it constitutes a light form of screw jack. Guard board clips are used to secure the ordinary decking to the putlogs or the guard boards to the standards.

Typical scaffolds are illustrated on page 547. On high buildings double or treble tube standards, linked by couplers, are required for the lower part. Similar strengthening is necessary for a mason's scaffolding when heavy blocks of stone must be supported.

METAL SCAFFOLDING FRAMES

These are prefabricated tubular units which can be built up to form scaffolding. Their use saves time in erection and avoids the use of specialized labour. They are, therefore, very useful on smaller building jobs.

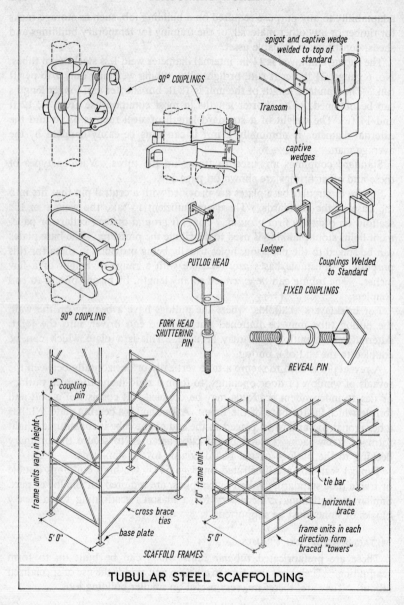

90° COUPLINGS

spigot and captive wedge welded to top of standard

Transom

captive wedges

Ledger

Couplings Welded to Standard

FIXED COUPLINGS

PUTLOG HEAD

90° COUPLING

FORK HEAD SHUTTERING PIN

REVEAL PIN

coupling pin

frame units vary in height

cross brace ties

base plate

5' 0"

SCAFFOLD FRAMES

2' 0" frame unit

tie bar

horizontal brace

frame units in each direction form braced "towers"

5' 0"

TUBULAR STEEL SCAFFOLDING

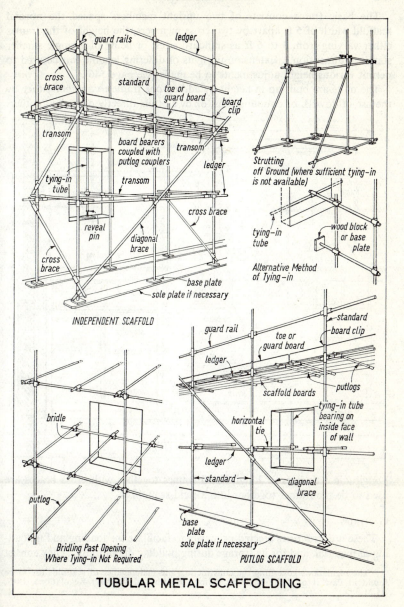

INDEPENDENT SCAFFOLD

guard rails
ledger
cross brace
standard
toe or guard board
board clip
transom
board bearers coupled with putlog couplers
transom
ledger
tying-in tube
transom
cross brace
reveal pin
diagonal brace
cross brace
base plate
sole plate if necessary

Strutting off Ground (where sufficient tying-in is not available)

tying-in tube

wood block or base plate

Alternative Method of Tying-in

Bridling Past Opening Where Tying-in Not Required

bridle

putlog

PUTLOG SCAFFOLD

standard
board clip
guard rail
toe or guard board
ledger
scaffold boards
putlogs
horizontal tie
tying-in tube bearing on inside face of wall
ledger
standard
diagonal brace
base plate
sole plate if necessary

TUBULAR METAL SCAFFOLDING

The basic frame consists of two upright members spaced the normal scaffold width of 5 ft apart by two cross members, the height of the frames either varying from 3 to 6 ft as standard sizes, or being of a single smaller standard dimension. Extension uprights of differing lengths can be used to permit various height adjustments to be made (see page 546).

The units are built up in height by adding one frame to another either by the use of dowels, or coupling pins, or by slotting directly one into another.

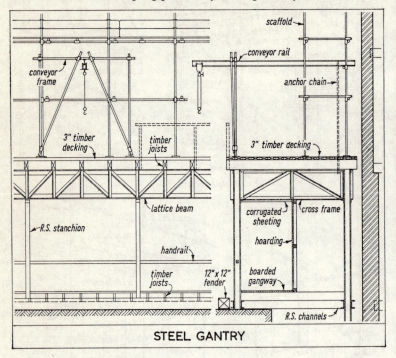

STEEL GANTRY

Longitudinal tie-bars or longitudinal frames together with cross braces are used to tie the frames together into a rigid scaffold.[1]

GANTRIES

These are structures erected primarily to facilitate the loading and unloading of material, and for its storage during building operations. They consist

[1] The regulations governing the construction and maintenance of scaffolds are to be found in Part II of "The Building (Safety, Health and Welfare) Regulations, 1948, (H.M.S.O.)

of an elevated staging erected in front of buildings in course of erection, designed to act as unloading platforms. They extend usually from the face of the intended structure to a short distance from the edge of the kerb, covering the footways. A gangway is provided under the staging for the convenience of the public. Some form of hoisting tackle is provided for raising material from lorries on to the platform. The use of the tower crane reduces the value of the gantry for this particular purpose, but it is still useful on sites where it is essential to have room outside the site for the storage of materials and for agents' huts.

Gantries are constructed of tubular scaffolding or of steel, as shown on page 548. The uprights here consist of light steel joists and these are connected by steel channels at their bottom, which act as sleepers. Their upper ends are connected with a light framework forming a lattice beam bolted on the face of the columns and resting on cleats. The two frames are connected with cross frames bolted to them. The various parts are standardized, which ensures simplicity and rapidity in erection, and enables them to be used many times. The inner frames of both timber and steel gantries frequently have to be taken down to a basement level for a bearing. In this case either longer standards are employed, or a subsidiary frame is erected to support the upper frame, being cleated to the upper lengths of the pillars by fish-plates through the web.

If the gantry is over the public way, it must be double-boarded to prevent dust, rubbish or water falling upon pedestrians, or be under-decked with corrugated iron sheeting.

FORMWORK

Concrete must be given form by casting it in a mould. These moulds are known as formwork or shuttering.[1] Reference has already been made in Chapter 5 to the fact that the cost of the formwork may be as much as one-third or more of the total cost of the concrete work as a whole, and to the effect that the nature of the formwork can have on its cost. The formwork for any job must be considered at the design stage. Economy is more likely to be achieved if it is designed and worked out in detail before work commences on the site, taking into consideration the nature of the elements to be cast and the methods of handling likely to be used on the site. For example, handling by crane makes possible the use of much larger sizes of wall and floor shutters than if manually handled.

---

[1] *Formwork* is a general term which covers all types of mould for cast *in situ* concrete. The word *shuttering* is correctly applied only to the flat panels which are fixed together to make the complete formwork. Parts of the formwork such as column and beam boxes are called *forms*. Boxes for precast concrete are called *moulds*.

19

The general requirements governing the design and construction of formwork are as follows:

(i) It should be strong enough to bear the weight of the wet concrete and all incidental working loads and it should be rigid enough to prevent excessive deflection during the placing of the concrete.

(ii) The joints should be tight enough to prevent the loss of fine material from the concrete.

(iii) It should be so designed and constructed that erection and stripping is orderly and simple and all units are of such a size that they can be easily handled. It should be possible for the side forms to be removed before the soffit shuttering is struck.

(iv) If the concrete is to be fair-face the formwork in actual contact with the concrete should be so arranged and jointed that the resulting concrete has a good appearance.

In horizontal work the formwork must support its own weight, the weight of the wet concrete and reinforcement placed upon it, and the weight of men and any transporting equipment which is being used for the work. The formwork for vertical work must resist the pressure of the wet concrete pushing it outwards, and wind pressure. The outward pressure of the concrete depends upon its stiffness, the depth of concrete placed at one time and the way in which it is consolidated. The outward pressure will increase with increased wetness of mix and an increased height of concrete placed. As a general rule the pressure in pounds per square foot may be taken as 100 times the depth of the wet concrete in feet, but with tamping by vibrators, the pressure is more nearly 144 times the depth of the concrete. When vibration is used, board joints must be tight, any wedges must be nailed and the whole must be sufficiently braced to prevent any movement. For floor and beam forms, the weight of wet concrete may be taken as 144 lb per cu. ft. Thus the weight in pounds per square foot may be obtained simply by multiplying the thickness of the floor by twelve. The weight in pounds per foot run of a poured beam is obtained by multiplying together the depth and width of the beam. The live load during construction is generally taken as 75 lb per sq. ft of floor, but this may need to be increased to take account of loads arising from the transport of reinforcement or concrete.[1]

The formwork must be designed and constructed so that it may easily be removed or "stripped" without damage to the formwork itself or to the hardened concrete. To facilitate this, nailing in timber forms should be kept to a minimum. Erection should be such that the formwork can be

---

[1] Research is being carried out by the Royal College of Science and Technology, Glasgow, to obtain reliable data concerning the pressure exerted by concrete on formwork.

struck in the following order: One side of columns, sides of beams, bottoms of slabs and beams, the remaining sides of columns (see Table 32, p. 563).

Formwork may be constructed of any suitable material. Timber was once always used for this purpose and, by its nature, still has the advantage of the flexibility of forms which may be produced by its use. Plywood is widely used in place of boards for the working faces. On *in situ* work timber forms are usually unfit for further use after four to six times, although they may then be cut up and parts used in the construction of other forms. If reasonable care is taken in fixing and striking, plywood will give about thirty to forty re-uses.

In precast work, particularly in factory production, up to twenty re-uses are possible with timber forms. Steel shutters are available, generally in standard units of suitable sizes, and are designed to eliminate timber. They can be quickly erected and dismantled and can be used a greater number of times than timber forms, the actual number of times depending on the way in which they are handled and dismantled. In factory produced precast work as many as 100 re-uses are possible.

Timber Formwork

Timber should be sound and well seasoned and may be dressed on all four sides, on one side and one edge, or on one side and two edges. Timber dressed on all four sides is uniform in size and therefore more easily adapted for different purposes. The advantages arising from this often make it more economical to use than timber dressed in the other ways.

Timber of any one size should be dressed to a uniform thickness so that each piece will match up, particularly in the case of boarding. Close, square-edge boarding is most commonly used but tongued and grooved boarding gives best results, particularly for face work. When a good finish is required, used and new boards should not be incorporated in the same panel. Plywood used instead of boards or as a lining to forms should be resin-bonded external grade. The thicknesses of the timbers will depend on the loads to be carried and on the available supply. The latter is generally the governing factor as any ordinary size can be used by adjusting the spacing of supports.

As mentioned earlier, nailing should be kept to a minimum and, where used, the nail heads should not be quite driven home, as this makes it easier to draw them with a claw hammer or nail bar. Bolts and wedges are preferable to nailing, but are more costly.

Column Forms. In the case of rectangular columns, the forms consist of four shutters or panels made up of boards nailed securely to cleats and held together by a series of yokes or clamps to form the column casing, as shown on pages 553 and 555. The thickness of the boards varies between 1 in. and 2 in. depending on the size of the column and the spacing of the yokes. In practice it is usually the thickness of the board which dictates the number and spacing of the yokes, which are more closely spaced at the bottom where the outward pressure is greatest, than at the top. This is shown on page 553.

The yokes are made up of 3 or 4 in. × 4 in. timber, with $\frac{1}{2}$ in. or $\frac{5}{8}$ in. diameter bolts to clamp together the two longer pieces, the other two being tightened against the shutter by pairs of wedges driven between the bolts. Where convenient, when the column is very tall and large it is usual to erect and strut three sides only of the box and to fix the fourth side in 3 ft sections as concreting proceeds. This facilitates hand tamping of the concrete after each pouring and avoids the provision of hand holes at the bottom of the column form, although it is still essential to make certain that the bottom is quite clear of rubbish before the concrete is deposited.

Adjustable steel yokes or clamps as shown on page 553 are now widely used, as they reduce the amount of timber required, have a long life and are quickly fitted and dismantled.

Circular column forms are built up from narrow vertical boards, called "staves", shaped to the correct curve and fixed to shaped yokes. The latter are in two halves which are bolted together (see page 553).

Beam Forms. Beam sides are generally built up of 1 in. boards nailed to 4 in. × 1 in. battens at 2 ft or 2 ft 6 in. centres; the bottom should be thicker, about 2 in., and where practicable should be made from a single width of board (see page 553). In erection, the bottoms are first placed in position between the column boxes and are supported by props, to the top of which are fixed cross pieces or headtrees about 15 in. longer than the width of the beam. These are braced to the props by pairs of struts. The beam bottom is carefully levelled by means of wedges placed between the lower ends of the props and the sill pieces on which they rest. The bottom board is usually given a slight camber of about $\frac{1}{4}$ in. in 10 ft of length to allow for deflection. The sides are then placed in position and nailed to the edges of the bottom and secured to the column boxes. Stops or stop boards with wedges are sometimes preferred to nailing the sides to the edges of the bottom. The sides are braced apart to the correct width by temporary strainers.

The free side of an outer beam is braced at the top by struts off the ends of the headtrees, which are extended for this purpose (page 555).

To avoid construction on scaffolding, whenever possible beam forms should be made at ground level and hoisted into position.

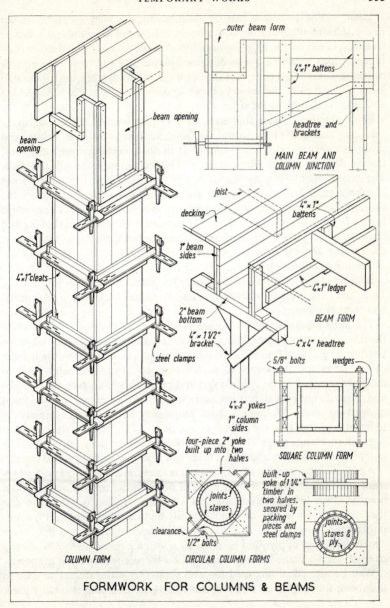

outer beam form

4"x1" battens

headtree and brackets

MAIN BEAM AND COLUMN JUNCTION

beam opening

beam opening

joist

decking

4" x 1" battens

1" beam sides

4"x1" ledger

4"x1" cleats

2" beam bottom

BEAM FORM

4" x 1 1/2" bracket

4"x4" headtree

steel clamps

5/8" bolts   wedges

4"x3" yokes

1" column sides

four-piece 2" yoke built up into two halves

SQUARE COLUMN FORM

joints staves

built-up yoke of 1 1/4" timber in two halves, secured by packing pieces and steel clamps

clearance

joints staves & ply

1/2" bolts

COLUMN FORM   CIRCULAR COLUMN FORMS

FORMWORK FOR COLUMNS & BEAMS

When secondary beams bear on main beams, openings for them are cut in the sides of the main beam shutter in the correct position and a bearer nailed on to receive the soffit board of the secondary beam form, the construction of which is carried out as described above.   A 4 in. × 1 in. ledger or runner is nailed to the battens of the beam sides to form a bearing for the slab joists.   The tops of the ledgers are set at such a level that the slab decking will bear on the top of the sides.

Floor Shutters.   Floor shuttering or centering is made up of boards or "decking" on which the concrete is placed, supported by joists, ledgers and props as shown on page 555.   1 in. or 1¼ in. thick decking is generally used, thinner decking necessitating a closer and less economic spacing of the joists. The boards should run the length of the floor panels so that they do not require cutting into short lengths, and so that the joists span across the shortest dimension.   The usual size of joist is 6 in. × 2 in., but may range from 4 in. × 2 in. to 10 in. × 3 in.   The actual thickness of the decking and the sizes of the joists used will depend upon the loads the forms must carry, the spacing and the span of the joists and the maximum deflection of the shuttering which may have been specified.

Boarding used for formwork is usually one standard size on a job, 6 in. × 1¼ in. being the most common size.   This facilitates the ordering of material and reduces wastage.

The joists are supported on ledgers fixed to the beam sides.   To minimize the size of the joists intermediate ledgers are sometimes used, carried on props bearing on the floor below.   Folding wedges are placed between the bottom of the joists and the ledger to permit final adjustment of height and to facilitate removal.   The size of joists and props should be such that ledgers and props do not have to be too closely spaced, causing excessive obstruction of working space.   Adjustable steel props may be used which are simple to install and avoid the use of wedges (see page 561).   Tubular steel scaffolding with forkheads (page 546) may also be used for the same purpose.   The latter is particularly suitable where the height from the floor or ground is great.

Adequate cross bracing of all supports is essential in order to avoid movement and failure.   Long narrow areas of floor shutter may be made up in a number of smaller panels consisting of a number of joists or cleats carrying the decking.   These may be handled easily and facilitate re-use.   Plywood, rather than boards, is now widely used for floor shutters, and very large panels consisting of plywood on joists with framing round all four edges can be used when a crane is being employed on the site for handling purposes.

Wall Forms.   Boarding used for wall shuttering varies from 1 to 2 in. in thickness; for heights up to about ten feet 1½ in. boarding is usually used.

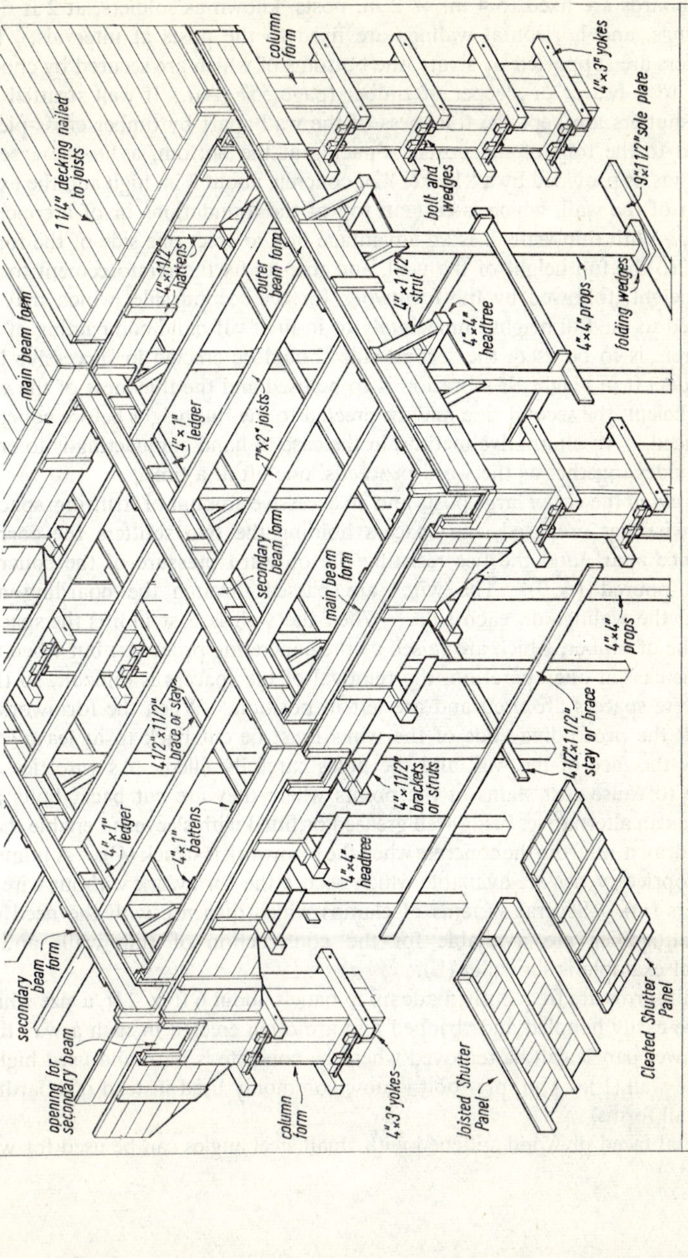

1 1/4" decking nailed to joists
column form
4"×3" yokes
bolt and wedges
9"×1 1/2" sole plate
4"×1 1/2" battens
outer beam form
4"×1 1/2" strut
folding wedges
4"×4" props
4"×4" headtree
main beam form
4"×1" ledger
7"×2" joists
secondary beam form
main beam form
4"×4" props
4 1/2"×1 1/2" brace or stay
4"×1 1/2" brackets or struts
4 1/2"×1 1/2" stay or brace
4"×1" ledger
4"×1" battens
4"×4" headtree
secondary beam form
opening for secondary beam
column form
4"×3" yokes
Joisted Shutter Panel
Cleated Shutter Panel

FORMWORK FOR REINFORCED CONCRETE FLOOR

The boards are fixed to 4 in. × 2 in. posts, known as soldiers, at 2 ft 6 in. spacings, and horizontal walings are fixed to the posts at intervals. The shutters are supported by struts, the bottoms of which are secured by chocks fixed to a bearer or sleeper of timber (page 557 (A)). If well strutted the two shutters are kept the thickness of the wall apart by timber cross-pieces nailed to the tops of the posts. Spacing at the bottom, as in the case of columns, is provided by a "kicker" of concrete about 2 in. high and the exact width of the wall, which is cast on top of the foundations or of a concrete floor. With thin walls it is an advantage first to erect one side of the form-work to the full height of the wall, and then to fix the reinforcement to the full height, followed by the formwork for the second side, which may be erected to the full height immediately or in lifts. If hand compacting of the concrete is to be used, the second side should be erected in successive lifts of 2 or 3 ft in height; if vibration is to be used and the thickness of the wall is sufficient, the second side may be erected to the full height before concrete is placed. An alternative method in the case of hand compacting is to erect both sides together as the work proceeds, one lift at a time.

To avoid the use of large posts and an excessive amount of strutting, spacers and wire ties are used, the spacers holding the two shutters the correct distance apart, and the ties resisting the outward pressure of the concrete when poured (A,B). The wires are passed through the boarding and round the walings on each side. When the wall is cast in lifts the spacers may be of timber, which are raised as the concreting proceeds; but when the wall is cast in one operation, the removal of the spacers is difficult, so that concrete spacers are used and are left in position. When the formwork is struck the protruding ends of the wires must be cut back to at least $\frac{1}{2}$ in. below the face of the wall and the holes carefully filled. As wire ties are likely to cause rust stains at the points where they are cut back, bolts are used as an alternative, being well greased or fitted with sleeves to enable them to be drawn out from the concrete when the formwork is struck (C). A number of proprietary ties are available which secure the formwork without wire or spacers (D). Several systems of clamps which dispense with the need for ties altogether are available for the construction of thin walls and a typical example is shown at (E).

Wall forms are frequently made up in panels about 6 ft × 2 ft, a size which can be easily handled and stripped and are often erected in such a way that the lower panels can be removed when the concrete is hard and used higher up the wall (F). $\frac{5}{8}$ in. plywood is now commonly used instead of boarding for wall forms.

Metal faced plywood stiffened with small steel angles can be used for wall

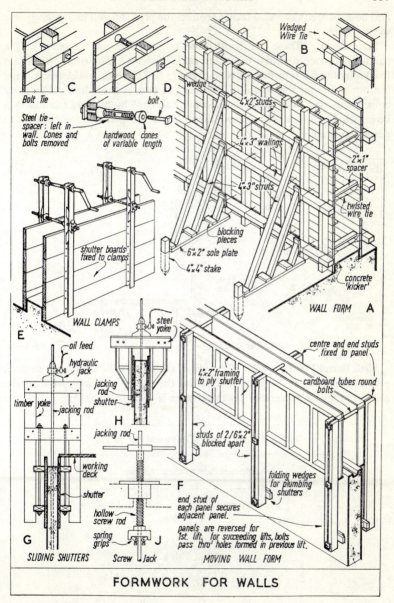

C Bolt Tie

Steel tie- spacer: left in wall. Cones and bolts removed

bolt

hardwood cones of variable length

D

Wedged Wire Tie

B

wedge

4"×2" studs

4"×3" walings

4"×3" struts

2"×1" spacer

twisted wire tie

blocking pieces

6"×2" sole plate

4"×4" stake

concrete 'kicker'

WALL FORM **A**

shutter boards fixed to clamps

WALL CLAMPS

E

oil feed

hydraulic jack

timber yoke

jacking rod

working deck

shutter

G SLIDING SHUTTERS

steel yoke

jacking rod

shutter

H

jacking rod

F

hollow screw rod

spring grips

J Screw Jack

centre and end studs fixed to panel

4"×2" framing to ply shutter

cardboard tubes round bolts

studs of 2/6"×2" blocked apart

folding wedges for plumbing shutters

end stud of each panel secures adjacent panel.

panels are reversed for 1st. lift. for succeeding lifts, bolts pass thro' holes formed in previous lift.

MOVING WALL FORM

FORMWORK FOR WALLS

and floor panels; the metal facing protects the plywood and increases the life of the panels.

Stair Forms. These are constructed on the lines shown below. The shutter is carried on cross joists and raking ledgers. The risers, which are fixed after the reinforcement is placed, are $1\frac{1}{2}$ to 2 in. thick and bevelled at the bottom to permit the whole of the tread face to be trowelled. The outer ends are carried by a cut string and the wall ends by hangers secured to a board fixed to, or strutted against, the wall face. The treads are left open to permit concreting.

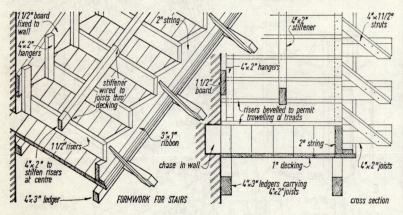

Shell Barrel Vault Forms. The radii of these vaults in most cases permits plywood decking to be bent cold round the curve. An indication of the radii appropriate to various ply thicknesses is given in Table 31.

Table 31 Bending of plywood for forms

Thickness in inches	Approximate minimum radius in inches	
	Across grain	Parallel to grain
$\frac{3}{8}$	36	54
$\frac{1}{2}$	72	96
$\frac{5}{8}$	96	120
$\frac{3}{4}$	120	144

The decking is supported by straight joists, spaced at intervals appropriate to the thickness of the plywood. For a 3 to 4 in. thick barrel these would be 25 in. for $\frac{1}{2}$ in., 29 in. for $\frac{5}{8}$ in., and 36 in. for $\frac{3}{4}$ in. ply. The joists bear on curved ledgers. For smaller radii curves, where boards or plywood cannot be bent, shaped joists, carried by longitudinal ledgers, are used to carry longitudinal decking. In each case the formwork is carried on a system of braced shores. End diaphragms are deep thin beams, and are formed in the same way as thin walls, the whole formwork being supported by braced shoring. Edge beams are formed as normal beams. Typical examples are shown on page 560.

Shell Dome Forms. Narrow board decking is used for these, carried on curved radiating built-up ribs, some of which stop short of the crown to avoid jointing difficulties. The boarding is laid in "panels" at different angles to minimize curvature and taper cutting. Noggings are inserted between the ribs where required to take the ends of the boards. With small radius domes it may be necessary to use two layers of thin boarding ($\frac{3}{8}$ in.) in order to bend it to the required curve. The built-up ribs are carried by a braced framework bearing on ledgers supported, usually, by braced scaffolding.

Doubly Curved Shell Forms. As explained in Chapter 9, the hyperbolic paraboloid form can be developed from straight lines. The formwork can, therefore, be made up entirely from straight members. In principle, therefore, the construction is the same as for floor slabs, with decking, joists, ledgers and props. The edge beam forms are framed up, braced and supported as normal outer floor beams (see page 560).

STEEL FORMWORK

This type of formwork is designed to eliminate timber and to be quickly erected and dismantled, and being in panel units the lower panels can be released individually and used at a higher level. Many systems are available, generally consisting of panels made of steel sheet on light steel angle framing similar to that shown on page 561. The sizes of the panels are usually about 3 ft × 2 ft or 2 ft square, and narrow width units and strips for making up dimensions are available. Special panels for circular work may be obtained. Steel forms are commonly used for wall and floor shutters, although they can be used for columns, particularly if the latter are large. This type of formwork can be re-used a great many times, but if roughly handled needs considerable maintenance in straightening and in welding up broken and cracked edges. This must be put against the savings arising from the greater number of re-uses. Telescopic steel beam units can be used for the support

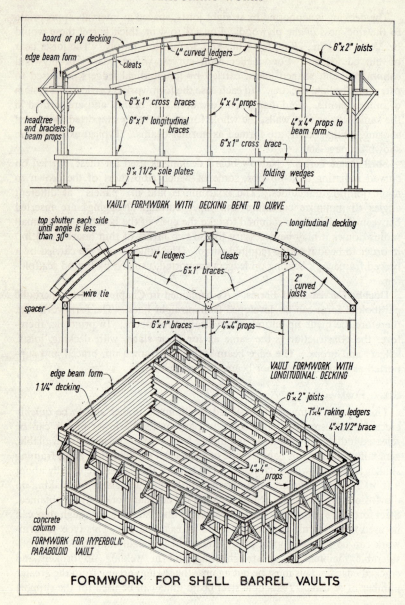

VAULT FORMWORK WITH DECKING BENT TO CURVE

board or ply decking
edge beam form
cleats
4" curved ledgers
6"x 2" joists
6"x 1" cross braces
6"x 1" longitudinal braces
4" x 4" props
4" x 4" props to beam form
headtree and brackets to beam props
6"x1" cross brace
9"x 11/2" sole plates
folding wedges

top shutter each side until angle is less than 30°
longitudinal decking
4" ledgers
cleats
6"x1" braces
2" curved joists
wire tie
spacer
6"x 1" braces
4"x 4" props

VAULT FORMWORK WITH LONGITUDINAL DECKING

edge beam form
1 1/4" decking
6"x 2" joists
7"x4" raking ledgers
4"x1 1/2" brace
4"x 4" props
concrete column
FORMWORK FOR HYPERBOLIC PARABOLOID VAULT

FORMWORK FOR SHELL BARREL VAULTS

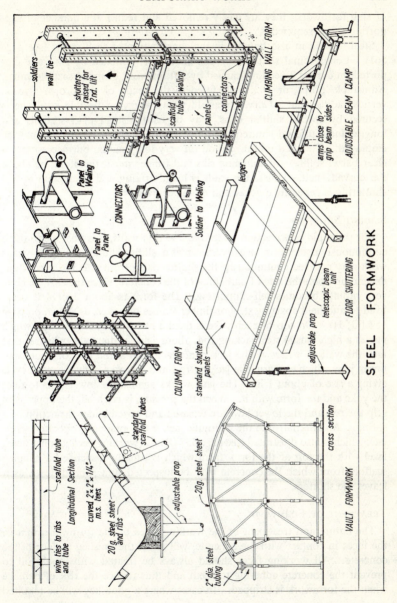

soldiers

wall tie

shutters raised for 2nd. lift

scaffold tube

waling

panels

connectors

CLIMBING WALL FORM

arms close to grip beam sides

ADJUSTABLE BEAM CLAMP

Panel to Waling

CONNECTORS

Panel to Panel

Soldier to Waling

ledger

telescopic beam unit

adjustable prop

FLOOR SHUTTERING

COLUMN FORM

standard shutter panels

scaffold tube

Longitudinal Section

curved 2" 2" × 1/4" m.s. tees

standard scaffold tubes

adjustable prop

20 g. steel sheet and ribs

wire ties to ribs and tube

20g. steel sheet

cross section

VAULT FORMWORK

2" dia. steel tubing

STEEL FORMWORK

of slab formwork; they are easily removed and reduce the number of supporting props required.

Steel forms can also be used in the construction of shell vaults (see page
561). Longitudinal shutters, of thin sheet steel stiffened by ribs, are supported on curved T-sections carried by a framework of metal scaffold tubes.
Adjustable props, or jack bolts fitted to the heads of the props, provide
vertical adjustment. Curved scaffold tubes, carrying flexible steel sheets
secured by special shutter clips, may be used instead of T-sections and
longitudinal stiffened shutters. Mobile scaffolds running on rails may be
employed. This is a useful method on very long vaults, but necessitates a
clear barrel soffit. All stiffening ribs and frames must, therefore, be above
the curved shell. Unless the vault is long, striking and re-erection of the
shuttering is generally quicker and more accurate.

Sliding Shutters

For the rapid construction of constant section walls, it is possible to use a
continuously rising form, usually known as a sliding shutter. By this means
work may proceed continuously, the shutter rising from 6 to 12 in. per hour
depending upon the rate of hardening of the concrete, since the cast concrete
very rapidly becomes self-supporting. The form is about 3 or 4 ft deep,
fixed to and held apart by steel or timber frames or yokes, as shown on page
557 (G, H). On top of each yoke is fixed a hydraulic jack, through which
passes a high tensile steel jacking rod, about 1 in. in diameter, which is cast
into the wall as it rises. The jack contains a ram and a pair of upper and
lower jaws which can grip the jacking rod and it works in cycles, each cycle
giving a rise of about 1 in. The jack works against the lower jaws to raise
the yoke and the form with it. When the pressure is released, the upper jaws
grip the rod and the lower jaws are released and raised under the action of a
spring. An alternative to the hydraulic jack is the manually operated screw
jack which is also illustrated (see page 557 (J)). A working deck is constructed
level with the top of the form, from which is usually suspended a hanging
scaffold from which the concrete may be inspected and rubbed down as it
leaves the shutters.

Treatment of Formwork

The nature and treatment of the working faces of the formwork, that is,
the faces in contact with the concrete, will affect the finished surface of the
concrete. All working faces should always be treated with mould oil to
prevent the concrete adhering to them and thus reduce the risk of damage
when the formwork is stripped. In cases where a good key will be required

on the final surface or where it is desired ultimately to expose the aggregate on the surface, a retarding liquid may be applied to the formwork. This prevents the setting of the cement at the surface, so that when the formwork is struck, the concrete face may be brushed down with stiff brushes to form a rough surface of exposed aggregate. Alternatively, aggregate transfer may be used. This consists of sticking selected aggregate to shutter liners with a suitable water-soluble adhesive. On stripping the shutters the aggregate is transferred to the concrete to which it is, by then, bonded.[1] To produce a good smooth face, the formwork may be lined with plywood, hardboard or plastic sheeting, or where a patterned surface is required, a patterned tough rubber sheet is used as a lining. Very deep patterning may be produced in this way because the rubber is sufficiently elastic to be pulled away reasonably easily from the set concrete.

Permanent shuttering of precast concrete may be used to provide the final finished face. Concrete pipes may be used for circular columns and concrete slabs for walls (see "Facings", Chapter 4). Wood wool slabs used for thermal insulation to a wall may be used as an inside permanent shutter.

Stripping times for formwork are given in Table 32 below. These are intended as a general guide only. Actual times will vary on each job according to the size of members, type of structure and day to day weather conditions.

Table 32   Period before formwork should be removed (in days)

Formwork	Ordinary Portland cement concrete		Rapid-hardening Portland cement concrete	
	Cold weather (just above freezing)	Normal weather (about 60°F)	Cold weather (just above freezing)	Normal weather (about 60°F)
Beam sides, walls and columns	6	2	5	1
Slabs (props left under)	10	3	7	2
Beam soffits (props left under)	14	7	10	4
Removal of props to slabs	21	7 to 10	14	4
Removal of props to beams	28	16	21	8

[1] See Cement and Concrete Association Advisory Note No. 4, "Aggregate Transfer".

INDEX

Page references in italic figures refer to illustrations